3
3
3
3
3
3
3

Study Manual

Course 3

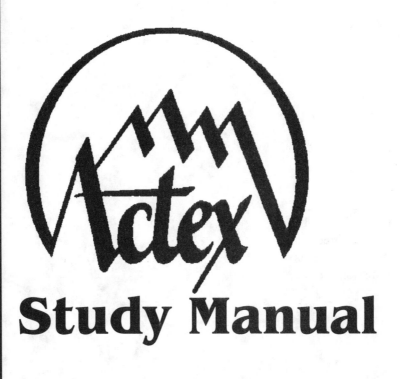

Examination of the Society of Actuaries

Exam 3

of the Casualty Actuarial Society

Volume II
(Aggregate Loss Models, Stochastic Processes, Simulation)

2000 Edition

Michael A. Gauger, Ph.D.

Printed in the United States of America

ISBN: 1-56698-370-3

TABLE OF CONTENTS

Section IV: Stochastic Process Models

Section V: Simulation

Preface

This two-volume manual has been designed as a self-contained introduction to the topics covered by the new Course 3 Exam. It could also serve as a stand-alone text for a year-long University Course. We have endeavored to address all of the Learning Objectives set forth in the Report of the Joint CAS/SOA Working Group on Courses 3 and 4. Volume I is devoted to Survival Models (2 units) and Contingent Payment Models (6 units). As suggested in the Report of the Working Group, relevant business applications with contingent payments supplement the usual life insurance and annuity models. Volume II includes Aggregate Loss Models (4 units), Stochastic Processes (4 units), and Simulation (1 unit). The multiple-decrement model developed in Volume I is integrated with the treatment of continuous-time stochastic processes to describe the mathematics of "transition to the next state." Application of stochastic process theory is then made to contingent payment models in the Unit Review Questions.

Each of the 17 units contains Introductory Discussion, Condensed Review Notes, a Conceptual Review Test (to reinforce basic concepts and reasoning), a Computational Review Test (more central and elementary computations), and Unit Review Questions. In Volume I, many of the Unit Review Questions are from past SOA 150 exams. Additional questions have been created featuring business applications of contingent payment models to try to prepare the student for the style of question likely to be encountered on the Course 3 Examination. In Volume II, some questions from past SOA 151 exams concerning aggregate loss and ruin models remain relevant and have been included. Most questions are newly-created, and, wherever possible, the questions are applied to business problems.

The Unit Review Questions in these two volumes are the best questions we can offer at this point for the student seeking to prepare for the Course 3 Exam. However, the Course 3 Sample Exam produced by the Working Group makes it clear that the style of exams is changing dramatically compared to the recent past. Fewer questions will involve heavy symbolic manipulation and parametric model algebra. Many questions will require integrating ideas from several topics and applying them to solve a problem set in a business context. Solutions will require reasoning from first principles. Memorizing lists of equations from parametric models, and being prepared to do heavy computation or algebra with these equations is not the way to prepare for the Course 3 Exam. Understanding concepts, being able to integrate ideas from different topics, and applying these things to business problems will be paramount.

We commend the Working Group for the care with which they have undertaken the design of this new course and for their adherence in the Sample Exam to the principles set forth in their report. It is clear that actuarial education is evolving in a new direction, with the result that successful exam candidates will have to demonstrate not only computational mathematical skill, but also conceptual understanding and an ability to apply these concepts to solve business problems.

We would like also to express appreciation to the peer review group who read the first draft of these manuals and made valuable suggestions for improvement. This group includes James W. Daniel, ASA, University of Texas; Thomas N. Herzog, ASA, Department of HUD; Dick London, FSA, University of Connecticut; and Brian Lowrey, graduate student of the Actuarial Science Program at the University of Connecticut.

Michael A. Gauger
July 1999

YOUR OPINION IS IMPORTANT TO US

We here at ACTEX are eager to provide you, the actuarial student, with helpful study material to assist you in gaining the necessary knowledge to become a successful actuary. In turn we would like your help in evaluating our manuals so we can help you meet that end. We invite you to provide us with a critique of this manual by sending this form to us at your convenience.

Course 3 Volume II

In preparing for my exam I found this manual: (Check one)

☐ Very Good ☐ Good ☐ Satisfactory ☐ Unsatisfactory

I found the following helpful:

____

I found the following problems:
(Please be specific as to area, i.e., section, specific item, and/or page #)

____

To improve this manual I would:

____

Name: ______________________________

Address: ______________________________

Phone: ______________________________

(Please provide name and phone number in case clarification is needed)

Send to: Denise Rosengrant
ACTEX Publications
P.O. Box 974
Winsted, CT 06098

We appreciate your time and value your input. THANK YOU!

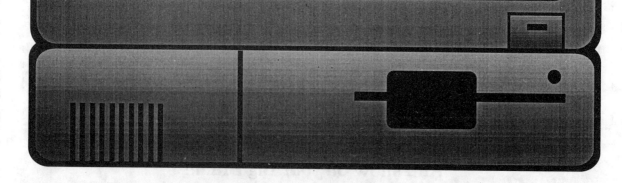

SECTION III

AGGREGATE LOSS MODELS

INTRODUCTORY NOTE

This section of the manual contains four units. For each unit there is a package of five items:

(1) ***Introductory Notes.*** While not as complete as many textbooks, it is designed to cover all the learning objectives set forth in the SOA - Working Group Report on Course 3.

(2) ***Condensed Review Notes and Advanced Topics.*** These notes constitute a list of the major relations with additional comments on more exotic topics. They should be useful as a reference when solving the Unit Review Questions, and as a final checklist of facts you should be familiar with for the exam.

(3) ***Conceptual Review Test.*** This material should be used in conjunction with reading and rereading the Introductory notes.

(4) ***Computational Review Test.*** These questions are more elementary than the Unit Review Questions and emphasize very basic calculations related to the unit reading.

(5) ***Unit Review Questions.*** This is a compilation of past SOA exam questions which still appear to be relevant, and newly created questions to reflect the new learning objectives and syllabus.

UNIT 1: INTRODUCTION TO AGGREGATE LOSS MODELS

Introduction

The goal of this section of the manual is to develop a probability distribution for the total sum of losses or payments over a period of time resulting from a portfolio of contracts or block of business. The amounts summed could be the actual losses sustained by the contract holders, the payments to them by the insurer as a result of their claims, or the payments by a reinsurer to the insurer resulting from a reinsurance arrangement. Suppose the random payment amounts ("losses") are denoted by X_1, X_2, ..., X_N. N is the random number of payments ("losses" or "claims") generated by the block of business over a period of time, say a year. It is typically assumed that the X_i are all distributed like X (a loss or claim amount model) and that N, X_1, X_2, ..., X_N are independent. In the **collective risk model** the aggregate loss (total sum of losses or payments), S, is viewed as a random sum,

$$S = X_1 + X_2 + \cdots + X_N,$$

of a random number of random amounts. It is sometimes referred to as a compound distribution of the X ("severity") and N ("frequency") distributions. The separation of S into frequency and severity components has several modeling advantages. Underwriting changes or growth in the number of contracts in the block of business can be incorporated by revising the N-distribution. Inflationary effects on payments or coverage modifications such as deductibles, limits or coinsurance lead to modifications in the X-distribution.

In the **individual risk model** claims are first sorted by policy and then totaled. Let n be the number of policies in the block of business. Denote by Y_i the sum of the X_j which are due to claims on the ith policy. Then $S = Y_1 + Y_2 + \cdots + Y_n$. If N_i is the random number of claims against the ith policy over the time period then Y_i can be viewed as $X_1 + X_2 + \cdots + X_{N_i}$ (a compound distribution) and N may be viewed as $N_1 + N_2 + \cdots + N_n$. This points out the intertwining nature of the collective and individual methods and makes it apparent that the collective model is the most basic.

In the first unit of this section of the manual we cover the fundamental ideas needed in developing the distribution of S from either the collective or individual method. Following this, two units are devoted to severity (i.e., X) distributions and frequency (i.e., N) distributions. Heavy emphasis here will be given to popular parametric models and methods for expanding the parametric families. In the final unit of this section we will return to the model of S in more detail making use of the parametric models for frequency and severity in Units 2 and 3. Issues such as recursive calculation of the S-density, reinsurance and setting of the premium will be treated.

Sums of Independent Random Variables

In both the individual and collective risk models one needs to be able to calculate the density function of a sum of two independent variables. We begin by examining the method of convolution and then turn to using moment generating functions.

Since all the loss variables we need to work with are non-negative let's assume X and Y are independent, non-negative random variables. The convolution of f_X and f_Y, denoted $f_X * f_Y$, is the density function of $S = X + Y$. If both X and Y are discrete then so is S, and the event decomposition

$$\{S = s\} = \bigcup_{0 \leq x \leq s} \{X = x \text{ and } Y = s - x\}$$

leads to

$$f_S(s) = Pr(S = s) = \sum_{0 \leq x \leq s} Pr(X = x \text{ and } Y = s - x) \qquad \text{(disjointedness)}$$

$$= \underbrace{\sum_{0 \leq x \leq s} f_X(x) f_Y(s - x)}_{f_X * f_Y(s),\text{ the convolution of } f_X \text{ with } f_Y} \qquad \text{(independence).}$$

The equivalent version when X and Y are continuous is

$$f_S(s) = \int_{x=0}^{s} f_X(x) f_Y(s - x)\, dx$$

Example 1 If $f_X(0) = \frac{1}{2}$, $f_X(1) = \frac{1}{4}$, $f_X(2) = \frac{1}{4}$ and X_1, X_2, X_3 are independent and identically distributed like X, find the density of $S = X_1 + X_2 + X_3$.

Solution First we calculate $f_{X_1} * f_{X_2}$ and then use this result to find $(f_{X_1} * f_{X_2}) * f_{X_3}$.

S	$f_{X_1} * f_{X_2}(s) = \sum_{x=0}^{s} f_{X_1}(x) f_{X_2}(s-x)$
0	$\frac{1}{2} \cdot \frac{1}{2} = \frac{1}{4}$
1	$\frac{1}{2} \cdot \frac{1}{4} + \frac{1}{4} \cdot \frac{1}{2} = \frac{1}{4}$
2	$\frac{1}{2} \cdot \frac{1}{4} + \frac{1}{4} \cdot \frac{1}{4} + \frac{1}{4} \cdot \frac{1}{2} = \frac{5}{16}$
3	$\frac{1}{2} \cdot 0 + \frac{1}{4} \cdot \frac{1}{4} + \frac{1}{4} \cdot \frac{1}{4} + 0 \cdot \frac{1}{2} = \frac{2}{16}$
4	$\frac{1}{2} \cdot 0 + \frac{1}{4} \cdot 0 + \frac{1}{4} \cdot \frac{1}{4} + 0 \cdot \frac{1}{4} + 0 \cdot \frac{1}{2} = \frac{1}{16}$

It is left for the reader to verify that the distribution of $S = X_1 + X_2 + X_3$ is

S	0	1	2	3	4	5	6
$f_S(s)$	$\frac{1}{8}$	$\frac{3}{16}$	$\frac{9}{32}$	$\frac{13}{64}$	$\frac{9}{64}$	$\frac{3}{64}$	$\frac{1}{64}$

e.g., $f_S(3) = \sum_{x=0}^{3}(f_{X_1}*f_{X_2}(x)) \cdot f_{X_3}(3-x) = \frac{1}{4}\cdot 0 + \frac{1}{4}\cdot\frac{1}{4} + \frac{5}{16}\cdot\frac{1}{4} + \frac{2}{16}\cdot\frac{1}{2} = \frac{13}{64}$ □

Example 2 Suppose X is uniform on $[0,100]$ and Y is independent and uniform on $[0,150]$. If $S = X + Y$ what is $f_S(175)$?

Solution Since these are continuous variables

$$f_S(175) = f_X*f_Y(175) = \int_{x=0}^{175} f_X(x)\cdot f_Y(175-x)\,dx$$

where

$$f_X(x) = \frac{1}{100} \quad 0 \le x \le 100$$

$$f_Y(y) = \frac{1}{150} \quad 0 \le y \le 150.$$

Over some portions of [0,175] the integrand is zero. It is non-zero when

$$0 \le x \le 100 \quad \text{and} \quad 0 \le 175 - x \le 150$$

since this makes both integral factors non-zero. From $0 \le 175-x \le 150$ it follows that $25 \le x \le 175$. The intersection of this interval with $0 \le x \le 100$ is $25 \le x \le 100$. Thus

$$f_S(175) = \int_{x=25}^{100} \frac{1}{100}\cdot\frac{1}{150}\,dx = \frac{75}{100\cdot 150} = \frac{1}{200}$$

It is somewhat tedious to derive a general $f_S(s)$ formula but the picture looks like the following:

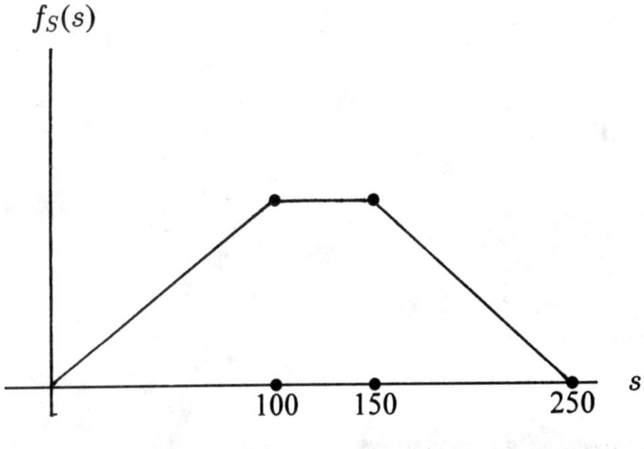

□

Another method of identifying the distribution of $S = X+Y$ is based on moment generating functions. (See Appendix A for a summary of basic facts about $M_X(t) = E[e^{tX}]$, the moment generating function of X.) This techniques works best with parametric families of distributions which are closed under addition. It hinges on the idea that if $M_X(t) = M_Z(t)$, then X and Z have identical distributions.

Example 3 If X and Y are independent Poisson variables with parameters λ_1 and λ_2 find the distribution of $S = X+Y$.

Solution The Poisson λ generating function is $e^{\lambda(e^t-1)}$ so

$$\begin{aligned} M_S(t) &= M_X(t)M_Y(t) && \text{(independence)} \\ &= e^{\lambda_1(e^t-1)} \cdot e^{\lambda_2(e^t-1)} && \text{(poisson facts)} \\ &= e^{(\lambda_1+\lambda_2)(e^t-1)} && \text{(algebra)} \end{aligned}$$

The latter is the generating function of a Poisson distribution with parameter $\lambda_1 + \lambda_2$. Hence, by the uniqueness of generating functions, S has a Poisson distribution with parameter $\lambda_1 + \lambda_2$. □

The Double Expectation Theorem

Suppose X and Y are "related" (i.e., dependent) and we wish to compute $E[X]$ and $Var(X)$. The double expectation theorem is a device to break this into smaller pieces corresponding to values of Y. Suppose the blob below represents the sample space S for the random variable X. We can use values of Y to decompose S disjointly. Here we have assumed for convenience that possible Y values are 1, 2, ..., n.

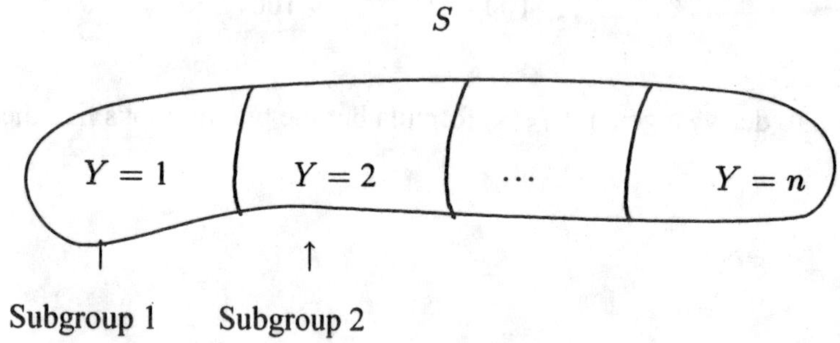

As a first step in the calculation of $E[X]$ one could compute the "subgroup" averages $E[X \mid Y = 1], \ldots, E[X \mid Y = n]$. The "overall" average, $E[X]$, should be a "weighted average" of the subgroup-averages. Intuitively the weights should correspond to the relative likelihood of the subgroups, that is

$$E[X] = E[X \mid Y = 1] \cdot Pr(Y = 1) + \cdots + E[X \mid Y = n] Pr(Y = n).$$

Observing that $E[X \mid Y = y]$ varies as y varies, we see that it is a function of Y. Since the sum above is of a product of this function and Y probabilities, it may be interpreted as the expected value of $E[X \mid Y]$:

$$E[X] = E[\underbrace{E[X \mid Y]}_{\text{function of Y}}].$$

This is the more compact form of the double expectation theorem, although the expression preceding it is more intuitive.

Now let's consider variability of X in terms of the subgroups. Here we will be totally descriptive and intuitive. There should be two contributions to variability in X, variance *within* the subgroups, and variability *between* them. $Var(X \mid Y = 1), \ldots, Var(X \mid Y = n)$ represents variability within the subgroups, so $E[Var(X \mid Y)]$ is average variance within the subgroups. Representing each subgroup by its average value, *i.e.*, $E[X \mid Y]$, we could measure variance between them in calculating $Var(E[X \mid Y])$, the variance in subgroup averages as a function of Y. The second part of the double expectation theorem asserts

$$Var(X) = \underset{\substack{\text{average vari-}\\ \text{ance within}\\ \text{subgroups}}}{E[Var(X \mid Y)]} + \underset{\substack{\text{variance between}\\ \text{subgroup averages}}}{Var(E[X \mid Y])}$$

Finally, we will indicate three examples of how these ideas influence the development of the collective claims model.

In the collective claims model, aggregate claims, S, is expressed as

$$S = X_1 + X_2 + \cdots + X_N$$

where

$N =$ random number of claims,

$X_1, \ldots, X_N$ independent and distributed like X, and

$X_1, \ldots, X_N$ and N are independent.

Here the difficulty is due to the random number of terms in the sum. If we knew (*i.e.*, were given) the number of terms, this would be a much simpler problem. This suggests conditioning S on the related variable N:

$$S|_{N=n} = X_1 + \cdots + X_n \qquad \text{(sum of a given number of terms)}$$

$$\Rightarrow \begin{cases} E[S \mid N=n] = E[X_1 + \cdots + X_n] = nE[X] \\ Var(S \mid N=n) = Var(X_1 + \cdots + X_n) = nVar(X). \end{cases}$$

These results can be written generally as

$$E[S \mid N] = N \cdot \underbrace{E[X]}_{\text{number}} \qquad \text{(a linear function of } N\text{)}$$

$$Var(S \mid N) = N \cdot \underbrace{Var(X)}_{\text{number}} \qquad \text{(a linear function of } N\text{)}$$

The double expectation theorem can be applied to obtain

$$E[S] = E[E[S \mid N]] = E[N \cdot \underbrace{E[X]}_{\text{number}}] = E[X] \cdot E[N]$$

$$\begin{aligned} Var(S) &= E[Var(S \mid N)] + Var(E[S \mid N]) \\ &= E[N \cdot \underbrace{Var(X)}_{\text{number}}] + Var(N \cdot \underbrace{E[X]}_{\text{number}}) \\ &= E[N] \cdot Var(X) + (E[X])^2 \cdot Var(N). \end{aligned}$$

The first relation says $E[S]$ is the product of the expected number of claims and the expected claim amount. The second says that variance in aggregate claims has two sources of contribution. The term $E[N] \cdot Var(X)$ corresponds to variability in claim amounts, whereas $(E[X])^2 Var(N)$ is related to variability in the number of claims.

Suppose there is again a random number of claims, N, and possible claim amounts are $X = 1, 2, \ldots$. Another way to write S is

$$S = \underbrace{1 \cdot N_1}_{\substack{\text{sum of} \\ \$1 \text{ claims}}} + \underbrace{2 \cdot N_2}_{\substack{\text{sum of} \\ \$2 \text{ claims}}} + \cdots,$$

where N_k is the number of claims equal k. What is the distribution of an N_k? N_k is related to the random number of claims, N. If we knew (*i.e.*, were given) that $N = n$, each of the n claims can be viewed as a Bernoulli trial where "success" means the claim amount is k and "failure" means it is not k.

Thus

$$N_{k|N=n} = \text{Binomial } (n \text{ trials}, p = Pr(X = k))$$

From binomial facts, $E[N_k \mid N = n] = n \cdot p$, $Var(N_k \mid N = n) = n \cdot p \cdot q$. So more generally

$$E[N_k \mid N] = pN, \quad Var(N_k \mid N) = pqN.$$

By the double expectation theorem

$$E[N_k] = E[E[N_k \mid N]] = E[pN] = p \cdot E[N]$$

$$= \text{(prob. a claim } = k\text{)(expected number of claims)}$$

$$\begin{aligned} Var(N_k) &= E[Var(N_k \mid N)] + Var(E[N_k \mid N]) \\ &= E[pqN] + Var(pN) \qquad\qquad p = Pr(X = k) \\ &= pqE[N] + p^2 Var(N). \end{aligned}$$

Suppose we have the following data for a group dental plan where claims are broken down by sex:

	Average Claim	Claim Variance
Male	525	40,000
Female	375	28,000

Suppose an employee group of 100 people has an unknown (random) number of males. How can we find the expected value and variance of aggregate claims, S, for this group? Let X be the claim amount for a randomly selected individual and let Y be a sex-indicator variable for this person ($Y = 0$ for males, $Y = 1$ for females). The table can be interpreted as giving

$$E[X \mid Y = 0] = 525 \qquad E[X \mid Y = 1] = 375$$

$$Var(X \mid Y = 0) = 40{,}000 \qquad Var(X \mid Y = 1) = 28{,}000.$$

Aggregate claims is related to N, the random number of males. If we knew (*i.e.*, were given) that $N = n$, then there are n males and $(100-n)$ females. Thus

$$\begin{aligned} E[S \mid N=n] &= nE[X \mid Y=0] + (100-n)E[X \mid Y=1] \\ &= n(525) + (100-n)375 \\ &= 37{,}500 + 150n \end{aligned}$$

and

$$\begin{aligned} Var(S \mid N=n) &= nVar(X \mid Y=0) + (100-n)Var(X \mid Y=1) \\ &= n(40{,}000) + (100-n)(28{,}000) \\ &= 2{,}800{,}000 + 12{,}000n. \end{aligned}$$

Generically

$$E[S \mid N] = 37{,}500 + 150N,\ Var(S \mid N) = 2{,}800{,}000 + 12{,}000N.$$

So by the double expectation theorem ($p = Pr(\text{"male"})$)

$$E[S] = E[37{,}500+150N] = 37{,}500 + 150(100p)$$

$$\begin{aligned} Var(S) &= E[2{,}800{,}000+12{,}000N] + Var(37{,}500+150N) \\ &= 2{,}800{,}000 + (12{,}000)(100p) + 150^2(100pq). \end{aligned}$$

The common thread in these three examples is that if N were given then S and N_k were easier to envision. Furthermore, the conditional expectations and variances always turned out to be ***linear*** functions of N.

Theory of Compound Distributions

Here we assume N is the random number of claims and $X_1, X_2, \ldots, X_N$ are the random claim (loss) amounts. All X_i are assumed to be distributed like X, and $N, X_1, \ldots, X_N$ are assumed to be independent. Aggregate claims, S, is represented by $S = X_1 + X_2 + \cdots + X_N$ in the collective risk model. We have just seen how the following important relations are derived from the double expectation theorem:

$$E[S] = \underbrace{E[N]}_{\substack{\text{expected}\\\text{number of}\\\text{claims}}} \cdot \underbrace{E[X]}_{\substack{\text{expected claim}\\\text{amount}}}$$

$$Var(S) = \underbrace{E[N]Var(X)}_{\substack{\text{part due to variability}\\\text{in claim amounts}}} + \underbrace{(E[X])^2 Var(N)}_{\substack{\text{part due to variability}\\\text{in the number of claims}}}.$$

Similarly, for the third central moment of S we have

$$E[(S-E[S])^3] = E[N]E[(X-E[X])^3] + 3Var(N)E[X]Var(X) + E[(N-E[N])^3](E[X])^3$$

as an expression in terms of moments of X and N.

Next we wish to examine the distribution and density functions of S. The event decomposition

$$\{S \le x\} = \bigcup_{n=0}^{\infty} \{N = n \text{ and sum of } n \text{ claims } \le x\}$$

leads to

$$F_S(x) = \sum_{n=0}^{\infty} \underbrace{Pr(N=n)}_{f_N(n)} \cdot \underbrace{Pr(X_1 + \cdots + X_n \le x)}_{\text{denoted } F_X^{*n}(x)}$$

due the independence of N, X_1, ..., X_N. In this relation the n-fold convolution notation, $F_X^{*n}(x)$, denotes the distribution function of $X_1 + \cdots + X_n$. Just as with density functions, it can be shown that

$$F_X{*}F_Y(s) = Pr(X+Y \le s) = Pr(S \le s) = \begin{cases} \sum\limits_{0 \le x \le s} f_X(x)F_Y(s-x) & \text{(discrete case)} \\ \int_{x=0}^{s} f_X(x)F_Y(s-x)\,dx & \text{(continuous case)} \end{cases}$$

The parallel density function relation is

$$f_S(x) = \sum_{n=0}^{\infty} f_N(n) \cdot f_X^{*n}(x)$$

where $f_X^{*n}(x)$ denotes the density function of $X_1 + \cdots + X_n$. A necessary convention in these expressions is that a 0-fold convolution of X (i.e., a sum of no X's) is a zero random variable:

$$f_X^{*0}(0) = 1, \quad F_X^{*0}(x) = 1 \qquad \text{if } x \ge 0.$$

From the density relation one can see that S is discrete if X is discrete. Also, if X is continuous, then S has a mixed distribution with a point mass of $Pr(N=0)$ at $S=0$ (i.e., the $n=0$ term in the sum) and $\sum_{n=1}^{\infty} f_N(n) \cdot f_X^{*n}(x)$ as $Pr(N \ne 0) \cdot$ (density of the continuous part). Of course it could happen that $Pr(N=0)=0$ and then S would be continuous. Due to the reliance of these formulas on n-fold convolutions of all orders they are difficult to implement in practice. In Unit 4 we will return to the question of calculating $f_S(x)$ and look at recursion methods that are available for certain types of N-distributions introduced in Unit 3 (Poisson, Negative Binomial, and Binomial).

A final technical point concerns the generating function relation

$$M_S(t) = M_N(lnM_X(t)),$$

which is obtained as follows from the double expectation theorem:

$$M_S(t) = E[e^{tS}] = E[E[e^{tS}|N]] = E[\underbrace{E[e^{t(X_1+\cdots+X_n)}|N=n]}_{M_X^n(t)}]$$

$$= \sum_{n=0}^{\infty} M_X^n(t) Pr(N=n)$$

$$= E[M_X(t)^N] = E[e^{lnM_X(t)N}] = M_N(lnM_X(t)).$$

For example, if N has the Poisson-λ distribution (i.e., S is **compound Poisson**), then $M_N(t) = e^{\lambda(e^t-1)}$ so

$$M_S(t) = M_N(lnM_X(t)) = e^{\lambda(M_X(t)-1)}.$$

This relation can be used to obtain more compact formulas for $E[S]$, $Var(S)$ and the third central moment than the general relations derived earlier:

$$R_S(t) = lnM_S(t) = \lambda[M_X(t) - 1]$$

$$\Rightarrow \quad \frac{d^k}{dt^k}[R_S(t)]\bigg|_{t=0} = \lambda \cdot \frac{d^k}{dt^k}[M_X(t)]\bigg|_{t=0}$$

$$\Rightarrow \quad E[S] = R_S'(0) = \lambda \cdot M_X'(0) = \lambda \cdot E[X]$$

$$Var(S) = R_S''(0) = \lambda \cdot M_X''(0) = \lambda \cdot E[X^2]$$

$$E[(S - E[S])^3] = R_S'''(0) = \lambda \cdot M_X'''(0) = \lambda \cdot E[X^3]$$

(See Appendix A for information on $R_X(t) = ln(M_X(t))$.)

An Example Contrasting the Individual and Collective Risk Models

Suppose that 80% of the policies in a block of business experience a single claim during a one-year period where the claim amount, X, has density function

$$f_X(x) = \frac{2}{100^2}[100 - x] \text{ for } 0 \leq x \leq 100.$$

The other 20% experience no claim. Suppose there are $n = 100$ such policies in a portfolio. The aggregate claims are denoted by S.

We begin with the individual risk model of S. Let N_i be the number of claims against the ith policy over this year and let $Y_i = X_1 + \cdots + X_{N_i}$ be the total claim against the ith policy. From the above $N_i = 0$ or 1 and $f_{N_i}(0) = .20$, $f_{N_i}(1) = .80$. From results earlier in this unit we have the following:

$$f_{Y_i}(x) = \sum_{n=0}^{\infty} f_{N_i}(n) f_X^{*n}(x) = .20 \underbrace{f_X^{*(0)}(x)}_{\substack{\text{density of a} \\ \text{0-variable}}} + .80 \underbrace{f_X^{*(1)}(x)}_{\text{density of } X}$$

$$\text{Claim Amount Distribution:} \begin{cases} E[X] = \displaystyle\int_0^{100} x \cdot \frac{2}{100^2}[100 - x]dx = \frac{100}{3} \\ E[X^2] = \displaystyle\int_0^{100} x^2 \cdot \frac{2}{100^2}[100 - x]dx = 1666.6\overline{6} \\ \sigma_X^2 = 555.5\overline{5} \end{cases}$$

$$\text{Total Claims Against a Single Policy:} \begin{cases} E[Y_i] = E[N_i] \cdot E[X] = (.8)\left(\frac{100}{3}\right) = 26.6\overline{6} \\ Var(Y_i) = E[N_i] \cdot Var(X) + (E[X])^2 \cdot Var(N_i) \\ \qquad = (.8)(555.5\overline{5}) + \left(\frac{100}{3}\right)^2 (.8)(.2) = 622.\overline{2} \end{cases}$$

$$\text{Aggregate Claims:} \begin{cases} E[S] = 100 \cdot E[Y] = 2666.6\overline{6} \\ Var(S) = 100 \cdot Var(Y) = 62{,}222.2\overline{2} \\ f_S = f_Y^{*(100)} \quad \text{(a formidable problem!)} \end{cases}$$

In the collective risk model $N = N_1 + \cdots + N_{100}$ is a binomial distribution with $n = 100$ trials and $p = .8 = Pr(\text{"Success"})$ since each N_i is a Bernoulli variable with $p = .8$. Thus we have

$$E[S] = E[N] \cdot E[X] = (100(.8))\left(\frac{100}{3}\right) = 2666.6\bar{6} \qquad \text{(same as earlier)}$$

$$\begin{aligned} Var(S) &= E[N] \cdot Var(X) + (E[X])^2 \cdot Var(N) \\ &= (100)(.8)(555.5\bar{5}) + \left(\frac{100}{3}\right)^2 (100)(.8)(.2) = 62{,}222.\bar{2} \qquad \text{(same as earlier)} \end{aligned}$$

$$f_S(x) = \sum_{n=0}^{\infty} f_N(n) \cdot f_X^{*n}(x) = \sum_{n=0}^{100} \underbrace{\binom{100}{n}(.2)^{100-n}(.8)^n}_{\text{Binomial}} \cdot f_X^{*n}(x)$$

In both cases the calculation of $f_S(x)$ is a formidable problem. Higher order convolutions, binomial coefficients $\binom{100}{n}$, and powers $(.2)^{100-n}$ and $(.8)^n$ will create a considerable computational challenge with accumulating rounding errors. One might have to approximate the distribution of S in some way while preserving $E[S]$, $Var(S)$ and perhaps the 3rd Central Moment so that probability in the right tail of the S-distribution will not be badly underestimated.

CONDENSED REVIEW NOTES AND ADVANCED TOPICS

Sums of Positive Valued Independent Random Variables

$$\underbrace{f_{X+Y}(s)}_{\substack{\text{denoted } f_X * f_Y \\ \text{convolution of} \\ f_X \text{ and } f_Y}} = \begin{cases} \displaystyle\sum_{0 \le x \le s} f_X(x) \cdot f_Y(s-x) & X, Y \text{ discrete} \\ \displaystyle\int_{x=0}^{s} f_X(x) \cdot f_Y(s-x)\,dx & X, Y \text{ continuous} \end{cases}$$

$M_{X+Y}(t) = M_X(t) \cdot M_Y(t)$ can be used with lists of moment generating functions of well known distributions to identify $X + Y$ since $M_{X+Y}(t) = M_Z(t)$ means $X + Y$ and Z are identically distributed.

Double Expectation Theorem

1. $$E\underbrace{[E[W \mid V]]}_{\substack{\text{a function} \\ \text{of } V}} = E[W]$$

2. $$Var(W) = \underbrace{Var\underbrace{(E[W \mid V])}_{\substack{\text{average of } W \\ \text{given } V}}}_{\substack{\text{Variability in these} \\ \text{averages due to} \\ \text{different } V \text{ values}}} + \underbrace{E\underbrace{[Var(W \mid V)]}_{\substack{\text{variability in} \\ W \text{ values given } V}}}_{\substack{\text{Average variability} \\ \text{in } W \text{ values} \\ \text{given } V}}$$

Example: Suppose we have a group of 70 males whose average weight is 175 and 30 females whose average weight is 135. Suppose the variance in weight is 400 for males and 250 for females. Let W be the weight of a randomly selected member of this group of 100, and let V be an indicator variable for the sex of the chosen member ($V = 0$ if male and $V = 1$ if female).

Then $E[W \mid V = 0]$ is the average weight given the member is male, which is 175, and $E[W \mid V = 1]$ is the average weight given the member is female, which is 135. Notice that

$$E[E[W \mid V]] = \sum_v \underbrace{E[W \mid V = v]}_{\text{function of } v} \cdot f_V(v)$$
$$= 175 \cdot f_V(0) + 135 \cdot f_V(1)$$
$$= 175 \cdot \frac{70}{100} + 135 \cdot \frac{30}{100}.$$

The last line can be rearranged as $\frac{70(175) + 30(135)}{100} = \frac{\text{total weight for group of 100}}{\text{total number in group}}$, which is the average weight, $E[W]$, for the entire group.

Similarly, from the given information, $Var(W|V=0) = 400$ and $Var(W|V=1) = 250$. Since $.70 = Pr(V=0)$, we have $\underbrace{E[Var(W \mid V)]}_{\substack{\text{average of variance} \\ \text{within the male group} \\ \text{and female group}}} = 400(.70) + 250(.30) = 355.$

Also for $E[W \mid V]$ we have the discrete distribution

$E[W \mid V]$	Probability	
175	.70	(male: $Pr(V=0) = .70$)
135	.30	(female: $Pr(V=1) = .30$)

having variance

$$\begin{aligned} Var(E[W \mid V]) &= (\text{second moment}) - (\text{first moment})^2 \\ &= (175^2(.70) + 135^2(.30)) - (175(.70) + 135(.30))^2 \\ &= 336. \end{aligned}$$

This number represents variability between average weights for the two groups. For the combined groups $Var(W)$, variability in weights, is then calculated as

$$\begin{aligned} Var(W) &= E[Var(W \mid V)] + Var(E[W \mid V]) \\ &= \underset{\substack{\text{average variability} \\ \text{within the subgroups}}}{355} + \underset{\substack{\text{variability between} \\ \text{the subgroup} \\ \text{averages}}}{336} \\ &= 691 \end{aligned}$$

Compound Distributions

$S = X_1 + \cdots + X_N =$ aggregate claims

$N =$ random number of claims during period (claim frequency)

$X =$ random claim amount model (claim severity)

$N, X_1, \ldots, X_n$ independent and all X_i distributed like X

Then

(1) $$E[S] = \underbrace{E[N]}_{\substack{\text{expected}\\ \text{number}\\ \text{of claims}}} \cdot \underbrace{E[X]}_{\substack{\text{expected}\\ \text{claim}\\ \text{amount}}}$$

(2) $$Var(S) = \underbrace{E[N] \cdot Var(X)}_{\substack{\text{part due to}\\ \text{variability in}\\ \text{claim amounts}}} + \underbrace{(E[X])^2 \cdot Var(N)}_{\substack{\text{part due to variability}\\ \text{in the number of claims}}}$$

(3) $$E[(S - E[S])^3] = E[N] \cdot E[(X - E[X])^3] + 3Var(N) \cdot E[X] \cdot Var(X) + E[(N - E[N])^3](E[X])^3$$

(4) $$F_S(x) = \sum_{n=0}^{\infty} f_N(n) \cdot \underbrace{F_X^{*n}(x)}_{\substack{\text{probability a sum}\\ \text{of } n \text{ claims} \le x}}$$

$$f_S(x) = \sum_{n=0}^{\infty} f_N(n) \cdot \underbrace{f_X^{*n}(x)}_{\substack{\text{density of } X_1 + \cdots + X_n\\ \text{where all } X_i \sim X}}$$

Note: For the $n = 0$ terms a 0-fold convolution (i.e., a sum of no X's) is a zero variable, that is $f_X^{*0}(0) = 1$.

(5) $$M_S(t) = M_N(ln M_X(t))$$

$$P_S(t) = P_N(P_X(t))$$

where $P_N(t) = E[t^N]$ is the probability generating function.

CONCEPTUAL REVIEW TEST

1. Describe the individual risk model for aggregate claims against a block of business over a period of time.

2. Describe the collective risk model for aggregate claims against a block of business over a period of time.

3. Suppose X_1, X_2 are independent and distributed like X where $f_X(1) = .6$, $f_X(2) = .3$ and $f_X(3) = .1$. Explain why $f_{X_1+X_2}(4) = f_X(1) \cdot f_X(3) + f_X(2) \cdot f_X(2) + f_X(3) \cdot f_X(1)$.

4. Explain the double expectation theorem in terms of subgroups.

5. Assume X is a discrete claim amount model. Then $S = X_1 + \cdots + X_N$ is also discrete. Explain how $f_S(x)$ is a weighted average of convolutions of $f_X(x)$ by using the additive probability law and a disjoint decomposition of $\{S = x\}$.

6. Explain how the expected value and variance of S are obtained in the collected risk model from the frequency and severity distributions.

CONCEPTUAL REVIEW TEST SOLUTIONS

1. Aggregate claims, S, is viewed as $Y_1 + \cdots + Y_n$ where n is the number of policies and Y_i is the total claim against the ith policy during the period. The Y_i are assumed to be independent.

2. Aggregate claims, S, is viewed as $X_1 + \cdots + X_N$ where N is the random number of claims and X_i is the random amount of the ith claim. $N, X_1, \ldots, X_N$ are assumed independent and all X_i are distributed like X.

3. If $S = X_1 + X_2$ then $\{S = 4\}$ is the disjoint union $\{X_1 = 1 \text{ and } X_2 = 3\} \cup \{X_1 = 2 \text{ and } X_2 = 2\} \cup \{X_1 = 3 \text{ and } X_2 = 1\}$. Furthermore $Pr(X_1 = a \text{ and } X_2 = b) = Pr(X_1 = a)Pr(X_2 = b)$ due to independence. The formula in the question is the convolution identity $f_{X_1} * f_{X_2}(s) = \sum_{x=0}^{\infty} f_{X_1}(x) \cdot f_{X_2}(s - x)$.

4. $E[X|Y = i]$ is the average value of X within the subgroup of the sample space corresponding to $Y = i$. Intuitively, the overall average, $E[X]$, is the weighted average, $\sum Pr(Y = i) \cdot E[X|Y = i]$, of subgroup averages. The summation can be written as $E[E[X|Y]]$. $Var(X) = E[Var(X|Y)] + Var(E[X|Y])$ is the sum of the average variance within the subgroups and the variance between the subgroup averages.

5. The event $\{S = x\}$, sum of claims equal to x, can be written as $\bigcup_{n=0}^{\infty} \{S = x \text{ and } N = n\}$. Thus

$$f_S(x) = Pr(S = x) = \sum_{n=0}^{\infty} Pr(\{S = x\} \text{ and } \{N = n\})$$

$$= \sum_{n=0}^{\infty} \underbrace{Pr(N = n)}_{\text{weights}} \cdot \underbrace{Pr(S = x|N = n)}_{\substack{f_X^{*n}(x)=\text{probability} \\ \text{that a sum of } n \text{ claims} \\ \text{equals } x}}$$

6. $E[S] = E[N] \cdot E[X]$, the expected number of claims times the expected claim amount, and $Var(S) = E[N] \cdot Var(X) + (E[X])^2 \cdot Var(N)$. The first term is due to variability in claim amounts and the second term is due to variability in the number of claims.

COMPUTATIONAL REVIEW TEST

1. If the density function of X is given by

$X = x$	0	100	200
$f(x)$	.80	.15	.05

and $S = X_1 + X_2 + X_3$, where the X_i are independent and distributed like X, calculate the density of S using convolutions. Then calculate $E[S]$ in two ways.

2. Suppose $S = B_1 + B_2$, where the B_i are independent and distributed like B with

$$f_B(b) = \frac{2}{100^2}(100 - b), \quad 0 < b \leq 100.$$

Then $0 < S \leq 200$. Use convolutions to calculate $f_S(50)$ and $f_S(150)$. Be careful with the latter in determining the limits of integration.

3. Suppose $f_X(1) = .60$ and $f_X(2) = .40$ gives the distribution of the claim amount variable X, and $Pr(N = 0) = .7$, $Pr(N = 1) = .2$ and $Pr(N = 2) = .1$ gives the distribution of the claim number variable N.

(i) Calculate $E[X]$, $Var(X)$, $E[N]$ and $Var(N)$.

(ii) Calculate f_X^{*2}.

(iii) What are $E[S|N]$ and $Var(S|N)$?

(iv) What are $E[S]$ and $Var(S)$

(v) Since S is the sum of 0, 1, or 2 claim amounts of size 1 or 2, the possible values of S are $0, 1, 2, 3, 4$. Calculate $f_S(x)$ for these five values of x.

COMPUTATIONAL REVIEW TEST SOLUTIONS

1. Let $Y = X_1 + X_2$. Possible Y amounts are 0, 100, 200, 300 and 400:

$f_Y(0) = f_X(0)f_X(0) \;=\; (.8)(.8) \;=\; .6400$

$f_Y(100) = f_X(0)f_X(100) + f_X(100)f_X(0) = 2(.8)(.15) = .2400$

$f_Y(200) = f_X(0)f_X(200) + f_X(100)f_X(100) + f_X(200)f_X(0) = .1025$

$f_Y(300) = f_X(100)f_X(200) + f_X(200)f_X(100) = .0150$

$f_Y(400) = f_X(200)f_X(200) = .0025$

NOTE: Check $\sum f_Y(y) = 1.0000$ to catch mistakes.

Then $S = Y + X_3$, and possible S values are 0, 100, ..., 600:

$f_S(0) = f_Y(0)f_X(0) \;=\; (.6400)(.8) \;=\; .512$

$f_S(100) = f_Y(0)f_X(100) + f_Y(100)f_X(0) = .288$

$f_S(200) = f_Y(0)f_X(200) + f_Y(100)f_X(100) + f_Y(200)f_X(0) = .1500$

$f_S(300) = f_Y(100)f_X(200) + f_Y(200)f_X(100) + f_Y(300)f_X(0) = .039375$

$f_S(400) = f_Y(400)f_X(0) + f_Y(300)f_X(100) + f_Y(200)f_X(200) = .009375$

$f_S(500) = f_Y(400)f_X(100) + f_Y(300)f_X(200) = .001125$

$f_S(600) = f_Y(400)f_X(200) = .000125$

Thus $E[S] = \sum s \cdot f_X(s) = 75.00$ (hard way)

$= 3 \cdot E[X] = 3(\Sigma x \cdot f_X(x)) = 3(25.00) = 75.00$ (easy way)

2. $$f_S(50) \;=\; \int_0^{50} f_B(50-x)\cdot f_B(x)\,dx \;=\; \int_0^{50} \left(\frac{2}{100^2}\right)^2 (100-50+x)(100-x)\,dx \;=\; .0108\overline{3}$$

In calculating $f_S(150) = \int_0^{150} f_B(150-s)f_B(s)\,ds$, it is critical to note that the two integrand factors are nonzero only when their arguments are between 0 and 100:

$$\left.\begin{array}{l} 0 < 150 - s \le 100 \\ 0 < s \le 100 \end{array}\right\} \Rightarrow \left\{\begin{array}{l} 50 \le s \\ 0 < s \le 100 \end{array}\right\} \Rightarrow 50 \le s \le 100$$

Thus

$$f_S(150) \;=\; \int_{50}^{100} \left(\frac{2}{100^2}\right)^2 (100-150+x)(100-x)\,dx \;=\; .0008\overline{3}$$

3. (i)

$X=x$	$f_X(x)$
1	.6
2	.4

$$\Rightarrow \begin{cases} E[X] = 1(.6)+2(.4) = 1.4 \\ E[X^2] = 1^2(.6)+2^2(.4) = 2.2 \\ Var(X) = 2.2 - 1.4^2 = .24 \end{cases}$$

$N=n$	$Pr(N=n)$
0	.7
1	.2
2	.1

$$\Rightarrow \begin{cases} E[N] = .4 \\ E[N^2] = .6 \\ Var(N) = .44 \end{cases}$$

(ii) Possible values of $X_1 + X_2$ are $1+1$, $1+2$, $2+2$; then

$f_X^{*2}(2) = f_X(1) \cdot f_X(1) = .36$

$f_X^{*2}(3) = f_X(1) \cdot f_X(2) + f_X(2) \cdot f_X(1) = .48$

$f_X^{*2}(3) = f_X(2) \cdot f_X(2) = .16$

(Note: Check that they sum to one to avoid arithmetic errors)

(iii) $E[S|N] = E[X] \cdot N = 1.4N$

$Var(S|N) = Var(X) \cdot N = .24N$

(iv) $E[S] = E[X] \cdot E[N] = (1.4)(.4) = .56$

$Var(S) = E[N] \cdot Var(X) + (E[X])^2 \cdot Var(N) = .9584$

(v) In general

$$f_S(x) = \sum_{n=0}^{\infty} Pr(N=n) \cdot f_X^{*n}(x),$$

so in this case

$f(x) = (.7)f_X^{*0}(x) + (.2)f_X^{*1}(x) + (.1)f_X^{*2}(x)$:

x	$f_X^{*0}(x)$	$f_X^{*1}(x)$	$f_X^{*2}(x)$	$f(x)$
0	1	0	0	.7
1	0	.6	0	.12
2	0	.4	.36	.116
3	0	0	.48	.048
4	0	0	.16	.016

$\Sigma = 1.000$ o.k.!

UNIT REVIEW QUESTIONS

The list of Review Questions in the first three Units of this section of the manual is rather short. A much more extensive list follows Unit 4 and integrates ideas from all 4 units.

1. Let S be the total amount of claims. The number of claims, N, has probability function:

n	$Pr(N=n)$
0	.50
1	.25
2	.25

The claim size distribution is Poisson with $\lambda = 2$. Calculate $Var(S)$.

(A) 2.50 (B) 2.75 (C) 3.25 (D) 4.00 (E) 4.25

2. You have been asked by a city planner to analyze office cigarette smoking patterns. The planner has provided the following information about the distribution of the number of cigarettes smoked during a workday:

	Male	Female
Mean	6	3
Variance	64	31

The number of male employees in a randomly selected office of N employees has a binomial distribution with parameters N and .40. Determine the mean plus the standard deviation of the number of cigarettes smoked during a workday in a randomly selected office of 8 employees.

(A) 50.9 (B) 51.4 (C) 51.9 (D) 52.4 (E) 52.9

3. X_1, X_2, and X_3 are mutually independent random variables with probability functions as follows:

x	$f_1(x)$	$f_2(x)$	$f_3(x)$
0	p	.60	.25
1	$1-p$	.20	.25
2	0	.10	.25
3	0	.10	.25

If $S = X_1 + X_2 + X_3$ and $f_S(5) = .06$, determine p.

(A) .10 (B) .20 (C) .50 (D) .80 (E) .90

4. An insurance portfolio produces N claims, where:

n	$Pr(N=n)$
0	.50
1	.40
3	.10

Individual claim amounts have the following distribution:

x	$p(x)$
1	.90
10	.10

Individual claim amounts and N are mutually independent. Calculate the probability that the ratio of aggregate claims to expected claims will exceed 3.0.

(A) .05 (B) .07 (C) .09 (D) .11 (E) .13

5. A farmer has observed that the amount of rainfall in a month can be modeled as follows:

(i) The probability of rain in any day is .10.
(ii) The daily amounts of rain are mutually independent.
(iii) If rain occurs on a given day, the amount of rain has a gamma distribution with mean .50 and variance .50.

S is the total rainfall in a month of 30 days. Which of the following are true?

I. $E[S]=1.5$ II. $Var[S]=1.5$ III. $M_S(t)=\dfrac{.90}{1-.10(1-t)^{-.50}}$

(A) I and II only (B) I and III only (C) II and III only (D) I, II, and III
(E) The correct answer is not given by (A), (B), (C) or (D).

6. Individual members of an insured group have independent claims. The claim distributions have the following statistics:

	Mean	Variance
Males	2	4
Females	4	10

The premium for a group with future claims S is the mean of S plus 2 times the standard deviation of S.

If the genders of the members of a group of n members are not known, the number of males is assumed to have a binomial distribution with parameters n and $p=.40$.

P is the premium for a group of 100 for which the genders of the members are not known.

Q is the premium for a group of 40 males and 60 females.

Determine P/Q.

(A) 1.000 (B) 1.005 (C) 1.010 (D) 1.015 (E) 1.020

7. When an individual is admitted to the hospital, the hospital charges have the following characteristics:

(i)

Charges	Mean	Standard Deviation
Room	1000	500
Other	500	300

(ii) the covariance between an individual's Room Charges and Other Charges is 100,000.

An insurer issues a policy that reimburses 100% for Room Charges and 90% for Other Charges. The number of hospital admissions has a Poisson distribution with parameter 4.

Determine the variance of the insurer's payout for the policy.

(A) 9,600,000 (B) 9,700,000 (C) 9,800,000 (D) 9,900,000 (E) 10,000,000

8. An insurance company is developing a medical insurance policy. The actuary assumes the following:

(i) The probability that a policyholder will file a claim is .01.
(ii) A policyholder will file at most one claim.
(iii) The claim amount distribution is Gamma with mean 500 and variance 2500.

Determine the mean and variance of claims for a policy.

	Mean	Variance
(A)	5	2500
(B)	5	3000
(C)	50	2000
(D)	50	2500
(E)	50	3000

9. For aggregate claims S, you are given:

(i) $f_S(x) = \sum_{n=0}^{\infty} f_X^{*n}(x) \binom{n+2}{n} (.6)^3 (.4)^n$; and

(ii)

x	$f_X(x)$
1	.30
2	.60
3	.10

Determine $Var[S]$.

(A) 7.5 (B) 8.5 (C) 9.5 (D) 10.5 (E) 11.5

10. For aggregate claims S, you are given:

(i) $f_S(x) = \sum_{n=0}^{\infty} f_X^{*n}(x) \frac{e^{-50}(50)^n}{n!}$; and

(ii)

x	$f_X(x)$
1	.40
2	.50
3	.10

Determine $Var[S]$.

(A) 20.5 (B) 85.0 (C) 144.5 (D) 165.0 (E) 205.0

11. Suppose $f_{X_i}(x) = \beta_i e^{-\beta_i x}$. If X_1 and X_2 are independent which of the following is the density of $X_1 + X_2$? Assume $\beta_1 \neq \beta_2$.

(A) $\frac{\beta_1}{\beta_1 - \beta_2} e^{-\beta_1 x} + \frac{\beta_2}{\beta_1 - \beta_2} e^{-\beta_2 x}$

(B) $\frac{\beta_1 \beta_2}{\beta_1 - \beta_2} e^{-\beta_1 x} + \frac{\beta_1 \beta_2}{\beta_2 - \beta_1} e^{-\beta_2 x}$

(C) $\frac{\beta_1 \beta_2}{\beta_2 - \beta_1} e^{-\beta_1 x} + \frac{\beta_1 \beta_2}{\beta_2 - \beta_1} e^{-\beta_2 x}$

(D) $\frac{\beta_1 \beta_2}{\beta_2 - \beta_1} e^{-\beta_1 x} + \frac{\beta_1 \beta_2}{\beta_1 - \beta_2} e^{-\beta_2 x}$

(E) $\frac{\beta_1}{\beta_1 - \beta_2} e^{-\beta_2 x} + \frac{\beta_2}{\beta_2 - \beta_1} e^{-\beta_1 x}$

12. If X_1, X_2 are as in Question 11 with $\beta_1 = \frac{1}{2}$ and $\beta_2 = \frac{1}{3}$ what is the probability that $X_1 + X_2 > 5$?

(A) .38 (B) .40 (C) .42 (D) .44 (E) .50

13. Suppose $S = X_1 + \cdots + X_N$ is a compound-Poisson λ distribution. It is to be approximated by $Z = a + Y$ where $f_Y(y) = \left(\frac{\beta^\alpha}{\Gamma(\alpha)}\right) y^{\alpha-1} e^{-\beta y}$ is a Gamma distribution. The three parameters of the approximating distribution (i.e., a, α, β) are obtained by matching the mean, variance, and 3rd central moments of S and Z. Which of the following is the correct expression for a in terms of λ and moments of X?

(A) $\lambda\left(E[X] - \frac{E[X^3]}{2(E[X^2])^2}\right)$ (B) $\lambda\left(\frac{E[X]E[X^2]}{E[X^3]}\right)$ (C) $\lambda\left(E[X] - 2\frac{E[X^2]}{E[X^3]}\right)$

(D) $\lambda\left(E[X] - \frac{1}{2}\frac{(E[X^2])^2}{E[X^3]}\right)$ (E) $\lambda\left(E[X] - 2\frac{(E[X^2])^2}{E[X^3]}\right)$

SOLUTIONS TO UNIT REVIEW QUESTIONS

1. A straightforward use of basic relations in the collective risk model:

$$\begin{aligned}E[N] &= .75,\ E[N^2] = 1.25,\ Var(N) = \tfrac{11}{16}\\ E[X] &= Var(X) = \lambda = 2\\ Var(S) &= E[N]Var(X) + (E[X])^2 Var(N)\\ &= (.75)(2) + (2)^2\left(\tfrac{11}{16}\right) = 4.25,\end{aligned}$$

ANSWER E

2. Let S be the number of cigarettes smoked by the 8 people in a workday, and let X be the number of males in the group of 8. According to the description X is binomial with 8 trials and $p = .4$, thus

$$E[X] = 8(.4) = 3.2,\ Var(X) = 8(.4)(.6) = 1.92.$$

If X is known (i.e., given) then

$$E[S|X] = \underset{\text{males}}{X} \cdot \underset{\substack{\text{exp. male}\\ \text{smokes}}}{6} + \underset{\text{females}}{(8-X)} \cdot \underset{\substack{\text{exp. female}\\ \text{smokes}}}{3} = 24 + 3X$$

$$Var(S|X) = \underset{\text{males}}{X} \cdot \underset{\substack{\text{male}\\ \text{variance}}}{64} + \underset{\text{females}}{(8-X)} \cdot \underset{\substack{\text{female}\\ \text{variance}}}{31} = 248 + 33X.$$

By the double expectation theorem

$$E[S] = E[E[S|X]] = E[24+3X] = 24 + (3)(3.2) = 33.6$$

$$\begin{aligned}Var(S) &= E[Var(S|X)] + Var(E[S|X])\\ &= E[248+33X] + Var(24+3X)\\ &= 248 + 33E[X] + 9Var(X) = 370.88\end{aligned}$$

So $E[S] + \sigma_S = 33.6 + \sqrt{370.88} = 52.86,$ ANSWER E

3. $f_S(5)$ is the probability that 3 claims sum to 5: $X_1 + X_2 + X_3 = 5$. Simple combinatorics results in:

X_1	X_2	X_3	Probability
0	3	2	$p(.1)(.25)$
0	2	3	$p(.1)(.25)$
1	3	1	$(1-p)(.1)(.25)$
1	2	2	$(1-p)(.1)(.25)$
1	1	3	$(1-p)(.2)(.25)$

$\Rightarrow\ .06 = f_S(5) = .025p + .025p + .025(1-p) + .025(1-p) + .050(1-p)$

$\Rightarrow\ p = .8,$ ANSWER D

4. We seek the probability that $S > 3E[S] = 3E[N]E[X] = 3(.7)(1.9) = 3.99$. There are either 0, 1, or 3 claims each of which is 1 or 10. The only ways S exceeds 3.99 is with one claim of amount 10 (probability equals $Pr(N{=}1)Pr(X{=}10) = (.4)(.1) = .04$) or with three claims not all equal to 1 (probability equals $Pr(N{=}3)Pr(\text{not all } X_i = 1) = (.1)(1-.9^3) = .0271$).
So $Pr(S > 3.99) = .04 + .0271 = .0671$, ANSWER B

5. S = monthly rainfall $= X_1 + \cdots + X_N$ where N is the number of days of rain and X_i is the amount of the ith rainfall. From the description N is binomial with 30 trials and $p = .10$ so

$$E[N] = 30(.10) = 3,\ Var(N) = 30(.10)(.90) = 2.7,\ M_N(t) = (.90 + .10e^t)^{30}.$$

X has a $\Gamma(\alpha, \beta)$ distribution (i.e., $f_X(x) = \frac{\beta^\alpha}{\Gamma(\alpha)} x^{\alpha-1} e^{-\beta x}$, $E[X] = \frac{\alpha}{\beta}$, $Var(X) = \frac{\alpha}{\beta^2}$, $M_X(t) = \left(1 - \frac{t}{\beta}\right)^{-\alpha}$) and $.5 = \mu = \frac{\alpha}{\beta}$, $.5 = \sigma^2 = \frac{\alpha}{\beta^2}$ implies $\alpha = \frac{1}{2}$, $\beta = 1$. So $M_X(t) = (1-t)^{-.5}$.

I. $E[S] = E[N] \cdot E[X] = (3)(.5) = 1.5$, True.

II. $Var(S) = E[N] \cdot Var(X) + (E[X])^2 Var(N) = (3)(.5) + (.5)^2(2.7) = 2.175$. False.

III. $M_S(t) = M_N(\ln M_X(t)) = (q + pM_X(t))^{30} = (.90 + .10(1-t)^{-.5})^{30}$, False, ANSWER E

6. The premium $Q = \mu_S + 2\sigma_S$ is based on a group of 40 males and 60 females:

$$\mu_S = 40\mu_M + 60\mu_F = 320$$
$$\sigma_S^2 = 40\sigma_M^2 + 60\sigma_F^2 = 760$$

since $S = \sum_{i=1}^{40} X_i^{Male} + \sum_{j=1}^{60} X_j^{Female}$. Thus $Q = 320 + 2\sqrt{760} = 375.14$.
When the number of males, N, is binomial with $n = 100$ and $p = .40$ there are a random number of male terms in S and a random number (i.e. $100 - N$) of female terms. This is a clue to apply the double expectation theorem with conditioning on N:

$$E[S|N] = N\mu_M + (100-N)\mu_F = 400 - 2N$$

$$Var(S|N) = N\sigma_M^2 + (100-N)\sigma_F^2 = 100 - 6N$$

$$E[N] = 100(.4) = 40,\ Var(N) = 100(.4)(.6) = 24,$$

thus

$$\mu_S = E[E[S|N]] = E[400 - 2N] = 400 - 2(40) = 320$$

$$\begin{aligned} \sigma_S^2 &= E[Var(S|N)] + Var(E[S|N]) \\ &= E[1000-6N] + Var(400-2N) \\ &= 1000 - 6(40) + (-2)^2 24 = 856. \end{aligned}$$

Hence $P = \mu_S + 2\sigma_S = 320 + 2\sqrt{856} = 378.51$ and $P/Q = 1.009$. ANSWER C

7. Aggregate claims, S, is compound Poisson:

$S = X_1 + \cdots + X_N$, $N \sim$ Poisson ($\lambda = 4$)

X_i = claim from i^{th} hospitalization.

The claim payout can be written as $X = R + (.8)O$ (R = room charge, O = other, with R and O dependent). From given data

$$E[X] = E[R] + (.8)E[O] = 1400$$

$$Var(X) = Var(R) + (.8)^2 Var(O) + 2(1)(.8)Cov(R, O) = 467{,}600.$$

Thus $E[X^2] = Var(X) + (E[X])^2 = 2{,}427{,}600$ and from the compound-Poisson formula $Var(S) = \lambda E[X^2] = 4(2{,}467{,}600) = 9{,}710{,}400$. ANSWER B

8. Claims against a single policy, S, is either 0 or X where $E[X] = 500$, $Var(X) = 2500$. It is convenient to view S as $X_1 + \cdots + X_N$ where $Pr(N = 0) = .99$, $Pr(N = 1) = .01$ (i.e., there is at most one claim and the probability of a claim is .01) Hence, from the collective model,

$$E[S] = E[N]E[X] = (.01)(500) = 5$$

$$Var(S) = E[N]Var(X) + (E[X])^2 Var(N) = (.01)2500 + (500)^2(.01)(.99) = 2500.$$

ANSWER A

9. For the collective model $S = X_1 + \cdots + X_N$ we know $f_S(x) = \sum_{n=0}^{\infty} Pr(N = n) f_X^{*n}(x)$. Comparing this with $\sum_{n=0}^{\infty} f_X^{*n}(x)\binom{n+2}{n}(.6)^3(.4)^n$, we see that $f_N(n) = Pr(N = n) = \binom{n+2}{n}(.6)^3(.4)^n$, which is the Negative Binomial distribution. From the given information $E[X] = \sum x \cdot f_X(x) = 1.8$, $E[X^2] = \sum x^2 f_X(x) = 3.6$ and $Var(X) = 3.6 - 1.8^2 = .36$. If N is the number of failures until r successes are obtained in a sequence of Bernoulli trials with $p = Pr(\text{Success})$, then

$$f_N(n) = \binom{n+r-1}{n} p^r q^n$$

$$E[N] = \frac{rq}{p},\ Var(N) = \frac{rq}{p^2}.$$

Here $r = 3$, $p = .6$ so $E[N] = \frac{3(.4)}{(.6)} = 2$, $Var(N) = \frac{E[N]}{p} = \frac{2}{.6} = \frac{10}{3}$. Finally,

$$Var(S) = E[N]Var(X) + (E[X])^2 Var(N) = 2(.36) + (1.8)^2\left(\frac{10}{3}\right) = 11.52.$$

ANSWER E

10. The format is the same as Question 9 above. This time $f_N(n) = e^{-50}\frac{50^n}{n!}$ so that N is Poisson with parameter $\lambda = 50$: $E[N] = Var(N) = \lambda = 50$. A routine calculation with (ii) gives $E[X] = 1.7$, $E[X^2] = 3.3$, $Var(X) = .41$. Hence

$$Var(S) = E[N]Var(X) + (E[X])^2 Var(N) = 50(.41) + (1.7)^2(50) = 165. \qquad \text{ANSWER D}$$

11. In general

$$f_{X_1+X_2}(x) = \int_{y=0}^{x} f_{X_1}(y) f_{X_2}(x-y)\,dy = \int_{y=0}^{x} \beta_1 e^{-\beta_1 y} \beta_2 e^{-\beta_2(x-y)}\,dy$$

$$= \beta_1\beta_2 e^{-\beta_2 x} \int_{y=0}^{x} e^{-(\beta_1-\beta_2)y}\,dy$$

$$= \beta_1\beta_2 e^{-\beta_2 x}\left[\frac{1-e^{-(\beta_1-\beta_2)x}}{\beta_1-\beta_2}\right]$$

$$= \frac{\beta_1\beta_2}{\beta_1-\beta_2} e^{-\beta_2 x} + \frac{\beta_1\beta_2}{\beta_2-\beta_1} e^{-\beta_1 x} \qquad \text{ANSWER D}$$

12. $f_{X_1+X_2}(x) = \frac{(1/6)}{(1/6)} e^{-x/3} + \frac{(1/6)}{(-1/6)} e^{-x/2} = e^{-x/3} - e^{-x/2}$. Hence

$$Pr(X_1 + X_2 > 5) = \int_5^\infty (e^{-x/3} - e^{-x/2})dx$$

$$= -3e^{-x/3} + 2e^{-x/2}\Big|_5^\infty = 0 - (-3e^{-5/3} + 2e^{-5/2}) = .402. \qquad \text{ANSWER B}$$

13.

	S-distribution		Z-distribution
mean:	$\lambda \cdot E[X]$	=	$a + \frac{\alpha}{\beta}$
variance:	$\lambda \cdot E[X^2]$	=	$\frac{\alpha}{\beta^2}$
3rd Central:	$\lambda \cdot E[X^3]$	=	$\frac{2\alpha}{\beta^3}$
	Compound Poisson facts		Gamma facts

Dividing equations (2) and (3) yields $\beta = \frac{2E[X^2]}{E[X^3]}$. Substituting this expression into Equation (2) gives $\alpha = \beta^2 \lambda E[X^2] = 4\lambda \frac{(E[X^2])^3}{(E[X^3])^2}$. Finally, substituting these results into Equation (1) results in $a = \lambda E[X] - 2\lambda \frac{(E[X^2])^2}{E[X^3]}$ ANSWER E

Note: Z is known as a translated Gamma distribution. Since the compound Poisson is skewed to the right the translated Gamma (also skewed to the right) approximation has more accuracy in the right tail than a normal approximation to a compound-Poisson would have.

APPENDIX A
Moment Generating Functions

$M_X(t)$ = moment generating function of X, a real valued function of t

$$\equiv E[\underbrace{e^{tX}}_{\substack{\text{function of}\\ X \text{ for each } t}}] = \sum \text{ or } \int e^{tx} \cdot f_X(x)$$

Properties (1) $M_X(0) = 1,\ \underbrace{E[X^n]}_{\substack{n^{th} \text{ moment}\\ \text{about origin}}} = \underbrace{M_X^{(n)}(0)}_{\substack{n^{th} \text{ derivative}\\ \text{at the origin}}}$

$\therefore\ \mu_X = M_X'(0)$ and $\sigma_X^2 = M_X''(0) - (M_X'(0))^2$

(2) Set $R(t) = ln\, M_X(t)$; then $R(0) = 0$, $\mu_X = R'(0)$, $\sigma_X^2 = R''(0)$ and the third central moment of X is given by $E[(X - \mu_X)^3] = R'''(0)$ (measures skewness or non-symmetry of the distribution; many claim and loss models are skewed to the right meaning a positive third central moment and a long thin tail at the right).

density of a distribution skewed to right

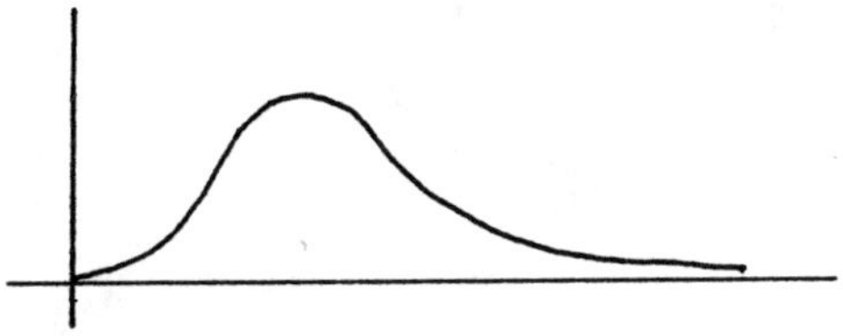

(3) (i) $M_{aX}(t) = M_X(at)$

(ii) $M_{X+Y}(t) = M_X(t) \cdot M_Y(t)$, if X and Y are independent

(iii) If $X_1, \ldots, X_n$ are independent and identically distributed like X, then

$$M_{\Sigma X_i}(t) = M_{X_1}(t) \cdots M_{X_n}(t) = (M_X(t))^n$$

$$M_{\bar{X}}(t) = M_{\frac{1}{n}\Sigma X_i}(t) = M_{\Sigma X_i}(t/n) = (M_X(t/n))^n$$

(4) If $M_X(t) = M_Y(t)$ then X and Y have the same distribution. (e.g., if $M_X(t) = e^{t^2/2}$, then X has the $N(0,1)$ distribution since if $Y = N(0,1)$ one has $M_Y(t) = e^{t^2/2}$.) This property is used with a list of generating functions of well-known discrete and continuous parametric families to identify distributions as belonging to one of these families. Generating functions for commonly used parametric families are given in Units 2 and 3 to follow.

Example Suppose X has the Poisson density function $f(x) = \frac{e^{-\lambda} \cdot \lambda^x}{x!}$ for $x = 0, 1, 2, \ldots$. Since X is discrete, then

$$M_X(t) = E[e^{tX}] = \sum_{x=0}^{\infty} e^{tx} \cdot \frac{e^{-\lambda} \cdot \lambda^x}{x!} = e^{-\lambda} \cdot \sum_{x=0}^{\infty} \frac{(\lambda e^t)^x}{x!} = e^{-\lambda} \cdot e^{\lambda e^t} = e^{\lambda(e^t - 1)}.$$

So if X_i has a Poisson distribution with parameter λ_i, and if the X_i are independent, the generating function of ΣX_i is

$$\begin{aligned} M_{\Sigma X_i}(t) &= M_{X_1}(t) \cdots M_{X_n}(t) \\ &= e^{\lambda_1(e^t-1)} \cdots e^{\lambda_n(e^t-1)} \\ &= e^{(\Sigma\lambda_i)(e^t-1)} \\ &= \text{generating function of a Poisson variable with parameter } \Sigma\lambda_i. \end{aligned}$$

Thus ΣX_i is Poisson with parameter $\Sigma\lambda_i$.

APPENDIX B

Mixed Distributions

1. MAKING A MIXED DISTRIBUTION

Ingredients: D (discrete variable), C (continuous variable), and a number α satisfying $0 < \alpha < 1$

Procedure: Use ingredients to determine the value of a random variable X having a mixed distribution

Step 1 Flip a coin such that $\alpha = Pr(\text{Heads})$. (Let I be the number of heads; I is an indicator or Bernoulli variable.)

Step 2 If the flip produced a Head do the experiment producing a value of the discrete variable D and take this number as the value of X. If the flip produced a tail do the experiment producing a value of the continuous variable C and take this number as the value of X.

Consequence: $X|_{I=0} = C$, $\quad X|_{I=1} = D$, $\quad \alpha = Pr(I = 1)$

$$\Rightarrow \quad F_X(x) = Pr(X \le x) = Pr(X \le x \mid I = 0) \cdot Pr(I = 0) + Pr(X \le x \mid I = 1) \cdot Pr(I = 1)$$

$$= Pr(C \le x) \cdot (1-\alpha) + Pr(D \le x) \cdot \alpha$$

$$= (1-\alpha) \cdot F_C(x) + \alpha \cdot F_D(x)$$

$=$ weighted average of the two given distribution functions

2. DECOMPOSING A MIXED DISTRIBUTION

Recall that any distribution function $F_X(x)$ is right continuous and

$$Pr(X = c) + Pr(X < c) = Pr(X \le c) = F_X(c)$$

$$\Rightarrow Pr(X = c) = F_X(c) - Pr(X < c)$$

$$= F_X(c) - \lim_{x \to c^-} F_X(x)$$

$$= \begin{cases} 0 \text{ if } F_X \text{ is continuous at } c, \text{ or} \\ \text{height of jump discontinuity at} \\ c \text{ if } F_X \text{ is not continuous at } c \end{cases}$$

Therefore points at which F_X has jump discontinuities are connected with the "discrete part" of the distribution. The following example shows how to use this idea in order to split F_X into its discrete and continuous parts.

Example

Suppose the distribution function is given by

$$F_X(x) = \begin{cases} 0 & x < 0 \\ .25 & x = 0 \\ .70\,\frac{x}{1000} + .25 & 0 < x < 1000 \\ 1 & 1000 \le x \end{cases}$$

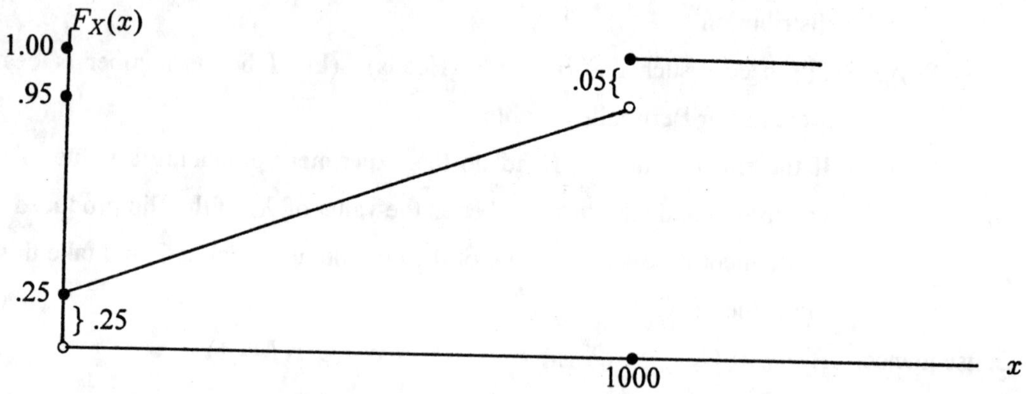

Note the jump discontinuities at $x = 0$ and 1000. Consider a discrete variable D defined by

$$f_D(0) = \frac{.25}{.25 + .05} = \frac{5}{6},\ f_D(1000) = \frac{.05}{.25 + .05} = \frac{1}{6}$$

where the probability assigned at a jump discontinuity point is the fraction of the total of all jumps. Then

$$F_D(x) = \begin{cases} 0 & x < 0 \\ \frac{5}{6} & 0 \le x < 1000 \\ 1 & 1000 \le x \end{cases}$$

and $F_X(x) - .30\ F_D(x)$ is calculated as

$$\underbrace{F_X(x) - .30F_D(x)}_{\text{graph below}} = \begin{cases} 0 - (.3)(0) = 0 & x < 0 \\ .25 - (.3)\left(\frac{5}{6}\right) = 0 & x = 0 \\ .70\,\frac{x}{1000} + .25 - (.3)\left(\frac{5}{6}\right) = \frac{.70x}{1000} & 0 < x < 1000 \\ 1 - (.3)(1) = .7 & 1000 \le x \end{cases}$$

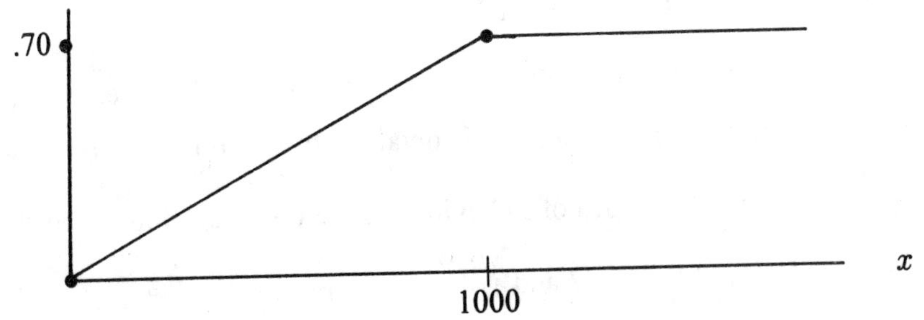

Note that this difference is non-decreasing and continuous but is not a distribution function since it "levels off" at .70 instead of at 1. Set $F_C(x) = \frac{1}{.70}\left[F_X(x) - .30F_D(x)\right]$:

$$F_C(x) = \begin{cases} 0 & x < 0 \\ \frac{x}{1000} & 0 \le x < 1000 \\ 1 & 1000 \le x \end{cases}$$

This is the distribution function of a continuous variable C which is uniform over the range of 0 to 1000. Solving the equation above for F_X in terms of F_C and F_D yields

$$F_X(x) = \underbrace{.70\ F_C(x)}_{\text{cont. part}} + \underbrace{.30F_D(x)}_{\text{disc. part}}$$

How could such a distribution arise in a natural way? Suppose a group dental plan has a 100 annual deductible and reimburses the individual for all his dental expenses over 100 up to a max annual reimbursement of 1000.

X = reimbursement

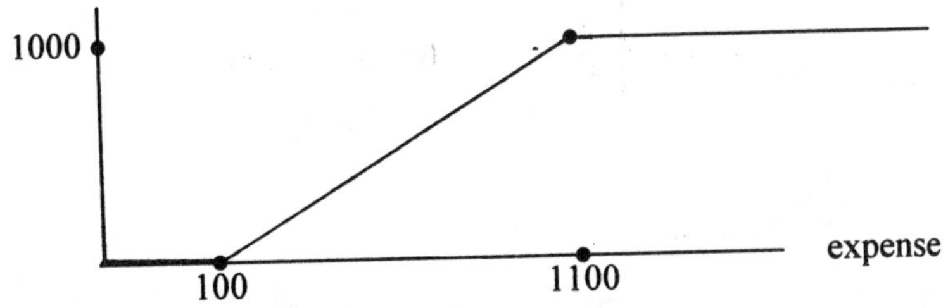

Suppose 25% of those covered have expenses less than 100 and 5% of those covered have expenses greater than 1100, and suppose the expenses of the other 70% are uniformly distributed between 100 and 1100. Then

$$F_X(0) = Pr(\text{expense} \le 100) = .25$$

$$F_X(1000) - \lim_{x \to 1000} F_X(x) = Pr(X = 1000) = Pr(\text{expense} \ge 1100) = .05$$

and $F_X(x)$ is linear between 0 and 1000. This is exactly the picture with which we began.

3. CALCULATING MOMENTS OF MIXED DISTRIBUTIONS

Suppose $F_X = (1-\alpha)F_C + \alpha F_D$ where C is continuous and D is discrete. Then there is a similar decomposition of f_X where $f_C = F_C'$ and f_D is obtained from F_D by differencing.

That is, if $x_1 < \cdots < x_k$ are the values of D having non-zero probabilities, then

$f_D(x_i) = F_D(x_i) - F_D(x_{i-1})$ for $i \geq 2$ and $f_D(x_1) = F_D(x_1)$.

Example

$F_X = .70F_C + .30F_D$ in 2, above.

$$F_C(x) = \begin{cases} 0 & x \leq 0 \\ \frac{x}{1000} & 0 \leq x \leq 1000 \\ 1 & 1000 \leq x \end{cases} \quad \Rightarrow \quad f_C(x) = \frac{1}{1000},\ 0 < x < 1000$$

$$F_D(x) = \begin{cases} 0 & x < 0 \\ \frac{5}{6} & 0 \leq x < 1000 \\ 1 & 1000 \leq x \end{cases} \quad \Rightarrow \quad x_1 = 0, \quad x_2 = 1000$$

$$f_D(x_1) = \frac{5}{6},\ f_D(x_2) = \frac{1}{6}$$

Notice that f_D is non-zero only at $x = 0$ and 1000, whereas f_C is non-zero at $0 < x < 1000$. It can always be arranged so that the points where f_D is non-zero have nothing in common with the set where f_C is non-zero since points have no probability in continuous models (*i.e.*, there is no difference between $f_C(x) = \frac{1}{1000}$ for $0 \leq x \leq 1000$ and $f_C(x) = \frac{1}{1000}$ for $0 < x < 1000$).

Due to this non-overlapping we can write

$$f_X(x) = .70f_C(x) + .30f_D(x)$$

$$= \begin{cases} .70 \cdot \frac{1}{1000} & 0 < x < 1000 \\ 0 & \text{otherwise} \end{cases} + \begin{cases} (.3)\frac{5}{6} & x = 0 \\ (.3)\frac{1}{6} & x = 1000 \\ 0 & \text{otherwise} \end{cases}$$

$$= \begin{cases} .25 & x = 0 \\ .05 & x = 1000 \\ \frac{.70}{1000} & 0 < x < 1000 \\ 0 & \text{otherwise} \end{cases} \quad \begin{matrix} \left.\right\} \text{disc. part} \\ \\ - \text{ cont. part} \\ \end{matrix}$$

Moments about the origin are then calculated as $E[X^k] = .70 \cdot E[C^k] + .30 \cdot E[D^k]$ in terms of f_C and f_D, or as the following in terms of f_X:

$$E[X^k] = \sum_{\substack{x \text{ such} \\ \text{that} \\ f_D(x) \neq 0}} x^k \cdot f_X(x) + \int_{\substack{x \text{ such} \\ \text{that} \\ f_C(x) \neq 0}} x^k \cdot f_X(x)\, dx.$$

Using the first of these approaches for $E[X]$ results in $E[C] = 500$, since C is uniform over (0,1000), and $E[D] = 0 \cdot \frac{5}{6} + 1000 \cdot \frac{1}{6} = 166.\bar{6}$, so

$$E[X] = .7(500) + .3(166.\bar{6}) = 400$$

The second approach yields

$$\begin{aligned} E[X] &= 0 \cdot f_X(0) + 1000 \cdot f_X(1000) + \int_0^{1000} x \cdot \frac{.70}{1000}\, dx \\ &= 0(.25) + 1000(.05) + .70 \left. \frac{x^2}{2000} \right|_0^{1000} \\ &= 0 + 50 + (.70)(500) = 400. \end{aligned}$$

<u>Warning:</u>

$$\begin{aligned} Var(X) &\neq .70 \cdot Var(C) + .30 \cdot Var(D) \\ Var(X) &= E[X^2] - (E[X])^2 \\ &= (.70 \cdot E[C^2] + .30 \cdot E[D^2]) \\ &\quad - (.70 \cdot E[C] + .30 \cdot E[D])^2 \end{aligned}$$

Linearity only works for moments about the origin!

APPENDIX C

Convex Combinations

Convex combinations are a generalization of the idea that a mixed distribution X is a "weighted average" of a discrete part and a continuous part. With convex combinations one can form a weighted average of more than 2 variables. If they are all discrete, the resulting combination is discrete. If they are all continuous, it is continuous. If some are discrete and others continuous, then the resulting combination has a mixed distribution.

Suppose an insurer has n different classes of claims, and suppose claims of the ith class are distributed like C_i having density function f_i. Let $100\alpha_i$ be the percentage of all claims which are of class i. If C is a randomly chosen claim where all classes are mixed together, it is intuitive that its distribution is a "blend" or "weighted average" of the distributions of the various C_i. In fact

$$\begin{aligned} F_C(c) &= Pr(C \le c) = Pr(\text{Randomly selected claim} \le c) \\ &= \sum_{i=1}^{n} Pr(\{C \le c\} \cap \text{Claim of Class } i) \\ &= \sum_{i=1}^{n} Pr(\text{Claim of Class } i) \cdot Pr(C \le c \mid \text{Claim of Class } i) \\ &= \sum_{i=1}^{n} \alpha_i \cdot Pr(C_i \le c) \\ &= \sum_{i=1}^{n} \alpha_i \cdot F_i(c), \end{aligned}$$

which is a convex combination (all $\alpha_i > 0$ and $\Sigma\alpha_i = 1$) of the distribution functions of $C_1, \ldots, C_n$.

It follows that

(i) $f_C(c) = \sum_{i=1}^{n} \alpha_i \cdot f_i(c)$

(ii) $E[C^k] = \sum_{i=1}^{n} \alpha_i \cdot E[C_i^k]$

(iii) $M_C(t) = \sum_{i=1}^{n} \alpha_i \cdot M_{C_i}(t)$

Example

70% of claims are distributed like C_1, with $f_{C_1}(c_1) = \dfrac{2(1000 - c_1)}{1000^2}$ for $0 \le c_1 \le 1000$, and 30% of claims are distributed like C_2, with $f_{C_2}(c_2) = \dfrac{2(5000 - c_2)}{5000^2}$ for $0 \le c_2 \le 5000$. Find the density of C and the average overall claim.

By (i) above

$$f_C(c) = .70 \cdot f_{C_1}(c) + .30 \cdot f_{C_2}(c)$$

$$= \begin{cases} \dfrac{1.4(1000-c)}{1000^2} & 0 < c < 1000 \\ 0 & \text{otherwise} \end{cases} + \begin{cases} \dfrac{.6(5000-c)}{5000^2} & 0 < c < 5000 \\ 0 & \text{otherwise} \end{cases}$$

$$= \begin{cases} .00152 - .000001424c & 0 < c < 1000 \\ .00012 - .000000024c & 1000 < c < 5000 \\ 0 & \text{otherwise} \end{cases}$$

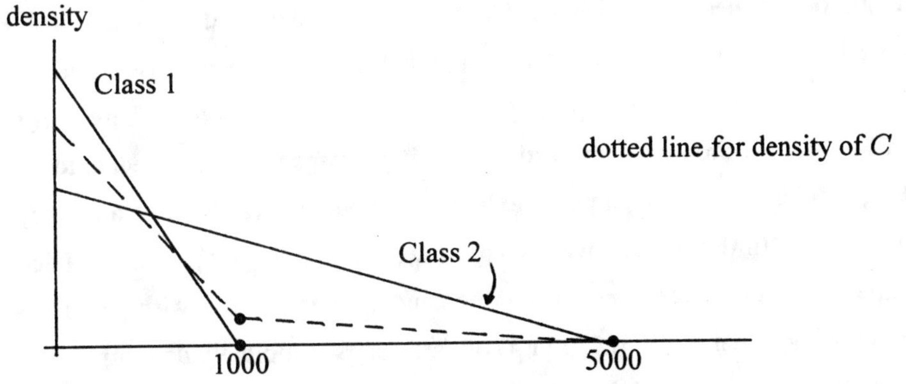

The simplest way to get $E[C]$ is as $.70 \cdot E[C_1] + .30 \cdot E[C_2]$, which is

$$.70 \int_0^{1000} c \cdot \frac{2(1000-c)}{1000^2}\, dc + .30 \int_0^{5000} c \cdot \frac{2(5000-c)}{5000^2}\, dc = .70\left(\frac{1000}{3}\right) + .30\left(\frac{5000}{3}\right) = 733.3\overline{3}$$

UNIT 2: LOSS DISTRIBUTIONS

Parametric Versus Empirical Models

In the collective risk model for aggregate losses, $S = X_1 + \cdots + X_N$, where the X_i are independent and identically distributed like X, the term **loss variable** is used in reference to X. Its distribution is called a **loss distribution** and X serves as a model for the amount of a single payment or loss. It might represent the actual dollar loss of a policyholder as a result of a covered loss event, it might represent the claim amount for this loss paid by the insurer, or it might be the amount received by the insurer from a reinsurer as a result of this loss and a reinsurance agreement.

The question immediately arises: How should one model the distribution of X? If one assumes that the future is another random sample from the distribution of past losses, and if there are a large number of past observations, it is appealing to use an empirical model where $F_X(x)$, the **empirical distribution function**, is simply the proportion of all past losses less than or equal to x. Simplicity is the key here. But, problems include (i) a possible lack of smoothness, (ii) extrapolation beyond the past data to reflect future trends (inflation) or coverage adjustments (removing or increasing a deductible), and (iii) lack of parsimony. All of these concerns can be handled theoretically with parametric models for the loss distribution where a handful[1] (1, 2, 3 or 4) of parameters completely determines the $f_X(x)$ graph and all moments of the X-distribution. The difficult practical side of parametric modeling is the estimation of the parameters from incomplete data (i.e., truncated or censored) and the numerical procedures necessary to approximate likelihood (or other types of) estimators.

There is a rich variety of parametric families of models available to the practitioner as well as a number of transformation techniques for enlarging the families. Virtually any smooth, regular $f_X(x)$ graph can be suitably approximated by a member of one or more of these families. Next we take a look at some of these families and these enlargement techniques.

Operations on Loss Models Used to Enlarge Parametric Families

The discussion in this section concerns specific 1-to-1 transformations, $Y = g(X)$, and the relation of the Y and X density functions. In general we know that

$$f_Y(y) = f_X(g^{-1}(y))\left|\frac{dg^{-1}(y)}{dy}\right|.$$

Throughout we assume $Pr(X \geq 0) = 1$.

The first of these transformations to be examined is $Y = \theta X$ where θ is a positive scale factor that could be used to represent an inflationary trend in X.

---

[1] parsimonious in contrast with the empirical $F_X(x)$ which defies compact expression.

Scalar Multiplication: $Y = \theta X,\ x = g^{-1}(y) = \left(\frac{y}{\theta}\right),\ \theta > 0$

$$f_Y(y) = f_X\left(\frac{y}{\theta}\right) \cdot \frac{1}{\theta}$$

This idea can be used to explain how the family of exponential distributions arises from the simplest exponential model, $f_X(x) = e^{-x}$, having an expected value of 1. If $Y = \theta X$, by the above

$$f_Y(y) = f_X\left(\frac{y}{\theta}\right) \cdot \frac{1}{\theta} = \frac{1}{\theta}e^{-y/\theta},$$

the **exponential density** with parameter θ. It can also be used to show that aY is exponential with parameter $a\theta$ if Y is exponential with parameter θ, that is, scalar multiplication keeps you within the exponential family.

This same technique can be used to enlarge a **1-parameter gamma family** into the usual 2-parameter family. Consider $f_X(x) = x^{\alpha-1}e^{-x}/\Gamma(\alpha)$ where

$$\Gamma(\alpha) = \int_0^\infty x^{\alpha-1}e^{-x}dx$$

is the so-called **gamma function**[2]. If $Y = \theta X$, then

$$f_Y(y) = f_X\left(\frac{y}{\theta}\right) \cdot \frac{1}{\theta} = \frac{1}{\theta}\left(\frac{y}{\theta}\right)^{\alpha-1} e^{-(y/\theta)}/\Gamma(\alpha) = \left(\frac{1}{\theta^\alpha\Gamma(\alpha)}\right)y^{\alpha-1}e^{-y/\theta}$$

is the usual **two-parameter gamma distribution** with $E[Y] = \alpha\theta$, $Var(Y) = \alpha\theta^2$ and $M_Y(t) = (1-\theta t)^{-\alpha}$ for $t < \frac{1}{\theta}$. $F_Y(y) = Pr(Y \le y) = Pr(\theta X \le y) = Pr(X \le \frac{y}{\theta}) = \Gamma(\alpha; \frac{y}{\theta})$ where $\Gamma(\alpha; x)$, the **incomplete gamma function**, is given by

$$\Gamma(\alpha; x) = Pr(X \le x) = \int_0^x \frac{t^{\alpha-1}e^{-t}}{\Gamma(\alpha)}dt,$$

i.e., the distribution function of the 1-parameter gamma distribution. Similarly, if Y has a gamma distribution with parameters α, θ, then aY has a gamma distribution with parameters α, $a\theta$.

Next we examine the transformation $Y = X^{1/\tau}$. When τ is positive the Y distribution is called the **transformed X-distribution**. When τ is negative we change the notation to $Y = X^{1/(-\tau)} = X^{-1/\tau}$ so that we may keep the parameter positive. In this case Y is called the **inverse transformed X-distribution** (special case: $Y = X^{-1}$ is called the **inverse X-distribution**).

---

2 Recall $\Gamma(1) = 1$, $\Gamma(\alpha) = (\alpha-1)\Gamma(\alpha-1)$, and $\Gamma(n) = (n-1)!$ if n is a positive integer.

Transformed: $\begin{cases} Y = X^{1/\tau}, x = g^{-1}(y) = y^{\tau}, \left|\frac{dx}{dy}\right| = \tau y^{\tau-1}, \tau > 0 \\ f_Y(y) = \tau y^{\tau-1} f_X(y^{\tau}) \end{cases}$

Inverse Transformed: $\begin{cases} Y = X^{-1/\tau}, x = g^{-1}(y) = y^{-\tau}, \left|\frac{dx}{dy}\right| = \tau y^{-\tau-1}, \tau > 0 \\ f_Y(y) = \tau y^{-\tau-1} f_X(y^{-\tau}) \end{cases}$

Inverse: $\begin{cases} Y = X^{-1}, x = y^{-1}, \left|\frac{dx}{dy}\right| = y^{-2} \\ f_Y(y) = y^{-2} f_X(y^{-1}) \end{cases}$

Example 1 Let X have the exponential density $f_X(x) = e^{-x}$. Compute the densities of $Y_1 = X^{(1/2)}$ (a transformed exponential) and $Y_2 = X^{-(1/2)}$ (an inverse transformed exponential).

Solution From the equations preceding the example

$$f_{Y_1}(y) = 2y^{2-1} f_X(y^2) = 2ye^{-y^2} = \frac{2y}{e^{y^2}}$$

$$f_{Y_2}(y) = 2y^{-2-1} f_X(y^{-2}) = \frac{2e^{-y^{-2}}}{y^3} = \frac{2}{y^3 e^{1/y^2}}$$

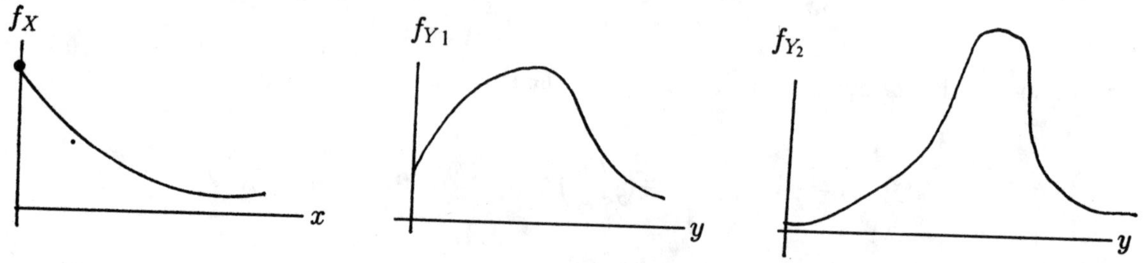

Note: These are just a rough indication of the shapes available from the transformation $Y = X^{1/\tau}$ and the exponential distribution of X.

□

The final type of transformation considered is **exponential**:

Exponential: $\begin{cases} Y = e^X, x = ln(y), \left|\frac{dx}{dy}\right| = \frac{1}{y} \\ f_Y(y) = \frac{1}{y} f_X(ln(y)) \\ E[Y^k] = E[(e^X)^k] = E[e^{kX}] = M_X(k) \end{cases}$

This is the technique by which a **lognormal** distribution is created from a normal distribution. Suppose X is normally distributed with parameters μ, σ^2. Then $Y = e^X$ is said to have a log-normal distribution (i.e., its log is normally distributed - perhaps not the best choice of terminology).

Y a log-normal:
$$\begin{cases} f_Y(y) = \frac{1}{y} f_X(ln(y)) = \frac{1}{y\sqrt{2\pi}\sigma} \cdot exp\left(-\frac{1}{2}\left(\frac{lny-\mu}{\sigma}\right)^2\right) \\ E[Y^k] = M_X(k) = e^{\mu k + \sigma^2 k^2/2} \end{cases}$$

If $\mu = 0, \sigma^2 = 1$ (i.e., X is the Standard Normal) then $f_Y(y) = \frac{1}{y\sqrt{2\pi}} \cdot exp\left[-\frac{1}{2}(ln\, y)^2\right]$ has the graph in the figure below.

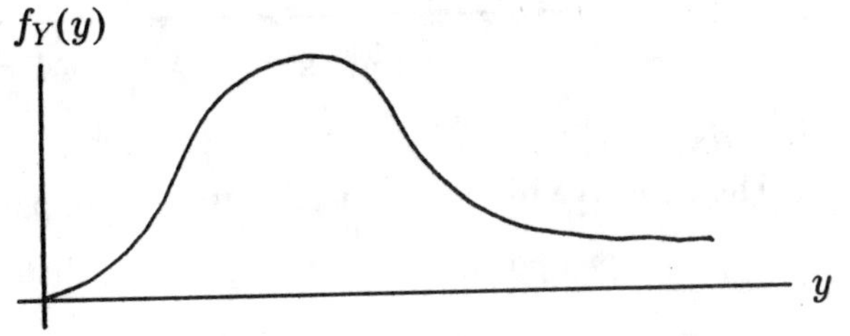

Mixing of Distributions

There are both continuous and discrete versions of this technique. We begin with the continuous version. An example is used to introduce the ideas. Mixing parametric families can result in the creation of other parametric families.

Suppose N has a Poisson distribution. Then $f_N(n) = e^{-\lambda}\frac{\lambda^n}{n!}$, $E[N] = Var(N) = \lambda$. N is often used to model the random number of occurrences of some "rare" event over a period of time, for example, the number of claims against a car insurance policy over a policy year. In a portfolio of car insurance policies the same λ is not appropriate for all policies. Certain variables such as location (urban versus rural) and the number of miles a car is driven in a year would tend to affect the expected number of claims, λ. So it might be helpful to view $e^{-\lambda}\frac{\lambda^n}{n!}$ as $f_N(n|\Lambda = \lambda)$ rather than as $f_N(n)$, and to think of the "parameter" Λ as having a probability distribution reflecting the variation in λ over the portfolio. In this case one can obtain the joint density of N and Λ as $f_N(n|\Lambda = \lambda)f_\Lambda(\lambda)$, and then the N-marginal density, $f_N(n)$, by integrating out (or summing out) the λ variable in the joint density. N would then represent the random number of claims from a randomly selected policy in the portfolio. $E[N]$ would represent the average number of claims per car in the portfolio.

Example 2 Suppose $f_N(n|\Lambda = \lambda) = e^{-\lambda} \cdot \frac{\lambda^n}{n!}$ for $n = 0, 1, \ldots$ and suppose Λ has a gamma distribution[3] with parameters α and θ: $f_\Lambda(\lambda) = \frac{1}{\theta^\alpha \Gamma(\alpha)}\lambda^{\alpha-1}e^{-\lambda/\theta}$ for $0 \le \lambda < \infty$. Show that N has the negative binomial distribution and relate its parameters to α and θ.

---

[3] For some authors, $f(x) = \frac{\theta^\alpha}{\Gamma(\alpha)}x^{\alpha-1}e^{-\theta x}$ with $E[X] = \frac{\alpha}{\theta}$ and $Var(X)=\frac{\alpha}{\theta^2}$. The way to avoid confusion is to say that X is gamma with given mean and variance. It is then up to you calculate the parameters in the form you are familiar with.

Solution We leave to the reader to verify that

$$f_N(n) = \int_0^\infty f_N(n|\lambda) f_\Lambda(\lambda) d\lambda$$

$$= \int_0^\infty e^{-\lambda} \cdot \frac{\lambda^n}{n!} \cdot \frac{1}{\theta^\alpha \Gamma(\alpha)} \cdot \lambda^{\alpha-1} \cdot e^{-\lambda/\theta} d\lambda$$

$$= \frac{\left(\frac{\theta}{1+\theta}\right)^{n+\alpha} \cdot \Gamma(n+\alpha)}{n! \Gamma(\alpha) (\theta)^\alpha} \int_0^\infty \underbrace{\frac{1}{\left(\frac{\theta}{1+\theta}\right)^{n+\alpha} \cdot \Gamma(n+\alpha)} \cdot \lambda^{n+\alpha-1} \cdot e^{-\lambda/\left(\frac{\theta}{1+\theta}\right)}}_{\text{Gamma density with parameters } n+\alpha \text{ and } \frac{\theta}{1+\theta}} d\lambda$$

The remaining integral is thus 1. The **negative binomial distribution**[4] with parameters r, p has density function $f(n) = \binom{r+n-1}{n} q^n p^r$. When r is a positive integer it gives the distribution of the number of failures in a series of Bernoulli trials until one obtains r successes. Now $\binom{r+n-1}{n} = \frac{(r+n-1)!}{n!(r-1)!} = \frac{\Gamma(r+n)}{n!\Gamma(r)}$. Following a little rearrangement we have from the above that

$$f_N(n) = \frac{\Gamma(\alpha+n)}{n!\Gamma(\alpha)} \cdot \frac{\theta^n}{(1+\theta)^{n+\alpha}} = \binom{n+\alpha-1}{n} \left(\frac{\theta}{1+\theta}\right)^n \left(\frac{1}{1+\theta}\right)^\alpha.$$

Thus N is negative binomial with $r = \alpha$ and $p = \frac{1}{1+\theta}$. □

In general suppose $f_X(x; \lambda)$ is a parametric family of densities with parameter λ. If we view λ as a realization of Λ, a random variable with density $f_\Lambda(\lambda)$, then $f_X(x; \lambda)$ is reinterpreted as $f_X(x|\Lambda = \lambda)$. We then obtain the joint density of X and Λ as

$$f_{X,\Lambda}(x, \lambda) = f_\Lambda(\lambda) f_X(x|\Lambda = \lambda),$$

and the X-marginal (unconditional) density as

mixing
$$f_X(x) = \begin{cases} \int_\lambda f_\Lambda(\lambda) f_X(x|\Lambda = \lambda)\, d\lambda & \Lambda \text{ continuous} \\ \text{or} & \\ \sum_\lambda f_\Lambda(\lambda) f_X(x|\Lambda = \lambda) & \Lambda \text{ discrete} \end{cases}$$

The discrete case of mixing is really the same thing as taking a convex combination of distributions (see Appendix C at the end of this section of the manual). For example, suppose X_1 and X_2 are

[4] This is another distribution where definitions of the parameters and the variable itself tend to vary from one text to the next. See Unit 3 to follow for more details. For some authors X is the number of the trial on which the rth success ocurs, so that $X = r, r+1, \ldots$.

exponentially distributed with parameters θ_1, θ_2 respectively. A **convex combination** of these distributions has density

$$f_X(x) = a \cdot f_{X_1}(x) + b \cdot f_{X_2}(x) = a\left(\frac{1}{\theta_1}e^{-x/\theta_1}\right) + b\left(\frac{1}{\theta_2}e^{-x/\theta_2}\right)$$

where a, b are positive and $a+b=1$. Now consider $f_X(x;\theta) = \frac{1}{\theta}e^{-x/\theta}$ as being $f_X(x|\Theta=\theta)$ where $f_\Theta(\theta_1) = a$ and $f_\Theta(\theta_2) = b$. Then

$$f_X(x) = \sum_{i=1}^{2} \underbrace{f_X(x|\Theta=\theta_i)f_\Theta(\theta_i)}_{\text{joint density of } X,\,\Theta} = \left(\frac{1}{\theta_1}e^{-x/\theta_1}\right)a + \left(\frac{1}{\theta_2}e^{-x/\theta_2}\right)b$$

just as above. So mixing with a discrete distribution produces the same thing as a convex combination – a weighted average of densities where the weights are positive and sum to 1.

Example 3 Suppose $N|_{\Lambda=\lambda}$ has the Poisson λ distribution and Λ has a binomial distribution with parameters n, p. Obtain $E[N]$, $Var(N)$ without obtaining the N marginal density by the mixing procedure above.

Solution The double expectation theorem comes to our rescue:

$$\left.\begin{array}{l} E[N|\Lambda=\lambda] = \lambda \\ Var(N|\Lambda=\lambda) = \lambda \end{array}\right\} \text{Poisson-distribution facts.}$$

In general the way to write this is $E[N|\Lambda] = \Lambda$ and $Var(N|\Lambda) = \Lambda$. Thus, by the double expectation theorem

$$E[N] = E[E[N|\Lambda]] = E[\Lambda] = np$$

$$Var(N) = E[Var(N|\Lambda)] + Var(E[N|\Lambda]) = E[\Lambda] + Var(\Lambda) = np + np(1-p) = np(2-p).$$

□

Modeling an Inflationary Effect on a Loss Distribution

Suppose X represents the loss distribution for the current year of an ongoing claims process generated by a portfolio of risks. How could you model the effect of inflation to describe Y, next year's loss distribution? In the simplest view $Y = (1+r)X$ where r represents the inflation rate. Consequently we would have $E[Y] = (1+r)E[X]$, $Var(Y) = (1+r)^2 Var(X)$ and $f_Y(y) = f_X\left(\frac{y}{1+r}\right)\frac{1}{(1+r)}$. The problem with this simplistic approach is that it requires knowing a year in advance what next years inflation rate will be, when in fact there is some uncertainty in any economic forecast. A better approach would be to consider the model

$$Y = CX, C \text{ and } X \text{ independent}$$
$$C \text{ a random inflation factor,}$$

incorporating the uncertainty in the inflation forecast. For example, if the forecast for next year is for inflation to be between 2% and 6%, with the low end more likely, one might use the function

$f_C(c) = \frac{1}{a} \cdot \frac{1}{c}$

$1.02 \leq c \leq 1.06$

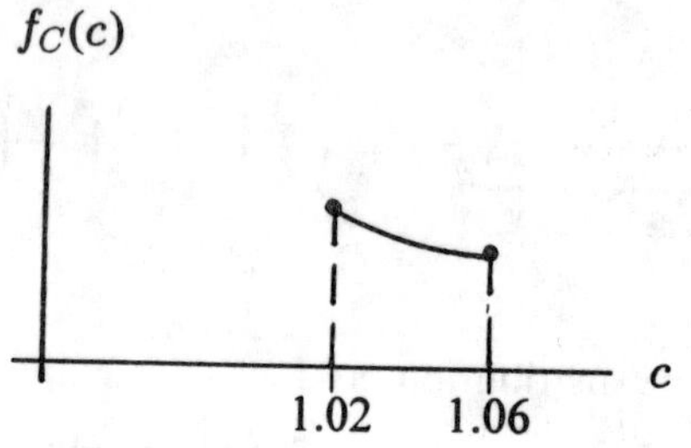

where

$$a = \int_{1.02}^{1.06} \frac{1}{c}\, dc = ln\left(\frac{1.06}{1.02}\right) = .038466$$

$$E[C] = \int_{1.02}^{1.06} c \cdot \frac{1}{a} \cdot \frac{1}{c}\, dc = \frac{1.06 - 1.02}{a} = 1.0399$$

$$E[C^2] = \int_{1.02}^{1.06} c^2 \cdot \frac{1}{a} \cdot \frac{1}{c}\, dc = \frac{1.06^2 - 1.02^2}{2a} = 1.0815$$

$$\sigma_C = .0115.$$

This model is used to illustrate general relations in the remainder of this section.

It follows from this model that

$$E[Y] = E[C]E[X]$$

$$E[Y^2] = E[C^2]E[X^2] \qquad \text{(independence of } C, X\text{)}$$

$$Var(Y) = E[C^2]E[X^2] - (E[C]E[X])^2$$

A slightly rearranged form of these relations, following from the double expectation theorem, results in a variance formula that has an appealing interpretation. Notice that $E[Y|C = c] = E[CX|C = c]$ $= E[cX] = c \cdot E[X]$. It is better to write this relation in the form $E[Y|C] = CE[X]$. Similarly, $Var(Y|C) = C^2 Var(X)$. Thus

$$E[Y] = E[E[Y|C]] = E[C \cdot \underbrace{E[X]}_{\text{number}}] = E[X]E[C]$$

$$\begin{aligned} Var(Y) &= E[Var(Y|C)] + Var(E[Y|C]) \\ &= E[C^2 \cdot \underbrace{Var(X)}_{\text{number}}] + Var(C \cdot \underbrace{E[X]}_{\text{number}}) \\ &= \underbrace{Var(X)}_{\substack{\text{variance in} \\ \text{current losses}}} E[C^2] + (E[X])^2 \underbrace{Var(C)}_{\substack{\text{variance due to} \\ \text{uncertainty in the} \\ \text{inflation forecast}}} \end{aligned}$$

which is more intuitively appealing. It is easy to see from $Var(X) = E[X^2] - (E[X])^2$, $Var(C) = E[C^2] - (E[C])^2$ that this form of the variance agrees with the earlier one.

If, for example, X is exponentially distributed with parameter $\theta = 10$ ($f_X(x) = \frac{1}{10}e^{-x/10}$), then

$$E[Y] = E[C]E[X] = 1.03987(10) = 10.3987$$

$$Var(Y) = E[C^2]Var(X) + (E[X])^2 Var(C) = (1.081466)(10^2) + (10)^2(.000133) = 108.16$$

in contrast with $E[X] = 10$, $Var(X) = 10^2 = 100$. (These same results will be duplicated later in Example 5, where we also derive $f_Y(y)$ for the set of assumptions in this paragraph. The following discussion leads up to that calculation.)

A slightly more difficult problem lies in the calculation of the Y density. But first lets consider two possible interpretations of the model $Y = CX$:

(1) All of next year's losses will be distributed like cX for some realization c of C. Then Y represents a *forecast of next year's losses reflecting the uncertainty about inflation*; or

(2) Next year's losses will each be inflated by a factor c which varies from loss to loss like C. In this case Y can be interpreted as the distribution of next year's losses.

The first step in computing the Y density is the relation

$$f_Y(y) = \int_c f_Y(y|C = c) f_C(c)\, dc = \int_c f_{c \cdot X}(y) f_C(c)\, dc = \int_c f_X\left(\frac{y}{c}\right)\frac{1}{c} \cdot f_C(c)\, dc.$$

This form would be good enough to proceed from formulas for f_X, f_C to a formula for f_Y. We examine next what the evaluation would look like if X belonged to a parametric family having a **scale parameter**. In this case the relation above looks like a mixing of the parametric family with the C distribution. A desirable choice for a parametric family for C can result in the mixture having a desirable parametric form that would allow playing "what if ..." games with the model in a simple way, due to a compact expression for $f_Y(y)$ involving several parameters, which are functions of the parameters of the loss distribution (i.e., X) and the inflation forecast (i.e., C distribution). (See the results of Example 4 ahead.)

A parametric family of distributions is called a **scale** family if aX remains in the family when X is from the family. Among others, this is true of the normal family and the gamma family. A slightly more restrictive form of this idea is a parametric family having a **scale parameter**. In this case the parameters of aX are the same as those of X except that the scale parameter is multiplied by a. For example, if X has the normal distribution with parameters μ, σ^2, then aX has the normal distribution with parameters $a\mu$, $a^2\sigma^2$. So μ is not a scale parameter. On the other hand if X has the gamma distribution with parameters α, θ (i.e., $f_X(x) = \frac{1}{\theta^\alpha \Gamma(\alpha)} x^{\alpha-1} e^{-x/\theta}$), then aX has the gamma distribution with parameters α, $a\theta$; θ is a scale parameter. A special case, $\alpha = 1$, gives the exponential family.

Now suppose that this year's loss distribution, X, has a parametric density, $f(x;\theta)$, where θ is a scale parameter. We could interpret this density as $f(x|\Theta = \theta)$, where Θ has a distribution of its own. In this case, if X has density $f(x;\theta)$ then cX has density $f(x;c\theta)$. With these ideas in mind lets return to the $Y = CX$ model incorporating an inflationary effect into next year's losses. Recall from earlier that

$$f_Y(y) = \int_c f_Y(y|C = c) f_C(c)\, dc = \int f_{cX}(y) f_C(c)\, dc.$$

If $f_X(x) = f(x;\theta_0)$ for some θ_0 (the parameter for the current year), then $f_{cX}(x) = f(x;c\theta_0)$ since θ is a scale parameter. In this case the above relation becomes

$$f_Y(y) = \int_c f(y;c\theta_0) f_C(c)\, dc.$$

If one substitutes $\theta = c \cdot \theta_0$ into the above and defines $g(\theta) = f_C\left(\frac{\theta}{\theta_0}\right)\frac{1}{\theta_0}$, the above relation can be made to look like a mixing of the $f(x;\theta)$ family with the distribution $g(\theta)$:

$$f_Y(y) = \int_\theta f(y;\theta) g(\theta)\, d\theta$$

mixing interpretation $\begin{cases} f(y;\theta) = f(y|\Theta = \theta) \\ f_\Theta(\theta) = g(\theta) \end{cases}$

It is sometimes possible to choose $g(\theta)$ from a parametric family in such a way that Y is from a parametric family with parameters expressed in terms of the parameters of the loss distribution and the parameters of the inflation forecast. This idea is illustrated in the following example.

Example 4 Suppose $Y = CX$ where C and X are independent, X is exponentially distributed with parameter θ_0, and

$$f_C(c) = \frac{1}{ln(b/a)} \cdot \frac{1}{c} \text{ for } a \leq c \leq b$$

(C has 2 parameters - a, b). Derive formulas for the Y density, $E[Y]$ and $E[Y^2]$.

Solution From the above

$$\begin{aligned} f_Y(y) &= \int_c f(y; c\cdot\theta_0) f_C(c)\, dc \\ &= \int_a^b \frac{1}{c\cdot\theta_0} \cdot e^{-y/c\cdot\theta_0} \cdot \frac{1}{ln(b/a)} \cdot \frac{1}{c}\, dc \\ &= \frac{1}{\theta_0 \cdot ln(b/a)} \int_a^b \frac{1}{c^2} \cdot e^{-y/c\cdot\theta_0}\, dc \\ &= \frac{1}{\theta_0 \cdot ln(b/a)} \left(e^{-y/c\cdot\theta_0} \cdot \frac{\theta_0}{y} \Big|_{c=a}^{b} \right) \\ &= \frac{1}{y \cdot ln(b/a)} \left(e^{-y/b\cdot\theta_0} - e^{-y/a\cdot\theta_0} \right) \end{aligned}$$

Notice how the parametric form of the Y-density involves the parameter θ_0 of the loss distribution and the parameters a, b of the inflation forecast. Now one could play "what if ..." games with the model. Furthermore, using $\int_0^\infty e^{-ay}\, dy = \frac{1}{a}$ and $\int_0^\infty y \cdot e^{-ay}\, dy = \frac{1}{a^2}$, we have

$$E[Y] = \int_0^\infty y \cdot f_Y(y)\, dy = \int_0^\infty \frac{1}{ln(b/a)} \left(e^{-y/b\cdot\theta_0} - e^{-y/a\cdot\theta_0} \right) dy = \frac{b\theta_0 - a\theta_0}{ln(b/a)} = \frac{\theta_0}{ln(b/a)}(b - a)$$

$$\begin{aligned} E[Y^2] &= \int_0^\infty y^2 \cdot f_Y(y)\, dy = \int_0^\infty \frac{1}{ln(b/a)} \left(y \cdot e^{-y/b\cdot\theta_0} - y \cdot e^{-y/a\cdot\theta_0} \right) dy \\ &= \frac{(b\theta_0)^2 - (a\theta_0)^2}{ln(b/a)} = \frac{\theta_0^2}{ln(b/a)}(b^2 - a^2) \end{aligned}$$

□

Example 5 Suppose this year's loss distribution, X, is exponential with mean 10 (i.e., $\theta_0 = 10$, $f(x; \theta_0) = \frac{1}{10} e^{-x/10}$) and suppose C has the distribution

$$f_C(c) = \frac{1}{ln(1.06/1.02)} \cdot \frac{1}{c} \text{ for } 1.02 \leq c \leq 1.06$$

given earlier. Calculate the Y density, $E[Y]$ and $Var(Y)$. Compare the $Y = CX$ and X densities.

Note: These were the assumptions used earlier in the calculation of $E[Y]$, $Var(Y)$ before we discussed the calculation of $f_Y(y)$.

Solution We may use the results of Example 4 with $\theta_0 = 10$, $a = 1.02$, $b = 1.06$ to obtain the following:

$$f_Y(y) = \frac{1}{y \cdot ln(1.06/1.02)}\left(e^{-y/10.6} - e^{-y/10.2}\right)$$

$$E[Y] = \frac{10}{ln(1.06/1.02)} \cdot (1.06 - 1.02) = 10.3987$$

$$E[Y^2] = \frac{10^2}{ln(1.06/1.02)} \cdot (1.06^2 - 1.02^2) = 216.2933$$

$$Var(Y) = 108.16$$

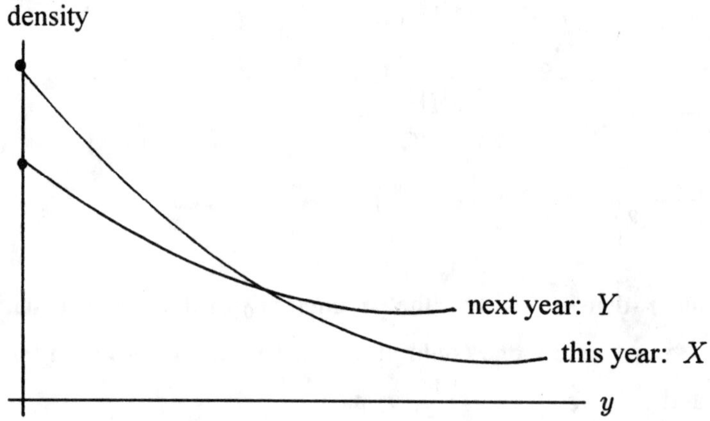

For this year $E[X] = \theta_0 = 10$, $Var(X) = \theta_0^2 = 100$, and we see $E[Y] = 10.3987$, $Var(Y) = 108.16$. These numbers agree with our earlier calculations using

$$E[Y] = E[C]E[X],\ Var(Y) = E[C^2]Var(X) + (E[X])^2 Var(C).$$

One can see several related effects of incorporating the inflation factor into the loss distribution:

(1) Variance increases from $Var(X)$ due to both $E[C]$ and the uncertainty in C (i.e., $Var(C)$. (See the Variance formula above.)

(2) The Y density has a "fatter tail" than the X density. □

The Gamma, Transformed Gamma and Inverse Transformed Gamma Families[5]

We have seen earlier the 1-parameter gamma density, $f(x) = \frac{x^{\alpha-1}e^{-x}}{\Gamma(\alpha)}$, which gives rise to the two parameter family with density function $\frac{x^{\alpha-1}e^{-x/\theta}}{\theta^{\alpha}\Gamma(\alpha)}$. If X has the 1-parameter density above then θX has the two-parameter density given next and θ is a scale parameter.

The 3-parameter, **transformed gamma family** is obtained from X, the 1-parameter distribution, in two steps: $X \rightarrow X^{1/\tau} \rightarrow \theta(X^{1/\tau})$ where $\tau > 0$. It is necessary to do the construction in this order to retain θ as a scale parameter. Thus, if Y has the transformed gamma distribution with parameters α, θ, τ, it follows that $\left(\frac{Y}{\theta}\right)^{\tau}$ has the 1-parameter gamma distribution with parameter α. In case $\tau = 1$, Y has the 2-parameter gamma distribution with parameters α, θ.

The 3-parameter, **inverse transformed gamma family** is obtained from X in a similar manner: $X \rightarrow X^{-1/\tau} \rightarrow \theta(X^{-1/\tau})$ where $\tau > 0$. If Y has the inverse transformed gamma distribution with parameters α, θ, τ, then it follows that $\left(\frac{Y}{\theta}\right)^{-\tau}$ has the 1-parameter gamma distribution with parameter α.

Density and moment formulas for these families can be found in the Condensed Review Notes section of this unit.

The Beta and Transformed Beta Families

A **two-parameter beta distribution** has a density function given by

$$f_X(x) = \frac{\Gamma(a+b)}{\Gamma(a)\Gamma(b)} x^{a-1}(1-x)^{b-1} \qquad 0 < x < 1, a > 0, b > 0.$$

The **incomplete beta function**, the distribution function of X, is denoted by

$$\beta(a,b;x) = \int_0^x \frac{\Gamma(a+b)}{\Gamma(a)\Gamma(b)} t^{a-1}(1-t)^{b-1}\, dt$$

for $0 \le x \le 1$. It requires numerical evaluation.

It requires several steps and the introduction of two new parameters to progress from X (above) to Y having the **4-parameter, transformed beta** distribution. First X is transformed to $\frac{X}{1-X}$ by a 1-1 increasing transformation of $(0,1)$ onto $(0,\infty)$, which increases the support to the entire real line. Then $\frac{X}{1-X}$ is transformed to $\theta\left(\frac{X}{1-X}\right)^{1/\tau} = Y$. So if Y has the 4-parameter, transformed beta distribution, then $\frac{(Y/\theta)^{\tau}}{1+(Y/\theta)^{\tau}}$ has the 2-parameter beta distribution.

Density and moment formulas for this family can be found in the Condensed Review Note section of this unit.

---

[5] Important facts about all parametric families are summarized in the Condensed Review Notes to follow.

The Effect of Coverage Adjustments on a Loss Distribution

In this section we investigate the effect of coverage modifications on a loss distribution. Here X denotes the **loss** as a result of a **single loss event**, the amount that would be paid by an insurance if the loss were fully covered. X is also known as the **ground-up loss**. It is assumed in the following that $1 = Pr(X > 0)$. Y is used to denote the **amount paid per loss** as a result of an insurance not fully covering the loss X due to policy modifications such as a limit, a deductible, or co-insurance. Y could be zero. For example, if there is a deductible d, and if $X < d$, then there is no payment made. In contrast, Z is used to denote the **amount paid per payment**, that is, $Z = Y|_{Y>0}$.

If N is used to model the frequency of losses, then aggregate losses are modeled by $S = X_1 + \cdots + X_N$ and aggregate claims are modeled by $C = Y_1 + Y_2 + \cdots + Y_N$. The Y_i's however do not all represent claims since some losses, X, result in $Y = 0$. Let M be the random number of losses resulting in claims, that is, the claim frequency distribution. Then it is better to model C, aggregate claims, by $C = Z_1 + \cdots + Z_M$. There is some set, S, of positive real numbers so that if X falls in S then $Y > 0$ (i.e., a claim is paid). For example, if the policy has a deductible d, then $X > d$ means that $Y = X - d$ (the claim amount) is positive. Thus $S = (d, \infty)$. Let N_S be the random number of losses such that the loss X falls in S. N_S is what we first called M above. It is the claim frequency variable. In Unit 3 we will look more carefully at N_S as we study claim frequency distributions. For now let us just note the following:

$$N_S|_{N=n} = \text{Binomial } (n \text{ trials, } p = Pr(X \in S)$$

view a loss as a "success " if it falls in S and triggers a claim

$$\left.\begin{array}{l} E[N_S|N] = Np \\ Var(N_S|N) = Np(1-p) \end{array}\right\} \text{ Conditional Binomial Facts.}$$

Thus, by the double expectation theorem

$$\underbrace{E[N_S]}_{\substack{\text{expected number} \\ \text{of claims}}} = E[E[N_S|N]] = E[Np] = E[N]p = \underbrace{E[N]}_{\substack{\text{expected number} \\ \text{of losses}}} \underbrace{Pr(X \in S)}_{\substack{\text{probability that} \\ \text{a loss produces a} \\ \text{a claim}}}.$$

This relation illustrates how a coverage modification can affect the expected number of claims. For example, if a policy has a deductible and $S = (d, \infty)$, then $Pr(X \in (d,\infty)) = 1 - F_X(d)$ goes down as d goes up. One can also use the equation above to examine the effect of removing a deductible and giving full coverage. The expected number of claims would increase from $E[N_S]$ to $E[N_S]/(1 - F_X(d)) = E[N]$. These ideas will be explored again in Units 3 and 4 to follow. Now let's return to analyzing coverage modifications and how they affect loss distributions, that is, how the Y and Z described earlier are related to X.

If a **deductible** d is applied to a loss, X, then

$$Y = \begin{cases} 0 & X \le d \\ X - d & X > d \end{cases}$$

is the amount paid per loss, and $Z = X - d|_{X>d}$ is the amount paid per payment (i.e, per claim). Y is often denoted[6] by $I_d(X)$. One can think of the loss as being split into the insured piece and the retained piece:

$$\underset{\text{(loss)}}{X} = \underset{\text{(insured part)}}{I_d(X)} + \underset{\text{(retained part)}}{(X - I_d(X))}$$

$$X - I_d(X) = \begin{cases} X & X \le d \\ d & X > d \end{cases} \qquad \text{(a right censored form of } X\text{).}$$

The retained loss above is related to the idea of a policy limit. If the loss X faces a **policy limit**[7] L, then the loss is fully covered up to a maximum claim payment of L. In this case, $Y = Z$, the amount paid per loss/claim, is often denoted by

$$Y = (X \wedge L) = min\{X, L\} = \begin{cases} X & X \le L \\ L & X > L \end{cases} = X - I_L(X) \quad \text{(see above).}$$

Because every loss results in $Y > 0$ we have $Y = Z$. Thus we have in general that

$$X = I_d(X) + (X - I_d(X)) = I_d(X) + (X \wedge d).$$

A third type of coverage modification is a so-called **coinsurance factor**, α, where $0 < \alpha < 1$. In this case $Y = Z = \alpha X$ and we have

$$\underset{\text{(loss)}}{X} = \underset{\text{(insured part)}}{\alpha(X)} + \underset{\text{(retained part)}}{(1-\alpha)X}.$$

First we will examine the separate effect that each of these modifications has on the X-distribution. Later, an example incorporating all 3 modifications simultaneously will be given.

---

[6] Another common notation is $(X - d)_+$.

[7] In general the policy limit refers to the X distribution. If there is no deductible or coinsurance then it also equals the maximal claim payment.

Effect of a Deductible

$$Y = \begin{cases} 0 & X \le d \\ X-d & X > d \end{cases} = I_d(X)$$

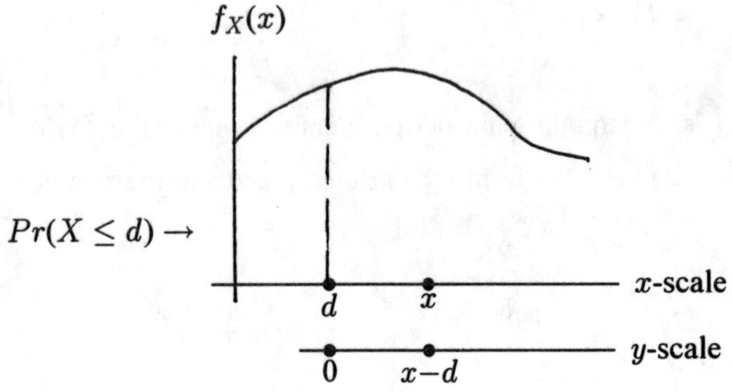

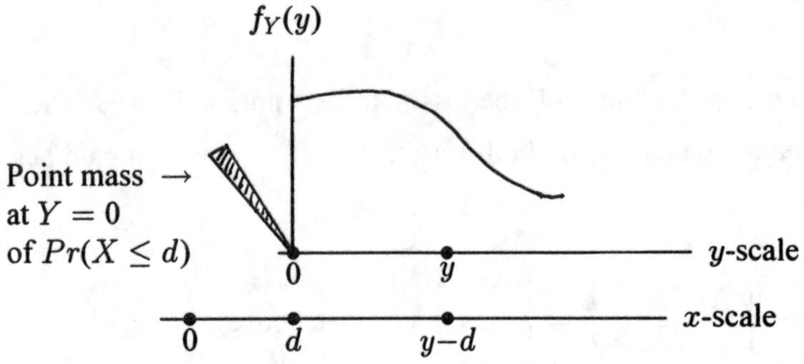

$$f_Y(y) = \begin{cases} Pr(X \le d) & y = 0 \quad \text{(discrete part)} \\ f_X(d+y) & y > 0 \quad \text{(continuous part)} \end{cases}$$

$$f_Z(z) = f_X(d+z)/[1 - Pr(X \le d)], \; z > 0$$

$$\underbrace{E[Z]}_{\text{expected claim amount per claim}} = E[Y|Y>0] = E[X-d|X>d]^8 = \frac{\int_d^\infty (x-d) f_X(x)}{1 - Pr(X \le d)}\,dx$$

Note: $\frac{E[X \wedge d]}{E[X]} = 1 - \frac{E[I_d(X)]}{E[X]}$ is called the **loss elimination ratio**. It is the fraction of the expected loss which is eliminated by imposing the deductible d.

[8] If X were a lifetime distribution, we saw earlier that $\mathring{e}_x = E[X - x|X > x]$ is the expected future lifetime at age x.

Effect of a Policy Limit

$$Z = Y = min\{X, L\} = (X \wedge L)$$

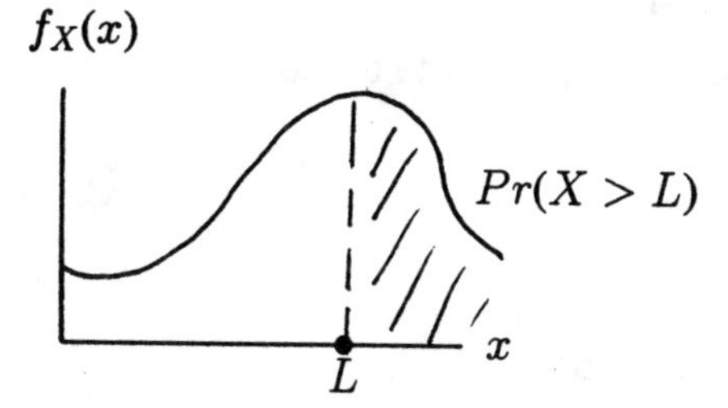

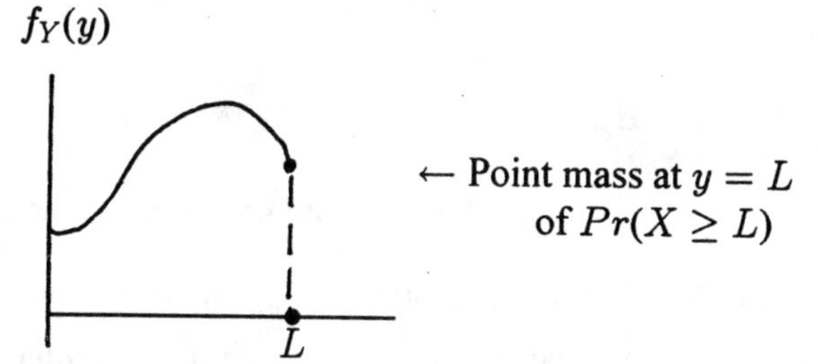

$$f_Y(y) = \begin{cases} f_X(y) & y < L \quad \text{(continuous part)} \\ Pr(X \geq L) & y = L \quad \text{(discrete part)} \end{cases}$$

$$\begin{aligned} E[Z] = E[Y] = E[X \wedge L] &= \int_0^L x \cdot f_X(x)\,dx + \int_L^\infty L \cdot f_X(x)\,dx \\ &= \int_0^L x \cdot f_X(x)\,dx + L \cdot Pr(X \geq L) \\ &= \int_0^L (1 - F_X(x))\,dx\ ^9 \qquad \text{(Alternate method of evaluation)} \end{aligned}$$

Effect of Coinsurance Factor

$$Z = Y = \alpha X \qquad 0 < \alpha < 1$$

$$f_Y(y) = f_X\left(\frac{y}{\alpha}\right)\frac{1}{\alpha}$$

$$E[Y] = \alpha E[X]$$

---

[9] Integration by parts

Example 6 Suppose X has an exponential density with parameter θ: $f_X(x) = \frac{1}{\theta}e^{-x/\theta}$ for $x > 0$.

(1) Calculate $E[Y]$, $E[Z]$, $f_Y(y)$, $f_Z(z)$ for a deductible d applied to the loss X.

(2) Calculate $E[Y]$, $f_Y(y)$ for a policy limit of L applied to the loss X.

(3) Calculate $E[Y]$, $f_Y(y)$ for a a coinsurance factor α applied to the loss X.

Solution

(1) From the above summary

$$f_Y(y) = \begin{cases} 1 - e^{-d/\theta} & y = 0 \quad \text{discrete part} \\ \frac{1}{\theta}e^{-(d+y)/\theta} & y > 0 \quad \text{continuous part} \end{cases}$$

since $1 - e^{-d/\theta} = \int_0^d f_X(x)\,dx = Pr(X \leq d)$,

and $f_Z(z) = \frac{f_X(d+z)}{1 - Pr(X \leq d)} = \frac{\frac{1}{\theta}e^{-(d+z)/\theta}}{e^{-d/\theta}} = \frac{1}{\theta}e^{-z/\theta}$ (the same exponential distribution as X – this is the "memoryless" property of the exponential distribution that we saw earlier in the form $T(x) \sim Exp(\theta)$ if $X \sim Exp(\theta)$ in the survival model portion of this manual.). So clearly $E[Z] = E[X] = \theta$ and

$$\begin{aligned} E[I_d(X)] = E[Y] = \int_d^\infty (x - d)f_X(x)\,dx &= \int_d^\infty (x - d)\frac{1}{\theta}e^{-x/\theta}\,dx \\ &= \int_d^\infty (x - d)\frac{1}{\theta}e^{-(x-d)/\theta} \cdot e^{-d/\theta}\,dx \\ &= e^{-d/\theta}\int_0^\infty u\frac{1}{\theta}e^{-u/\theta}\,du \qquad (u = x - \theta) \\ &= e^{-d/\theta} \cdot \theta. \end{aligned}$$

The last integral is the expected value of an exponential θ variable. Note the consistency of these results with

$$\begin{aligned} \underbrace{E[Y]}_{\substack{e^{-d/\theta}.\theta \\ \text{above}}} &= E[Y|X \leq d]Pr(X \leq d) + E[Y|X > d]Pr(X > d) \\ &= \underbrace{E[0]}_{0}(1 - e^{-d/\theta}) + \underbrace{E[Z]}_{\theta \text{ above}}e^{-d/\theta} \end{aligned}$$

Note: It is useful to know both $E[Y]$ and $E[Z]$. $E[Y]$ is the **pure premium** (i.e., expected payment) needed to cover the portion of a single loss exceeding a deductible d. It reflects the fact that $Y = 0$ with probability $Pr(X \leq d)$. $E[Z]$ represents the expected claim payment for a single, payment-generating loss.

(2) From the summary preceding this example, if $Y = (X \wedge L) = min\{X, L\}$, then $Y = Z$ and

$$f_Y(y) = \begin{cases} f_X(y) & y < L \\ Pr(X \geq L) & y = L \end{cases} = \begin{cases} \frac{1}{\theta}e^{-y/\theta} & y < L \\ \frac{1}{\theta}e^{-L/\theta} & y = L \end{cases} \quad \text{(a right-censored exponential density).}$$

One could compute $E[Y]$ either as

$$E[Y] = \int_0^L y \cdot \frac{1}{\theta}e^{-y/\theta}\, d\theta + L \cdot e^{-L/\theta} = -ye^{-y/\theta} - \theta e^{-y/\theta}\Big|_0^L + L \cdot e^{-L/\theta} = \theta(1 - e^{-L/\theta}),$$

or from the identity below seen earlier and part (1) of this example:

$$\underbrace{E[X]}_{\substack{\theta \\ \text{exp. dist.}}} = \underbrace{E[I_L(X)]}_{\substack{e^{-L/\theta}\cdot\theta \\ \text{part (1)}}} + \underbrace{E[X \wedge L]}_{\text{part (2)}}.$$

(3) If $Y = \alpha X$ and X is exponential with parameter θ (a scale parameter), then Y is exponential with parameter $\alpha\theta$. Thus $Y = Z$ and $f_Y(y) = \frac{1}{\theta\alpha}e^{-y/\theta\alpha}$, $E[Y] = \alpha\theta$. □

Finally, let's look at an example of a policy modification incorporating all three features analyzed separately above. Suppose X is the loss (i.e., cost) to an individual as a result of a single visit to a dentist. As a result of a group dental plan, a payment of 80% of the excess of the loss over a deductible of 100 and up to a limit[10] of 1000 is paid by the insurance carrier. Then Y, the payment per loss, is given as

$$Y = \begin{Bmatrix} 0 & X \leq 100 \\ .80(X - 100) & 100 < X \leq 1000 \\ .80(1000 - 100) & 1000 < X \end{Bmatrix} = .80(I_{100}(X) - I_{1000}(X)).$$

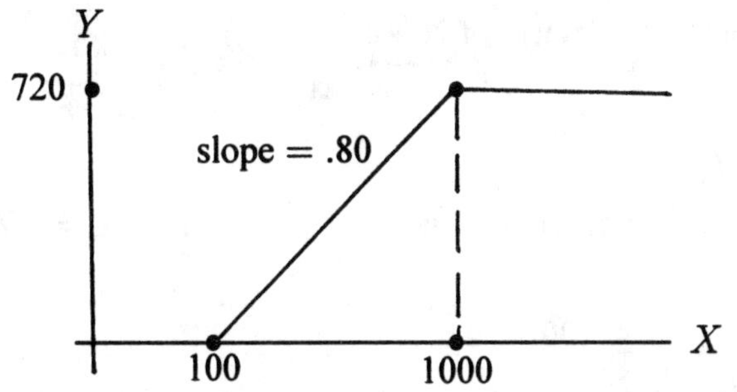

[10] The limit refers to an X-value, not the maximum claim payment.

Z, the amount paid per payment (i.e., $Y|_{Y>0}$) is given as

$$Z = \begin{cases} .80(X-100) & 100 < X \le 1000 \\ .80(1000-100) & 1000 < X \end{cases},$$

and is conditional on $X > 100$ (i.e., $Y > 0$).

Example 7 For the group dental problem above calculate $E[Y]$, $E[Z]$, $F_Y(y)$, $F_Z(z)$ assuming X is exponentially distributed with mean 150.

Solution $\theta = E[X] = 150$ so $f_X(x) = \frac{1}{150}e^{-x/150}$. Now

$$E[Y] = E[.80(I_{100}(X) - I_{1000}(X))] = .80(\underbrace{E[I_{100}(X)]}_{e^{-100/150}\cdot 150} - \underbrace{E[I_{1000}(X)]}_{\substack{e^{-1000/150}\cdot 150 \\ \text{(Se Ex. 6)}}}) = 61.46$$

(expected claim per visit), and

$$E[Y] = E[Y|Y=0]Pr(Y=0) + E[Y|Y>0]Pr(Y>0)$$

$$61.46 = 0 \cdot Pr(X \le 100) + E[Z]Pr(X > 100).$$

Hence $E[Z] = \frac{61.46}{Pr(X > 100)} = \frac{61.46}{e^{-100/150}} = 119.70$ (the expected claim payment per claim).

Note: If there were 200 expected visits over the next year from the insured group (i.e., $E[N] = 200$), then there are $E[N]Pr(Y > 0) = E[N]Pr(X > 100) = 200(e^{-100/150})$ expected claim payments. The expected cost to the insurer can be viewed as either

$$\underbrace{E[N]}_{\substack{\text{expected} \\ \text{visits}}} \cdot \underbrace{E[Y]}_{\substack{\text{expected} \\ \text{cost/visit}}} = (200)(61.46) = 12{,}292$$

or

$$\text{(Expected number of claims)} \cdot \text{(Expected amount per claim)} = \underbrace{(200(e^{-100/150}))}_{102.683} \cdot \underbrace{\left(\frac{61.46}{e^{-100/150}}\right)}_{119.70}.$$

To calculate the distribution function it is easiest to first forget the policy limit $L = 1000$. Without this limit

$$Y = \begin{cases} 0 & X \le 100 \\ .8(X-100) & X > 100 \end{cases},$$

and for $y \ge 0$

$$F_Y(y) = Pr(Y \le y|X \le 100)Pr(X \le 100) + Pr(Y \le y|X > 100)Pr(X > 100)$$

$$= Pr(0 \le y|X \le 100)(1 - e^{-100/150}) + Pr(.8(X-100) \le y|X > 100)e^{-100/150}$$

$$= \underbrace{1 \cdot (.4866)}_{\text{discrete part}} + \underbrace{(1-e^{-y/120})(.5134)}_{\text{continuous part}}.$$

The "1" above is the distribution function of a zero-variable, and $(1 - e^{-y/120})$ is the distribution function of an exponential with parameter 120. First, $X - 100|_{X>100}$ is exponential with parameter 150, and thus $.8(X - 100)|X > 100$ is exponential with parameter $(.8)(150) = 120$. To build back in the policy limit of $L = 1000$ we merely need to kick the $F_Y(y)$ formula above up to 1 at $Y = 720$. So including this policy limit

$$F_Y(y) = (.4866)1 + (.5134) \cdot \begin{cases} 1 - e^{-y/120} & y < 720 \\ 1 & y \ge 720 \end{cases}.$$

Y has a mixed distribution with point masses of .4866 at $y = 0$ and $.5134e^{-720/120} = .0013$ at $y = 720$.

The distribution of Z is a little simpler. Without the policy limit $Z = Y|_{Y>0} = .8(X - 100|_{X>100})$, an exponentially distributed variable with parameter 120. Including the limit of $L = 1000$ gives a maximum Y of 720, so Z is censored at 720 at the right:

$$f_Z(z) = \begin{cases} \frac{1}{120}e^{-z/120} & 0 \le z < 720 & \text{continuous part} \\ e^{-720/120} & z = 720 & \text{point mass} \end{cases}$$

□

The details with a discrete loss distribution for X are a lot simpler to work out by hand. A difficult continuous model could be approximated by a discrete one.

Example 8 Suppose the table below gives the distribution of X. Suppose an insurance policy provides a reimbursement of 80% of the excess over 1.5 up to a policy limit of 4. Let Y be the payment per loss and Z be the payment per payment event. Calculate $f_Y(y)$, $f_Z(z)$ and the expected values.

x	1	2	3	4	5
$f_X(x)$	.40	.25	.15	.10	.10

Solution The y-values corresponding to $x = 1, 2, \ldots, 5$ are 0, .40, 1.20, 2.0, 2.0 respectively. Thus the Y-density looks like

y	0	.4	1.2	2.0
$f_Y(y)$	.40	.25	.15	.20

Since $Z = Y|_{Y>0}$ and $Pr(Y > 0) = 1 - .40 = .60$ the Z-density looks like

z	.4	1.2	2.0
$f_Z(z)$	.25/.60	.15/.60	.20/.60

It is elementary from these tables to see that $E[X] = 2.25$, $E[Y] = .68$, $E[Z] = 1.1\overline{3}$. □

Before considering a final example it is useful to point out a connection here between the Z (amount paid per payment variable) related to a deductible d applied to a loss X, and the future lifetime after age x, $T(x)$, in a survival model:

Loss Distributions	Survival Model
X a loss variable	X a waiting time
$Y_d = \begin{cases} X-d & X>d \\ 0 & X \le d \end{cases}$	
$Z_d = Y_d|_{Y_d>0} = X - d|_{X>d}$	$T(x) = X - x|_{X>x}$ = future lifetime after age x
$E[Z_d]$ = Expected payment amount per payment	$\overset{\circ}{e}_x = E[T(x)]$

Setting $x = d$ one sees that Z_d and $T(x)$ are identical. Recall the 2-parameter survival model given by one of the following equivalent relations:

$$\mu(x) = \frac{r}{\omega - x}, \quad f_X(x) = \frac{r}{\omega}\left(1 - \frac{x}{\omega}\right)^{r-1}, \qquad s_X(x) = \left(1 - \frac{x}{\omega}\right)^r.$$

We saw in section one of this manual that

$$\overset{\circ}{e}_x = \frac{\omega - x}{r+1}, \quad Var(T(x)) = \frac{(\omega-x)^2 r}{(r+1)^2(r+2)}$$

for this survival model. These results can be rephrased in the context of a deductible applied to a loss distribution in the following form:

$f_X(x) = \frac{r}{\omega}\left(1 - \frac{x}{\omega}\right)^{r-1}$ $\quad 0 \le x \le \omega$

$F_X(x) = 1 - \left(1 - \frac{x}{\omega}\right)^r$ $\quad \omega =$ maximum loss

$E[Z_d] = \frac{\omega-d}{r+1}$ $\quad d =$ deductible

$$Var(Z_d) = \frac{(\omega-d)^2 r}{(r+1)^2(r+2)}$$

$f_{Z_d}(z) = \frac{r}{\omega - d}\left(1 - \frac{z}{\omega-d}\right)^{r-1}$ $\quad 0 \le z \le \omega-d$

(Same parametric family as X; r preserved and ω replaced by $\omega-d$ as the max claim payment.)

Example 9 Suppose $S = X_1 + \cdots + X_N$ is a collective risk model for aggregate losses where $E[N] = 1000$, $f_X(x) = \frac{r}{\omega}\left(1 - \frac{x}{\omega}\right)^{r-1}$.

(a) Compute the expected value of aggregate claims for a deductible $d = 0$, 25 or 50 if $r = 2$ and $\omega = 250$ is the maximum loss.

(b) What is the smallest deductible so that expected aggregate claims are less than or equal to 50,000?

(c) What is the percentage increase in expected aggregate claims if you move from a deductible of $d = 25$ to no deductible?

Solution

(a) Let S_d be aggregate claims if a deductible d applies to each loss. Then

$$E[S_d] = \underbrace{E[N]}_{\substack{\text{expected number}\\ \text{of losses}}} \cdot \underbrace{E[Y_d]}_{\substack{\text{expected}\\ \text{payment per loss}}} \qquad Y_d = I_d(X)$$

$$= \underbrace{(E[N]Pr(X > d))}_{\substack{\text{expected number}\\ \text{of payments}}}\underbrace{(E[Y_d]/Pr(X > d))}_{\substack{\text{expected payment}\\ \text{per payment event}}}$$

$$= (1000 S_X(d))E[Z_d]$$

$$= \left(1000\left(\frac{250-d}{250}\right)^2\right)\left(\frac{250-d}{2+1}\right) \qquad (\omega = 250, r = 2)$$

$$= \frac{1000(250-d)^3}{3(250)^2}$$

d	0	25	50
$E[S_d]$	83,333.33	60,750	42,666.66
$E[Z_d]$	83.33	75	66.66
Expected Number of Claims	1000	810	640

(b) If $50{,}000 = E[S_d] = \dfrac{1000(250-d)^3}{3(250)^2}$ then $d = 39.14$. As d goes up $E[Z_d]$ goes down and hence $E[S_d]$ goes down.

(c) From the table above the percent increase is

$$\frac{83{,}333.33 - 60{,}750}{60{,}750} \times 100\% = 37.17\%.$$

Tail Behavior

The worrisome right tail of a loss distribution is related to the probability of catastrophic losses. For any distribution on $[0, \infty)$ it follows that $\lim_{x\to\infty} f(x) = 0$. How rapidly $f(x)$ approaches zero relates to how thick the right tail is. If $\lim_{x\to\infty} f_X(x)/f_Y(x) = c$, then X is said to have the **lighter tail** if $c = 0$, or the **heavier tail** if $c = \infty$. If $0 < c < \infty$ the tails are **proportional** (similar). For example, if $f_X(x) = \dfrac{1}{(x+1)^2}$ and $f_Y(x) = \frac{1}{2}e^{-x/2}$, then

$$\lim_{x\to\infty} f_X(x)/f_Y(x) = \lim_{x\to\infty} \frac{2e^{x/2}}{(x+1)^2} = \lim_{x\to\infty} \frac{(\frac{1}{2}e^{x/2})}{2(x+1)} = \lim_{x\to\infty} \frac{1}{2}\frac{e^{x/2}}{2} = \infty.$$

So X has a heavier tail than Y.

Recall from the theory of survival models that $S_X(x) = Pr(X > x) = \int_x^\infty f_X(t)\,dt$, the survival function, satisfies $\lim_{x\to\infty} S_X(x) = 0$ and $-S'_X(x) = f_X(x)$. Thus, by L'Hopital's rule

$$\lim_{x\to\infty} \frac{S_X(x)}{S_Y(x)} = \lim_{x\to\infty} \frac{f_X(x)}{f_Y(x)}.$$

This offers an alternative method of calculating the same limit. The question of which to use hinges on the complexity of the functions.

Other tail-weight comparisons are based on a ratio of hazard rates (recall $h_X(x) = \dfrac{f_X(x)}{S_X(x)}$) or a ratio of mean excess losses ($E[X - x | X > x]$; called mean residual life in survival models and denoted by $\mathring{e}_x$). Since $S(x) = exp(-\int_0^x h(y)\,dy)$, an increasing $h(y)$ function causes $S(x)$ to approach zero rapidly. Thus, for example, if $\lim_{x\to\infty} \dfrac{h_X(x)}{h_Y(x)} = \infty$, then $S_X(x)$ approaches zero more rapidly than $S_Y(x)$ does.

In constructing a parametric model of a loss distribution, X, an important step following the estimation of parameters from a data set would be to compare the right tail of the empirical distribution to the right tail of the estimated parametric distribution. If the parametric model significantly underestimates right tail probabilities in the empirical distribution, then the model is in need of revision.

CONDENSED REVIEW NOTES AND ADVANCED TOPICS

Transformations of Loss Distributions

1. $Y = \theta X, x = g^{-1}(y) = \frac{y}{\theta}, \left|\frac{dx}{dy}\right| = \frac{1}{\theta}, \theta > 0 \quad \Rightarrow \quad f_Y(y) = f_X\left(\frac{y}{\theta}\right) \cdot \frac{1}{\theta}$

2. $Y = X^{(1/\tau)}, \tau > 0$ ("transformed" X-distribution)

   $x = y^{\tau}, \left|\frac{dx}{dy}\right| = \tau y^{\tau-1} \quad \Rightarrow \quad f_Y(y) = \tau y^{\tau-1} f_X(y^{\tau})$

   $Y = X^{(1/-\tau)}, \tau > 0$ ("inverse transformed" X-distribution)

   $x = y^{-\tau}, \left|\frac{dx}{dy}\right| = \tau y^{-\tau-1} \quad \Rightarrow \quad f_Y(y) = \tau y^{-\tau-1} f_X(y^{-\tau})$

   Note: With $\tau = 1$, Y is called the "inverse X-distribution".

3. $Y = e^X, x = g^{-1}(y) = ln(y), \left|\frac{dx}{dy}\right| = \frac{1}{y} \quad \Rightarrow \quad f_Y(y) = f_X(ln(y))\frac{1}{y}$

   Note: $E[Y^k] = E[(e^X)^k] = E[e^{kX}] = M_X(k)$ where $M_X(t)$ is the moment generating function.

Mixing of Distributions

Suppose X has a parametric density $f(x\colon\theta)$. View θ as a realization of a random variable Θ having a distribution of its own. Then $f(x\colon\theta)$ is really $f(x|\Theta = \theta)$. The joint density of X and Θ is then $f(x\colon\theta)f_\Theta(\theta) = f(x|\Theta = \theta)f_\Theta(\theta)$. The X-marginal distribution is then obtained by integrating out the θ in the joint density (Θ a continuous random variable) or summing out the θ in the joint density.

Example Suppose X is geometric[11] with parameter p. Suppose p is a realization of P which is uniformly distributed on $(0,1)$. Then $f_X(x) = (1-p)^x p$ for $x = 0, 1, 2, \ldots$. Here we view this as $f_X(x|P = p)$. So $f_{X,P}(x,p) = f_X(x|P = p)f_P(p) = (1-p)^x p \cdot 1$ for $x = 0, 1, 2, \ldots$ and $0 < p < 1$. Thus

$$f_X(x) = \int_{p=0}^{1} (1-p)^x p\, dp = \frac{\Gamma(2)\Gamma(x+1)}{\Gamma(x+3)} = \frac{(1)!(x)!}{(x+2)!} = \frac{1}{(x+1)(x+2)}.$$

The trick above is based on the fact that integrating a beta density from 0 to 1 gives 1:

$$1 = \int_0^1 \frac{\Gamma(a+b)}{\Gamma(a)\Gamma(b)} x^{a-1}(1-x)^{b-1} dx$$

---

[11] Discussed in Unit 3 to follow.

Model of An Inflationary Effect on a Loss Distribution

$Y = CX$ where C, X are independent and the distribution of C reflects uncertainty about next years inflation. X represents the current year's loss distribution. Then

$$E[Y] = E[CX] = E[C]E[X] \qquad \text{(independence)}$$

$$Var(Y) = E[C^2]E[X^2] - (E[X])^2(E[C])^2 = E[C^2]Var(X) + (E[X])^2 Var(C)$$

Two views of Y:

(1) All of next year's losses will be distributed like cX for some realization c of C. Then Y represents a forecast of next year's losses reflecting the uncertainty about inflation.

(2) Next year's losses will each be inflated by a factor c which varies from loss to loss like C. Then Y can be interpreted as next year's loss distribution.

Computing the Y-density:

$$f_Y(y) = \int_c f_Y(y|C=c) f_C(c)\,dc = \int_c f_{cX}(y) f_C(c)\,dc = \int_c f_X\left(\tfrac{y}{c}\right) \cdot \tfrac{1}{c} \cdot f_C(c)\,dc$$

Note: This can be viewed as "mixing" of two distributions if X is from a parametric family $f(x;\theta)$ where θ is a scale parameter. If θ_0 is this year's parameter $f_X(x) = f(x;\theta_0)$ and $f_{cX}(x) = f(x;c\theta_0)$. Substituting $\theta = c\theta_0$ into the final integral above makes the integral look like mixing.

The Gamma Family

$$f_X(x) = \frac{1}{\theta^\alpha \Gamma(\alpha)} \cdot x^{\alpha-1} e^{-x/\theta}, \quad 0 < x < \infty, \ \alpha > 0, \ \theta > 0$$

$$\Gamma(\alpha) = \int_0^\infty x^{\alpha-1} e^{-x}\,dx, \ \ \Gamma(\alpha) = (\alpha-1)\Gamma(\alpha-1), \ \ \Gamma(n) = (n-1)!$$

if n is integral, and $\Gamma(1) = 1$

$$M_X(t) = (1-\theta t)^{-\alpha} \qquad \text{for } t < \frac{1}{\theta}$$

$$E[X^k] = \theta^k(\alpha+k-1)(\alpha+k-2)\cdots(\alpha) = \begin{cases} \theta\alpha & k=1 \\ \theta^2\alpha(\alpha+1) & k=2 \end{cases}$$

$\alpha = 1 \ \Rightarrow \ X$ has the exponential density

aX is gamma with parameters α, $a\theta$

Incomplete Gamma Function: $\Gamma(\alpha; x) = \int_0^x \frac{t^{\alpha-1}e^{-t}}{\Gamma(\alpha)}\,dt$ is the distribution function if $\theta = 1$

$F_X(x) = Pr(X \le x) = Pr\left(\frac{X}{\theta} \le \frac{x}{\theta}\right) = \Gamma\left(\alpha; \frac{x}{\theta}\right)$ since $\frac{1}{\theta}X$ is gamma with parameters α, 1

The Transformed Gamma Family

$f_X(x) = \frac{\tau u^{\alpha} e^{-u}}{x\Gamma(\alpha)}$ where $u = \left(\frac{x}{\theta}\right)^{\tau}$, $0 < x < \infty, \alpha > 0,\ \theta > 0, \tau > 0$

$\left(\frac{1}{\theta}X\right)^{\tau}$ has a gamma distribution with parameters α, 1

$F_X(x) = Pr(X \le x) = Pr\left(\left(\frac{1}{\theta}X\right)^{\tau} \le \left(\frac{x}{\theta}\right)^{\tau}\right) = \Gamma\left(\alpha; \left(\frac{x}{\theta}\right)^{\tau}\right)$

$E[X^k] = \frac{\theta^k \Gamma(\alpha + k/\tau)}{\Gamma(\alpha)}$

The Inverse Transformed Gamma Family

$f_X(x) = \frac{\tau u^{\alpha} e^{-u}}{x\Gamma(\alpha)}$ where $u = \left(\frac{x}{\theta}\right)^{-\tau} = \left(\frac{\theta}{x}\right)^{\tau}$, $0 < x < \infty, \alpha > 0,\ \theta > 0, \tau > 0$

$\left(\frac{1}{\theta}X\right)^{-\tau} = \left(\frac{\theta}{X}\right)^{\tau}$ has a gamma distribution with parameters α, 1

$F_X(x) = 1 - \Gamma\left(\alpha; \left(\frac{\theta}{x}\right)^{\tau}\right)$

$E[X^k] = \frac{\theta^k \Gamma(\alpha - k/\tau)}{\Gamma(\alpha)}$

The Beta Family

$f_X(x) = \frac{\Gamma(a+b)}{\Gamma(a)\Gamma(b)} x^{a-1}(1-x)^{b-1}, 0 \le x \le 1, a > 0,\ b > 0$

Incomplete Beta Function: $\beta(a, b, x) = \int_0^x \frac{\Gamma(a+b)}{\Gamma(a)\Gamma(b)} t^{a-1}(1-t)^{b-1}\,dt = F_X(x)$ for $0 \le x \le 1$

$E[X^k] = \frac{\Gamma(a+b)\Gamma(a+k)}{\Gamma(a)\Gamma(a+b+k)}$

The Transformed Beta Family

$$f_X(x) = \frac{\Gamma(a+b)}{\Gamma(a)\Gamma(b)} \cdot \frac{\gamma(x/\theta)^{\gamma a}}{x[1+(x/\theta)^\gamma]^{a+b}},\ 0 < x < \infty, \text{ all four parameters positive}$$

$\dfrac{(X/\theta)^\gamma}{1+(X/\theta)^\gamma}$ has a Beta distribution with parameters a, b

$$E[X^k] = \frac{\theta^k\Gamma(a+k/\gamma)\Gamma(b-k/\gamma)}{\Gamma(a)\Gamma(b)},\quad -a\gamma < k < b\gamma$$

The Lognormal Family

$$f_X(x) = \frac{1}{x\sqrt{2\pi}\sigma} exp\left[-\frac{1}{2}\left(\frac{ln(x)-\mu}{\sigma}\right)^2\right],\ 0 < x < \infty,\ \sigma > 0$$

$ln(X)$ has a normal distribution with parameters μ, σ^2

$$E[X^k] = e^{\mu k+\sigma^2 k^2/2}$$

The Inverse Gaussian Family

$$f_X(x) = \left(\frac{\theta}{2\pi x^3}\right)^{1/2} \cdot exp\left[-\frac{\theta}{2x}\left(\frac{x-\mu}{\mu}\right)^2\right],\ 0 < x < \infty$$

$$E[X] = \mu,\ Var(X) = \frac{\mu^3}{\theta},\quad \theta > 0$$

Coverage Modifications

X is the loss resulting from a single loss event ($Pr(X > 0) = 1$) (the **ground-up loss**)
Y is the amount paid per loss by the insurer/reinsurer
$Z = Y|_{Y>0}$ is the amount paid per payment event
$S = X_1 + \cdots + X_N$ = aggregate losses/collective model
$C = Y_1 + \cdots + Y_N$ = aggregate claims/collective model $= Z_1 + \cdots + Z_M$
where M is the random number of losses during the period resulting in a claim payment. (Modeled by an N_S below.)

Let S be a set of numbers such that $X \in S$ implies that $Y > 0$ (i.e., a claim payment is made). Let N_S be the random number of losses, X, which fall in S. Then

$$N_S|_{N=n} = \text{Binomial } (n \text{ trials}, p = Pr(X \in S)), \text{ i.e., a loss is a " success" if it falls in } S$$

Thus, by the double expectation theorem

$$\underbrace{E[N_S]}_{\substack{\text{expected number}\\ \text{of claims}}} = \underbrace{E[N]}_{\substack{\text{expected number}\\ \text{of losses}}} \underbrace{Pr(X \in S)}_{\substack{\text{fraction of losses}\\ \text{producing a claim}}}.$$

So if $C = Z_1 + \cdots + Z_{N_S}$ then

$$\underbrace{E[C]}_{\substack{\text{expected agg.}\\ \text{claims}}} = \underbrace{E[N_S]}_{\substack{\text{expected number}\\ \text{of claims}}} \underbrace{E[Z]}_{\substack{\text{expected}\\ \text{claim amount}}}.$$

1. A deductible d is applied to the loss X.

$$Y = \begin{cases} 0 & X \leq d \\ X - d & X > d \end{cases} = \underbrace{I_d(X)}_{\text{notation}} = \underbrace{(X-d)_+}_{\text{alternate notation}}$$

$$Z = Y|_{Y>0} = X - d|_{X>d}$$

$$f_Y(y) = \begin{cases} Pr(X \leq d) & y = 0 \quad \text{(point mass/disc. part)} \\ f_X(d+y) & y > 0 \quad \text{(cont. part)} \end{cases}$$

$$f_Z(z) = \frac{1}{1 - Pr(X \leq d)} \cdot f_X(d+z)$$

Here $S = (d, \infty)$ and $E[N_S] = E[N]Pr(X > d)$

2. A limit L is applied to the loss X. Note: L refers to the max loss amount used in computing the claim, it is not necessarily the maximum claim amount.

$$Z = Y = \begin{cases} X & X \leq L \\ L & X > L \end{cases} = \underbrace{\{X \wedge L\}}_{\text{notation}} = X - I_L(X)$$

$$f_Y(y) = \begin{cases} f_X(y) & y < L \quad \text{(continuous part)} \\ Pr(X > L) & y = L \quad \text{(discrete part)} \end{cases}$$

Here every loss produces a claim.

3. A coinsurance factor α, $0 < \alpha < 1$, is applied to the loss X

$$Z = Y = \alpha X$$

$$f_Y(y) = f_X\left(\frac{y}{\alpha}\right) \cdot \frac{1}{\alpha}$$

Here every loss produces a claim.

4. All three modifications: a coinsurance factor α is applied to the excess of a loss over a deductible d, up to a policy limit of L.

$$Y = \left\{\begin{array}{ll} 0 & X \le d \\ \alpha(X-d) & d < X \le L \\ \alpha(L-d) & L < X \end{array}\right\} = \alpha(I_d(X) - I_L(X))$$

$$Z = Y|_{Y>0} = \left\{\begin{array}{ll} \alpha(X-d) & d < X \le L \\ \alpha(L-d) & L < X \end{array}\right\}\Bigg|_{X>d}$$

$$f_Z(z) = \left\{\begin{array}{ll} \dfrac{\left(\frac{1}{\alpha}\right) f_X\left(\frac{z}{\alpha}+d\right)}{1-F_X(d)} & 0 < z < \alpha(L-d) \\ \dfrac{1-F_X(L)}{1-F_X(d)} & z = \alpha(L-d)\text{: a point mass/discrete part.} \end{array}\right.$$

Here $S = (d, \infty)$ and $E[N_S] = E[N]Pr(X > d)$

Measures of Tail Weight

1. $$\lim_{x\to\infty} \frac{f_X(x)}{f_Y(x)} = \left\{\begin{array}{ll} \infty & X \text{ has the “heavier tail”} \\ 0 & X \text{ has the “lighter tail”} \\ 0 < c < \infty & \text{tails are “proportional”/similar} \end{array}\right.$$

L'Hopitals Rule $\Rightarrow \displaystyle\lim_{x\to\infty} \frac{S_X(x)}{S_Y(x)} = \lim_{x\to\infty} \frac{f_X(x)}{f_Y(x)}$

2. $\displaystyle\lim_{x\to\infty} \frac{E[X-x|X>x]}{E[Y-x|Y>x]}$ used with same conclusions although this limit is not the same as above. It is simply a different measure of tail weight than in (1).

3. $\displaystyle\lim_{x\to\infty} \frac{h_X(x)}{h_Y(x)} = \infty$ means $h_X(x)$ is much larger than $h_Y(x)$. Hence $H_X(x) > H_Y(x)$ and $S_X(x) = exp(-H_X(x)) < S_Y(x) = exp(-H_Y(x))$. So X has a lighter tail. Recall from survival models that $H_X(x)$ is the cumulative hazard rate.

CONCEPTUAL REVIEW TEST

1. What is the general relation of f_Y to f_X if $Y = g(X)$ is a one-to-one function? What is the specific relation if $Y = \theta(X^{1/\tau})$ where $\tau > 0$?

2. If X has a gamma distribution with parameters $\alpha = 3$ and $\theta = 2$, express $Pr(X \leq 12)$ in terms of the incomplete gamma function.

3. Suppose X has a geometric density with parameter p (i.e., $f_X(x) = (1-p)^x \cdot p$ for $x = 0, 1, 2, \ldots$) and suppose p is a realization of P which is uniformly distributed on $(0, 1)$. In other words, $f_X(x|P = p) = (1-p)^x \cdot p$. Explain how the X distribution is mixed with the uniform to obtain the unconditional X density.

4. X is the year's loss distribution. Two models for next year's losses, Y, are given as follows:
   (i) $Y = 1.03X$, or
   (ii) $Y = CX$ where C and X are independent, $E[C] = 1.03$ and $Var(C) = .0001$.
   Contrast $E[Y]$, $Var[Y]$ for these two models.

5. If Y has a transformed gamma distribution with parameters α, θ, τ explain how to calculate $Pr(Y \leq y)$ in terms of the incomplete gamma function.

6. X is a loss variable. An insurance covers 60% of the excess loss over 50, if there is an excess, up to a policy limit of 1000. Write expressions for Y (the payment per loss variable) and Z (the payment per payment event variable).

7. In Question 6, express $F_Y(500)$, $F_Z(500)$ in terms of $F_X(x)$.

8. What is the relation between $I_L(X)$ (an insurance with a deductible of L) and $X \wedge L = min\{X, L\}$ (an insurance with a policy limit of L)? X is the loss being insured.

9. Why is the right tail of a loss distribution so important?

CONCEPTUAL REVIEW TEST SOLUTIONS

1. In general $f_Y(y) = f_X(g^{-1}(y))\left|\frac{dx}{dy}\right|$. Solving the specific relation $y = \theta(x)^{1/\tau}$ results in $x = \left(\frac{y}{\theta}\right)^{\tau}$ and $f_Y(y) = f_X\left(\left(\frac{y}{\theta}\right)^{\tau}\right) \cdot \frac{\tau}{\theta}\left(\frac{y}{\theta}\right)^{\tau-1}$.

2. $\frac{X}{2} = \frac{X}{\theta}$ has a gamma distribution with parameters $\alpha = 3$, $\theta = 1$. Thus $Pr(X \leq 12) = Pr\left(\frac{X}{2} \leq 6\right) = \Gamma(3;6) = \int_0^6 \frac{t^2 e^{-t}}{2!}\,dt$.

3. The joint X, P density is

$$f_{X,P}(x,p) = f_X(x|P=p)f_P(p) = (1-p)^x \cdot p \cdot 1$$

for $x = 0, 1, 2, \ldots$ and $0 < p < 1$.

Thus $f_X(x) = \int_{p=0}^{1} f_{X,P}(x,p)\,dp$. (See the Condensed Review Notes for more detail.)

4. If $Y = 1.03X$ then $E[Y] = 1.03E[X]$, $Var(Y) = 1.03^2 Var(X) = 1.0609Var(X)$. Both $E[X]$ and σ_X will increase by 3% next year. In the $Y = CX$ model $E[Y] = E[C]E[X] = 1.03E[X]$ (same as the model above), but

$$Var(Y) = E[C^2]Var(X) + (E[X])^2 Var(C) = (1.03^2 + .0001)Var(X) + (E[X])^2(.0001)$$

$$= 1.0610Var(X) + (E[X])^2(.0001)$$

is larger due to the uncertainty in the inflation forecast, C.

5. $X = \left(\frac{Y}{\theta}\right)^{\tau}$ is a gamma distribution with parameters α, 1. Thus $Pr(Y \leq y) = Pr\left(\left(\frac{Y}{\theta}\right)^{\tau} \leq \left(\frac{y}{\theta}\right)^{\tau}\right) = F_X\left(\left(\frac{y}{\theta}\right)^{\tau}\right) = \Gamma\left(\alpha; \left(\frac{y}{\theta}\right)^{\tau}\right)$.

6. $$Y = \begin{cases} 0 & X \leq 50 \\ (X-50).60 & 50 < X \leq 1000 \\ 570 & 1000 < X \end{cases}$$

$$Z = Y|_{Y>0} = \begin{cases} (X-50).60 & 50 < X \leq 1000 \\ 570 & 1000 < X \end{cases}$$

and is conditional on $X > 50$.

7. If $y = 500 = .60(x - 50)$ then $x = 883.\overline{3}$. Thus $F_Y(500) = Pr(Y \leq 500) = Pr(X \leq 883.\overline{3}) = F_X(883.\overline{3})$. Similarly

$$F_Z(500) = Pr(Y \leq 500|Y > 0) = Pr(X \leq 883.\overline{3}|X > 50)$$
$$= \frac{Pr(50 < X \leq 883.\overline{3})}{Pr(50 < X)} = \frac{F_X(883.\overline{3}) - F_X(50)}{1 - F_X(50)}.$$

8. $$I_L(X) = \begin{cases} 0 & X \leq L \\ X - L & X > L \end{cases}, \qquad X \wedge L = \begin{cases} X & X \leq L \\ L & X > L \end{cases}$$

and from these definitions it is clear that $I_L(X) + X \wedge L = X$.

9. The probability of "large" losses resides in the right tail. If a parametric model for X is used, once the parameters are estimated one should compare the right tail of the parametric model with the right tail of the empirical distribution to make sure you are not badly underestimating risk.

COMPUTATIONAL REVIEW TEST

1. If X has the exponential density $f_X(x) = e^{-x}$ for $0 < x < \infty$, then find the density function and expected value of $Y = X^{-1/2}$ (an inverse transformed exponential). The expected value should be expressed in terms of the gamma function.

2. Suppose $N|_{\Lambda=\lambda}$ is Poisson λ and $f_\Lambda(\lambda) = \frac{1}{2}e^{-\lambda/2}$ for $0 < \lambda < \infty$. Calculate $Pr(N = 2)$.

3. Suppose $N|_{\Lambda=\lambda}$ is Poisson λ and Λ has the inverse Gaussian distribution with parameters θ, μ. (See the Condensed Review Notes). Calculate $E[X]$ and $Var(N)$ in terms of θ and μ.

4. Suppose X and C are independent where X is this year's loss distribution. Assume that X is exponentially distributed with mean 10. Suppose C has the inverse exponential density $f_C(c) = \frac{11}{10c^2}e^{-11/10c}$. Let $Y = CX$ represent next year's losses.
   (a) Using $f_Y(y) = \int_{c=0}^{\infty} f_{cX}(y) f_C(c)\, dc$ as a starting point, calculate $f_Y(y)$. Hint: a substitution $u = \frac{1}{c}$ is needed to integrate and the trick $\theta^\alpha\Gamma(\alpha) = \int_0^\infty u^{\alpha-1}e^{-u/\theta}du$ based on the gamma distribution.
   (b) Calculate next year's expected loss.
   (c) Find the 90th percentile of Y.

5. A loss variable X has density function $f_X(x) = \frac{2}{200}\left(1 - \frac{x}{200}\right)$. An insurance covers 80% of the excess loss over 50, if there is an excess, up to a policy limit of 150. Let Y be the payment per loss variable and let Z be the payment per payment event variable.
   (a) Write expressions for Y and Z in terms of X.
   (b) Calculate $E[Y]$ and $E[Z]$.
   (c) Find the Z density.

6. Consider again the insurance in problem 5. Suppose that with the current deductible of 50 there are 200 expected claims.
   (a) Calculate the expected aggregate claims.
   (b) Recalculate the expected aggregate claims if the deductible of 50 is dropped. What is the percent increase?

COMPUTATIONAL REVIEW TEST SOLUTIONS

1. $x = y^{-2}$ means $f_Y(y) = f_X(y^{-2})\frac{2}{y^3} = \frac{2}{y^3}e^{-1/y^2}$. Thus $E[Y] = \int_0^\infty y \cdot \frac{2}{y^3}e^{-1/y^2}dy$. Now substitute $u = \frac{1}{y^2}$, $y = u^{-1/2}$, $dy = -\frac{1}{2}u^{-3/2}\,du$ to obtain

$E[Y] = \int_\infty^0 2ue^{-u}\left(-\frac{1}{2}u^{-3/2}\right)du = \displaystyle\int_0^\infty u^{-1/2}e^{-u}\,du = \Gamma\left(\frac{1}{2}\right)$.

2. $Pr(N = 2)$ is the same as $f_N(2)$. From the given information

$$\begin{aligned}
f_N(2) = \int_{\lambda=0}^\infty f_N(2|\Lambda = \lambda)f_\Lambda(\lambda)\,d\lambda &= \int_{\lambda=0}^\infty e^{-\lambda}\frac{\lambda^2}{2!}\frac{1}{2}e^{-\lambda/2}\,d\lambda \\
&= \frac{1}{4}\int_{\lambda=0}^\infty e^{-(3\lambda/2)}\lambda^2\,d\lambda \\
&= \frac{1}{4}\int_{\lambda=0}^\infty e^{-u}\frac{4}{9}u^2\frac{2}{3}\,du \qquad \left\{\begin{array}{l} u = 3\lambda/2 \\ du = 3/2\,d\lambda \end{array}\right. \\
&= \frac{2}{27}\int_{\lambda=0}^\infty e^{-u}u^2\,du = \frac{2}{27}\Gamma(3) = \frac{2}{27}(2!) = \frac{4}{27}.
\end{aligned}$$

Shortcut: If Λ is a gamma variable with parameters α (an integer) and θ then it was shown in Example 2 that N is negative binomial with $r = \alpha$ and $p = \frac{1}{1+\theta}$. Here $\alpha = 1$ (i.e., Λ is exponential), $\theta = 2$, so $f_N(2) = q^2p = \left(\frac{2}{3}\right)^2\left(\frac{1}{3}\right) = \frac{4}{27}$ as above.

3. Since $N|_\Lambda$ is Poisson we know $E[N|\Lambda] = \Lambda$ and $Var(N|\Lambda) = \Lambda$. So, by the double expectation theorem,

$$E[N] = E[E[N|\Lambda]] = E[\Lambda] = \mu$$

$$Var(N) = E[\underbrace{Var(N|\Lambda)}_{\Lambda}] + Var(\underbrace{E[N|\Lambda]}_{\Lambda\text{ (above)}}) = \mu + \frac{\mu^3}{\theta} \qquad \text{(Inv. Gaussian facts)}$$

Note: N is called Poisson-Inverse Gaussian!

4. (a) First, $f_{cX}(y) = f_X\left(\frac{y}{c}\right) \cdot \frac{1}{c} = \frac{1}{10}e^{-y/10c} \cdot \frac{1}{c} = \frac{1}{10c}e^{-y/10c}$ (i.e., exponential with parameter $10c$). Thus

$$f_Y(y) = \int_{c=0}^{\infty} \frac{1}{10c}e^{-y/10c} \cdot \frac{11}{10c^2}e^{-11/10c}\,dc = \frac{11}{100}\int_{c=0}^{\infty} \frac{1}{c^3}e^{-\frac{1}{c}\left(\frac{y+11}{10}\right)}dc$$

Now, substitute $u = \frac{1}{c}$, $dc = \frac{-1}{u^2}du$ to obtain

$$f_Y(y) = \frac{11}{100}\int_{u=0}^{\infty} u^3 \cdot \frac{1}{u^2}e^{-u/(10/11+y)}du = \underbrace{\frac{11}{100}\left(\frac{10}{11+y}\right)^2\Gamma(2)}_{\text{(see the hint)}} = \underbrace{\frac{11}{(11+y)^2}}_{\text{(a Pareto density)}}$$

(b) $$E[Y] = \int_{y=0}^{\infty} y \cdot f_Y(y)\,dy = \int_{y=0}^{\infty}\frac{11y}{(11+y)^2}\,dy = 11\left[\int_{y=0}^{\infty}\frac{y+11-11}{(11+y)^2}\,dy\right]$$

$$= 11\left[\int_{y=0}^{\infty}\frac{1}{11+y} - \frac{11}{(11+y)^2}dy\right]$$

$$= 11\left[ln(11+y) + \frac{11}{11+y}\Big|_{y=0}^{\infty}\right]$$

Surprise? The integral diverges.

(c) $$F_Y(y) = \int_0^y \frac{11}{(11+x)^2}\,dx = \frac{-11}{11+x}\Big|_{x=0}^{y} = 1 - \frac{11}{11+y} = \frac{y}{11+y}.$$

$$.90 = \frac{y}{11+y} \quad \Rightarrow \quad 9.9 + .9y = y \quad \Rightarrow \quad y = 99.$$

5. (a) $$Y = \begin{cases} 0 & X \le 50 \\ (X-50).8 & 50 < X \le 150 \\ 80 & 150 < X \le 200 \end{cases}$$

$$Z = \begin{cases} .8(X-50) & 50 < X \le 150 \\ 80 & 150 < X \le 200 \end{cases} \quad \text{(conditional on } X > 50\text{)}$$

Note: A policy limit refers to the X distribution and is usually not the maximal possible claim payment.

(b) $$E[Y] = \int_{50}^{150} .8(x-50)\frac{2}{200}\left(1 - \frac{x}{200}\right)dx + \int_{150}^{200} 80 \cdot \frac{2}{200}\left(1 - \frac{x}{200}\right)dx$$

$$= 16\tfrac{2}{3} + 5 = 21\tfrac{2}{3} = 21.6\overline{6}$$

So $E[Y] = E[Y|Y=0]Pr(Y=0) + E[Y|Y>0]Pr(Y>0)$

$21.6\overline{6} = 0 \cdot Pr(X \le 50) + E[Z]Pr(X > 50)$.

Now $Pr(X > 50) = \int_{50}^{200} \frac{2}{200}\left(1 - \frac{x}{200}\right)\,dx = -\left(1 - \frac{x}{200}\right)^2\Big|_{50}^{200} = \frac{9}{16}$,
so $E[Z] = \frac{16}{9}E[Y] = 38.52$.

(c) It is easiest to begin with $Z_1 = X - 50|_{X>50}$ and then add the coinsurance factor, .80, and the policy limit of 150 (i.e., max Z-value = 80). Now $f_{Z_1}(z) = \frac{f_X(50+z)}{Pr(X>50)} = \frac{2}{200}\left(\frac{200-(50+z)}{200}\right)\cdot\frac{16}{9} = \frac{2}{150}\left(1-\frac{z}{150}\right)$ for $0 \le z \le 150$. Net let $Z_2 = .8Z_1$. Then $f_{Z_2}(z) = f_{Z_1}(\frac{z}{.8})\frac{1}{.8} = \frac{2}{120}\left(1-\frac{z}{120}\right)$ for $0 \le z \le 120$. Now $Pr(Z_2 > 80) = \left(1-\frac{80}{120}\right)^2 = \frac{1}{9}$. Finally,

$$Z = \begin{cases} Z_2 & Z_2 < 80 \\ 80 & Z_2 \ge 80 \end{cases}$$

so

$$f_Z(z) = \begin{cases} \frac{2}{120}\left(1-\frac{z}{120}\right) & 0 \le z \le 80 \quad \text{(cont. part)} \\ \frac{1}{9} & z = 80 \quad \text{(disc. part)} \end{cases}$$

6. (a) Expected aggregate claims is

$$\underbrace{(200)}_{\substack{\text{Expected} \\ \text{No. of Claims}}} \cdot \underbrace{(38.52)}_{\substack{\text{Expected payment} \\ \text{per claim}}} = 7704$$

(b) Let $E[N]$ be the expected number of losses. Without a deductible this is also the expected number of claims. Furthermore,

$$\underbrace{E[N]}_{\substack{\text{Expected} \\ \text{No. of losses}}} \cdot \underbrace{Pr(X>50)}_{\substack{\text{fraction of losses} \\ \text{producing claims}}} = \underbrace{200}_{\substack{\text{Exp. No.} \\ \text{Claims if } d=50}}$$

and $Pr(X>50) = \left(1-\frac{50}{200}\right)^2 = \frac{9}{16}$ result in $E[N] = \frac{200(16)}{9} = 355.\overline{5}$.

Also, with no deductible,

$$Z = Y = \begin{cases} .8X & 0 \le X \le 150 \\ 120 & 150 < X \le 200 \end{cases}.$$

Hence

$$E[Z] = \int_0^{150} .8x\frac{2}{200}\left(1-\frac{x}{200}\right)dx + 120Pr(X>150) = 45 + \frac{120}{16} = 52.5$$

Finally, expected aggregate claims equal $(355.\overline{5})(52.5) = 18{,}666.\overline{6}$. The percent increase is thus 142.3%.

UNIT REVIEW QUESTIONS

1. The distribution of the number of claims, N, given Λ, is Poisson. The distribution of Λ is exponential with parameter 1. Determine $Pr(N = 0)$.

(A) .00 (B) .05 (C) .20 (D) .35 (E) .50

2. (2 points) For an insured, Y is the total time spent in the hospital in a year. The distribution of the number of hospital admissions in a year is:

Number of Admissions	Probability
0	0.60
1	0.30
2	0.10

The distribution of the length of stay for each admission is gamma with $\alpha = 1$ and $\beta = 0.2$. $f_X(x) = \left(\frac{\beta^\alpha}{\Gamma(\alpha)}\right) x^{\alpha-1} e^{-\beta x}$. Determine the variance of Y.

(A) 20 (B) 24 (C) 28 (D) 32 (E) 36

3. (2 points) A population is equally divided into two classes of drivers. The number of accidents per individual driver is Poisson for all drivers.

For a driver selected at random from Class I, the expected number of accidents is uniformly distributed over (0.2, 1.0).

For a driver selected at random from Class II, the expected number of accidents is uniformly distributed over (0.4, 2.0).

For a driver selected at random from this population, determine the probability of zero accidents.

(A) 0.41 (B) 0.42 (C) 0.43 (D) 0.44 (E) 0.45

4. (2 points) For aggregate claims $S = \sum_{i=1}^{N} X_i$ you are given:

(i) the conditional distribution of N, given Λ, is Poisson with parameter Λ;
(ii) Λ has a gamma distribution with $\alpha = 3$ and $\beta = 4$;
(iii) $X_1, X_2, X_3, \ldots$ are identically distributed with $p(1) = p(3) = 0.5$; and
(iv) $N, X_1, X_2, \ldots$ are mutually independent.

Determine $Var[S]$.

(A) 4.4 (B) 4.5 (C) 4.6 (D) 4.7 (E) 4.8

5. (2 points) A population has two classes of drivers. The number of accidents per individual driver has a geometric distribution.

For a driver selected at random from Class I, the geometric distribution[12] parameter has a uniform distribution over the interval $(0, 1)$. 25% of the drivers are in Class I.

All drivers in Class II have expected number of claims 0.25.

For a driver selected at random from this population, determine the probability of exactly two accidents.

(A) 0.030 (B) 0.035 (C) 0.040 (D) 0.045 (E) 0.050

6. For aggregate claims $S = \sum_{i=1}^{N} X_i$, you are given:

(i) X_i has distribution

x	$p(x)$
1	p
2	$1-p$

(ii) Λ is a Poisson random variable with parameter $\frac{1}{p}$;
(iii) given $\Lambda = \lambda$, N is Poisson with parameter λ;
(iv) the number of claims and claim amounts are mutually independent; and
(v) $Var(S) = \frac{19}{2}$.

Determine p.

(A) $\frac{1}{6}$ (B) $\frac{1}{5}$ (C) $\frac{1}{4}$ (D) $\frac{1}{3}$ (E) $\frac{1}{2}$

7. If X is exponentially distributed with mean 2, find $E[Y]$ and $f_Y(y)$ where $Y = X^{-1/2}$, an inverse transformed exponential

	Mean	Density
A.	$\frac{1}{\sqrt{2}}\Gamma\left(\frac{1}{2}\right)$	$\frac{2y^3}{e^{(1/2y^2)}}$
B.	$\frac{1}{2}\Gamma\left(\frac{1}{2}\right)$	$\frac{2y^{-3}}{e^{(1/2y^2)}}$
C.	$\frac{1}{\sqrt{2}}\Gamma\left(-\frac{1}{2}\right)$	$\frac{2y^{-3}}{e^{(1/2y^2)}}$
D.	$\frac{1}{2}\Gamma\left(\frac{1}{2}\right)$	$\frac{1}{y^3 e^{(1/2y^2)}}$
E.	$\frac{1}{\sqrt{2}}\Gamma\left(\frac{1}{2}\right)$	$\frac{1}{y^3 e^{(1/2y^2)}}$

---

12 $f_N(n) = q^n p$, $E[N] = \frac{q}{p}$, $Var(N) = \frac{q}{p^2}$, $q + p = 1$; $p =$ "parameter".

8. Suppose $Y = CX$ where C and X are independent. You are also given:

(i) X is exponentially distributed with mean 2;
(ii) $f_C(c) = \frac{1}{ln(1.25)} \cdot \frac{1}{c}$ for $1 \leq c \leq 1.25$.

Calculate $f_Y(y)$ and $E[Y]$.

	$E[Y]$	$f_Y(y)$
A.	$\frac{1}{2\,ln(1.25)}$	$\frac{1}{2y\,ln(1.25)}[e^{-y/2} - e^{-y/2.5}]$
B.	$\frac{1}{ln(1.25)}$	$\frac{1}{y\,ln(1.25)}[e^{-y/2.5} - e^{-y/2}]$
C.	$\frac{1}{2\,ln(1.25)}$	$\frac{1}{y\,ln(1.25)}[e^{-y/2.5} - e^{-y/2}]$
D.	$\frac{1}{ln(1.25)}$	$\frac{1}{y\,ln(1.25)}[e^{-y/2.5} - e^{-y/2}]$
E.	$\frac{1}{2\,ln(1.25)}$	$\frac{1}{2y\,ln(1.25)}[e^{-y/2} - e^{-y/2.5}]$

9. Suppose the distribution of $M|_{N=n}$ is Binomial with n trials and $p = Pr(\text{Success}) = .2$. You are also given that N is Poisson with parameter $\lambda = 5$. Calculate $f_M(m)$ for $m = 0, 1, 2, \ldots$.

A. $e^{-4}\frac{4^m}{m!}$ B. $\binom{m+2}{m}(.2)^3(.8)^m$ C. $\binom{m+1}{m}(.2)^2(.8)^m$

D. $\binom{n}{m}(.2)^m(.8)^{n-m}$ E. $e^{-1} \cdot \frac{1}{m!}$

Use the following information for Questions 10-14.

A loss variable, X, is exponentially distributed with mean 10 and aggregate claims, S, is given by $S = X_1 + \cdots + X_N$ where $E[N] = 100$ and $Var(N) = 125$.

10. If each loss is subjected to a deductible of 2 what is the expected number of claims? (nearest integer)

(A) 80 (B) 82 (C) 84 (D) 86 (E) 88

11. What is the expected value of aggregate claims after the deductible of 2 is imposed? (nearest 10)

(A) 780 (B) 790 (C) 800 (D) 810 (E) 820

12. What deductible d (applied to each claim) will result in a 30% reduction in expected aggregate claims? (nearest tenth)

(A) 3.4 (B) 3.5 (C) 3.6 (D) 3.7 (E) 3.8

13 Calculate the ratio of the standard deviation of aggregate claims to the expected aggregate claims with no deductible and with a deductible of 2 applied to each loss.

	$\sigma/\mu,\ d=0$	$\sigma/\mu,\ d=2$
A.	.125	.150
B.	.150	.164
C.	.150	.180
D.	.175	.164
E.	.175	.180

14. Calculate expected aggregate claims if a policy limit of 15 is imposed on each loss. (nearest 1)

(A) 777 (B) 790 (C) 802 (D) 815 (E) 887

Use the following information for Questions 15-18.

A ground-up loss X has density function $f(x) = .0004xe^{-.02x}$ for $x > 0$.

15. An insurance applies a deductible d to the loss X. Calculate the probability that a loss results in a claim payment.

(A) $e^{-.02d}$ (B) $.02de^{-.02d}$ (C) $1 - e^{-.02d}$ (D) $(.02d+1)e^{-.02d}$ (E) $.02d(1 - e^{-.02d})$

16. An insurance applies a deductible d to the loss X. What is the expected claim payment given that a payment is made?

(A) $\dfrac{50d+500}{d+5}$ (B) $\dfrac{50d+5000}{d+50}$ (C) $\dfrac{5d+5000}{d+50}$ (D) $\dfrac{50d+5}{d+.02}$ (E) $100(1-.02d)$

17. An insurance applies a deductible d to the loss X. What is the percent decrease in the expected claim payment if d is increased from 50 to 100?

(A) 8.88 (B) 9.25 (C) 10.00 (D) 11.11 (E) 12.50

18. An insurance applies a deductible $d = 50$ to the loss X. Which of the following is closest to the loss elimination ratio?

(A) .35 (B) .40 (C) .45 (D) .47 (E) .50

SOLUTIONS TO UNIT REVIEW QUESTIONS

A more extensive list of questions integrating topics from this entire section of the manual will follow Unit 4.

1. This is a standard situation which results in N having a Negative Binomial distribution. In general, if $N|_{\Lambda=\lambda}$ is Poisson λ, and if Λ has a Gamma distribution with parameters α and θ (i.e., $f_\Lambda(\lambda) = \frac{1}{\theta^\alpha \Gamma(\alpha)} \lambda^{\alpha-1} e^{-\lambda/\theta}$), then N has a Negative Binomial distribution:

$$f_N(n) = \binom{n+\alpha-1}{n}\left(\frac{\theta}{1+\theta}\right)^n \left(\frac{1}{1+\theta}\right)^\alpha.$$

(See Example 2 in this Unit.) Thus $Pr(N=0) = \binom{\alpha-1}{0}\left(\frac{1}{1+\theta}\right)^\alpha = (1)\left(\frac{1}{2}\right)^1 = \frac{1}{2}$ since $\alpha = 1$ and $\theta = 1$ (i.e., Λ is exponential ($\alpha = 1$) with parameter 1 ($\theta = 1$). ANSWER E

2. Let N be the random number of admissions and let X be the length of a stay. Then $Y = X_1 + \cdots + X_N$ - a random sum. So

$$Var(Y) = E[N]Var(X) + (E[X])^2 Var(N)$$

$$\left.\begin{array}{l} E[N] = 0(.60) + 1(.30) + 2(.10) = .50 \\ E[N^2] = 0^2(.60) + 1^2(.30) + 2^2(.10) = .70 \end{array}\right\} Var(N) = .7 - .5^2 = .45$$

$$E[X] = \frac{\alpha}{\beta} = \frac{1}{.2} = 5,\ Var(X) = \frac{\alpha}{\beta^2} = \frac{1}{.04} = 25$$

Plugging in

$$Var(Y) = (.50)(25) + (5)^2(.45) = 23.75$$

ANSWER B

3. In each class $f_N(n|\Lambda = \lambda) = e^{-\lambda} \cdot \frac{\lambda^n}{n!}$. Also for Class I $f_\Lambda(\lambda) = \frac{1}{.8}$ for $.2 \le \lambda \le 1.0$ and for Class II $f_\Lambda(\lambda) = \frac{1}{1.6}$ for $.4 \le \lambda \le 2.0$. Hence

(Class I)

$$f_N(0) = \int_{\lambda=.2}^{1.0} f_N(0|\Lambda=\lambda) f_\Lambda(\lambda)\,d\lambda = \int_{\lambda=.2}^{1.0} e^{-\lambda}\frac{\lambda^0}{0!}\frac{1}{.8}\,d\lambda = 1.25(e^{-.2} - e^{-1.0}) = .564$$

(Class II)

$$f_N(0) = \int_{\lambda=.4}^{2.0} f_N(0|\Lambda=\lambda) f_\Lambda(\lambda)\,d\lambda = \int_{\lambda=.4}^{2.0} e^{-\lambda}\frac{\lambda^0}{0!}\frac{1}{1.6}\,d\lambda = .625(e^{-.4} - e^{-2.0}) = .334$$

Therefore

$$Pr(0 \text{ accidents}) = Pr(0 \text{ accidents}|\text{I})Pr(I) + Pr(0 \text{ accidents}|\text{II})Pr(\text{II})$$
$$= .564(.50) + .334(.50) = .449$$

ANSWER E

4. N is Negative Binomial: $r = \alpha = 3, p = \frac{\beta}{1+\beta} = \frac{4}{5} = .8, q = .2$

$$\Rightarrow E[N] = \frac{rq}{p} = \frac{3}{4},\ Var(N) = \frac{rq}{p^2} = \frac{3}{3.2}$$

$$\left.\begin{array}{l} E[X] = \sum x \cdot p(x) = 2 \\ E[X^2] = \sum x^2 \cdot p(x) = 5 \end{array}\right\} \Rightarrow \quad Var(X) = 1$$

$$Var(S) = E[N]Var(X) + (E[X])^2 Var(N) = \left(\tfrac{3}{4}\right)(1) + (2^2)\left(\tfrac{3}{3.2}\right) = 4.5$$ ANSWER B

5. $Pr(\text{2 accidents}) = \underbrace{Pr(\text{Class I})}_{.25 \text{ given}} \underbrace{Pr(\text{2 Accidents}|I)}_{\frac{1}{12} \text{ below}} + \underbrace{Pr(\text{Class II})}_{.75 \text{ given}} \underbrace{Pr(\text{2 Accidents}|\text{II})}_{.032 \text{ below}} = .0448$

ANSWER D

Class I: $f_N(n|P = p) = (1-p)^n p \quad n = 0, 1, \ldots$

$f_p(p) = 1 \quad 0 \le p \le 1$

Thus $f_N(n) = \int_{p=0}^{1} f_{N,P}(n,p)\,dp = \int_{p=0}^{1} f_N(n|P=p) f_P(p) dp,$

$$f_N(2) = \int_{p=0}^{1} f_N(2|P=p) f_P(p)\,dp$$
$$= \int_{p=0}^{1} (1-p)^2 p \cdot 1\,dp = \int_0^1 p - 2p^2 + p^3\,dp = \frac{p^2}{2} - \frac{2p^3}{3} + \frac{p^4}{4}\Big|_0^1 = \frac{1}{12}.$$

Class II: $f_N(n) = (1-p)^n p, \qquad n = 0, 1, 2, \ldots$

$E[N] = \frac{q}{p} = .25 \quad \text{(given)} \quad \Rightarrow \quad p = .8$

$f_N(2) = (.2)^2(.8) = .032$

6. From (i), $E[X] = 2 - p$, $E[X^2] = 4 - 3p$, and $Var(X) = p - p^2$. From (ii) and (iii), $N|_\Lambda$ is Poisson with parameter Λ (hence $E[N|\Lambda] = \Lambda$ and $Var(N|\Lambda) = \Lambda$) and Λ is Poisson with parameter $\frac{1}{p}$ (hence $E[\Lambda] = Var(\Lambda) = \frac{1}{p}$). Putting this together, by the double expectation theorem

$$E[N] = E[E[N|\Lambda]] = E[\Lambda] = \frac{1}{p}$$

$$Var(N) = E[Var(N|\Lambda)] + Var(E[N|\Lambda]) = E[\Lambda] + Var[\Lambda] = \frac{1}{p} + \frac{1}{p} = \frac{2}{p}.$$

From (v)

$$\frac{19}{2} = Var(S) = E[N]Var(X) + (E[X])^2 Var(N) = \left(\tfrac{1}{p}\right)(p-p^2) + (2-p)^2\left(\tfrac{2}{p}\right)$$

$$\Rightarrow \qquad 19p = 2(p-p^2) + 4(2-p)^2$$

$$\Rightarrow \qquad p = \frac{33 \pm 31}{4} = 16 \text{ or } \frac{1}{2}: \text{ since } p \text{ is a probability } p = \frac{1}{2}.$$ ANSWER E

7. We are given $f_X(x) = \frac{1}{2}e^{-x/2}$ for $x > 0$ and $Y = X^{-1/2}$. Hence $X = Y^{-2}$ and, since we have a 1-1 transformation,

$$f_Y(y) = f_X(y^{-2})\left|\frac{dy^{-2}}{dy}\right| = \frac{1}{2}\cdot e^{-1/(2y^2)}\cdot\left(\frac{2}{y^3}\right) = \frac{1}{y^3\cdot e^{1/(2y^2)}}$$

So $E[Y] = \int_0^\infty y\cdot f_Y(y)\,dy = \int_0^\infty \frac{1}{y^2}e^{-1/(2y^2)}dy.$

Let $u = \frac{1}{2y^2}$ so that $y = (2u)^{-1/2}$, $dy = -\frac{1}{2}(2u)^{-3/2}\cdot 2\,du.$

Then

$$E[Y] = -\int_\infty^0 2u\cdot e^{-u}(2u)^{-3/2}\,du = \frac{1}{\sqrt{2}}\int_0^\infty e^{-u}u^{-1/2}\,du = \frac{1}{\sqrt{2}}\Gamma\left(\frac{1}{2}\right).$$

ANSWER E

8. Due to the independence $E[Y] = E[C]E[X] = 2E[C]$ where $E[C] = \int_1^{1.25} c\cdot\frac{1}{ln(1.25)}\frac{1}{c}\,dc = \frac{.25}{ln\,(1.25)}$. Thus $E[Y] = \frac{.50}{ln(1.25)}$.

From the reading in the unit we saw

$$\begin{aligned}
f_Y(y) &= \int_c f_Y(y|C=c)f_C(c)dc \\
&= \int_c f_{cX}(y)f_C(c)dc \\
&= \int_c f_X\left(\frac{y}{c}\right)\cdot\frac{1}{c}f_C(c)dc \\
&= \int_{1.0}^{1.25}\frac{1}{2}e^{-(y/2c)}\cdot\frac{1}{c}\cdot\frac{1}{ln(1.25)}\cdot\frac{1}{c}\,dc \\
&= \frac{1}{2\,ln(1.25)}\int_{1.0}^{1.25}\frac{1}{c^2}e^{-(y/2c)}dc.
\end{aligned}$$

Substituting $u = \frac{-y}{2c}$, $du = \left(\frac{-y}{2}\right)\left(\frac{-1}{c^2}\right)dc$ gives

$$f_Y(y) = \frac{1}{2\,ln(1.25)}\int_{-y/2}^{-y/2.5} e^u\frac{2}{y}du = \frac{1}{y\,ln(1.25)}[e^{-y/2.5} - e^{-y/2}]$$

ANSWER C

9. $$f_M(m) = \sum_{n=0}^{\infty} f_{M,N}(m,n) = \sum_{n=0}^{\infty} f_N(n) f_M(m|N=n)$$

$$= \sum_{n=m}^{\infty} \underbrace{e^{-5} \cdot \frac{5^n}{n!}}_{\text{Poisson}} \underbrace{\binom{n}{m}(.2)^m(.8)^{n-m}}_{\text{Binomial: need } n \geq m \text{ to have non-zero probability}}$$

$$= e^{-5}\left(\frac{.2}{.8}\right)^m \sum_{n=m}^{\infty} \frac{5^n}{n!} \frac{n!}{m!(n-m)!}(.8)^n$$

$$= \frac{e^{-5}}{m!4^m} \sum_{n=m}^{\infty} \frac{4^n}{(n-m)!}$$

$$= \frac{e^{-5}}{m!4^m} \sum_{k=0}^{\infty} \frac{4^{m+k}}{k!} \qquad \text{(set } k = n - m\text{)}$$

$$= \frac{e^{-5}}{m!4^m} \cdot 4^m \cdot \underbrace{\sum_{k=0}^{\infty} \frac{4^k}{k!}}_{e^4} = \frac{e^{-1}}{m!}$$

ANSWER E

Note: This is a Poisson density with parameter 1. The general result is: If $M|_{N=n}$ is Binomial with parameters n and p, and if N is Poisson λ, then M is Poisson with parameter λp.

10. Let M be the number of losses such that $X > 2$. Then $M|_{N=n}$ is Binomial with n trials and $p = Pr(Success) = Pr(X > 2) = \int_2^{\infty} \frac{1}{10} e^{-x/10}\, dx = e^{-.20}$. Thus $E[M|N=n] = np = ne^{-.20}$ (Binomial formula). If $E[M|N] = e^{-.20}N$, by the double expectation theorem,

$$E[M] = E[E[M|N]] = E[e^{-.20}N] = e^{-.20}E[N] = e^{-.20}(100) = 81.87. \qquad \text{ANSWER B.}$$

11. There are 2 ways to view aggregate claims after the deductible: $I_d(X) = (X-d)_+ = X - d$ if $X > d$.

Method 1: $\widetilde{S} = I_2(X_1) + \cdots + I_2(X_N)$

$$\Rightarrow \quad E[\widetilde{S}] = E[N]E[I_2(X)] = (100)\int_2^{\infty} (x-2)\frac{1}{10}e^{-x/10}\, dx$$

$$= (100)\left[\int_2^{\infty} (x-2)\frac{1}{10}e^{-(x-2)/10}\, dx\right] e^{-2/10}$$

$$= 100e^{-.20} \underbrace{\int_0^{\infty} y \cdot \frac{1}{10} e^{-y/10}\, dy}_{\text{mean of exponential with parameter 10}}$$

$$= (100)e^{-.20}(10) = 1000e^{-.20} = 818.7$$

ANSWER E

11. (cont.)

Method 2: In method 1 a lot of terms in $\widetilde{S}$ are zero (i.e., when $X < 2$). If M is the number of losses in excess of 2 (see the solution to Question 10 above), then aggregate claims with a deductible of 2 can be viewed as

$$\widetilde{S} = Y_1 + \cdots + Y_M, \qquad M = \#\text{ claims}$$

where $Y = X - 2|_{X>2}$, an exponential with the same mean as X (memoryless property). Thus

$$E[\widetilde{S}] = E[M]E[Y] = (e^{-.20}E[N])E[Y] = (e^{-.20}100)(10) = 1000e^{-.20}$$

as above. Y here is the claim per payment event whereas $I_2(X)$ is the payment per loss event. Not all losses result in a claim.

12. Following the reasoning in 10 and 11 above,

$$\widetilde{S} = I_d(X_1) + \cdots + I_d(X_N).$$

By method 1 above,

$$E[\widetilde{S}] = E[N]E[I_d(X)] = 100\int_d^{\infty} \frac{(x-d)}{10} e^{-x/10}\,dx$$

$$= 100(e^{-d/10}\int_0^{\infty} \frac{y}{10} e^{-y/10}\,dy) = 100(e^{-d/10})(10) = 1000e^{-d/10}.$$

To obtain a 30% reduction it is clear that $e^{-d/10}$ must be .70: $e^{-d/10} = .70$, or $d = -10ln(.70) = 3.57$. ANSWER C.

13. With no deductible,

$$E[S] = E[N]E[X] = (100)(10) = 1000 \text{ and}$$

$$Var(S) = E[N]Var(X) + (E[X])^2 Var(N) = 100(10)^2 + (10^2)(125) = 22{,}500:$$

$$\sigma/\mu = 150/1000 = .15.$$

With the deductible of 2 we saw in Question 11 that $E[\widetilde{S}] = (100e^{-.2})(10) = 1000e^{-.2}$. Writing $\widetilde{S} = Y_1 + \cdots + Y_M$ as in method 2 of the solution to Question 11 above, we have

$$E[Y] = 10,\ Var(Y) = 10^2 \qquad (Y \text{ is exponential, mean } 10)$$

$$E[M] = E[N]Pr(X > 2) = 100e^{-.2}$$

We still need to calculate $Var(M)$.

13 (cont.)

We know that $M|_{N=n}$ is Binomial with n trials and $p = Pr(X > 2) = e^{-.2}$. Hence

$E[M|N] = Ne^{-.2}$

$Var(M|N) = Ne^{-.2}(1 - e^{-.2})$,

and, by the double expectation theorem,

$$\begin{aligned} Var(M) &= E[Var(M|N)] + Var(E[M|N]) \\ &= E[Ne^{-.2}(1-e^{-.2})] + Var(Ne^{-.2}) \\ &= (e^{-.2}-e^{-.4})\underbrace{E[N]}_{\text{given } 100} + (e^{-.4})\underbrace{Var(N)}_{\text{given } 125} = 98.631. \end{aligned}$$

Finally, putting all the results above together,

$$Var(\widetilde{S}) = \underbrace{E[M]}_{100e^{-.2}}\underbrace{Var(Y)}_{10^2} + \underbrace{(E[Y])^2}_{(10)^2}\underbrace{Var(M)}_{98.631} = 18{,}050,$$

$\frac{\sigma}{\mu} = \frac{\sqrt{18{,}050}}{818.7} = .164.$ ANSWER B

14. If $\widetilde{S}$ represents aggregate claims with a limit of 15, then $\widetilde{S} = (X_1 \wedge 15) + \cdots + (X_N \wedge 15)$. Hence

$$E[\widetilde{S}] = \underbrace{E[N]}_{100,\ \text{given}} E[X \wedge 15].$$

$E[X \wedge 15]$ can be computed from

$$\int_0^{15} x \cdot \frac{1}{10}e^{-x/10}\,dx + \int_{15}^{\infty} 15 \cdot \frac{1}{10}e^{-x/10}\,dx = 7.769,$$

or from $X = X \wedge 15 + I_{15}(X)$:

$$\begin{aligned} E[X \wedge 15] &= E[X] - E[I_{15}(X)] \\ &= 10 - E[I_{15}(X)|X > 15]Pr(X > 15) \\ &= 10 - (10)e^{-15/10} \\ &= 10(1 - e^{-1.5}) = 7.769 \end{aligned}$$

Note: memoryless property $\Rightarrow$ $(X - d)|_{X>d}$ is the same exponential distribution as X.

Finally, $E[\widetilde{S}] = E[N]E[X \wedge 15] = 100(7.769) = 776.9.$ ANSWER A

15. $f(x) = (.02)^2 x e^{-.02x}$ is a Gamma density with $\alpha = 2,\ \theta = 50$ $(f(x) = \frac{1}{\theta^\alpha \Gamma(\alpha)} x^{\alpha-1} e^{-x/\theta}$, $E[X] = \alpha\theta)$. Now the survival function is

$$S(x) = \int_x^\infty f(y)\,dy = \int_x^\infty (.02)^2 y e^{-.02y}\,dy = (.02x+1)e^{-.02x} \qquad \textbf{(integration by parts)}$$

With a deductible of d the probability of a claim payment is

$$Pr(X > d) = S(d) = (.02d+1)e^{-.02d}.$$

ANSWER D

16. $E[X-d|X>d]$, the expected claim payment given that a payment is made, can be calculated by identifying the distribution of $X-x|_{X>x}$ as a mixture of an Exponential density and a Gamma density. If $Y = X-d|_{X-d}$ (also known as the future lifetime after age d if X were a survival model; $\mathring{e}_d = E[X-d|X>d]$), then

$$f_Y(y) = \frac{f(y+d)}{S(d)} = \frac{(.02)^2(y+d)e^{-.02(y+d)}}{(.02d+1)e^{-.02d}}$$

$$= \underbrace{\left(\frac{.02d}{.02d+1}\right)}_{\text{weight}} \underbrace{(.02e^{-.02y})}_{\substack{\text{Exponential density}\\ \text{with mean 50}}} + \underbrace{\left(\frac{1}{.02d+1}\right)}_{\text{weight}} \underbrace{(.02^2 y e^{-.02y})}_{\substack{\text{Gamma density}\\ \text{with mean 100}}},$$

which is a weighted average of an Exponential with mean $\theta = 50$ and a Gamma with mean $\alpha\theta = 2(50) = 100$. Thus

$$E[Y] = \left(\frac{.02d}{.02d+1}\right)50 + \left(\frac{1}{.02d+1}\right)100 = \frac{d+100}{.02d+1} = \frac{50d+5000}{d+50}.$$

ANSWER B

17. From the solution to Question 16 we have

d	$E[X-d\|X>d] = \frac{50d+5000}{d+50}$
50	75
100	$66.\overline{6}$

so the percent decrease is

$$100 \times \frac{75 - 66.\overline{6}}{75} = 11.\overline{1}.$$

ANSWER D

18. The loss X can be split into

$$X = \underbrace{(X \wedge d)}_{\text{retained}} + \underbrace{(X-d)_+}_{\text{insured}}$$

where

(i) $X \wedge d = min\{X, d\}$ = loss retained if a deductible d applies

(ii) $Pr(X > 50) = 2e^{-1}$ (see #15)

(iii) $E[X - 50|X > 50] = 75$ (see #17).

Since $E[X] = 100$ we have

$$E[(X \wedge 50)] = 100 - (2e^{-1})(75) = 44.82$$

and

$$LER = \frac{E[X \wedge 50)]}{E[X]} = \frac{44.82}{100} = .4482.$$

ANSWER C

UNIT 3: FREQUENCY DISTRIBUTIONS

Introduction

Keep in mind the collective risk model $S = X_1 + \cdots + X_N$, where the X_i are distributed like X and N, $X_1, X_2, \ldots, X_N$ are independent. X is a loss model and N models the frequency of loss occurrences during a period of time. In this unit we consider the most commonly used frequency models. Since possible N values are 0, 1, 2, ... it is sometimes called a **counting distribution**.

The Poisson Distribution

The Poisson distribution is derived in a standard way by a limiting process from a binomial distribution. It is designed to model the number of occurrences of some "rare" event over a period of time or space. As a result, the number of claims (claim occurrence = rare event) against a portfolio over a period of time can often be successfully modeled by a Poisson distribution. The most important facts about a variable, N, having a Poisson distribution are summarized below:

1. Probability (density) function

$$f_N(k) = p_k = e^{-\lambda} \cdot \frac{\lambda^k}{k!} \qquad \lambda > 0,\ k = 0, 1, 2, \ldots.$$

Note: $f_N(k)$ will be shortened to p_k throughout this unit.

2. Moments

$$E[N] = Var(N) = E[(N - E[N])^3] = \lambda$$

3. Generating functions

(moment) $\quad M_N(t) = E[e^{tN}] = e^{\lambda(e^t - 1)}$

(probability) $\quad P_N(t) = E[t^N] = M_N(ln(t)) = e^{\lambda(t-1)}$

Note: $E[N^k] = \left.\frac{d^k}{dt^k}(M_N(t))\right|_{t=0}$

$$E[(N)(N-1)\cdots(N-k+1)] = \left.\frac{d^k}{dt^k}(P_N(t))\right|_{t=1}$$

Two properties of the Poisson family are particularly useful in insurance models. Both properties involve sums. Using the moment generating functions above, and general properties of these functions, it is easy to show that a sum of independent Poisson variables is also a Poisson variable. The parameter of the sum is the sum of the parameters. For example, suppose claims against a portfolio of policies are of two distinct types. Suppose the number of claims of type (i), N_i, is Poisson with parameter λ_i. Assuming independence, $N = N_1 + N_2$, the total number of claims of all types, is Poisson with parameter $\lambda_1+\lambda_2$. We will use this idea in Unit Four when we consider sums of independent compound Poisson distributions (i.e., $S_i = X_1 + \cdots + X_{N_i}$ where N_i is Poisson; a compounding of the X and N_i distributions).

The second property concerns decomposing a Poisson distribution into a sum. Suppose claims can be classified into m distinct categories $C_1, \ldots, C_m$. E_i is the event that a claim belongs to category C_i and p_i is $Pr(E_i)$, the probability that a claim belongs to this category. Let N_i be the number of claims during the period which belong to category i. Then, since the categories are distinct, $N = N_1 + \cdots + N_m$. So far we have not relied on N being Poisson. The next step does not require this assumption either.

Consider the conditional distribution of N_i given $N = n$. Viewing each claim as a "trial" where "success" is thought of as the claim belonging to category C_i, one sees that $N_i|_{N=n}$ is Binomial with n trials and $p_i = Pr(E_i)$ as the probability of success: $N_i|_{N=n} =$ Binomial $(n, p_i = Pr(E_i))$. Thus, using well-known facts about the Binomial distribution (summarized later),

$$E[N_i|N] = Np_i, \quad Var(N_i|N) = Np_i(1 - p_i).$$

Applying the double expectation theorem result in

$$\underbrace{E[N_i]}_{\substack{\text{expected no.}\\ \text{of claims in}\\ \text{category } i}} = \underbrace{E[N]}_{\substack{\text{expected}\\ \text{no. of}\\ \text{claims}}} \cdot \underbrace{p_i}_{\substack{\text{fraction of}\\ \text{claims in}\\ \text{category } i}}$$ [13]

$$Var(N_i) = E[N] \cdot p_i(1 - p_i) + p_i^2 Var(N).$$

Notice that we still have not assumed N to be Poisson in this development. The results directly above, along with $N = N_1 + N_2 + \cdots + N_m$, are generally true. In addition, if **N is Poisson λ**, then

(1) $N_1, \ldots, N_m$ are independent, and

(2) N_i is Poisson λ_i where $\lambda_i = E[N_i] \underset{\text{(above)}}{=} E[N]p_i = \lambda p_i$.

Note the consistency of the second part of this statement with the variance formula above. The variance of Poisson λ_i is λ_i, and, by the formula above,

$$Var(N_i) = E[N] \cdot p_i(1 - p_i) + p_i^2 Var(N) = \lambda(p_i - p_i^2) + p_i^2\lambda = \lambda p_i = \lambda_i.$$

---

[13] Also discussed briefly in Unit Two. See Examples 7 and 9 of this Unit.

There are at least three situations where the above decomposition is useful:

(1) Suppose N, a Poisson λ variable, is the annual number of claims against a portfolio. Divide the claims into 4 categories corresponding to the quarter of the year in which a claim occurs. Assuming claims are evenly spread over the year, then (i) $p_1 = p_2 = p_3 = p_4 = \frac{1}{4}$, (ii) $N = N_1 + \cdots + N_4$ where the N_i are independent, and (iii) N_i is Poisson - $\left(\frac{\lambda}{4}\right)$. Here the categorization of claims is according to the time of occurrence.

(2) Suppose N is the annual number of claims against a group dental plan and you are considering dropping coverage of annual x-rays, which represent 8% of the claims. Here we divide claims into two categories: category one is for x-rays, category two is all other types. If N is Poisson λ, then $N = N_1 + N_2$ and N_2 is Poisson with parameter $.92\lambda$. N_2 would be the model for annual claim frequency if coverage of x-rays were dropped.

(3) Claims could also be categorized by amounts. Suppose we are considering instituting a deductible, $d = 25$, on each claim for the group dental plan in (2). Category one consists of claims $X \leq 25$, and category two consists of claims $X > 25$. Then $p_1 = Pr(X \leq 25) = F_X(25)$ and $p_2 = Pr(X > 25) = 1 - F_X(25)$. If N is Poisson λ, then N_2 is Poisson with parameter λp_2. N_2 would be the annual claim frequency model if the deductible were instituted.

The Negative Binomial Distribution

The Negative Binomial family has two parameters $r > 0$, $\beta > 0$. In case r is an integer there is a description of a Negative Binomial variable, N, as the number of "failures" in a sequence of Bernoulli trials until r successes are obtained. The probability of "success", usually denoted p, is expressed as $\frac{1}{1+\beta}$ in terms of β. With this description of N it is easy to show the following:

(1) Probability (density) function

$$f_N(k) = p_k = \binom{k+r-1}{k}\left(\frac{\beta}{1+\beta}\right)^k\left(\frac{1}{1+\beta}\right)^r, \quad k = 0, 1, 2, \ldots$$

(2) Moments

$$E[N] = r\beta, \; Var(N) = r\beta(1+\beta)$$

(3) Generating Functions

$$M_N(t) = [1 - \beta(e^t - 1)]^{-r}$$

$$P_N(t) = [1 - \beta(t-1)]^{-r}$$

Note:

(1) The description of the Negative Binomial as the number of failures in a sequence of Bernoulli trials until r successes are obtained, requires that $r = 1, 2, \ldots$. With any $r > 0$ the above density formula is still a density (i.e., $p_k > 0$ and $\sum p_k = 1$), but the Binomial symbol,

$$\binom{k+r-1}{k} = \frac{(k+r-1)!}{k!(r-1)!} = \frac{(k+r-1)(k+r-2)\cdot\cdots\cdot r}{k!},$$

must be calculated by the final form if r is not integral.

(2) Textbooks often disagree about the form "the" parameters take in a density function. For some authors an exponential density with parameter β means $f(x) = \beta e^{-\beta x}$, and for others it means $f(x) = \frac{1}{\beta}e^{-x/\beta}$. For a Negative Binomial it is common to use p and q in place of $\left(\frac{1}{1+\beta}\right)$, $\left(\frac{\beta}{1+\beta}\right)$.

(3) When r is integral some authors define N as the number of the trial on which the rth success occurs.

Notice that $Var(N) = (1+\beta)E[N] > E[N]$. Contrast this with $\lambda = E[N] = Var(N)$ for this Poisson distribution. We pointed out in Unit Two, Example 2, that the Negative Binomial can be obtained by mixing a Poisson distribution with a Gamma Distribution. More precisely, suppose that the annual number of claims against a single policy in a portfolio is Poisson λ, but λ varies from policy to policy according to a variable Λ having a Gamma distribution with parameters α and θ. We saw in the solution of the aforementioned Example two, that the resulting marginal distribution of N is Negative Binomial where $r = \alpha$ and $\beta = \theta$.

When $r = 1$, the Negative Binomial distribution is called **geometric**. The geometric distribution has a "memoryless property" just like the continuous exponential family:

$$N \text{ geometric - } \beta \quad \Rightarrow \quad N - n|_{N \geq n} \text{ is geometric - } \beta$$
$$T \text{ exponential - } \theta \quad \Rightarrow \quad T - t|_{T>t} \text{ is exponential - } \theta.$$

The Binomial Distribution

The most common description of a variable N having a Binomial distribution is as the number of "successes" in a string of n Bernoulli trials where p is the probability of success on each trial and $q = 1 - p$. The most important facts about N are:

1. Probability (density) function

$$p_k = f_N(k) = \binom{n}{k}p^k q^{n-k}, \qquad k = 0, 1, \ldots, n\,,\ 0 < p < 1,\ n = \text{positive integer},\ p+q = 1$$

2. Moments

$$E[N] = np,\ Var(N) = npq$$

3. Generating Functions

$$M_N(t) = (q + pe^t)^n$$

$$P_N(t) = (q + pt)^n$$

Several observations about this 2-parameter family should be noted in contrast with the Poisson and Negative Binomial families:

(i) $Var(N) = npq = E[N] \cdot q < E[N]$ whereas $E[N] = Var(N)$ for a Poisson and $E[N] < Var(N)$ for a Negative Binomial; and

(ii) A Binomial has finite **support**[14] in contrast with Poisson and Negative Binomial variables which have infinite support.

An obvious situation where a Binomial model is the natural choice for a claim frequency model is a portfolio of one-year term insurances to individuals all having the same age, x. "Success" means death of the individual in the age range $(x, x+1]$ and $p = q_x$, the probability that (x) dies within the next year. The number of trials is the number of policies in the portfolio. With this application in mind one might prefer to use q as the symbol of the probability of success.

The $(a, b, 0)$ Family

The $(a, b, 0)$ family of distributions is a two-parameter family of counting distributions. Using p_k as a shorthand for $f_N(k)$, the p_k are defined recursively by

$$\frac{p_k}{p_{k-1}} = a + \frac{b}{k} \qquad k = 1, 2, \ldots$$

In other words, beginning with a p_0 where $0 < p_0 < 1$, one calculates p_1, p_2, ... recursively from the above relation. Not all combinations of p_0, a, b will result in a density function. This combination of three numbers must be chosen such that each p_k satisfies $0 \leq p_k < 1$, and such that $\sum_{k=0}^{\infty} p_k = 1$. However, if some combination of p_0, a, b results in $0 \leq p_k$ and $\sum_{k=0}^{\infty} p_k = S < \infty$, then $p'_k = \frac{1}{S} p_k$ also satisfies $\frac{p'_k}{p'_{k-1}} = a + \frac{b}{k}$ and is thus a density. Recursive calculation of a probability density function is extremely

[14] The support is the collection of non-negative x's where $f_N(x) \neq 0$.

useful in conjunction with computers and formulas involving huge numbers like $k!$, or very small numbers like p^k, when k itself is large. In the collective risk model, $S = X_1 + \cdots + X_N$, where N belongs to the $(a,b,0)$ family, there is also a closely related recursive method for calculating the probability density function of S when X is discrete with possible values 1, 2, 3, ... This will be illustrated in Unit Four to follow.

It can be shown that the Poisson, Binomial and Negative Binomial families are $(a,b,0)$ distributions. In fact, they are the only $(a,b,0)$ distributions. The a,b values are illustrated below for these families in terms of the parameters for the family. The Geometric distribution is listed in addition to the Negative Binomial Family since it is the only $(a,b,0)$ distribution with $b = 0$.

Poisson:
$$\frac{p_k}{p_{k-1}} = \frac{e^{-\lambda}\lambda^k/k!}{e^{-\lambda}\lambda^{k-1}/(k-1)!} = 0 + \frac{\lambda}{k}$$

$$a = 0,\ b = \lambda,\ p_0 = e^{-\lambda}$$

Negative Binomial:
$$\frac{p_k}{p_{k-1}} = \frac{\binom{k+r-1}{k}\left(\frac{\beta}{1+\beta}\right)^k\left(\frac{1}{1+\beta}\right)^r}{\binom{k+r-2}{k-1}\left(\frac{\beta}{1+\beta}\right)^{k-1}\left(\frac{1}{1+\beta}\right)^r}$$
$$= \left(\frac{k+r-1}{k}\right)\left(\frac{\beta}{1+\beta}\right) = \left(\frac{\beta}{1+\beta}\right) + \frac{(r-1)\beta}{(1+\beta)} \cdot \frac{1}{k}$$

$$a = \frac{\beta}{1+\beta},\quad b = \frac{(r-1)\beta}{(1+\beta)},\quad p_0 = \left(\frac{1}{1+\beta}\right)^r$$

Geometric:
($r = 1$ above)
$$a = \frac{\beta}{1+\beta},\quad b = 0,\quad p_0 = \frac{1}{1+\beta}$$

Binomial:
$$\frac{p_k}{p_{k-1}} = \frac{\binom{n}{k}p^k q^{n-k}}{\binom{n}{k-1}p^{k-1}q^{n-k+1}} = \frac{n-k+1}{k} \cdot \frac{p}{q} = -\frac{p}{q} + \frac{(n+1)p}{q} \cdot \frac{1}{k}$$

$$a = -\frac{p}{q},\ b = \frac{(n+1)p}{q},\ p_0 = q^n$$

Note:

(1) In the Binomial case the recursion stops because $0 = p_{n+1} = p_{n+2}$ etc. The Binomial has finite support whereas the other three groups above have infinite support. If you use q as the probability of success in the description of the Binomial family, then p and q in the above $(a, b, 0)$ formulas must also be interchanged.

(2) From $k \cdot \frac{p_k}{p_{k-1}} = ak + b$ being linear in k, one could see which of the $(a, b, 0)$ models might fit a set of claim frequency data. Plot values of $k \cdot \frac{\widehat{p}_k}{\widehat{p}_{k-1}}$ based on a large sample so that no $\widehat{p}_k = 0$ for a good range of k values. The slope of $k \cdot \frac{p_k}{p_{k-1}}$, a, is zero for the Poisson family, negative for the Binomial Family, and positive for the Negative Binomial Family.

The $(a, b, 1)$ Family

Attempting to fit an $(a, b, 0)$ distribution to frequency data often results in a bad fit at $N = 0$. Sometimes $Pr(N = 0)$ is higher than expected and other times it is lower than expected, or even zero. Unique features of an insurance plan may dramatically affect this probability. Two operations can be performed on an $(a, b, 0)$ distribution to adjust $p_0 = Pr(N = 0)$ while preserving the recursive relation $\frac{p_k}{p_{k-1}} = a + \frac{b}{k}$ for $k \geq 2$. When the recursive relation only holds for $k \geq 2$, the distribution is said to be an $(a, b, 1)$ distribution. More will be said about the $(a, b, 1)$ family after we introduce the two operations on an $(a, b, 0)$ distribution which result in new $(a, b, 1)$ distributions. By definition, an unmodified $(a, b, 0)$ distribution is automatically an $(a, b, 1)$ family member.

We continue using p_k as a shorthand for $f_N(k) = Pr(N = k)$. The first operation on an $(a, b, 0)$ distribution to be discussed is called **zero-truncation**. Let p_k^T be the density function of $N^T = N|_{N>0}$. Note first that for $k \geq 1$

$$p_k^T = Pr(N = k|N > 0) = \frac{Pr(N = k \text{ and } N > 0)}{Pr(N > 0)} = \frac{Pr(N = k)}{Pr(N > 0)} = \frac{p_k}{1 - p_0}.$$

The important facts about this density function are

(i) $p_0^T = Pr(N^T = 0) = 0$, and

(ii) $\frac{p_k^T}{p_{k-1}^T} = \frac{p_k/(1 - p_0)}{p_{k-1}/(1 - p_0)} = a + \frac{b}{k}$
for $k \geq 2$, since p_k is an $(a, b, 0)$ distribution.

The moments and moment generating functions of the zero-truncation of N, N^T, are closely related to those of N:

(i) **Moments - Zero Truncation**

$$E[N^k] = E[\underbrace{N^k}_{\text{zero}}|N = 0]Pr(N = 0) + \underbrace{E[N^k|N > 0]}_{(N^T)^k} \underbrace{Pr(N > 0)}_{(1-p_0)}$$

$$\Rightarrow \quad E[(N^T)^k] = E[N^k]/(1 - p_0); \text{ and}$$

(ii) **Generating Function - Zero Truncation**

$$M_N(t) = E[e^{tN}] = E[\underbrace{e^{tN}}_{1}|N=0]\underbrace{Pr(N=0)}_{p_0} + E[\underbrace{e^{tN}|N>0}_{M_{N^T}(t)}]\underbrace{Pr(N>0)}_{(1-p_0)}$$

$$\Rightarrow \qquad M_{N^T}(t) = \frac{M_N(t) - p_0}{1 - p_0}.$$

The second operation to be discussed takes an $(a, b, 0)$ density, p_k, and modifies the probability at $k = 0$. The resultant new distribution is called **zero-modified** and we denote the corresponding random variable by N^{ZM}. (Zero truncation can be viewed as an extreme case of zero modification.). The idea here is to change p_0 to a chosen p_0^{ZM}, and then to adjust $p_1, p_2, \ldots$, to $p_1^{ZM}, p_2^{ZM}, \ldots$ in such a way that $1 = \sum_{k=0}^{\infty} p_k^{ZM}$ and $\frac{p_k^{ZM}}{p_{k-1}^{ZM}} = a + \frac{b}{k}$ for $k \geq 2$. The following algebraic rearrangement of $1 = \sum_{k=0}^{\infty} p_k$ illustrates how to accomplish the adjustment to p_k^{ZM}:

(i) Pick p_0^{ZM} in [0, 1) and set $p_k^{ZM} = cp_k$;

(ii) Solve for c to ensure $\sum_{k=0}^{\infty} p_k^{ZM} = 1$

$$1 = \sum_{k=0}^{\infty} p_k^{ZM} = p_0^{ZM} + \sum_{k=1}^{\infty} p_k^{ZM} = p_0^{ZM} + \sum_{k=1}^{\infty} cp_k = p_0^{ZM} + c\sum_{k=1}^{\infty} p_k = p_0^{ZM} + c(1-p_0)$$

$$\Rightarrow \qquad c = \frac{1 - p_0^{ZM}}{1 - p_0};$$

(iii) $$\frac{p_k^{ZM}}{p_{k-1}^{ZM}} = \frac{cp_k}{cp_{k-1}} = \frac{p_k}{p_{k-1}} = a + \frac{b}{k} \text{ for } k \geq 2.$$

Example 1 Suppose N is Poisson λ where $\lambda = 1$. Describe the zero modification so that $Pr(N^{ZM} = 0) = .50$.

Solution N is an $(a, b, 0)$ family member with $a = 0$ and $b = \lambda = 1$. We need to find c such that $c\sum_{k=1}^{\infty} p_k = 1 - p_0^{ZM} = 1 - .5 = .5$, and we know $\sum_{k=1}^{\infty} p_k = 1 - p_0 = 1 - e^{-\lambda} = 1 - e^{-1} = .632121$ (to six places). Thus

$$\sum_{k=1}^{\infty} \frac{.5p_k}{.632121} = \frac{.5}{.632121}\sum_{k=1}^{\infty} p_k = .5\left(\frac{.632121}{.632121}\right) = .5.$$

Hence $p_0^{ZM} = .5$, $p_k^{ZM} = \left(\frac{.5}{.632121}\right)e^{-1}\frac{(1)^k}{k!}$ for $k \geq 2$. □

Next we would like to illustrate that a zero-modified $(a, b, 0)$ distribution can be viewed as a mixture of a degenerate distribution (i.e., all probability at zero) and the corresponding zero-truncated $(a, b, 0)$ distribution. This fact is a result of substituting

$$p_k^{ZM} = cp_k = \left(\frac{1 - p_0^{ZM}}{1 - p_0}\right) p_k, \qquad k \geq 1$$

into $1 = \sum_{k=0}^{\infty} p_k^{ZM}$, and then slightly rearranging the relation:

$$1 = \sum_{k=0}^{\infty} p_k^{ZM} = p_0^{ZM} + \sum_{k=1}^{\infty}\left(\frac{1 - p_0^{ZM}}{1 - p_0}\right) p_k = \underbrace{p_0^{ZM}}_{\text{weight}} \cdot 1 + \underbrace{(1 - p_0^{ZM})}_{\text{weight}} \sum_{k=1}^{\infty} \underbrace{\frac{p_k}{1 - p_0}}_{p_k^T}.$$

This equation can be interpreted as saying that N^{ZM} is a mixture of a degenerate distribution and the N^T distribution of the same $(a, b, 0)$ density, where the corresponding weights are p_0^{ZM} (chosen arbitrarily in $[0, 1)$) and $1 - p_0^{ZM}$. It immediately follows that:

(i) **Moments - Zero Modification**

$$E[(N^{ZM})^k] = E[0^k] \cdot p_0^{ZM} + E[(N^T)^k] \cdot (1 - p_0^{ZM})$$

$$\Rightarrow \quad E[N^{ZM})^k] = E[(N^T)^k] \cdot (1 - p_0^{ZM}) = \frac{E[N^k]}{(1 - p_0)} \cdot (1 - p_0^{ZM})$$

(ii) **Generating Function - Zero Modification**

$$M_{N^{ZM}}(t) = M_0(t) \cdot p_0^{ZM} + M_{N^T}(t) \cdot (1 - p_0^{ZM}) = 1 \cdot p_0^{ZM} + \left[\frac{M_N(t) - p_0}{1 - p_0}\right] \cdot (1 - p_0^{ZM})$$

Example 2 Suppose N is Poisson λ where $\lambda = 1$

(i) Calculate $E[N^T]$, $Var(N^T)$ and $M_{N^T}(t)$ for the zero-truncation of N.

(ii) Make the parallel calculations for N^{ZM} if p_0^{ZM} is chosen to be .5.

Solution In Example 1 we considered this same distribution.

(i) For the Poisson λ distribution we know that $E[N] = Var(N) = \lambda$ (thus $E[N^2] = \lambda + \lambda^2$) and $M_N(t) = e^{\lambda(e^t - 1)}$. From the general relation

$$E[(N^T)^k] = \frac{E[N^k]}{1 - p_0}$$

we obtain

$$E[N^T] = \frac{\lambda}{1 - e^{-\lambda}}$$

$$E[(N^T)^2] = \frac{\lambda + \lambda^2}{1 - e^{-\lambda}}$$

for a Poisson variable N. Similarly, from the general relation

$$M_{N^T}(t) = \frac{M_N(t) - p_0}{1 - p_0},$$

we obtain

$$M_{N^T}(t) = \frac{e^{\lambda(e^t - 1)} - e^{-\lambda}}{1 - e^{-\lambda}},$$

for a Poisson variable N. Substituting $\lambda = 1$ into the above results in

$$\left.\begin{aligned} E[N^T] &= \frac{1}{1 - e^{-1}} = 1.58198 \\ E[(N^T)^2] &= \frac{1+1}{1 - e^{-\lambda}} = 3.16395 \end{aligned}\right\} Var(N^T) = .66130$$

$$M_{N^T}(t) = \frac{e^{(e^t - 1)} - e^{-1}}{1 - e^{-1}} = \frac{e^{e^t} - 1}{e - 1}.$$

(ii) For the zero-modified Poisson with $\lambda = 1$ and $p_0^{ZM} = .5$, we obtain the following from general relations and part (i) above:

$$\begin{aligned} E[N^{ZM}] &= E[N^T] \cdot (1 - p_0^{ZM}) && \text{(general)} \\ &= (1.58198)(.5) = .79099 && \text{((i) above)} \end{aligned}$$

$$\begin{aligned} E[(N^{ZM})^2] &= E[(N^T)^2] \cdot (1 - p_0^{ZM}) && \text{(general)} \\ &= (3.16395)(.5) = 1.58198 && \text{((i) above)} \end{aligned}$$

$$Var(N^{ZM}) = .95631$$

$$\begin{aligned} M_{N^{ZM}}(t) &= 1 \cdot p_0^{ZM} + M_{N^T}(t) \cdot (1 - p_0^{ZM}) && \text{(general)} \\ &= (1)(.5) + \left[\frac{e^{e^t} - 1}{e - 1}\right](.5) && \text{((i) above)} \end{aligned}$$

□

Note: The zero truncated distribution is a special case of zero-modified. It is important to single out this special case precisely because it has a simple relation with the original (a, b, 0) distribution (i.e., $p_k^T = \frac{p_k}{1 - p_0}$), and a general zero-modified distribution is a weighted average of a degenerate distribution (all probability at zero) and the zero-truncated one.

Now let's return to the problem of completely describing the $(a, b, 1)$ class of distributions. N is $(a, b, 1)$ if $\frac{p_k}{p_{k-1}} = a + \frac{b}{k}$ for $k \geq 2$. So far we have seen that if N is an $(a, b, 0)$ distribution, both N and N^{ZM} (special case: zero-truncated) are $(a, b, 1)$ distributions. In addition to these types there are several types of $(a, b, 1)$ distributions which do not arise from the $(a, b, 0)$ family. They have $p_0 = 0$ and arise in connection with the zero-truncated Negative Binomial from the $(a, b, 0)$ family.

Negative Binomial $\quad p_0 = (1+\beta)^{-r}$ (starting value)

$r > 0, \beta > 0$

$$\frac{p_k}{p_{k-1}} = \frac{\beta}{1+\beta} + \frac{(r-1)\beta}{(1+\beta)} \cdot \frac{1}{k} \quad \text{(recursion)}$$

if $k \geq 1$

Zero Truncated Negative Binomial

$r > 0, \beta > 0$

$$p_k^T = \frac{p_k}{1 - p_0} \quad \text{(general)}$$

$$p_1^T = \frac{p_1}{1 - p_0} \quad \text{(starting value)}$$

$$= \frac{p_0}{(1 - p_0)} \cdot \left[\frac{\beta}{1+\beta} + \frac{(r-1)\beta}{(1+\beta)} \cdot \frac{1}{1}\right]$$

$$= \frac{rp_0}{(1 - p_0)} \cdot \frac{\beta}{(1+\beta)} = \frac{r}{(1+\beta)^r - 1} \cdot \frac{\beta}{1+\beta}$$

$$\frac{p_k}{p_{k-1}} = \frac{\beta}{1+\beta} + \frac{(r-1)\beta}{(1+\beta)} \cdot \frac{1}{k} \quad \text{(recursion)}$$

if $k \geq 2$

These new types of $(a, b, 1)$ distributions, called **Extended[15] Truncated Negative Binomial[16]** distributions, arise from the zero-truncated Negative Binomial family above. Consider the same recursion relation,

$$\frac{p_k}{p_{k-1}} = \frac{\beta}{1+\beta} + \frac{(r-1)\beta}{(1+\beta)} \cdot \frac{1}{k} = \frac{\beta}{1+\beta}\left[1 + \frac{r-1}{k}\right], \qquad \text{if } k \geq 2$$

with $\beta > 0$ and $0 \geq r > -1$. Since $k \geq 2$ and $r > -1$, the factor $\left[1 + \frac{r-1}{k}\right]$ is positive for all $k \geq 2$. Thus, for an arbitrary $p_1 > 0$, and $p_2, p_3, \ldots$ generated recursively, all p_k are positive and $p_1 + p_2 + \cdots$ converges by the Ratio test since $\lim_{k\to\infty} \frac{p_k}{p_{k-1}} = \frac{\beta}{1+\beta} < 1$. Hence, for the proper choice of p_1, one can use the recursion to produce a density function (i.e., all $p_k > 0$ and $1 = p_1 + p_2 + \cdots$). The proper choice for p_1 is the same as $p_1^T = \frac{r}{(1+\beta)^r - 1} \cdot \frac{\beta}{1+\beta}$ in the zero-truncated Negative Binomial above, even though r is negative. The formula

$$p_1 = \frac{r}{(1+\beta)^r - 1} \cdot \frac{\beta}{1+\beta}$$

---

[15] $r > 0$ is extended to include $0 \geq r > -1$.

[16] Abbreviated to ETNB.

makes sense[17] if $0 > r > -1$, but not when $r = 0$. However, by L'Hopital's rule

$$\lim_{r\to 0} \frac{r}{(1+\beta)^r - 1} = \lim_{r\to 0} \frac{1}{(1+\beta)^r ln(1+\beta)} = \frac{1}{ln(1+\beta)}.$$

Thus the Extended Truncated Negative Binomial family with $r > -1$, $\beta > 0$ is exactly like the 0-truncated Negative Binomial with $r > 0$, $\beta > 0$ except when $r = 0$. In this case the starting value is

$$p_1 = \frac{1}{ln(1+\beta)} \cdot \frac{\beta}{1+\beta}$$

and the distribution is called **Logarithmic**.

From these new $(a, b, 1)$ distributions with $p_0 = 0$, one can also create new zero-modified $(a, b, 1)$ distributions, as earlier, by taking a weighted average of a degenerate distribution and an Extended Truncated Negative Binomial or Logarithmic distribution. The description below is meant to help visualize this large class of distributions.

The $(a, b, 1)$ Family

1. The $(a, b, 0)$ family: Poisson with $\lambda > 0$, Negative Binomial with $r > 0$ and $\beta > 0$, and Binomial distributions.
2. Zero-truncated $(a, b, 0)$ distributions: $p_0^T = 0$, $p_k^T = \frac{p_k}{1 - p_0}$ if $k \geq 1$, p_k an $(a, b, 0)$ type. Zero-modified distributions viewed as a weighted average of a degenerate distribution and a zero-truncated $(a, b, 0)$ distribution.
3. Extended Truncated Negative Binomial distributions with $0 \geq r > -1$, $\beta > 0$ (special case $r = 0$; Logarithmic).
4. Zero-modified distributions from group (3) - weighted averages of a degenerate distribution and an Extended Truncated Negative Binomial.

Example 3

(i) Give the starting value, recursion formula, mean and variance for an ETNB distribution with $r = -\frac{1}{2}$ and $\beta = 2$.

(ii) The truncated distribution in (i) is modified at zero such that $p_0^{ZM} = .25$. Give the starting value, recursion formula, mean and variance.

---

17 The two negative factors r, $(1+\beta)^r - 1$ give a positive ratio!

Solution

(i) ETNB, $r = -\frac{1}{2}$ and $\beta = 2$

Starting value: $p_1^T = \frac{r}{(1+\beta)^r - 1} \cdot \frac{\beta}{1+\beta} = \left[\frac{-.5}{3^{-.5} - 1}\right]\left(\frac{2}{3}\right) = .78868$

Recursion: $\frac{p_k^T}{p_{k-1}^T} = \frac{\beta}{1+\beta} + \frac{(r-1)\beta}{(1+\beta)} \cdot \frac{1}{k} = \frac{2}{3}\left[1 - \frac{1.5}{k}\right]$ for $k \geq 2$

Moments: The same formulas apply as when N^T is a truncated Negative Binomial with $r > 0$, $\beta > 0$. Some unusual negative factors occur when $0 > r > -1$, but they occur in pairs and the moments are positive as expected!

$E[(N^T)^k] = \frac{E[N^k]}{1 - p_0}$ where

$p_0 = (1+\beta)^{-r} = 3^{.5}$

$E[N] = r\beta = -1$

$E[N^2] = Var(N) + (E[N])^2 = r\beta(\beta+1) + (r\beta)^2 = -2$

$\Rightarrow$ $E[N^T] = \frac{E[N]}{1 - p_0} = \frac{-1}{1 - 3^{.5}} = 1.36603$

$E[(N^T)^2] = \frac{E[N^2]}{1 - p_0} = \frac{-2}{1 - 3^{.5}} = 2.73205$

$Var(N^T) = .86603$

(ii) Zero-modified ETNB, $r = -\frac{1}{2}$ and $\beta = 2$, $p_0^{ZM} = .25$

N^{ZM} is a 25%/75% mixture of a degenerate distribution and N^T in part (i).

Starting Value: $p_1^{ZM} = .75p_1^T = .75(.78868) = .59151$

($p_0^{ZM} = .25$ by choice!)

Recursion: $\frac{p_k^{ZM}}{p_{k-1}^{ZM}} = \frac{.75p_k^T}{.75p_{k-1}^T} = \frac{2}{3}\left[1 - \frac{1.5}{k}\right]$, $k \geq 2$

Moments: $E[(N^{ZM})^k] = .25E[0^k] + .75E[(N^T)^k]$

$E[N^{ZM}] = .75(1.36603) = 1.02452$

$E[(N^{ZM})^2] = .75(2.73205) = 2.04904$

$Var(N^{ZM}) = .99940$ □

Compound Counting Distributions

Suppose M and N are counting distributions (i.e., their support is 0, 1, 2, ...). If $M_1, \ldots, M_N$ are identically distributed like M, and if $N, M_1, \ldots, M_N$ are independent, then $S = M_1 + \cdots + M_N$ is a collective risk model for a compound counting distribution. N is called the **primary** distribution and M the **secondary** one. In Unit One we derived the following general properties of the collective model:

$$E[S] = E[N]E[M]$$

$$Var(S) = E[N]Var(M) + (E[M])^2 Var(N)$$

$$f_S(m) = \sum_{k=0}^{\infty} f_N(k) \cdot f_M^{*k}(m)$$

$$M_S(t) = M_N(lnM_M(t)).$$

From the last of these properties, along with $P_N(t) = M_N(ln\,(t))$, it follows that

$$P_S(t) = P_N(P_M(t)).$$

If N is the random number of loss events against a portfolio over a year, and if M is the number of claims generated by a loss event, then $S = M_1 + \cdots + M_N$ is the annual claim frequency distribution for the portfolio. The main focus here is on a recursive method of calculating $f_S(k)$ which is available when N is either an $(a, b, 0)$ or $(a, b, 1)$ type distribution. This method is more efficient than the general relation above requiring f_M^{*n} for $n = 0, 1, 2, \ldots$.

Suppose N is $(a, b, 0)$ and $f_N(k)$ is again shortened to p_k. Recall that this means $\frac{p_k}{p_{k-1}} = a + \frac{b}{k}$. Without indicating the method of derivation (technical and unintuitive), we present this recursion method:

(*a*, *b*, 0) recursion for f_S: $$f_S(k) = \left[\frac{1}{1 - af_M(0)}\right] \sum_{j=1}^{k} \left(a + \frac{bj}{k}\right) f_M(j) f_S(k-j)$$

If N is $(a, b, 1)$ the recursion formula is adjusted to

(*a*, *b*, 1) recursion for f_S: $$f_S(k) = \frac{[p_1 - (a+b)p_0] f_M(k) + \sum_{j=1}^{k} \left(a + \frac{bj}{k}\right) f_M(j) f_S(k-j)}{1 - af_M(0)}$$

These relations hold for $k \geq 1$, so we need a starting value $f_S(0)$. In general we have

$$f_S(0) = \sum_{k=0}^{\infty} f_N(k) \cdot f_M^{*k}(0),$$

where $f_M^{*k}(0) = Pr(M_1 + \cdots + M_k = 0) = Pr(\text{all } M_i = 0) = [Pr(M = 0)]^k = f_M(0)^k$. Substituting this into the above gives

starting value: $$f_S(0) = \sum_{k=0}^{\infty} f_N(k)[f_M(0)]^k = P_N(f_M(0)),$$

the probability generating function of N evaluated at the probability that M is zero.

Example 4 Suppose N is Poisson λ where $\lambda = 4$, and suppose $f_M(1) = f_M(2) = f_M(3) = \frac{1}{3}$. Let $S = M_1 + \cdots + M_N$.

(i) Find the starting value $f_S(0)$.

(ii) Obtain the recursion formula for $f_S(k)$.

(iii) Calculate $f_S(k)$ for $k = 1, 2, 3$.

Solution

(i) For a Poisson distribution $P_N(t) = e^{\lambda(t-1)}$. We saw above that the starting value is $f_S(0) = P_N(f_M(0))$. Since $\lambda = 4$ and $f_M(0) = 0$ we have $f_S(0) = e^{4(0-1)} = e^{-4}$. In this example we could also have reasoned this as follows: since $M =$ 1, 2, 3 the only way $0 = M_1 + \cdots + M_N$ is if $N = 0$. So $\{S = 0\} = \{N = 0\}$ and $Pr(N = 0) = e^{-\lambda}$ for N a Poisson distribution.

(ii) For the Poisson distribution

$$\frac{p_k}{p_{k-1}} = a + \frac{b}{k} = 0 + \frac{\lambda}{k}$$

($a = 0, b = \lambda; p_k = Pr(N = k) = f_N(k)$). So the $(a, b, 0)$ recursion relation for $f_S(k)$ is

$$\begin{aligned} f_S(k) &= \left[\frac{1}{1 - af_M(0)}\right]\sum_{j=1}^{k}\left(a+\frac{bj}{k}\right)f_M(j)f_S(k-j) \\ &= \left[\frac{1}{1-(0)(0)}\right]\sum_{j=1}^{3}\left(\frac{\lambda j}{k}\right)\cdot\frac{1}{3}\cdot f_S(k-j) \\ &= \frac{4}{3k}[f_S(k-1) + 2f_S(k-2) + 3f_S(k-3)], \end{aligned}$$

since $f_M(j) = \frac{1}{3}$ for $j = 1, 2, 3$ and $\lambda = 4$.

(iii) Using $f_S(0) = e^{-4}$ (and $f_S(-1) = f_S(-2) = 0$) and the recursive relation above

$$f_S(1) = \frac{4}{3\cdot 1}(f_S(0)) = \frac{4}{3}e^{-4}$$

$$f_S(2) = \frac{4}{3\cdot 2}(f_S(1) + 2f_S(0)) = \frac{2}{3}\left(\frac{4}{3}e^{-4} + 2e^{-4}\right) = \frac{20}{9}e^{-4}$$

$$f_S(3) = \frac{4}{3\cdot 3}(f_S(2) + 2f_S(1) + 3f_S(0)) = \frac{4}{9}\left(\frac{20}{9}e^{-4} + \frac{24}{9}e^{-4} + \frac{27}{9}e^{-4}\right) = \frac{284}{81}e^{-4}.$$ □

CONDENSED REVIEW NOTES AND ADVANCED TOPICS

The Poisson Distribution

Probability function: $f_N(k) = p_k = e^{-\lambda} \cdot \frac{\lambda^k}{k!} \qquad \lambda > 0, k = 0, 1, 2, \ldots.$

Moments: $E[N] = Var(N) = E[(N - E[N])^3] = \lambda$

Moment Generating Function: $M_N(t) = E[e^{tN}] = e^{\lambda(e^t - 1)}$

Probability Generating Function: $P_N(t) = E[t^N] = E[e^{ln(t) \cdot N}] = M_N(ln(t)) = e^{\lambda(t-1)}$

Summation Properties:

1. If $N_1, \ldots, N_k$ are independent Poisson variables with respective parameters $\lambda_1, \ldots, \lambda_k$ then $\sum_{i=1}^{k} N_i$ is Poisson with parameter $\sum_{i=1}^{k} \lambda_i$.
2. If Claims belong to distinct categories $C_1, \ldots, C_m$ and E_i is the event that a claim belongs to C_i, let $p_i = Pr(E_i)$. Let N be the number of claims during a period and let N_i be the number of these claims belonging to category C_i. Then $N = N_1 + \cdots + N_m$ and $N_i|_{N=n}$ is binomial where n is the number of trials and p_i is the probability of success:

   Binomial Facts: $E[N_i|N] = Np_i, \quad Var(N_i|N) = Np_i(1 - p_i).$

   Double Expectation Theorem $\Rightarrow$ $E[N_i] = E[N]p_i,$
   $Var(N_i) = E[N]p_i(1-p_i) + p_i^2 Var(N)$

   In addition, if N is Poisson λ, then

   (i) $N_1, \ldots, N_k$ are independent, and
   (ii) each N_i is Poisson λ_i, where $\lambda_i = E[N]p_i = \lambda p_i$

Note: three important ways of categorizing claims are by time of occurrence, "type" of claim, or by claim amounts.

The Negative Binomial Distribution

Probability function: $f_N(k) = p_k = \binom{k+r-1}{k}\left(\frac{\beta}{1+\beta}\right)^k\left(\frac{1}{1+\beta}\right)^r, \quad n = 0, 1, 2, \ldots$

where $\binom{k+r-1}{k} = \frac{(k+r-1)!}{k!(r-1)!} = \frac{(k+r-1)(k+r-2)\cdot\cdots\cdot(r)}{1\cdot 2\cdot \cdots \cdot k}$,

is calculated by the last form if r is not integral.

Moments: $E[N] = r\beta,\ Var(N) = r\beta(1+\beta)$

Moment Generating Function: $M_N(t) = [1 - \beta(e^t-1)]^{-r}$

Probability Generating Function: $P_N(t) = [1 - \beta(t-1)]^{-r}$

Notes:

1. If r is integral N can be viewed as the number of failures in a series of Bernoulli trials until r successes are obtained.
2. If $N|_{\Lambda=\lambda}$ is Poisson λ and Λ is a Gamma distribution with parameters α, θ, then N is negative binomial with $r = \alpha$ and $\beta = \theta$.
3. When $r = 1$, N is said to be geometric. In this case there is a "memoryless" property: $N - n|_{N\geq n}$ is also Geometric with the same parameter.
4. $Var(N) > E[N]$
5. Some authors use $q = \frac{\beta}{1+\beta}$, $p = \frac{1}{1+\beta}$ as parameters. When r is integral some authors define the variable as the number of the trial on which the rth success is obtained.

The Binomial Distribution

Probability function: $p_k = f_N(k) = \binom{n}{k}p^k q^{n-k}$, $\quad k = 0, 1, \ldots, n,\ 0 < p < 1,$

$n =$ positive integer, $p + q = 1$

Moments: $E[N] = np,\ Var(N) = npq$

Moment Generating Function: $M_N(t) = (1 + p(e^t-1))^n$

Probability Generating Function: $P_N(t) = (1 + p(t-1))^n$

Notes:

1. A Binomial has finite support whereas the Poisson and Negative Binomial families have infinite support.
2. $Var(N) < E[N]$ in contrast with the Poisson family (they are equal) and Negative Binomial family (inequality reversed).

(a, b, 0) Distributions

$f_N(k) = p_k$ is defined recursively from $\frac{p_k}{p_{k-1}} = a + \frac{b}{k}$. Beginning with a p_0 there are severe limitations on a, b such that all $p_k \geq 0$ and $\sum_{k=0}^{\infty} p_k = 1$. The only possibilities are the Poisson, Negative Binomial, and Binomial families.

Poisson: $p_0 = e^{-\lambda}$, $\frac{p_k}{p_{k-1}} = 0 + \frac{\lambda}{k}$ $\lambda > 0$

Negative Binomial: $p_0 = \left(\frac{1}{1+\beta}\right)^r$

$$\frac{p_k}{p_{k-1}} = \left(\frac{\beta}{1+\beta}\right) + \frac{(r-1)\beta}{(1+\beta)} \cdot \frac{1}{k}$$

$(r = 1$, Geometric, $\frac{p_k}{p_{k-1}} = \frac{\beta}{1+\beta})$ $r > 0,\ \beta > 0$

Binomial: $p_0 = q^n$,

$$\frac{p_k}{p_{k-1}} = -\frac{p}{q} + \frac{(n+1)p}{q} \cdot \frac{1}{k},\ n = \text{positive integer},\ p > 0,\ p + q = 1$$

Zero-Truncated (a, b, 0) Distributions

If N is $(a, b, 0)$ let $N^T = N|_{N>0}$ be derived from N by left-truncation at zero.

Notation: $p_k^T = f_{N^T}(k) = \frac{p_k}{1 - p_0}$ for $k \geq 1$.

Probability function: $p_0^T = 0$, $\frac{p_k^T}{p_{k-1}^T} = \frac{p_k/(1-p_0)}{p_{k-1}/(1-p_0)} = a + \frac{b}{k}$ for $k \geq 2$,

Moments $E[(N^T)^k] = \frac{E[N^k]}{1 - p_0}$

Generating Function $M_{N^T}(t) = \frac{M_N(t) - p_0}{1 - p_0}$

Zero-Modified (a, b, 0) Distributions

If N is $(a, b, 0)$, then N^{ZM}, a zero-modification of N, reassigns the probability at zero to an arbitrarily chosen p_0^{ZM} in $[0, 1)$ and sets $p_k^{ZM} = cp_k$ for $k \geq 1$ so as to ensure that the probabilities sum to 1.

Calculation of c:

$$1 = \sum_{k=0}^{\infty} p_k^{ZM} = p_0^{ZM} + c\sum_{k=1}^{\infty} p_k = p_0^{ZM} + c(1-p_0)$$

$$\Rightarrow \qquad c = \frac{1 - p_0^{ZM}}{1 - p_0};$$

Preservation of ratio: $\dfrac{p_k^{ZM}}{p_{k-1}^{ZM}} = \dfrac{cp_k}{cp_{k-1}} = a + \frac{b}{k}$ for $k \geq 2$.

Relation to zero-truncation: $1 = p_0^{ZM} \cdot 1 + (1-p_0^{ZM}) \sum_{k=1}^{\infty} \underbrace{\frac{p_k}{1 - p_0}}_{p_k^T}$

$\Rightarrow$ N^{ZM} is a mixture of a degenerate distribution (i.e., all probability at zero) and N^T with respective weights p_0^{ZM} (chosen arbitrarily form $[0, 1)$) and $1 - p_0^{ZM}$

Moments: $E[(N^{ZM})^k] = \dfrac{1 - p_0^{ZM}}{1 - p_0} \cdot E[N^k]$

Generating Function: $M_{N^{ZM}}(t) = 1 \cdot p_0^{ZM} + \left[\frac{M_N(t)-p_0}{1-p_0}\right] \cdot (1-p_0^{ZM})$

Notes:

1. Zero truncation is the special case of zero-modification where $p_0^{ZM} = 0$. It is mentioned because every zero-modification can be viewed as a weighted average of a degenerate distribution and the zero-truncated one.
2. These techniques allow more modeling flexibility in situations where p_0 might be a bad fit with the data due to some special circumstances with regard to the insurance process.

Extended Truncated Negative Binomial

The zero-truncated Negative Binomial satisfies $p_0^T = 0$,

(i) $p_k^T = \frac{p_k}{1-p_0} = \left[\frac{1}{1-(1+\beta)^{-r}}\right]\binom{k+r-1}{k}\left(\frac{\beta}{1+\beta}\right)^k\left(\frac{1}{1+\beta}\right)^r$, $k \geq 1$, and

(ii) $\frac{p_k^T}{p_{k-1}^T} = \frac{p_k/(1-p_0)}{p_{k-1}/(1-p_0)} = \frac{\beta}{1+\beta} + \frac{(r-1)\beta}{(1+\beta)} \cdot \frac{1}{k}$, $k \geq 2$

for $r > 0$ and $\beta > 0$. These relations still make sense if r is allowed to range over $0 \geq r > -1$, that is, with $p_1^T = \frac{r}{(1+\beta)^r - 1} \cdot \frac{\beta}{1+\beta}$ the p_k^T generated recursively are positive and sum to 1. With the extended range of r values this family is called the Extended Truncated Negative Binomial family (ETNB for short). With $r = 0$, $p_1^T = \lim_{r \to 0} \frac{r}{(1+\beta)^r - 1} \cdot \frac{\beta}{1+\beta} = \frac{1}{ln(1+\beta)} \cdot \frac{\beta}{1+\beta}$ and the distribution is called Logarithmic.

The (a, b, 1) Family

$\frac{p_k}{p_{k-1}} = a + \frac{b}{k}$ is assumed to hold for $k \geq 2$. The resulting family includes all $(a, b, 0)$ distributions, zero-truncated and zero-modified $(a, b, 0)$ distributions, the ETNB family, and zero modifications of the ETNB family. In addition to the list below one can do zero-modifications in each category as a weighted average of a degenerate distribution and the zero-truncated one. We list the starting value, recursion relation, and first two moments for each type of family except the zero-modifications.

I. Poisson type

Poisson: $p_0 = e^{-\lambda}$, $\frac{p_k}{p_{k-1}} = 0 + \frac{\lambda}{k}$, $k \geq 1$

$E[N] = Var(N) = \lambda$, $E[N^2] = \lambda + \lambda^2$

Zero Truncated: $p_0^T = 0$, $p_1^T = \frac{e^{-\lambda} \cdot \lambda}{1 - e^{-\lambda}} = \frac{\lambda}{e^{\lambda} - 1}$

$\frac{p_k^T}{p_{k-1}^T} = 0 + \frac{\lambda}{k}$, $k \geq 2$

$E[N^T] = \frac{\lambda}{1 - e^{\lambda}}$, $E[(N^T)^2] = \frac{\lambda + \lambda^2}{1 - e^{\lambda}}$

II. Negative Binomial Type

Negative Binomial: $p_0 = (1+\beta)^{-r},\ \frac{p_k}{p_{k-1}} = \frac{\beta}{1+\beta} + \frac{(r-1)\beta}{(1+\beta)} \cdot \frac{1}{k},\ k \geq 1,$

$r > 0, \beta > 0$ $E[N] = r\beta,\ Var(N) = r\beta(1+\beta),\ E[N^2] = r\beta(1+\beta+r\beta)$

ETNB: $p_0^T = 0,\ p_1^T = \frac{r \cdot \frac{\beta}{1+\beta}\left(\frac{1}{1+\beta}\right)^r}{1-(1+\beta)^{-r}} = \frac{\beta r}{(1+\beta)^{r+1} - (1+\beta)}$

$r > -1,\ \beta > 0$ $\frac{p_k^T}{p_{k-1}^T} = \frac{\beta}{1+\beta} + \frac{(r-1)\beta}{(1+\beta)} \cdot \frac{1}{k}$, for $k \geq 2$,

$$E[N^T] = \frac{r\beta}{1-(1+\beta)^{-r}},\quad E[(N^T)^2] = \frac{r\beta(1+\beta+r\beta)}{1-(1+\beta)^{-r}}$$

Notes:

(i) $r = 1$ is **Geometric** in both categories above. The $a + \frac{b}{k}$ recursion factor reduces to $a + \frac{0}{k} = \frac{\beta}{1+\beta}$.

(2) In the ETNB category, $r = 0$ is called **Logarithmic**. Since $\lim_{r\to 0} \frac{r}{(1+\beta)^r - 1} = \frac{1}{ln(1+\beta)}$ we have

$$p_0^T = 0,\ p_1^T = \frac{\beta}{(1+\beta)ln(1+\beta)}$$

$$\frac{p_k^T}{p_{k-1}^T} = \frac{\beta}{1+\beta} + \frac{(0-1)\beta}{1+\beta} \cdot \frac{1}{k} = \frac{\beta}{1+\beta}\left[1 - \frac{1}{k}\right]$$

$$E[N^T] = \frac{\beta}{ln(1+\beta)},\ E[(N^T)^2] = \frac{\beta(1+\beta)}{ln(1+\beta)}$$

III. Binomial Types

Binomial: $p_0 = (1-p)^n,\ \frac{p_k}{p_{k-1}} = \frac{-p}{1-p} + \frac{(n+1)p}{1-p} \cdot \frac{1}{k},\ k \geq 1,$

n = positive integer, $0 < p < 1$

$E[N] = np,\ Var(N) = np(1-p)$

Zero-Truncated: $p_0^T = 0,\ p_1^T = \frac{n(1-p)^{n-1}p}{1-(1-p)^n}$

Recursion - same as above for $k \geq 2$

$$E[N^T] = \frac{np}{1-(1-p)^n}$$

$$E[(N^T)^2] = \frac{n^2p^2 + np(1-p)}{1-(1-p)^n}$$

Compound Counting Distributions

$S = M_1 + \cdots + M_N$ where $M_1, \ldots, M_N, N$ are independent and all M_i are distributed like M. Both M and N are assumed to be counting distributions. N is called primary and M is called secondary. Then

$$E[S] = E[N]E[M]$$

$$Var(S) = E[N]Var(M) + (E[M])^2 Var(N)$$

$$f_S(m) = \sum_{k=0}^{\infty} f_N(k) \cdot f_M^{*k}(m)$$

$$M_S(t) = M_N(ln M_M(t)).$$

$$P_S(t) = P_N(P_M(t)).$$

If N is $(a, b, 0)$ then

$(a, b, 0)$ recursion : $f_S(k) = \left[\frac{1}{1 - af_M(0)}\right] \sum_{j=1}^{k} \left(a + \frac{bj}{k}\right) f_M(j) f_S(k-j)$

or if N is $(a, b, 1)$

$(a, b, 1)$ recursion: $f_S(k) = \dfrac{[p_1 - (a+b)p_0] f_M(k) + \sum_{j=1}^{k} \left(a + \frac{bj}{k}\right) f_M(j) f_S(k-j)}{1 - af_M(0)}$

The starting value is $P_N(f_M(0)) = f_S(0)$.

CONCEPTUAL REVIEW TEST

1. If $M_N(t) = e^{2e^t-2}$, what is the distribution of N?

2. For claim amounts, X, the distribution is given by $f_X(1) = .40$, $f_X(2) = .35$, $f_X(3) = .25$. The annual claim frequency, N, is Poisson with $\lambda = 200$. N_i is the annual number of claims of amount i. What can you say about N_1, N_2, N_3?

3. What can be said about the N_i in Question 2 if $E[N] = 200$ and $Var(N) = 300$ but it is not known that N is Poisson?

4. For the claim process in Question 2 a deductible of 1 is to be instituted. What can be said about annual claim frequency?

5. If $E[N] = 20$, $Var(N) = 24$ and N is Negative Binomial, what are r and β?

6. If N is geometric with $E[N] = 2$, what is the distribution of $N - 10|_{N\geq 10}$?

7. A portfolio consists of 1000, one-year term life insurances to 40-year-olds of varying face values. What is the distribution of annual claim frequency?

8. If N is Negative Binomial with $r = 3$ and $\beta = 2$ what is $\frac{p_k}{p_{k-1}}$ where $p_k = Pr(N = k) = f_N(k)$?

9. If $f_N(0) = .5$, $f_N(1) = .3$, $f_N(2) = .2$, what is $f_{N^T}(k)$ where $N^T = N|_{N>0}$ is the zero-truncation of N?

10. Discuss the zero-modification of N (in Question 9) where N^{ZM} has probability function p_k^{ZM} with $p_0^{ZM} = .20$.

11. How are the moments about the origin of N^T related to those of N? How is the moment generating function of N^T related to that of N.

12. Using Question 11 and viewing N^{ZM} as a weighted average of a degenerate distribution and N^T, relate the moments about the origin of N^{ZM} and its generating function to those of N^T and N.

13. What are the mean and variance of an ETNB (extended, truncated Negative Binomial) if $r = -.75$ and $\beta = 3$.

14. What types of distributions make up the $(a, b, 1)$ family?

CONCEPTUAL REVIEW TEST SOLUTIONS

1. Poisson with $\lambda = 2$. In general $M_N(t) = e^{\lambda(e^t-1)}$ for a Poisson distribution..

2. $N = N_1 + N_2 + N_3$ where the N_i are independent Poissons with parameters $\lambda_i = E[N]Pr(X = i) = 200f_X(i)$: $\lambda_1 = 80,\ \lambda_2 = 70,\ \lambda_3 = 50$.

3. $N = N_1 + N_2 + N_3$, but the independence of the N_i is not guaranteed. We can still calculate $E[N_i]$, $Var(N_i)$ as follows:

$$E[N_1] = E[N]Pr(X = 1) = 200(.40) = 80$$

$$\begin{aligned} Var(N_1) &= E[N]Pr(X = 1)(1 - Pr(X = 1)) + (Pr(X = 1))^2 Var(N) \\ &= 200(.4)(.6) + (.4)^2 300 = 96 \end{aligned}$$

4. Annual frequency is changed to $N_2 + N_3$ which is Poisson with parameter $\lambda_2 + \lambda_3 = 120$.

5. If $20 = r\beta,\ 24 = r\beta(1+\beta)$, then $(1+\beta) = \frac{24}{20}$. So $\beta = \frac{1}{5}$ and $r = 100$.

6. The same as N!

7. Each policy is a Bernoulli trial with $p = Pr(\text{Success}) = q_{40}$. Thus N is Binomial with $n = 100$, $p = q_{40}$. Note: We are assuming the lives to be independent.

8. $$p_k = \binom{k+r-1}{k}\left(\frac{\beta}{1+\beta}\right)^k\left(\frac{1}{1+\beta}\right)^r = \binom{k+2}{k}\left(\frac{2}{3}\right)^k\left(\frac{1}{3}\right)^r = \frac{(k+2)(k+1)}{1\cdot 2}\left(\frac{2}{3}\right)^k\left(\frac{1}{3}\right)^r$$

$$\Rightarrow \quad \frac{p_k}{p_{k-1}} = \frac{(k+2)(k+1)}{1\cdot 2}\left(\frac{2}{3}\right)^k\left(\frac{1}{3}\right)^r \cdot \frac{1\cdot 2}{k\cdot(k+1)}\left(\frac{2}{3}\right)^{-(k-1)}\left(\frac{1}{3}\right)^{-r}$$

$$= \left(\frac{2}{3}\right)\left(\frac{k+2}{k}\right) = \frac{2}{3} + \left(\frac{4}{3}\right)\left(\frac{1}{k}\right) \quad \text{(i.e., } a + \tfrac{b}{k} \text{ for } (a, b, 0)$$

9. $$p_k^T = Pr(N = k|N > 0) = \frac{Pr(N = k \text{ and } N > 0)}{Pr(N > 0)} = \frac{p_k}{1 - p_0}$$

$$\Rightarrow \quad p_1^T = \frac{.30}{.50} = .60,\ p_2^T = \frac{.20}{.50} = .40$$

10. $p_k^{ZM} = cp_k$ for $k \geq 1$ and $1 = \sum_{k=0}^{2} p_k^{ZM} = .20 + c(.3+.2)$

$\Rightarrow \quad c = \frac{8}{5}$: $p_1^{ZM} = \frac{8}{5}(.30) = .48,\ p_2^{ZM} = \frac{8}{5}(.20) = .32$ and p_0^{ZM} is chosen to be .20. N^{ZM} can be viewed as a weighted average of a degenerate distribution (all probability at 0; weight = $.20 = p_0^{ZM}$) and N^T (see Question 9; weight $= .80 = 1 - p_0^{ZM}$).

Degenerate

N_1	$Pr(N_1 = k)$
1	1
0	0
0	0

N^T	p_k^T
0	0
1	.60
2	.40

p_k^{ZM}

N^{ZM}	$.20Pr(N_1 = k) + .80p_k^T$
0	$.2(1) + .8(0) = .20$
1	$.2(0) + .8(.60) = .48$
2	$.2(0) + .8(.40) = .32$

11. $E[N^k] = E[N^k|N = 0]Pr(N = 0) + E[N^k|N > 0](1 - Pr(N = 0))$

$\Rightarrow \quad E[N^k] = 0 + E[(N^T)^k](1 - p_0)$

$\Rightarrow \quad E[(N^T)^k] = E[N^k]/(1 - p_0)$

Similarly, $M_N(t) = E[e^{tN}|N = 0]p_0 + E[e^{tN}|N > 0](1 - p_0)$

$\Rightarrow \quad M_{N^T}(t) = \dfrac{(M_N(t) - p_0)}{(1 - p_0)}$

12. $E[(N^{ZM})^k] = E[0^k]p_0^{ZM} + E[(N^T)^k](1 - p_0^{ZM}) = E[(N^T)^k](1 - p_0^{ZM}) = E[N^k] \cdot \dfrac{1 - p_0^{ZM}}{1 - p_0}$

$M_{N^{ZM}}(t) = 1 \cdot p_0^{ZM} + M_{N^T}(t) \cdot (1 - p_0^{ZM}) = 1 \cdot p_0^{ZM} + \dfrac{(M_N(t) - p_0)}{(1 - p_0)} \cdot (1 - p_0^{ZM})$

13. The starting point is $E[N] = r\beta$, $Var(N) = r\beta(1+\beta)$ if N is Negative Binomial and $r > 0$, $\beta > 0$. For N^T, the zero truncation, we know $E[(N^T)^k] = \dfrac{E[N^k]}{(1-p_0)}$ and $p_0 = (1+\beta)^{-r}$. Thus

$$E[N^T] = \frac{r\beta}{1-(1+\beta)^{-r}}, \qquad E[(N^T)^2] = \frac{r\beta(1+\beta) + (r\beta)^2}{1-(1+\beta)^{-r}}.$$

These same formulas work when $0 > r > -1$ (i.e., for the ETNB family). Here

$$E[N^T] = \frac{-.75(3)}{1-4^{.75}} = 1.2306$$
$$E[(N^T)^2] = \frac{-.75(3)(4) + (.75(3))^2}{1-4^{.75}} = 2.1535$$
$$Var(N^T) = .6392.$$

14. The Poisson and Binomial families together with their zero-truncations and zero-modifications, the Negative Binomial family, the ETNB family and its zero modifications.

COMPUTATIONAL REVIEW TEST

1. Suppose N is Negative Binomial with $r = 2$ and $\beta = 1/3$. A zero-modification is performed so that $p_0^{ZM} = \frac{1}{3}$. Calculate p_1^{ZM}, the recursion relation $\frac{p_k^{ZM}}{p_{k-1}^{ZM}} = a + \frac{b}{k}$, and then use it to calculate p_2^{ZM}, p_3^{ZM}.

2. For the zero-modification in Question 1 above, calculate $E[N^{ZM}]$, $Var(N^{ZM})$ and $M_{N^{ZM}}(t)$.

3. For the Logarithmic distribution with $\beta = 2$ calculate the following:
   (i) p_0, p_1 and the recursion relation for p_k with $k \geq 2$.
   (ii) The expected value and second moment about the origin.

4. Suppose N is Negative Binomial with $r = 2$, $\beta = 1$ and suppose $f_M(k) = \frac{1}{3}$ for $k = 1, 2, 3$. Let $S = M_1 + \cdots M_N$ be a collective model where the M_i are distributed like M above.
   (i) Find the starting value $f_S(0)$.
   (ii) Obtain the recursion relation for $f_S(k)$.
   (iii) Use it to calculate $f_S(1)$, $f_S(2)$.

COMPUTATIONAL REVIEW TEST SOLUTIONS

1. For the Negative Binomial with $r = 2$, $\beta = \frac{1}{3}$, we know $p_0 = (1+\beta)^{-r} = \left(\frac{4}{3}\right)^{-2} = \frac{9}{16}$ and $\frac{p_k}{p_{k-1}} = \frac{\beta}{1+\beta} + \frac{(r-1)\beta}{(1+\beta)} \cdot \frac{1}{k} = \frac{1}{4} + \frac{1}{4} \cdot \frac{1}{k} = \frac{1}{4}\left[1 + \frac{1}{k}\right]$. Thus $p_1 = \frac{9}{16} \cdot \frac{1}{4}\left[1+\frac{1}{1}\right] = \frac{9}{32}$. In general, we have seen that

$$1 = p_0^{ZM} + \sum_{k=1}^{\infty}\left(\frac{p_k}{1-p_0}\right)(1 - p_0^{ZM}),$$

so that $p_1^{ZM} = \left[\frac{p_1}{1-p_0}\right](1 - p_0^{ZM}) = \frac{(9/32)}{(7/16)}\left(\frac{2}{3}\right) = \frac{3}{7}$. Since $p_k^{ZM} = \left(\frac{1-p_0^{ZM}}{1-p_0}\right)p_k$, we still have the recursion relation

$$\frac{p_k^{ZM}}{p_{k-1}^{ZM}} = \frac{cp_k}{cp_{k-1}} = \frac{1}{4}\left[1 + \frac{1}{k}\right] \text{ for } k \geq 2.$$

Thus $\quad p_2^{ZM} = p_1^{ZM} \cdot \frac{1}{4}\left[1 + \frac{1}{2}\right] = \frac{3}{7} \cdot \frac{1}{4} \cdot \frac{3}{2} = \frac{9}{56}$,

$$p_3^{ZM} = p_2^{ZM} \cdot \frac{1}{4}\left[1 + \frac{1}{3}\right] = \frac{9}{56} \cdot \frac{1}{4} \cdot \frac{4}{3} = \frac{3}{56}.$$

2. If N is Negative Binomial with $r = 2$, $\beta = \frac{1}{3}$ then $E[N] = r\beta = \frac{2}{3}$, $Var(N) = r\beta(1+\beta) = \frac{8}{9}$ (hence $E[N^2] = \frac{8}{9} + \left(\frac{2}{3}\right)^2 = \frac{12}{9} = \frac{4}{3}$) and
$M_N(t) = (1 - \beta(e^t-1))^{-r} = (1 - \frac{1}{3}(e^t-1))^{-2} = \frac{9}{e^{2t}-8e^t+16}$.

From the general relation

$$E[(N^{ZM})^k] = \frac{E[N^k]}{(1-p_0)}(1 - p_0^{ZM}) = E[N^k]\frac{(2/3)}{(7/16)} = \frac{32}{21}E[N^k],$$

and results above, we have

$$E[N^{ZM}] = \frac{32}{21} \cdot \frac{2}{3} = \frac{64}{63}$$

$$E[(N^{ZM})^2] = \frac{32}{21} \cdot \frac{4}{3} = \frac{128}{63}$$

$$Var(N^{ZM}) = \frac{3{,}968}{(63)^2}.$$

2. (cont.)

From the general relation

$$M_{N^{ZM}}(t) = p_0^{ZM} \cdot 1 + (1 - p_0^{ZM}) \cdot \frac{M_N(t) - p_0}{1 - p_0}$$

if follows that

$$M_{N^{ZM}}(t) = \tfrac{1}{3} + \left(\tfrac{2}{3}\right)\frac{\left[\frac{9}{e^{2t}-8e^t+16}\right] - \frac{9}{16}}{\left(1 - \frac{9}{16}\right)} = -\tfrac{11}{21} + \tfrac{32}{21} \cdot \left[\frac{9}{e^{2t}-8e^t+16}\right].$$

3. The Logarithmic distribution is a special case, $r = 0$, of the extended truncated, Negative Binomial. We denote its probability function by p_k^T.

(i) Because it is truncated $p_0^T = 0$. The starting value, p_1^T, is calculated from

$$p_1^T = \lim_{r\to 0}\left[\frac{r}{(1+\beta)^r - 1} \cdot \frac{\beta}{1+\beta}\right] = \frac{1}{ln(1+\beta)} \cdot \frac{\beta}{1+\beta} = \frac{2}{3ln(3)}.$$

The recursion relation for a Negative Binomial or Zero-Truncated Negative Binomial is

$$\frac{p_k}{p_{k-1}} = \frac{p_k^T}{p_{k-1}^T} = \frac{\beta}{1+\beta} + \frac{\beta(r-1)}{(1+\beta)} \cdot \frac{1}{k} = \frac{2}{3}\left[1 - \frac{1}{k}\right] \qquad (k \geq 2)$$

(ii) From the Condensed Review Notes

$$E[N^T] = \lim_{r\to 0} \frac{r\beta}{1-(1+\beta)^{-r}} = \frac{\beta}{ln(1+\beta)} = \frac{2}{ln(3)}$$

$$E[(N^T)^2] = \lim_{r\to 0} \frac{r\beta(1+\beta+r\beta)}{1-(1+\beta)^{-r}} = \frac{\beta(1+\beta)}{ln(1+\beta)} = \frac{6}{ln(3)}$$

4. (i) In general, $f_S(0) = P_N(f_M(0)) = P_N(0)$. For the Negative Binomial family $P_N(t) = (1 - \beta(t-1))^{-r} = (2 - t)^{-2} = \frac{1}{4}$, when $t = 0$. Thus $f_S(0) = \frac{1}{4}$.

(ii) For the Negative Binomial we know

$$\frac{p_k}{p_{k-1}} = \frac{\beta}{1+\beta} + \frac{\beta(r-1)}{(1+\beta)} \cdot \frac{1}{k} = \underbrace{\frac{1}{2}}_{a} + \underbrace{\frac{1}{2}}_{b} \cdot \frac{1}{k} = \frac{1}{2}\left[1 + \frac{1}{k}\right].$$ So the recursion relation for f_S is

$$f_S(k) = \left[\frac{1}{1 - af_M(0)}\right]\sum_{j=1}^{k}\left(a+\frac{bj}{k}\right)f_M(j)f_S(k-j)$$

$$= \left[\frac{1}{1 - \frac{1}{2}\cdot 0}\right]\sum_{j=1}^{3}\left(\frac{1}{2}+\frac{j}{2k}\right)\cdot\frac{1}{3}\cdot f_S(k-j)$$

$$= \frac{1}{6}\left[\left(1+\frac{1}{k}\right)f_S(k-1) + \left(1+\frac{2}{k}\right)f_S(k-2) + \left(1+\frac{3}{k}\right)f_S(k-3)\right]$$

(iii) $f_S(1) = \frac{1}{6}\left[\left(1+\frac{1}{1}\right)f_S(0) + 0 + 0\right] = \frac{1}{3}f_S(0) = \frac{1}{3}\cdot\frac{1}{4} = \frac{1}{12}$

$f_S(2) = \frac{1}{6}\left[\left(1+\frac{1}{2}\right)f_S(1) + \left(1+\frac{2}{2}\right)f_S(0)\right] = \frac{1}{6}\left[\frac{3}{2}\cdot\frac{1}{12} + 2\cdot\frac{1}{4}\right] = \frac{5}{48}$

UNIT REVIEW QUESTIONS

1. The number of accidents incurred by an insured driver in a single year has a Poisson distribution with parameter 2. If an accident occurs, the probability that the damage amount exceeds the deductible is .25. The number of claims and the damage amounts are independent. What is the probability that there will be no damages exceeding the deductible in a single year?

(A) .46 (B) .51 (C) .56 (D) .61 (E) .66

2. N_2 is the number of claims of size 2 in a compound negative binomial distribution with:

(i) $r = 5$ and $p = 2/3$; and

(ii) the following claim size distribution:

x	$p(x)$
1	1/2
2	1/4
3	1/8
4	1/8

Determine $Var(N_2)$.

(A) $\frac{5}{64}$ (B) $\frac{5}{16}$ (C) $\frac{5}{8}$ (D) $\frac{45}{64}$ (E) $\frac{15}{4}$

3. The distribution of the number of claims, N, is negative binomial with parameter $p = 1/3$ and $Var[N] = 24$. The distribution of claim amounts is as follows:

x	$p(x)$
2	.10
3	.40
4	.50

Calculate the mean plus the variance of aggregate claims.

(A) 308 (B) 316 (C) 324 (D) 333 (E) 340

4. (2 points) A compound Poisson distribution S with discrete claim amounts can be expressed by the following sum:

$$S = 1N_1 + 2N_2 + 3N_3$$

You are given:

(i) $E[S] = 56$;
(ii) $Var[S] = 126$; and
(iii) $E[(S - E[S])^3] = 314$
(iv) N_k is the number of claims equal to k.

Determine $\lambda_2 = E[N_2]$.

(A) 7 (B) 8 (C) 9 (D) 10 (E) 11

5. For an insured portfolio, you are given:

(i) the number of claims has a geometric distribution with $p = .75$;
(ii) individual claim amounts can take values of 3, 4, or 5 with equal probability;
(iii) the number of claims and claim amounts are independent; and
(iv) the premium charged equals expected aggregate claims plus the variance of aggregate claims.

Determine the exact probability that aggregate claims exceeds the premium.

(A) .01 (B) .03 (C) .05 (D) .07 (E) .09

6. Aggregate claims S has a compound Poisson distribution with $\lambda = \log 4$ and individual claim amount p.f. given by

$$p(x) = \frac{2^{-x}}{x\,log2}, \quad x = 1, 2, 3, \ldots$$

Which of the following is true about the distribution of S?

(A) S is binomial with $p = \frac{1}{2}$

(B) S is binomial with $p = \frac{1}{4}$

(C) S is negative binomial with $r = 2$, $p = \frac{1}{2}$

(D) S is negative binomial with $r = 4$, $p = \frac{1}{2}$

(E) S is negative binomial with $r = 2$, $p = \frac{1}{4}$

7. Let S be the aggregate claims for a collection of insurance policies. You are given:

G is the premium with relative security loading[18] θ;
S has a compound Poisson distribution with parameter λ; and
$R = \frac{S}{G}$ (the loss ratio),

Which of the following is an expression for $Var(R)$?

(A) $\frac{E[X^2]}{E[X^1]} \cdot \frac{1}{(1+\theta)}$ (B) $\frac{E[X^2]}{E[X^1]^2} \cdot \frac{1}{\lambda(1+\theta)}$ (C) $\frac{E[X^2]^2}{E[X^1]^2} \cdot \frac{1}{\lambda(1+\theta)}$

(D) $\frac{E[X^2]}{E[X^1]^2} \cdot \frac{1}{\lambda(1+\theta)^2}$ (E) $\frac{E[X^2]^2}{E[X^1]^2} \cdot \frac{1}{\lambda(1+\theta)^2}$

8. If N is the annual claim frequency and X, the claim amount, what is the distribution of the annual number of claims exceeding 5? You are given that N is Poisson with mean 10 and that X is uniformly distributed on $[0, 20]$.

(A) Binomial with $n = 5$, $p = .75$
(B) Negative Binomial with mean 7.5
(C) Negative Binomial with mean 10
(D) Poisson with mean 10
(E) Poisson with mean 7.5

[18] $G = (1+\theta)E[S]$. Discussed in Unit 4 to follow.

9. Suppose N is a counting distribution. Let $p_k = Pr(N = k)$ for $k = 0, 1, 2, \ldots$. If

$$\frac{p_k}{p_{k-1}} = -\frac{1}{3} + \frac{4}{k} \quad \text{for } k = 1, 2, \ldots$$

then N has which of the following distributions?

(A) Binomial, $n = 12$, $p = \frac{1}{3}$

(B) Binomial, $n = 11$, $p = \frac{1}{4}$

(C) Negative Binomial, $r = 11$, $\beta = 3$

(D) Negative Binomial, $r = 12$, $\beta = 4$

(E) None of the above

The following information applies to Questions 10-12.

(i) $f_N(k) = Pr(N = k) = p_k$ for $k = 0, 1, 2, \ldots$.
(ii) N has a zero-modified, Poisson distribution with parameter $\lambda = ln(2)$.
(iii) $p_0 = \frac{1}{4}$.

10. Calculate $E[N]$.

(A) $.5\, ln(2)$ (B) $.75\, ln(2)$ (C) $ln(2)$ (D) $1.5\, ln(2)$ (E) $2\, ln(2)$

11. Calculate $Var(N)$. (nearest .01)

(A) .68 (B) .69 (C) .70 (D) .71 (E) .72

12. Calculate p_3.

(A) $\frac{1}{16}(ln(2))^3$ (B) $\frac{1}{8}(ln(2))^3$ (C) $\frac{1}{6}(ln(2))^3$ (D) $\frac{1}{4}(ln(2))^3$ (E) $\frac{1}{2}(ln(2))^3$

13. Suppose $f_M(0) = .8$, $f_M(1) = .2$. Suppose N is Poisson with parameter $\lambda = 5$. Let $S = M_1 + \cdots M_N$ where $N, M_1, \ldots, M_N$ are independent and all M_i are distributed like M. What is the distribution of S?

(A) Binomial, $n = 5$, $p = .2$
(B) Negative Binomial, $r = 5$, $\beta = 4$
(C) Logarithmic, $\beta = 4$
(D) Poisson, $\lambda = 1$
(E) None of the above

SOLUTIONS TO UNIT REVIEW QUESTION

1. The event {no damages exceeding deductible} is the disjoint union of events {n-accidents} ∩ {all n-damages ≤ deductible}. Thus we want

$$\sum_{n=0}^{\infty} \underbrace{Pr(n \text{ accidents})}_{e^{-2}\cdot\frac{2^n}{n!}} \cdot \underbrace{Pr(\text{all } n\text{-damages} \leq \text{deductible})}_{(.75)^n}$$

$$= e^{-2}\sum_{n=0}^{\infty}\frac{(1.5)^n}{n!} = e^{-2}(e^{1.5}) = e^{-.5} = .6065,$$

ANSWER D

2. When S is compound Poisson N_k, the number of claims equal to k, is Poisson with parameter $\lambda_k = \lambda p(k) = \lambda Pr(X{=}k)$. When S is not compound Poisson (this problem) the standard approach is as follows: view each claim as a "success" if it equals k and as a failure otherwise so that if we are given $N{=}n$ (*i.e.*, n claims occurred) then

$$N_k|_{N=n} = \text{Binomial } (n \text{ trials}, p = Pr(X{=}k))$$
$$E[N_k|N] = Np = Np(k)$$
$$Var(N_k|N) = Np(1-p) = Np(k)(1-p(k)).$$

Now apply the double expectation theorem:

$$E[N_k] = E[E[N_k|N]] = E[Np(k)] = E[N]p(k)$$

$$Var(N_k) = E[Var(N_k|N)] + Var(E[N_k|N])$$
$$= E[Np(k)(1-p(k))] + Var(Np(k))$$
$$= E[N]p(k)(1-p(k)) + Var(N)(p(k))^2$$

Here N is negative binomial with $r = 5$, $p = \frac{2}{3}$ so $E[N] = \frac{rq}{p} = \frac{5}{2}$, $Var(N) = \frac{rq}{p^2} = \frac{15}{4}$.

Finally, $Var(N_2) = \left(\frac{5}{2}\right)\left(\frac{1}{4}\right)\left(\frac{3}{4}\right) + \left(\frac{15}{4}\right)\left(\frac{1}{4}\right)^2 = \frac{45}{64}$, ANSWER D

Note: When N is Poisson and $E[N] = Var(N) = \lambda$ the formula above for $Var(N_k)$ reduces to $\lambda(p(k) - p(k)^2) + \lambda p(k)^2 = \lambda p(k) = \lambda_k$, which should be expected since N_k is Poisson $-\lambda_k$. Also, instead of saying $r = 5$, $p = \frac{2}{3}$ we could have used $r = 5$, $\beta = \frac{1}{2}$ to describe the negative binomial.

3. $24 = Var(N) = \frac{rq}{p^2}$, $E[N] = \frac{rq}{p} = Var(N) \cdot p = 24\left(\frac{1}{3}\right) = 8$

$E[X] = \sum x\,p(x) = 3.4$, $E[X^2] = \sum x^2 p(x) = 12$, $Var(X) = 12 - 3.4^2 = .44$.

Hence

$$E[S] = E[N]E[X] = 8(3.4) = 27.2$$

$$Var(S) = E[X]Var(X) + (E[X])^2 Var(N) = 280.96$$

$$E[S] + Var(S) = 308.16.$$

ANSWER A

4. From the given data, $56 = E[S] = 1 \cdot E[N_1] + 2E[N_2] + 3E[N_3] = 1 \cdot \lambda_1 + 2 \cdot \lambda_2 + 3 \cdot \lambda_3$

$126 = Var(S) = 1^2 Var(N_1) + 2^2 Var(N_2) + 3^2 Var(N_3) = \lambda_1 + 4\lambda_2 + 9\lambda_3$

$314 = 3^{rd}\text{ cent} = \lambda E[X^3] = \lambda[1^3 p(1) + 2^3 p(2) + 3^3 p(3)] = \lambda_1 + 8\lambda_2 + 27\lambda_3$

By Cramer's rule: $\lambda_2 = \dfrac{det\begin{vmatrix} 1 & 56 & 3 \\ 1 & 126 & 9 \\ 1 & 314 & 27 \end{vmatrix}}{det\begin{vmatrix} 1 & 2 & 3 \\ 1 & 4 & 9 \\ 1 & 8 & 27 \end{vmatrix}} = \frac{132}{12} = 11$

ANSWER E

5. From (i) $E[N] = \frac{q}{p} = \frac{1}{3}$, $Var(N) = \frac{q}{p^2} = \frac{4}{9}$, and from (ii) $E[X] = 4$, $Var(X) = \frac{2}{3}$. Thus $E[S] = E[N]E[X] = \frac{4}{3}$ and $Var(S) = E[N]Var(X) + (E[X])^2 Var(N) = \frac{66}{9}$. Hence the premium is $E[S] + Var(S) = \frac{78}{9} = 8.\bar{6}$, and
$Pr(S > 8.\bar{6}) = 1 - Pr(S \leq 8.6) = 1 - Pr(S \leq 8)$. With $X = 3$, 4 or 5 the following combinations result in $S \leq 8$:

N	X_1	X_2	Probability
0			(.75)
1	3, 4, or 5		(.25)(.75)(1)
2	3	3, 4, 5	$(.25)^2(.75)\left(\frac{1}{3}\right)^2 6$
	4	3, 4	
	5	3	
			Total = .969

Thus $Pr(S > \text{Premium}) = 1 - .969 = .031$.

ANSWER B

6. A direct solution is possible using generating functions, but it is simpler to work by elimination. Since $X = 1, 2, 3, \ldots$ if follows that $S = 0, 1, 2, \ldots$ has positive probability for each positive whole number. So S is clearly not Binomial.

$$E[X] = \sum_{x=1}^{\infty} x \cdot \frac{2^{-x}}{x \cdot ln(2)} = \frac{1}{ln(2)}\left[\frac{1}{2} + \frac{1}{4} + \cdots\right] = \frac{1}{ln(2)} \cdot 1,$$

hence $E[S] = E[N]E[X] = ln(4) \cdot \frac{1}{ln(2)} = \frac{2ln(2)}{ln(2)} = 2$. For Answers C, D, E respectively we have $E[S]$ is $2\left(\frac{1/2}{1/2}\right) = 2, 4\left(\frac{1/2}{1/2}\right) = 4, 2\left(\frac{3/4}{1/4}\right) = 6$. Thus C is the only possibility remaining.

ANSWER C

7. $$Var\left(\frac{S}{G}\right) = \frac{1}{G^2}Var(S) = \left[\frac{1}{(1+\theta)E[S]}\right]^2 [\lambda \cdot E[X^2]]$$

$$= \left[\frac{1}{\lambda(1+\theta)E[X]}\right]^2 [\lambda \cdot E[X^2]$$

$$= \frac{1}{\lambda(1+\theta)^2} \cdot \frac{E[X^2)}{(E[X])^2}$$

ANSWER D

8. Let C be the category of claims exceeding 5 and let $E = \{X > 5\}$: $pr(E) = \int_5^{20} \frac{1}{20} dx = \frac{15}{20} = .75$. Then the annual frequency of claims in category C is Poisson with parameter $\lambda \cdot pr(E) = 10(.75) = 7.5$

ANSWER E

9. Any $(a, b, 0)$ distribution is either Poisson ($a = 0$, $b = \lambda$), Negative Binomial ($a = \frac{\beta}{1+\beta}$, $b = \frac{(r-1)\beta}{1+\beta}$) or Binomial ($a = \frac{-p}{q}$, $b = \frac{(n+1)p}{q}$). In this problem $a = -\frac{1}{3}$ and $b = 4$. The only family with $a < 0$ is the Binomial. Hence $-\frac{1}{3} = -\frac{p}{q}$, $4 = \frac{(n+1)p}{q} = \frac{n+1}{3}$. This results in $n = 11, p = .25, q = .75$.

ANSWER B

10. Let N_1 be Poisson λ. Then N is a weighted average of a degenerate distribution with all probability at 0 (weight $= p_0 = \frac{1}{4}$) and the zero-truncation of N_1 (weight $= 1 - p_0 = \frac{3}{4}$). Hence

$$E[N] = \tfrac{1}{4}E[0] + \tfrac{3}{4}E[N_1^{ZT}] = 0 + \tfrac{3}{4}\left[\frac{E[N_1]}{1 - Pr(N_1 = 0)}\right]$$
$$= \tfrac{3}{4}\left[\frac{\lambda}{1 - e^{-\lambda}}\right] = \frac{3}{4}\frac{ln(2)}{(1 - \frac{1}{2})} = 1.5\,ln(2)$$

ANSWER D

11.
$$E[N^2] = \tfrac{1}{4}E[0^2] + \tfrac{3}{4}E[(N_1^{ZT})^2]$$
$$= 0 + \tfrac{3}{4}\left[\frac{E[N_1^2]}{1 - Pr(N_1 = 0)}\right]$$
$$= \; = \tfrac{3}{4}\left[\frac{(\lambda^2 + \lambda)}{1 - e^{-\lambda}}\right] = \frac{3}{4}\frac{ln(2) + (ln(2))^2}{(1 - \frac{1}{2})} = 1.5(ln(2) + (ln(2))^2),$$

hence

$$Var(N) = E[N^2] - E[N]^2$$
$$= 1.5(ln(2) + (ln(2))^2) - (1.5\,ln(2))^2$$
$$= 1.5ln(2) - .75\,(ln(2))^2 = .68$$

ANSWER A

12. Again, N is a weighted average of a degenerate distribution (weight $= \frac{1}{4}$) and the zero-truncated Poisson, N_1^{ZT} (weight $= \frac{3}{4}$). Thus

$$p_3 = Pr(N = 3) = \tfrac{1}{4}Pr(O = 3) + \tfrac{3}{4}Pr(N_1^{ZT} = 3)$$
$$= \tfrac{1}{4}(0) + \tfrac{3}{4}\left[\frac{Pr(N_1 = 3)}{1 - Pr(N_1 = 0)}\right]$$
$$= \tfrac{3}{4}\left[\frac{e^{-\lambda}\cdot\lambda^3/3!}{1 - e^{-\lambda}}\right] = \frac{3}{4}\cdot\frac{(\frac{1}{2})(ln(2))^3/6}{(1 - \frac{1}{2})} = \tfrac{1}{8}(ln(2))^3$$

ANSWER B

13. $M_S(t) = M_N(lnM_M(t))$ is a general relation for compound distributions. Here $M_N(t) = e^{5(e^t - 1)}$ and $M_M(t) = .8 + .2e^t$. Thus

$$M_S(t) = e^{5(.8 + .2e^t - 1)} = e^{e^t - 1},$$

which is the generating function of a Poisson distribution with parameter 1. ANSWER D

UNIT 4: MORE ON THE COLLECTIVE RISK MODEL

Premium and the S-Distribution in the Collective Model

The ideas here are a continuation from Unit 1 of the development of the collective risk model, $S = X_1 + \cdots + X_N$, for aggregate claims (losses) in light of the additional detail regarding the frequency (N) and severity (X) distributions in Units 2 and 3. From the relations (see Unit 1)

$$E[S] = E[N]E[X]$$

$$Var(S) = E[N]Var(X) + (E[X])^2 Var(N),$$

one can begin to determine an adequate premium to cover S. The premium, G, should be at least as big as $E[S]$ (the "**pure premium**"). There are several common ways to view G.

The **relative security loading,** θ, is determined from the relation

$$G = (1+\theta)E[S]$$

One can view $G - S$ as the random profit, and $E[G - S] = G - E[S] = (1+\theta)E[S] - E[S] = \theta E[S]$ as the expected profit. So θ can be viewed as either a profit margin or a margin needed to cover the risk that S exceeds $E[S]$. Using θ as a measure of security, however, is not advisable. If $E[S] = 100$, $Var(S) = 100$ and $\theta = .25$ and for another portfolio $E[S_1] = 100$, $Var(S_1) = 225$ and $\theta_1 = .25$, it is quite clear that there is a significantly greater risk in the latter portfolio even though $\theta = \theta_1$. In the first portfolio $G = 125$ is 2.5 deviations above the mean, whereas in the second portfolio $G = 125$ is $1.6\overline{6}$ deviations above the mean.

The profit margin interpretation of θ is useful in understanding reinsurance at an elementary level. Suppose an insurers original portfolio, S, is split into S^c, the **ceded** or reinsured portion, and S^r, the **retained** portion. If ζ is the relative security loading of the reinsurer, then $H = (1+\zeta)E[S^c]$ is the reinsurance premium and $G - H$ is the retained premium. If θ' is the relative security loading on the retained portfolio, $G - H = (1+\theta')E[S^r]$. The relation between θ, θ', and ζ is

$$\theta = \frac{E[S^r]}{E[S]}\theta' + \frac{E[S^c]}{E[S]}\zeta,$$

which can be interpreted as saying that the profit margin on the entire portfolio is a weighted average of the profit margins on the retained part and ceded part. The weights are the portions of $E[S]$ which are retained/ceded.

In addition to viewing G as $(1+\theta)E[S]$, one might also view G as $E[S]+k\cdot\sigma_S$ where k represents the number of deviations that G exceeds S by. Keep in mind Chebychev's inequality which says that $Pr(|S-E[S]|>k\sigma_S)\leq\frac{1}{k^2}$. This is a crude estimate. If this probability were equally split in the two tails we would know $Pr(S>E[S]+k\sigma_S)=Pr(S>G)\leq\frac{1}{2k^2}$. But, with the typically skewed-right distribution of S, the assumption of an equal split is a bit shaky.

It is also common to assume that S is approximately normal in distribution. If we view G as $E[S]+z_\alpha\cdot\sigma_S$ where $\alpha=Pr(N(0,1)>z_\alpha)$, then $\alpha\approx Pr(S>E[S]+z_\alpha\cdot\sigma_S)=Pr(S>G)$. Just as we noted above, however, the α calculated from a normal approximation might significantly understate the true probability that S exceeds G due to the right-skewness of a typical S distribution.

To accurately assess the risk that S exceeds G, one needs a precise calculation of $Pr(S>G)=1-F_S(G)$. This brings us back to the question of calculating the density or distribution function of aggregate claims, which is also necessary for evaluating possible reinsurance schemes. At the end of Unit one we saw that

$$f_S(x)=\sum_{n=0}^{\infty}f_N(n)\cdot f_X^{*n}(x),$$

$$F_S(x)=\sum_{n=0}^{\infty}f_N(n)\cdot F_X^{*n}(x).$$

The use of these formulas in practice will challenge the swiftest of computers.

If the frequency distribution, N, is from the $(a, b, 0)$ or $(a, b, 1)$ families, and if X is discrete with possible values 0, 1, 2, ..., there is a recursive method of calculating f_S which is essentially the same as the relations developed at the end of Unit 3 for compound frequency distributions with X here replacing M there:

$(a, b, 0)$ recursion : $$f_S(k)=\left[\frac{1}{1-af_X(0)}\right]\sum_{j=1}^{k}\left(a+\frac{bj}{k}\right)f_X(j)f_S(k-j)$$

$(a, b, 1)$ recursion: $$f_S(k)=\frac{[p_1-(a+b)p_0]f_X(k)+\sum_{j=1}^{k}\left(a+\frac{bj}{k}\right)f_X(j)f_S(k-j)}{1-af_X(0)}$$

where

$$p_k=Pr(N=k)=f_N(k)\qquad\text{(}N\text{-density shorthand)}$$

$$f_S(0)=P_N(f_X(0))\qquad\text{(starting value).}$$

These relations offer quicker calculation of $f_S(k)$ values than the f_S, F_S formulas relying on n-fold convolutions of f_X, F_X. Practical computer implementation of these recursions, however, can force one to deal with issues such as

(i) accumulation of roundoff errors in calculation of $f_S(1), f_S(2), \ldots$, and

(ii) the starting value $f_S(0) = P_N(f_X(0))$ being smaller than the smallest non-zero number representable in the computing system.

Discretization of the Severity Distribution

When X is continuous it must be approximated by a discrete distribution in order to use the recursion relations for f_S above. The approximation is referred to as a **discretization** or **arithmetization** of X. The idea is to replace the continuous distribution of X by point masses f_j at jh for $j = 0, 1, 2, \ldots$. The **span,** h, is a conveniently chosen unit of claim size measurement (e.g., $h = 10$, 100, or 1000).

In the method of **rounding (mass dispersal)** all claim amounts are rounded to the nearest multiple of h. Values of X in $[0, h/2)$ are rounded to 0, values of X in $[\frac{h}{2}, \frac{3h}{2})$ are rounded to h, and so on. So

$$f_0 = Pr\left(0 \leq X < \tfrac{h}{2}\right),$$

$$f_1 = Pr\left(\tfrac{h}{2} \leq X < \tfrac{3h}{2}\right),$$

etc.. One can think of f_k as $Pr(Y = k)$ where $Y = \frac{X}{h}$. Possible X-values are $0, h, 2h, \ldots$, whereas possible Y-values are $0, 1, 2, \ldots$. Use the recursion method to calculate f_{S_1} where $S_1 = Y_1 + \cdots + Y_N$, and then make the scale change adjustment $S = hS_1$:

$$f_S(jh) = f_{S_1}(j),$$

$$E[S] = hE[S_1]$$

$$Var(S) = h^2 Var(S_1).$$

Example 1 Suppose N is Poisson λ with $\lambda = 5$, and X is exponentially distributed with mean 100. Using a span of $h = 25$, describe the discretization of X by the method of rounding, set up the recursion relation for f_{S_1} calculation, and discuss the relations of $S = X_1 + \cdots + X_N$ and $S_1 = Y_1 + \cdots + Y_N$.

Solution The X density is $.01e^{-.01x}$, so

$$Pr(Y=0)=f_0=Pr(0\le X<12.5)=\int_0^{12.5}.01e^{-.01x}dx=1-e^{-.125}=.117503.$$

$$Pr(Y=1)=f_1=Pr(12.5\le X<37.5)=\int_{12.5}^{37.5}.01e^{-.01x}dx=e^{-.125}-e^{-.375}=.195208.$$

etc. For the Poisson $\lambda=5$ distribution we have

$$\frac{p_k}{p_{k-1}}=a+\frac{b}{k}=0+\frac{\lambda}{k}=\frac{5}{k}\qquad k\ge 1$$

and $P_N(t)=e^{\lambda(t-1)}=e^{5(t-1)}$.

Let $Y=\frac{X}{25}$ and $S_1=Y_1+\cdots+Y_N$. Then the starting value, $f_{S1}(0)$, is given by

$$f_{S_1}(0)=P_N(f_Y(0))=e^{5(.117503-1)}=.012125.$$

The S_1 recursion calculation looks like

$$f_{S_1}(k)=\left[\frac{1}{1-af_Y(0)}\right]\sum_{j=1}^{k}\left(a+\frac{bj}{k}\right)f_Y(j)f_{S_1}(k-j)$$

$$=\sum_{j=1}^{k}\left(\frac{5j}{k}\right)f_Y(j)f_{S_1}(k-j)\qquad (a=0,b=5)$$

$$=\frac{5}{k}\sum_{j=1}^{k}j\cdot f_Y(j)f_{S_1}(k-j).$$

For example,

$$f_{S_1}(1)=\frac{5}{1}\cdot 1\cdot f_Y(1)\cdot f_{S_1}(0)=5(.195208)(.012125)=.011835.$$

To complete the calculations, one would need to compute

$$f_Y(j)=Pr(25j-12.5\le X<25j+12.5)$$

$$=e^{-(.25j-.125)}-e^{-(.25j+.125)}$$

$$=e^{-.25j}(e^{.125}-e^{-.125})$$

$$=e^{-.25j}(.250652)$$

for $j=2,3,\ldots$, until it becomes negligible, and then compute values $f_{S_1}(2)$, $f_{S_1}(3)$, ... until they become negligible. Finally use $S=25S_1$ to compute $f_S(0)=f_{S_1}(0)=.012125$,
$f_S(25)=f_{S_1}(1)=.011835$, $f_S(50)=f_{S_1}(2)$ etc.. □

In the above example we can compute $E[S] = E[N]E[X] = (5)(100) = 500$, $Var(S) = E[N]Var(X) + (E[X])^2 Var(N) = (5)\frac{1}{(.01)^2} + \left(\frac{1}{.01}\right)^2 (5) = 100{,}000$ without using the S-density. If we compute the same quantities from the approximate S-density based on the discretization of X in Example 1, we would obtain different values. This leads to the idea of performing the discretization of X in such a way that some moments of the X-distribution are preserved. One can see from the above that if $E[X]$, $E[X^2]$ are preserved in the discretization, then $E[S]$ and $Var(S)$ are also preserved. If one also preserves $E[X^3]$ then the third central moment of S is preserved. The idea of the method of **local moment matching** is to discretize X while preserving several moments of X about the origin.

Using the data of Example 1 we illustrate how to begin the discretization of X by the method of local moment matching where the goal is to preserve $E[X]$, $E[X^2]$. Recall that $f_X(x) = .01e^{-.01x}$ and the span is $h = 25$. For each interval[19] $[2k(25), (2k+2)(25)]$, $k = 0, 1, \ldots$, one seeks point masses m_0^k, m_1^k, m_2^k, at the left, middle and right end of this interval so that

$$m_0^k + m_1^k + m_2^k = \int_{2k(25)}^{(2k+2)(25)} .01e^{-.01x}\,dx$$

$$(2k)(25)m_0^k + (2k+1)(25)m_1^k + (2k+2)(25)m_2^k = \int_{2k(25)}^{(2k+2)(25)} x \cdot .01e^{-.01x}\,dx$$

$$[(2k)(25)]^2 m_0^k + [(2k+1)(25)]^2 m_1^k + [(2k+2)(25)]^2 m_2^k = \int_{2k(25)}^{(2k+2)(25)} x^2 \cdot .01e^{-.01x}\,dx.$$

For each k this requires a solution of 3 linear equations in the 3 unknowns m_0^k, m_1^k, m_2^k. The diagram below illustrates how $f_0, f_1, \ldots$ are then calculated:

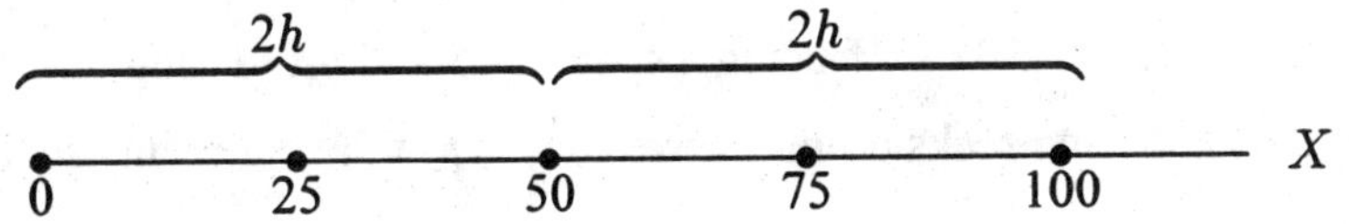

m_0^0 $\quad m_1^0$ $\quad m_2^0$

$\qquad\qquad m_0^1$ $\quad m_1^1$ $\quad m_2^1$

. . . .

$f_0 = m_0^0 \quad f_1 = m_1^0 \quad f_2 = m_2^0 + m_0^1 \qquad$ etc.

[19] A length of n spans is used when preserving n moments.

With $k = 0$ the calculation of the points masses m_0^0, m_1^0, m_2^0 at 0, 25, 50 requires solving

$$\begin{aligned} m_0^0 + m_1^0 + m_2^0 &= \int_0^{50} .01e^{-.01x}dx = .393469 \\ 25m_1^0 + 50m_2^0 &= \int_0^{50} x(.01)e^{-.01x}dx = 9.020401 \\ 25^2m_1^0 + 50^2m_2^0 &= \int_0^{50} x^2(.01)e^{-.01x}dx = 287.753559 \end{aligned}$$

This results in $m_2^0 = .049795$, $m_1^0 = .261226$, and $m_0^0 = .082448$. So far we would have $f_0 = .082448$, $f_1 = .261226$, $f_2 = .049795 + m_0^1$. The next three point masses m_0^1, m_1^1, m_2^1 at 50, 75 , 100 would be determined from

$$m_0^1 + m_1^1 + m_2^1 = \int_{50}^{100} f_X(x)\,dx$$

$$50m_0^1 + 75m_1^1 + 100m_2^1 = \int_{50}^{100} x \cdot f_X(x)dx$$

$$50^2m_0^1 + 75^2m_1^1 + 100^2m_2^1 = \int_{50}^{100} x^2 \cdot f_X(x)dx.$$

We could then finish the calculation of f_2 as $f_2 = \underbrace{.049795}_{m_2^0} + m_0^1$, calculate f_3 as m_1^1, and begin the calculation of f_4 as $m_2^1 + m_0^2$.

Note: Suppose you wish to discretize $f_X(x) = .01e^{-.01x}$ using a span of 25 and preserving just $E[X]$. For each interval $[k \cdot 25, (k+1) \cdot 25]$ one seeks point masses m_0^k, m_1^k at the endpoints such that

$$m_0^k + m_1^k = \int_{25k}^{25k+25} f_X(x)\,dx$$

$$(25k)m_0^k + (25k+25)m_1^k = \int_{25k}^{25k+25} x \cdot f_X(x)dx.$$

The Compound Poisson Collective Model

Suppose $S = X_1 + \cdots + X_N$ where N, X_1, ..., X_N are independent and all X_i are distributed like X, the severity model. In this section we assume the frequency model N to have a Poisson distribution with parameter λ. S is said to be compound-Poisson. Since $E[N] = Var(N) = \lambda$ and $M_N(t) = e^{\lambda(e^t-1)}$, the general collective risk model relations specialize to

$$E[S] = \lambda \cdot E[X],\ Var(S) = \lambda \cdot E[X^2]$$

$$E[(S - E[S])^3] = \lambda \cdot E[X^3],$$

$$M_S(t) = e^{\lambda(M_X(t)-1)}.$$

Also, recall that N is $(a, b, 0)$ with

$$\frac{p_k}{p_{k-1}} = a + \frac{b}{k} = 0 + \frac{\lambda}{k},\ k \geq 1,$$

where p_k is a shorthand for $f_N(k) = Pr(N = k)$, and $p_0 = e^{-\lambda}$. Thus, if X is discrete with possible values $0, 1, 2, \ldots$, we have a recursion relation for the density of aggregate claims given by

$$f_S(k) = \left[\frac{1}{1 - af_X(0)}\right]\sum_{j=1}^{k}\left(a + \frac{bj}{k}\right)f_X(j)f_S(k-j) = \sum_{j=1}^{k}\left(\frac{\lambda j}{k}\right)f_X(j)f_S(k-j) \quad (a = 0),$$

and a starting value of

$$f_S(0) = P_N(f_X(0)) = e^{\lambda(f_X(0)-1)}.$$

In this expression $\lambda \cdot f_X(j)$ is often shortened to λ_j. By results in Unit Three, N_j, the number of claims equal to j, is Poisson with parameter give by $E[N]Pr(X = j) = \lambda \cdot f_X(j) = \lambda_j$. Thus λ_j is the expected number of claims of amount j.

Next we introduce two results concerning a sum of independent, compound-Poissons. Suppose S_i is compound-Poisson with parameter λ_i and severity model X_i. Let $S = S_1 + \cdots + S_k$ and suppose the S_i are independent. Then, if $\lambda = \sum_{i=1}^{k}\lambda_i$, we have

$$M_S(t) = \prod_{i=1}^{k} M_{S_i}(t) = \prod_{i=1}^{k} e^{\lambda_i(M_{X_i}(t)-1)} = exp\left(\sum_{i=1}^{k}\lambda_i(M_{X_i}(t) - 1)\right) = exp\left(\lambda\left[\sum_{i=1}^{k}\frac{\lambda_i}{\lambda}M_{X_i}(t) - 1\right]\right),$$

which is the generating function of a compound-Poisson with parameter $\lambda = \sum_{i=1}^{k} \lambda_i$ and severity model X which is a weighted average of the X_i:

$$f_X(x) = \sum_{i=1}^{k} \frac{\lambda_i}{\lambda} \cdot f_{X_i}(x).$$

Hence S is also compound-Poisson.

Example 2 Suppose S_1 is compound-Poisson with $\lambda_1 = 10$ and $f_{X_1}(1) = .70$, $f_{X_1}(2) = .30$, and suppose S_2 is compound-Poisson with $\lambda_2 = 15$ and $f_{X_2}(1) = .50$, $f_{X_2}(2) = .30$, $f_{X_2}(3) = .20$. If S_1 and S_2 are independent, describe the distribution of $S = S_1 + S_2$.

Solution S is compound-Poisson with parameter $\lambda = 10 + 15 = 25$, and severity model X where $f_X(k) = \frac{10}{25} f_{X_1}(k) + \frac{15}{25} f_{X_2}(k)$:

$$f_X(1) = (.40)(.70) + (.60)(.50) = .58$$

$$f_X(2) = (.40)(.30) + (.60)(.30) = .30$$

$$f_X(3) = (.40)(0) + (.60)(.20) = .12.$$

□

One can also decompose a compound-Poisson into a sum of independent, compound Poissons using ideas about decomposing Poisson distributions discussed in Unit Three. So suppose $S = X_1 + \cdots + X_N$ is compound-Poisson with parameter λ. In addition, suppose that claims belong to distinct categories $C_1, \ldots, C_m$, where E_i is the event that a claim belongs to C_i and $p_i = Pr(E_i)$ $(1 = \sum_{i=1}^{m} p_i)$. Let N_i be the number of claims belonging to category C_i, and let $X^{(i)}$ be the conditional distribution of X given that X belongs to category C_i. Finally, let $S_i = X_1^{(i)} + \cdots + X_{N_i}^{(i)}$ be the sum of all claims belonging to category C_i. Then we can conclude that

(i) $S = S_1 + \cdots + S_m$, $N = N_1 + \cdots + N_m$

(ii) the S_i are independent,

(iii) S_i is compound-Poisson with parameter $\lambda_i = \lambda \cdot p_i$ and severity model $X^{(i)}$

Example 3 Suppose S is compound Poisson with parameter $\lambda = 10$ and severity model X where $f_X(1) = .50$, $f_X(2) = .30$, $f_X(3) = .20$. Suppose claims are broken into two categories: $C_1 = \{X | X \leq 2\}$, $C_2 = \{X | X > 2\}$. Decompose S using these categories.

Solution Note first that $p_1 = Pr(X \leq 2) = .50 + .30 = .80$ and $p_2 = Pr(X > 2) = .20$. The conditional distributions of $X^{(1)}$ and $X^{(2)}$ are given below:

x	$f_X(x)$	$f_{X^{(1)}}(x)$	$f_{X^{(2)}}(x)$
1	.50	.50/.80	0
2	.30	.30/.80	0
3	.20	0	.20/.20

If N_i represents the number of claims of type (i), then N_i is Poisson with parameter $\lambda_i = \lambda \cdot Pr(X \text{ belongs to } C_i) = 10p_i$: $\lambda_1 = 10(.80) = 8$, $\lambda_2 = 10(.20) = 2$. Finally, $S = S_1 + S_2$ where S_1 is compound-Poisson with parameter 8 and severity distribution $f_{X^{(1)}}(1) = \frac{5}{8}$, $f_{X^{(1)}}(2) = \frac{3}{8}$, and S_2 is compound-Poisson with parameter 2 and severity distribution $f_{X^{(2)}}(3) = 1$. □

Now we would like to use these ideas to explore an example of the effect of coverage modifications on a Compound-Poisson distribution modeling aggregate claims. (See Examples 7-9 of Unit Two.) Suppose X is the claim against a group dental plan as a result of a single visit by a plan member when there is no deductible (i.e., X is the bill for the services provided by the dentist). Suppose the annual frequency of visits, N, is adequately modeled by a Poisson distribution with $E[N] = \lambda = 100$ visits per year. Then aggregate annual claims, $S = X_1 + \cdots + X_N$, is compound-Poisson.

We will assume in the following discussion that X is from a parametric family described in Unit Two and that the parameters are $r = 2$ and $\omega = 250$. We summarize below the important results about this parametric family:

$$f_X(x) = \tfrac{r}{\omega}\left(1 - \tfrac{x}{\omega}\right)^{r-1} \qquad 0 \leq x \leq \omega \qquad (r > 0, \omega > 0)$$

$$= \tfrac{2}{250}\left(1 - \tfrac{x}{250}\right) \qquad 0 \leq x \leq 250 \qquad (r = 2, \omega = 250)$$

$$S_X(x) = Pr(X > x) = \left(1 - \tfrac{x}{\omega}\right)^r \qquad 0 \leq x \leq \omega$$

$$= \left(1 - \tfrac{x}{250}\right)^2 \qquad 0 \leq x \leq 250$$

$$E[X] = \frac{\omega}{r+1} = \frac{250}{3} = 83.\overline{3}$$

$$Var(X) = \frac{r\omega^2}{(r+1)^2(r+2)} = \frac{2(250)^2}{9 \cdot 4} = \frac{250^2}{18}$$

$$Y = X - d|_{X>d} \;\Rightarrow\; \underbrace{f_Y(y) = \frac{r}{\omega-d}\left(1-\frac{y}{\omega-d}\right)^r}_{\substack{\text{same } r\text{, new parameter } \omega-d \\ \text{same parametric family}}}$$

With these assumptions regarding aggregate annual claims with no deductible, we can calculate

$$E[S] = \lambda \cdot E[X] = 100(83.\overline{3}) = 8333.\overline{3}$$

$$Var(S) = \lambda \cdot E[X^2] = 100((E[X])^2 + Var(X)) = 100\left(\left(\frac{250}{3}\right)^2 + \frac{250^2}{18}\right) = 1{,}041{,}666.\overline{6}$$

$$\sigma_S = 1020.62.$$

To calculate $f_S(x)$ we might first discretize X while preserving $E[X]$, $E[X^2]$, and then use the compound-Poisson recursion formula for f_S with the discrete approximation to X.

Suppose next we want to analyze the effect of imposing a deductible $d = 50$ on each claim. Let C_1 be the category of claims ≤ 50 and let C_2 be those claims exceeding 50. Then $S = S_1 + S_2$ where:

$$\underline{S_1 = X^{(1)} + \cdots + X^{(1)}_{N_1} \quad \text{compound-Poisson}}$$

(frequency) $\begin{cases} N_1 = \text{number of claims in category 1, Poisson-}\lambda_1 \\ \lambda_1 = \lambda \cdot Pr(X \leq 50) = 100\left[1 - \left(1-\frac{50}{250}\right)^2\right] = 36 \end{cases}$

(severity) $X^{(1)} = X|_{X\leq 50}$; and

$$\underline{S_2 = X^{(2)}_1 + \cdots + X^{(2)}_{N_2} \quad \text{compound-Poisson}}$$

(frequency) $\begin{cases} N_2 = \text{number of claims in category 2, Poisson-}\lambda_2 \\ \lambda_2 = \lambda \cdot Pr(X > 50) = 100\left[\left(1-\frac{50}{250}\right)^2\right] = 64 \end{cases}$

(severity) $X^{(2)} = X|_{X>50}$

In order to study aggregate claims after the deductible $d = 50$ is imposed, rewrite $X^{(2)} = X|_{X>50}$ as $50 + (X-50)|_{X>50}$. Thus, in the above,

$$S_2 = X^{(2)}_1 + \cdots + X^{(2)}_{N_2} = 50N_2 + (Y_1 + \cdots + Y_{N_2})$$

where $Y = (X - 50)|_{X>50}$ (the claim amount given that a claim occurs with deductible $d = 50$). Let $S_3 = Y_1 + \cdots + Y_{N_2}$; this is the aggregate claim model for the group dental plan with $d = 50$. It is compound-Poisson with $E[N_2] = 64$, and

$$\begin{aligned} f_Y(y) &= \tfrac{r}{\omega-d}\left(1 - \tfrac{y}{\omega-d}\right)^{r-1} & \qquad 0 \le y \le \omega-d \\ &= \tfrac{2}{200}\left(1 - \tfrac{y}{200}\right) & \qquad 0 \le y \le 200 \end{aligned}$$

$$E[Y] = \tfrac{\omega-d}{r+1} = \tfrac{200}{3}$$

$$Var(Y) = \frac{r(\omega-d)^2}{(r+1)^2(r+2)} = \frac{2(200)^2}{9\cdot 4}.$$

Thus

$$E[S_3] = E[N_2]E[Y] = (64)\left(\tfrac{200}{3}\right) = 4{,}266.\overline{6},$$

$$Var(S_3) = E[N_2]E[Y^2] = (64)\left[\left(\tfrac{200}{3}\right)^2 + \tfrac{200^2}{18}\right] = 426{,}666.\overline{6}.$$

To calculate f_{S_3} (approximately) we might first discretize Y, and then use the compound-Poisson recursion formula.

The diagram below illustrates how we have split up the original S:

$$S = \underbrace{(X_1^{(1)} + \cdots + X_{N_1}^{(1)})}_{S_1} + \underbrace{(X_1^{(2)} + \cdots + X_{N_1}^{(2)})}_{S_2} =$$

$$= \underbrace{S_1 + \overbrace{50N_2}^{}}_{S_4} \quad \overbrace{+ \quad \underbrace{(Y_1 + \cdots + Y_{N_2})}_{S_3}}^{S_2}$$

Distribution:	Compound Poisson	Compound Poisson
Poisson Parameter:	$E[N_1 + N_2] = 100$	$E[N_2] = 64$
Severity:	$\begin{cases} X & \text{if } X \le 50 \\ 50 & \text{if } X > 50 \end{cases}$	$Y = X - 50\vert_{X>50}$

Note: S_4 and S_3 are not independent since N_2 shows up in both sums. S_3 represents aggregate annual claims with the deductible of 50, whereas S_4 represents the retained losses (i.e., deductibles) incurred by the insureds. In S_4 the severity distribution is a weighted average of the severity distribution in S_1, $X|_{X\le 50}$, and the severity distribution in $50N_2$, a degenerate distribution with all probability at 50.

Stop Loss Reinsurance on Aggregate Claims

Consider a collective risk model $S = X_1 + \cdots + X_N$ for aggregate annual claims. In Unit Two we considered the effect on the severity model, X, of imposing a deductible, d. The new severity model would look like $X - d|_{X>d}$. In this earlier Unit we wrote $I_d(X)$ for

$$\begin{cases} 0 & X \leq d \\ X - d & X > d \end{cases},$$

the payment per loss event. $X - d|_{X>d} = I_d(X)|_{X>d}$ is then the payment per payment event. When the deductible is applied to each individual loss X, the insurance is referred to as **excess of loss.** Here we want to consider a deductible d applied to $S = X_1 + \cdots + X_N$ when an insurer seeks reinsurance on the excess of S over d if there is an excess. This is referred to as **stop-loss reinsurance.** We will use the notation $(S - d)_+$ for

$$\begin{cases} S - d & \text{if } S > d \\ 0 & \text{if } S \leq d \end{cases},$$

which could also be denoted by $I_d(S)$ in the earlier format:

$$S = \begin{Bmatrix} S & S \leq d \\ d & S > d \end{Bmatrix} + \begin{Bmatrix} 0 & S \leq d \\ S - d & S > d \end{Bmatrix} = \underbrace{(S \wedge d)}_{\substack{\text{retained claims} \\ \text{after reinsurance}}} + \underbrace{(S - d)_+}_{\substack{\text{ceded or} \\ \text{reinsured claims}}}$$

Recall the Unit Two notation $S \wedge d = min\{S, d\}$.

The **pure** (net) **stop-loss premium,** $E[(S - d)_+]$, can be calculated as either $\int_d^\infty (x - d) f_S(x)\, dx$ or $\int_d^\infty (1 - F_S(x))\, dx$ if X is continuous. The second form is obtained via integration by parts from the first one. Remember that if X is continuous S may have a point mass at 0 of $Pr(N = 0)$, and its continuous part corresponds to $\sum_{n=1}^{\infty} f_N(n) \cdot f_X^{*n}(x)$. If X is discrete with possible values 0, 1, 2, ..., then S is discrete and, if d is a whole number,

$$\begin{aligned} E[(S - d)_+] = \sum_{x=d+1}^{\infty} (x - d) f_S(x) &= E[S] - d + \sum_{x=0}^{d-1} (d - x) f_S(x) \\ &= \sum_{x=d}^{\infty} (1 - F_S(x)) \\ &= (1 - F_S(d)) + E[(S - (d+1))_+]. \end{aligned}$$

If S is compound-Poisson $f_S(0)$, $f_S(1)$, ... can be generated recursively from the $(a, b, 0)$ method. Hence $F_S(0)$, $F_S(1)$, ... can be generated recursively, and by the last equation above,

$$E[S-(d+1))_+] = E[(S-d)_+] - (1-F_S(d)),$$

so can $E[(S-0)_+]$, $E[(S-1)_+]$, ... Notice that $(S-0)_+ = S$ so that $E[S] = E[N]E[X]$ is the starting value.

Example 4 Suppose S is compound-Poisson with $\lambda = 5$ and the severity distribution is given by $f_X(1) = .8$, $f_X(2) = .2$. Compute $f_S(x)$ and $E[(S-x)_+]$ for $x = 0, 1, 2, \ldots 6$.

Solution First notice that $f_S(0) = P_N(f_X(0)) = P_N(0) = e^{\lambda(0-1)} = e^{-5}$, and $E[(S-0)_+] = E[S] = \lambda \cdot E[X] = 5[1(.80) + 2(.20)] = 6.0$. The $(a, b, 0)$ recursion for $f_S(k)$ is

$$f_S(k) = \left[\frac{1}{1-af_X(0)}\right]\sum_{j=1}^{k}\left(a+\frac{bj}{k}\right)f_X(j)f_S(k-j)$$

$$=\sum_{j=1}^{2}\frac{\lambda j}{k}f_X(j)f_S(k-j)$$

$$=\frac{1}{k}[(1)(\lambda_1)f_S(x-1)+(2)(\lambda_2)f_S(x-2)]$$

where $\lambda_1 = \lambda \cdot Pr(X=1) = 5(.80) = 4.0$, $\lambda_2 = \lambda \cdot Pr(X=2) = 5(.20) = 1.0$. The reader may use this recursion to check that the following tables are correct:

x	0	1	2	3	4	5	6
$f_S(x)$	e^{-5}	$4e^{-5}$	$9e^{-5}$	$\frac{44}{3}e^{-5}$	$\frac{230}{12}e^{-5}$	$\frac{1272}{60}e^{-5}$	$\frac{7388}{360}e^{-5}$

x	0	1	2	3	4	5	6
$F_S(x)$	e^{-5}	$5e^{-5}$	$14e^{-5}$	$\frac{86}{3}e^{-5}$	$\frac{574}{12}e^{-5}$	$\frac{4142}{60}e^{-5}$	$\frac{32{,}240}{360}e^{-5}$

Using $E[(S-0)]_+ = E[S] = 6$ and the recursion $E[(S-(d+1)_+] = E[(S-d)_+] - (1-F_S(d))$ together with the table above, gives the next table:

x	0	1	2	3	4	5	6
$E[(S-d)_+]$	6	$5+e^{-5}$	$4+6e^{-5}$	$3+20e^{-5}$	$2+\frac{146}{3}e^{-5}$	$1+\frac{1158}{12}e^{-5}$	$\frac{9932}{60}e^{-5}$

□

The recursion method above generates $E[(S-d)_+]$ for integral d. What if d is not integral? The following **principle** makes this a simple linear interpolation in the table above:

$Pr(d_1 < S < d_2) = 0$ and $d_1 < d < d_2$

$$\Rightarrow \quad E[(S-d)_+] = \underbrace{\left(\frac{d_2-d}{d_2-d_1}\right)E[(S-d_1)_+] + \left(\frac{d-d_1}{d_2-d_1}\right)E[(S-d_2)_+]}_{\text{Linear Interpolation between } E[(S-d_1)_+] \text{ and } E[(S-d_2)_+]}$$

For example, in Example 4 above, we would have

$$E[(S-1.4)_+] = .6E[(S-1)_+] + .4E[(S-2)_+] = .6(5{+}e^{-5}) + .4(4{+}6e^{-5}) = 4.6 + 3.0e^{-5}$$

since $Pr(1 < S < 2) = 0$.

Suppose X is continuous and $S = X_1 + \cdots + X_N$ is compound-Poisson. One could use the preceding scheme for discrete X with possible values 0, 1, 2, ... in the following way:

Step 1: Discretize X with a convenient span h while preserving $E[X]$, $E[X^2]$ by the method of local moment matching. Let $f_0, f_1, \ldots$ be the probabilities assigned at $0, h, 2h, \ldots$ to $\widetilde{X}$, the discretization.

Step 2: Let $Y = \frac{1}{h}\widetilde{X}$ and $S_1 = Y_1 + \cdots + Y_N$. S_1 is compound Poisson with the same λ and severity model, Y, having possible values 0, 1, 2, ... Using the S_1 recursion

$$f_{S_1}(k) = \sum_{j=1}^{k} \frac{\lambda j}{k} f_Y(j) f_{S_1}(k-j) = \frac{\lambda}{k}\sum_{j=1}^{k} f_j \cdot f_{S_1}(k-j)$$

to calculate $f_{S_1}(1), f_{S_1}(2), \ldots$ from the starting value $f_{S_1}(0) = P_N(f_Y(0)) = e^{\lambda(f_0-1)}$. Then calculate $E[(S_1-d)_+]$ recursively, beginning with

$$E[S_1] = E[N]E[Y] = E[N]E[\tfrac{1}{h}\widetilde{X}] = \tfrac{1}{h}E[N]E[\widetilde{X}] = \tfrac{1}{h}E[N]E[X] = \tfrac{1}{h}E[S]$$

($E[\widetilde{X}] = E[X]$ due to local moment matching)

Step 3: $hS_1 = hY_1 + hY_2 + \cdots + hY_N = \widetilde{X}_1 + \cdots + \widetilde{X}_N$ is now a discrete approximation to S with probabilities at $0, h, 2h, \ldots$. Furthermore, for $k = 0, 1, 2, \ldots$

$Pr(hS_1 = kh) = Pr(S_1 = k)$ (done in Step 2)

$E[(hS_1 - hk)_+] = hE[(S_1-k)_+]$ (done in Step 2)

Example 5 Illustrate the mechanics of Steps 2 and 3 above if $S = X_1 + \cdots + X_N$ is compound-Poisson with $\lambda = 5$ and severity distribution $f_X(2) = .80$ and $f_X(4) = .20$. (X is like a discretization with span equal 2.)

Solution If $Y = \frac{1}{2}X$ then Y is 1 or 2 with probabilities .80 and .20 respectively. If we let $S_1 = Y_1 + \cdots + Y_N$, then using the data from Example 4 (Y here is the X-there) we have

x	0	1	2
$f_{S_1}(x)$	e^{-5}	$4e^{-5}$	$9e^{-5}$
$F_{S_1}(x)$	e^{-5}	$5e^{-5}$	$14e^{-5}$

and

d	0	1	2
$E[(S-d)_+]$	6	$5+e^{-5}$	$4+6e^{-5}$

Now $S = 2S_1$ and $E[(S-2d)_+] = 2E[(S_1-d)_+]$ so that we have

x	0	2	4
$f_S(x)$	e^{-5}	$4e^{-5}$	$9e^{-5}$
$F_S(x)$	e^{-5}	$5e^{-5}$	$14e^{-5}$
$E[(S-2x)_+]$	2(6)	$2(5+e^{-5})$	$2(4+6e^{-5})$

Furthermore, since $Pr(2 < S < 4) = 0$, by the linear interpolation principle

$$E[(S-2.8)_+] = \tfrac{1.2}{2}E[(S-2)_+] + \tfrac{.8}{2}E[(S-4)_+] = .6(2)(5+e^{-5}) + .4(2)(4+6e^{-5}) = 9.2 + 6e^{-5}.$$

The last result could also have been obtained from

$$E[(S-2.8)_+] = E[(2S_1 - 2(1.4)_+] = \underbrace{2E[(S_1-1.4)_+]}_{\substack{4.6+3.0e^{-5}\text{ from the}\\ \text{Example 4 follow-up}\\ \text{discussion.}}}.$$

CONDENSED REVIEW NOTES AND ADVANCED TOPICS

Premium/Collective Risk Model

$S = X_1 + \cdots + X_N$, $N =$ frequency model, $X =$ severity model

$G =$ premium $= (1+\theta)E[S]$, $\theta =$ relative security loading

Profit $=$ Gain $= G - S$, $E[\text{Gain}] = \theta \cdot E[S]$

Reinsurance

$S = S^r + S^c$ $\qquad r =$ retained, $c =$ ceded

$$(1+\theta)E[S] = G = \underbrace{(1+\theta')E[S^r]}_{\text{retained}} + \underbrace{(1+\zeta)E[S^c]}_{\text{reinsurance premium}}.$$

$$\Rightarrow \qquad \theta = \frac{E[S^r]}{E[S]}\theta' + \frac{E[S^c]}{E[S]}\zeta$$

where θ', ζ are the relative security loadings on the retained and ceded portfolios respectively

Premium Risk

$\alpha = Pr(S > G) = 1 - F_S(G)$ (probability that claims exceed premium)

Calculation requires knowing the right tail of $f_S(x)$. If X is discrete with possible values 0, 1, ... and if N is $(a, b, 0)$ or $(a, b, 1)$, $f_S(k)$ can be recursively calculated from

$(a, b, 0)$:
$$f_S(k) = \left[\frac{1}{1 - af_X(0)}\right]\sum_{j=1}^{k}\left(a+\frac{bj}{k}\right)f_X(j)f_S(k-j)$$

$(a, b, 1)$:
$$f_S(k) = \frac{[p_1 - (a+b)p_0]f_X(k) + \sum_{j=1}^{k}\left(a+\frac{bj}{k}\right)f_X(j)f_S(k-j)}{1 - af_X(0)}$$

and a starting value $f_S(0) = P_N(f_X(0))$: $\qquad p_k = Pr(N = k) = f_N(k)$

If X is discrete with values 0, h, $2h$, ..., set $Y = \frac{1}{h}X$, $S_1 = Y_1 + \cdots + Y_N$ and use the above to calculate f_{S_1}. Then $f_S(kh) = f_{S_1}(k)$. If X is continuous, perform a discretization on X and use the above to approximate f_S.

Discretization (Arithmetization) of a Continuous Variable

Replace the continuous distribution of X by point masses f_j at jh for $j = 0, 1, 2, \ldots$. $h = \text{span}$

1. Method 1: Rounding or Mass Dispersal.

   Set $f_0 = Pr\left(0 \le X < \frac{h}{2}\right)$, $f_1 = Pr\left(\frac{h}{2} \le X < 3\frac{h}{2}\right)$, etc.

2. Method 2: Local Moment Matching

   Assign the point masses in such a way that moments of X about the origin are preserved.

   a. Preserving $E[X]$ (hence $E[S]$)

   For each k assign point masses m_0^k, m_1^k at the endpoints of $[kh, (k+1)h]$ satisfying

$$m_0^k + m_1^k = \int_{kh}^{(k+1)h} f_X(x)\,dx$$

$$(kh)m_0^k + (k+1)(h)m_1^k = \int_{kh}^{(k+1)h} x \cdot f_X(x)\,dx.$$

The solution to this system of 2 linear equations is

$$m_1^k = \left[\frac{1}{h}\int_{kh}^{(k+1)h} (x - hk) f_X(x)\,dx\right]$$

$$m_0^k = \left[\frac{1}{h}\int_{kh}^{(k+1)h} (h(k+1) - x) f_X(x)\,dx\right]$$

Then set $f_0 = m_0^0$, $f_1 = m_1^0 + m_0^1$, $f_2 = m_1^1 + m_0^2$, etc.

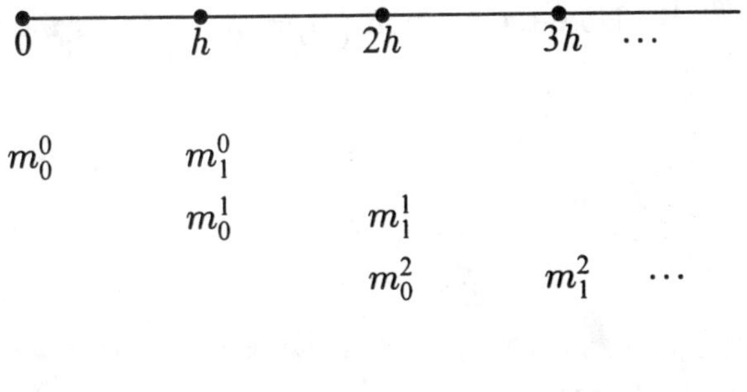

b. Preserving $E[X]$, $E[X^2]$ (hence $E[S]$, $Var(S)$)

For each k assign point masses m_0^k, m_1^k, m_2^k at the left, middle and right of the interval $[2kh, 2(k{+}1)h]$ (length = 2 spans) satisfying

$$m_0^k + m_1^k + m_2^k = \int_{2kh}^{(2k+2)h} f_X(x)\,dx$$

$$(2kh)m_0^k + (2k{+}1)(h)m_1^k + (2k{+}2)(h)m_2^k = \int_{2kh}^{(2k+2)h} x \cdot f_X(x)\,dx.$$

$$(2kh)^2 m_0^k + (2k{+}1)^2 h^2 m_1^k + (2k{+}2)^2 h^2 m_2^k = \int_{2kh}^{(2k+2)h} x^2 \cdot f_X(x)\,dx.$$

The solution to this system of 3 linear equations is straightforward: subtract a multiple of the first equation from the other equations to eliminate the m_0^k terms. Then eliminate m_1^k from the last equation so as to obtain m_2^k. Back substitute to obtain m_1^k and then m_0^k. The general algebraic formulas are quite messy. Then set $f_0 = m_0^0$, $f_1 = m_1^0$, $f_2 = m_2^0 + m_0^1$, $f_3 = m_1^1$, $f_4 = m_2^1 + m_0^2$ etc. (See computational review test Question 1.)

The Compound Poisson Collective Risk Model

$S = X_1 + \cdots + X_N$, where N is Poisson, parameter λ

$E[S] = \lambda \cdot E[X]$, $\qquad Var(S) = \lambda \cdot E[X^2]$

$E[(S - E[S])^3] = \lambda \cdot E[X^3]$, $M_S(t) = M_N(ln\, M_X(t)) = e^{\lambda(M_X(t)-1)}$

If $p_k = Pr(N = k)$ then $\frac{p_k}{p_{k-1}} = a + \frac{b}{k} = 0 + \frac{\lambda}{k}$, for $k \geq 1$, so if X is discrete with possible values 0, 1, 2, …., $f_S(k) = \sum_{j=1}^{k} \frac{\lambda j}{k} \cdot f_X(j) \cdot f_S(k-j)$ can be used to calculate recursively from $f_S(0) = P_N(f_X(0)) = e^{\lambda(f_X(0)-1)}$. Note on notation: $\lambda_j = \lambda \cdot f_X(j)$ is the expected number of claims equal to j.

Compound Poisson Summation Properties

1. If S_i is compound Poisson with parameter λ_i and severity model X_i, and if $S_1, S_2, \ldots, S_k$ are independent, then $S = S_1 + \cdots + S_k$ is compound Poisson with parameter $\lambda = \sum_{i=1}^{k} \lambda_i$ and severity model X, where $f_X(x) = \sum_{i=1}^{k} \left(\frac{\lambda_i}{\lambda}\right) f_{X_i}(x)$.

2. Suppose $S = X_1 + \cdots + X_N$ is compound-Poisson with parameter λ and severity model X. Suppose claims belong to distinct categories $C_1, \ldots, C_m$, where E_i the event $\{X \in C_i\}$ and $p_i = Pr(E_i)$: $1 = \sum_{i=1}^{m} p_i$. Let N be the number of claims belonging to C_i, and let $X^{(i)} = X|_{E_i}$. Let $S_i = X_1^{(i)} + \cdots + X_{N_i}^{(i)}$ be the sum of all claims in category C_i. Then

   (i) N_i is Poisson-λ_i where $\lambda_i = \lambda \cdot Pr(E_i) = \lambda \cdot p_i$

   (ii) $S = S_1 + \cdots + S_m$, $N = N_1 + \cdots + N_m$,

   (iii) $S_1, \ldots, S_m$ are independent, and

   (iv) S_i is compound-Poisson with parameter λ_i.

   Note: See Example 3 in the reading.

Stop-Loss Reinsurance

Let $S = X_1 + \cdots + X_N$ be aggregate claims to an insurer. Define $(S - d)_+$ by

$$(S - d)_+ = \begin{cases} S - d & \text{if } S > d \\ 0 & \text{if } S \le d \end{cases},$$

Typically used by an insurer in a scheme to reinsure the excess of aggregate claims over S, if there is an excess.

$$S = \underbrace{(S \wedge d)}_{\substack{\text{retained claims} \\ \text{after reinsurance}}} + \underbrace{(S - d)_+}_{\substack{\text{ceded or} \\ \text{reinsured claims}}}$$

Contrast this **stop-loss** reinsurance with $S = I_d(X_1) + \cdots + I_d(X_N)$, where each claim made to the insurer is subject to a deductible. This is referred to as **excess of loss** and $I_d(X)$ is another notation for $(X - d)_+$.

Pure Premium

1. If X is continuous

$$E[(S-d)_+] = \int_d^\infty (x-d) f_S(x)\, dx = \int_d^\infty (1 - F_S(x))\, dx$$

2. If X is discrete with possible values 0, 1, 2, ... and if $d = 0, 1, 2, \ldots$, then

$$\begin{aligned} E[(S-d)_+] &= \sum_{x=d+1}^{\infty} (x-d) f_S(x) = E[S] - d + \sum_{x=0}^{d-1} (d-x) f_S(x) \\ &= \sum_{x=d}^{\infty} (1 - F_S(x)) \\ &= (1 - F_S(d)) + E[(S-(d+1))_+]. \qquad \text{(recursive)} \end{aligned}$$

$E[(S-0)_+] = E[S] = E[N]E[X]$ is the starting value for a recursive calculation of $E[(S-d)_+]$ for $d = 0, 1, 2, \ldots$.

3. If X is discrete and $Pr(d_1 < S < d_2) = 0$ then one can **linearly interpolate** to find $E[(S-d)_+]$ if $d_1 < d < < d_2$:

$$E[(S-d)_+] = \left(\frac{d_2 - d}{d_2 - d_1}\right) E[(S-d_1)_+] + \left(\frac{d - d_1}{d_2 - d_1}\right) E[(S-d_2)_+]$$

4. If X is discrete with values $0, h, 2h, \ldots$, let $Y = \frac{1}{h}X$, $S_1 = X_1 + \cdots + X_N = \frac{1}{h}S$ and calculate as above. Then use $S = hS_1$, $f_S(hk) = f_{S_1}(k)$ etc..

CONCEPTUAL REVIEW TEST

1. If G is 50 and $E[S]$ is 40, what is the relative security loading?

2. Suppose 30% of each claim in Question 1 is reinsured and the reinsurer has a relative security loading of 40%. Describe the split of S/G into the retained and ceded portions.

3. What is a better measure of security than θ?

4. Describe the method of local moment matching as a way of discretizing a continuous severity model, X. Assume you want to preserve $E[X]$, $E[X^2]$.

5. Why would you want to discretize a continuous severity model?

6. If S_1 is compound-Poisson with $\lambda_1 = 10$ and $f_{X_1}(x) = .01e^{-.01x}$ and S_2 is compound-Poisson with $\lambda_2 = 15$ and $f_{X_2}(x) = .02e^{-.02x}$, what is the distribution of $S = S_1 + S_2$ if S_1 and S_2 are independent?

7. Describe stop-loss reinsurance on $S = X_1 + \cdots + X_N$ in contrast with excess of loss insurance $S = I_d(X_1) + \cdots + I_d(X_N)$.

CONCEPTUAL REVIEW TEST SOLUTIONS

1. $\frac{G}{E[S]} = \frac{50}{40} = 1.25 = 1+\theta;\ \theta = .25$

2. If $S = X_1 + \cdots + X_N$ then $S^r = .7X_1 + \cdots + .7X_N$ represents aggregate retained claims and $S^c = .3X_1 + \cdots + .3X_N$ represents aggregate ceded claims. The reinsurance premium is $(1+.40)E[S^c] = 1.4E[.3S] = .42E[S] = .42(40) = 16.80$. The retained premium is $50 - 16.80 = 33.20$ and $E[S^r] = E[.7S] = (.7)(40) = 28$. Thus $(1+\theta')28 = 33.20$, or $\theta' = .1857$ is the relative security on the retained claim portfolio. Check:

$$\underbrace{.25}_{\theta} = \left(\tfrac{28}{40}\right)\underbrace{.1857}_{\theta'} + \left(\tfrac{12}{40}\right)\underbrace{.40}_{\zeta}$$

3. $Pr(S > G) = 1 - F_S(G)$, the probability that claims exceed premium. This makes right tail knowledge of the S-distribution of central importance.

4. Point masses are assigned at $0, h, 2h, \ldots$ for some convenient h, the span, in such a way that both $E[X]$ and $E[X^2]$ are preserved.

5. If X is continuous, calculation of $f_S(x)$ from $\sum_{k=0}^{\infty} Pr(N = k) f_X^{*k}(x)$ is a formidable problem, making it difficult to calculate right tail probabilities such as $Pr(S > G)$ for some G. However, if N were $(a, b, 0)$ or $(a, b, 1)$ and $\widetilde{X}$ is a discrete approximation to X preserving $E[X]$ and $E[X^2]$, then $\widetilde{S} = \widetilde{X}_1 + \cdots + \widetilde{X}_N$ is a discrete approximation to S with $E[\widetilde{S}] = E[S]$, $Var(\widetilde{S}) = Var(S)$. Furthermore, $Pr(S > G) \approx Pr(\widetilde{S} > G)$ and values $f_{\widetilde{S}}(0)$, $f_{\widetilde{S}}(h)$, $f_{\widetilde{S}}(2h)$, $\ldots$ can be calculated recursively.

6. S is compound-Poisson with $\lambda = 10 + 15 = 25$ and severity model $f_X(x) = \frac{10}{25}(.01e^{-.01x}) + \frac{15}{25}(.02e^{-.02x})$, a weighted average of exponentials.

7. In stop-loss reinsurance, the excess of S over d, if there is an excess, $(S-d)_+$, is ceded to a reinsurer. The retained portfolio is then $S \wedge d = min\{S, d\} = \begin{cases} S & S \leq d \\ d & S > d \end{cases}$. The right tail of the S distribution is concentrated as a point mass at $S = d$ in the retained portfolio. With excess of loss insurance, each claim is the excess of an individual loss over a deductible.

COMPUTATIONAL REVIEW TEST

1. Suppose X is exponential with mean 100. Use local moment matching with a span of 25 to preserve $E[X]$, $E[X^2]$. What are the point masses f_0, f_1, f_2, f_3, f_4 assigned at 0, 25, 50, 75, 100.

   Note: Following Example 1 in the reading we calculated $m_0^0 = .082448$, $m_1^0 = .261226$, $m_2^0 = .049795$. Thus $f_0 = .082448$, $f_1 = .261226$ and $f_2 = .049795 + m_0^1$ where m_0^1, m_1^1, m_2^1 are assigned to 50, 75, and 100 in such a way that

$$m_0^1 + m_1^1 + m_2^1 = \int_{50}^{100} .01e^{-.01x}\,dx$$

$$50m_0^1 + 75m_1^1 + 100m_2^1 = \int_{50}^{100} x \cdot .01e^{-.01x}dx$$

$$50^2m_0^1 + 75^2m_1^1 + 100^2m_2^1 = \int_{50}^{100} x^2 \cdot .01e^{-.01x}dx$$

   Now solve for the m_k^1 given that the three integrals are .238651, 17.4037, and 1318.27.

2. Suppose S is compound-Poisson with parameter $\lambda = 10$ and severity model X where $f_X(1) = .5$, $f_X(2) = .3$, and $f_X(3) = .2$. A deductible of 1.5 is now imposed on each loss.
   (i) Describe the distribution of aggregate claims.
   (ii) Compute the expected value and variance of aggregate claims.
   (iii) Compute the moment generating function of aggregate claims.
   (iv) Discuss recursive calculation of the density of aggregate claims.

3. In Example 4, calculate the deductible so that the pure premium is 1.0 for the stop-loss reinsurance.

   Note: $E[(S-6)_+]$ was calculated in the example as $\frac{9932}{60}e^{-5} = 1.1154$. Calculate $E[(S-7)_+]$ by the recursion and then linearly interpolate.

COMPUTATIONAL REVIEW TEST SOLUTIONS

1. Using the first equation to eliminate m_1^0 from the next two gives

$$\begin{aligned} m_0^1 \quad + \quad m_1^1 \quad + \quad m_2^1 &= .238651 \\ 25m_1^1 \quad + \quad 50m_2^1 &= 5.47116 \\ 3125m_1^1 \quad + \quad 7500m_2^1 &= 721.645. \end{aligned}$$

Eliminating m_1^1 in the 3rd equation gives

$$\begin{aligned} m_0^1 \quad + \quad m_1^1 \quad + \quad m_2^1 &= .238651 \\ 25m_1^1 \quad + \quad 50m_2^1 &= 5.47116 \\ 1250m_2^1 &= 37.7496. \end{aligned}$$

Then $m_2^1 = .030199$, $m_1^1 = .158447$, $m_0^1 = .050004$. We can now finish the calculation of $f_2 = .049795 + m_0^1 = .099799$ (the probability at 50 in the discretization), $f_3 = .158447$ (the probability at 75) and begin the calculation of f_4 as $f_4 = m_2^1 + m_0^2 = .030199 + m_0^2$.

2. (i) There are several ways to go about obtaining the distribution of aggregate claims after a deductible of 1.5 is imposed on each loss. Call it S_3. Imitating the method described in the reading in Example 3, we break claims into 2 categories: C_1 is the category of claims greater than 1.5 ($E_1 = \{X > 1.5\}$, $p_1 = Pr(E_1) = .30 + .20 = .50$) and C_2 is the category of claims less than 1.5. Then $S = S_1 + S_2$ where S_1 is the sum of 2 and 3 dollar losses. S_1 is compound-Poisson with parameter $\lambda_1 = \lambda p_1 = 10(.5) = 5$ and severity model $X^{(1)} = X|_{X>1.5}$:

$X^{(1)}$	Probability	$X^{(1)}-1.5$
2	$\frac{.3}{.5} = .60$	.5
3	$\frac{.2}{.5} = .40$	1.5

Then $S_3 = S_1 - N_1 \cdot 1.5 = (X_1^{(1)} - 1.5) + \cdots + (X_{N_1}^{(1)} - 1.5)$ is also compound-Poisson with parameter $\lambda = 5$ and severity model $X^{(1)} - 1.5$ (table above).

2. (cont.)

The other method (less formal) is to write $S_3 = I_{1.5}(X_1) + \cdots + I_{1.5}(X_N)$ and recognize that it is compound-Poisson with parameter $\lambda = 10$ and severity model $I_{1.5}(X)$:

X	$I_{1.5}(X)$	Probability
1	0	.50
2	.50	.30
3	1.5	.20

In S_3, as written above, many terms are zero (i.e., no claim is made because the loss does not exceed the deductible.) The number of non-zero terms is Poisson with parameter $\lambda Pr(I_{1.5}(X) > 0) = 10(.5) = 5$, and the conditional distribution of $I_{1.5}(X)$ given that it is positive has probability .60 at .50 and probability .40 at 1.5.

(ii) $E[S_3] = 5 \cdot E[X^{(1)} - 1.5] = 5[.50(.60) + 1.5(.40)] = 4.5$

$Var(S_3) = 5 \cdot E[(X^{(1)} - 1.5)^2] = 5[.50^2(.60) + 1.5^2(.40)] = 5.25$

(iii) $M_{S_3}(t) = M_{N_1}(ln(M_{X^{(1)}-1.5}(t)) = e^{5(M_{X^{(1)}-1.5}(t)-1)} = exp[5(e^{.5t}(.60) + e^{1.5t}(.40) - 1)]$

Check: $E[S_3] = M'_{S_3}(0)$

$$M'_{S_3}(t) = M_{S_3}(t) \cdot \underbrace{\frac{d}{dt}[5(e^{.5t}(.60) + e^{1.5t}(.40) - 1)]}_{5((.50)(.60)e^{.5t} + (1.5)(.40)e^{1.5t})}$$

$$M'_{S_3}(0) = M_{S_3}(0) \cdot 5[.30 + .60] = 1 \cdot 5 \cdot (.90) = 4.5$$

(iv) S_3 is compound-Poisson with parameter $\lambda = 5$ and severity model Y where $f_Y(.50) = .60$ and $f_Y(1.5) = .40$. To use the recursive method of calculation consider $S_4 = 2S_3 = 2Y_1 + \cdots + 2Y_N$ where $Pr(2Y = 1) = .60$, $Pr(2Y = 3) = .40$. Use the following to recursively calculate $f_{S_4}(0)$, $f_{S_4}(1)$, ... and then use $Pr(S_3 = x) = Pr(S_4 = 2x)$ to obtain values of $f_{S_3}(x)$ for $x = 0, .5, 1.0$, etc.:

$$f_{S_4}(0) = Pr(N = 0) = e^{-5}$$

$$f_{S_4}(k) = \sum_{j=1}^{k} \left(a + \frac{bj}{k}\right) f_{2Y}(j) f_{S_4}(k-j)$$

$$= \underbrace{\frac{5 \cdot 1}{k}(.60)\, f_{S_4}(k-1)}_{j=1 \text{ term}} + \underbrace{\frac{5 \cdot 3}{k}(.40)\, f_{S_4}(k-3)}_{j=3 \text{ term}}$$

$$= \frac{1}{k}[3 \cdot f_{S_4}(k-1) + 6 \cdot f_{S_4}(k-3)].$$

3. $E[(S-7)_+] = E[(S-6)_+] - (1 - F_S(6)) = \frac{9932}{60}e^{-5} - \left(1 - \frac{32,240}{360}e^{-5}\right) = .7188$ (See Ex. 4)

$E[(S-6)_+] = 1.1154$

$1.0 = E[(S-d)_+]$ $\Rightarrow$ d is obtained by linear interpolation from deductibles of 6 and 7 since $Pr(6 < S < 7) = 0$

$$\frac{1.1154 - 1}{1.1154 - .7188} = .2909 \quad \Rightarrow \quad d = 6 + .2909 = 6.2909$$

Note: If $E[(S-d)_+]$ is obtained by linear interpolation between $E[(S-6)_+]$ and $E[(S-7)_+]$,

$$E[(S-d)_+] = \tfrac{7-d}{7-6}E[(S-6)_+] + \tfrac{d-6}{7-6}E[(S-7)_+],$$

then d is obtained by linear interpolation between 6 and 7.

d	$E[(S-d)_+]$
6	1.1154
6.2909	1.0
7	.7188

UNIT REVIEW QUESTIONS

1. A reinsurer pays aggregate claim amounts in excess of d, and in return receives a stop-loss premium $E[I_d]$. You are given the following:

   (i) $E[I_{100}] = 15$
   (ii) $E[I_{120}] = 10$
   (iii) The probability that the aggregate claim amounts are greater than 80 and less than or equal to 120 is 0.

   Determine the probability that the aggregate claim amounts are less than or equal to 80.

   (A) $\frac{1}{4}$ (B) $\frac{1}{3}$ (C) $\frac{1}{2}$ (D) $\frac{2}{3}$ (E) $\frac{3}{4}$

2. A random loss, X, has the following probability function:

x	$f(x)$	x	$f(x)$	x	$f(x)$
0	.05	4	.10	7	.05
1	.06	5	.05	8	.05
2	.25	6	.05	9	.12
3	.22				

   You are given that $E[X] = 4$ and $E[I_d] = 2$. Determine d.

   (A) $\frac{1}{4}$ (B) $\frac{5}{4}$ (C) $\frac{7}{4}$ (D) $\frac{9}{4}$ (E) $\frac{11}{4}$

3. The aggregate claims for a block of business has probability density function $f(x) = \beta e^{-\beta x}$. Find the expected amount of claims to be paid by a reinsurer under a stop-loss treaty with deductible, d.

   (A) $\frac{e^{-\beta d}}{\beta}$ (B) $\frac{e^{-\beta}}{\beta}$ (C) $\frac{e^{-\beta d}}{d}$ (D) $\frac{e^{-\beta d}}{\beta d}$ (E) $e^{-\beta d}$

4. On a given day a physician provides medical care to N_A adults and N_C children. N_A and N_C have Poisson distributions with parameters 3 and 2, respectively. The distributions of length of care per patient are as follows:

	Adult	Child
1 hour	.40	.90
2 hour	.60	.10

   N_A, N_C and the lengths of care for all individuals are independent. The physician charges 200 per hour of patient care. Determine the probability that the office income on a given day is less than or equal to 800.

   (A) .25 (B) .30 (C) .35 (D) .40 (E) .45

5. S has a compound-Poisson distribution with $\lambda = 1.0$ and claim amounts that are 1, 2, or 3 with probabilities .50, .25, and .25, respectively. Determine $f_S(3)$.

(A) .13 (B) .15 (C) .17 (D) .19 (E) .21

6. For a compound Poisson process, the expected number of claims is 2 and the claim amount distribution is lognormal. That is, the claim amount is a random variable X, where $X = e^Y$ and Y is normally distributed with expected value 1 and standard deviation 2.

What is the ratio of the variance of aggregate claims to the expected value of aggregate claims?

(A) e^5 (B) e^6 (C) e^7 (E) e^{12} (E) e^{13}

7. S has a compound Poisson distribution with $\lambda = .60$ and individual claim amounts that are 1, 2 or 3 with probability .20, .30, and .50, respectively. Determine $Pr(S \geq 3)$.

(A) .269 (B) .271 (C) .275 (D) .279 (E) .281

8. You are given two independent compound Poisson random variables S_A and S_B, where:

(i) $\lambda_A = \lambda_B = 1$ (ii) $f_A(1) = 1$ (claim amounts) (iii) $f_B(1) = f_B(2) = .50$

Let $F(x)$ be the claim size distribution function of $S_A + S_B$. Calculate $F^{*4}(6)$.

(A) .75 (B) .80 (C) .85 (D) .90 (E) .95

9. An insurer has an aggregate claims process that is compound Poisson with $\lambda = 1$ and claim amount density $f_X(x) = \frac{1}{12}e^{-x/12}$, $x > 0$. With no reinsurance, the insurer has a relative security loading of θ. The insurer purchases reinsurance that has expected claims 8. With the reinsurance, the insurer has a relative security loading of $3\theta/4$. Determine the reinsurer's relative security loading.

(A) $\frac{9\theta}{8}$ (B) $\frac{5\theta}{4}$ (C) $\frac{4\theta}{3}$ (D) $\frac{3\theta}{2}$ (E) 2θ

10. An insurer has a portfolio producing annual aggregate claims with a compound Poisson distribution with $\lambda = 1.5$, $f_X(1) = 2/3$ and $f_X(2) = 1/3$. The annual premiums received by the insurer are c. Stop-loss reinsurance can be obtained on the following bases:

Stop-loss Deductible	Net Stop-loss Premium	Insurer's Expected Gain with Reinsurance
3	.339	.462
4	.157	.644

The reinsurer uses a uniform relative security loading. Determine c.

(A) 2.4 (B) 2.5 (C) 2.6 (D) 2.7 (E) 2.8

11. S has a compound Poisson distribution with $\lambda = 2$ and $f_X(1) = f_X(2) = 1/2$. Determine $E[I_3]$.

(A) .82 (B) .84 (C) .86 (D) .88 (E) .90

12. For a compound Poisson distribution with positive integer claim amounts, the probability function is as follows:

$$f(x) = \frac{1}{x}[.16f(x-1) + k \cdot f(x-2) + .72f(x-3)], \; x = 1, 2, 3, \ldots$$

The expected value of aggregate claims is 1.68. Determine the expected number of claims.

(A) .60 (B) .70 (C) .80 (D) .90 (E) 1.00

13. S has a compound Poisson claims distribution with the following properties:

(i) Individual claim amounts equal to 1, 2 or 3
(ii) $E[S] = 56$
(iii) $Var(S) = 126$
(iv) $\lambda = 29$

Determine the expected number of claims of size 2.

(A) 10 (B) 11 (C) 12 (D) 13 (E) 14

14. A claim amount distribution is normal with $\mu = 100$ and $\sigma^2 = 9$. The distribution for the number of claims, N, is:

n	$Pr(N = n)$
0	.50
1	.20
2	.20
3	.10

Determine the probability that aggregate claims exceed 100.

(A) .20 (B) .30 (C) .40 (D) .50 (E) .60

15. An employer self-insures a life insurance program with the following characteristics:

(i) Given that a claim has occurred, the claim amount is 2000 with probability .40, or 3000 with probability .60.

(ii) The number of claims has the following distribution:

n	$f(n)$
0	1/16
1	1/4
2	3/8
3	1/4
4	1/16

The employer purchases aggregate stop-loss coverage that limits the employer's annual claims cost to 5000. The aggregate stop-loss coverage costs 1472. Determine the employer's expected annual cost of the program, including the cost of stop-loss coverage.

(A) 4000 (B) 4700 (C) 5200 (D) 5500 (E) 6200

16. For a portfolio for policies, the following information is given:

(i) The number of claims has a Poisson distribution.
(ii) Claim amounts can be 1, 2, or 3.
(iii) A stop-loss reinsurance contract has net premiums for various deductibles as follows:

Deductible	Net Premium
4	.20
5	.10
6	.04
7	.02

Determine the probability that aggregate claims will be either 5 or 6.

(A) .06 (B) .08 (C) .10 (D) .12 (E) .14

17. An insurance policy reimburses incurred expenses at the rate of 80% of the first 1000 in excess of 100, 90% of the next 1000 and 100% thereafter.

Express the coverage in terms of stop-loss premium notation.

(A) $(I_0 - 100) - .20I_{100} + .10I_{1000} + .10I_{2000}$
(B) $(I_0 - 100) - .20I_{100} + .10I_{1100} + .10I_{2100}$
(C) $I_0 - .20I_{100} + .10I_{1000} + .10I_{2000}$
(D) $.80I_{100} + .10I_{1000} + .10I_{2000}$
(E) $.80I_{100} + .10I_{1100} + .10I_{2100}$

18. Annual dental claims, X, for an individual have the following probability distribution:

x	$p(x)$
0	1/2
100	1/3
300	1/6

An insurance policy reimbursement is expressed as:

$$.80(I_{50} - I_{250})$$

The relative security loading is .20.

G is the annual gross premium the insurer will charge.

Determine G.

(A) 48 (B) 50 (C) 52 (D) 54 (E) 56

19. For a certain insurance, individual losses in 1994 were uniformly distributed over (0, 1000). A deductible of 100 is applied to each loss. In 1995 individual losses have increased 5%, and are still uniformly distributed. A deductible of 100 is still applied to each loss. Determine the percentage increase in the standard deviation of amount paid.

(A) 5.00% (B) 5.25% (C) 5.50% (D) 5.75% (E) 6.00%

20. An insurer issues a portfolio of 100 automobile insurance policies. Of these 100 policies, one-half have a deductible of 10 and the other half have a deductible of zero. The insurance policy pays the amount of damage in excess of the deductible subject to a maximum of 125 per accident. Assume:

(i) the number of automobile accidents per year per policy has a Poisson distribution with mean .03; and

(ii) given that an accident occurs, the amount of vehicle damage has the distribution:

x	$p(x)$
30	1/3
150	1/3
200	1/3

Compute the total amount of claims the insurer expects to pay in a single year.

(A) 270 (B) 275 (C) 280 (D) 285 (E) 290

21. A stop-loss reinsurance pays 80% of the excess of aggregate claims above 20, subject to a maximum payment of 5. All claim amounts are non-negative integers. You are given:

$E[I_{16}] = 3.89$ $\quad$ $E[I_{25}] = 2.75$
$E[I_{20}] = 3.33$ $\quad$ $E[I_{26}] = 2.69$
$E[I_{24}] = 2.84$ $\quad$ $E[I_{27}] = 2.65$

Determine the total amount of claims the reinsurer expects to pay.

(A) .46 (B) .49 (C) .52 (D) .54 (E) .56

22. S_1 has a compound Poisson distribution with parameter $\lambda_1 = 1$ and discrete claim amount distribution $p_1(x)$:

x	$p_1(x)$
1	.75
5	.25

S_2 has a compound Poisson distribution with parameter $\lambda_2 = 1$ and discrete claim amount distribution $p_2(x)$:

x	$p_2(x)$
3	.50
7	.50

S_1 and S_2 are independent. Determine $Pr\{(S_1 + S_2) \leq 3\}$.

(A) 0.21 (B) 0.28 (C) 0.35 (D) 0.42 (E) 0.49

23. A store sells two brands of a product. The revenue from sales of each brand has a compound Poisson distribution. The revenues are independent.

You are given:

	Price	Brand A	Brand B
Mean Units Sold		7	3
Percent of Sales (by number)	15	60%	
	25	40%	80%
	60		20%

Determine the probability that the total revenue from the sales of the two brands will be less than 50.

(A) 0.002 (B) 0.004 (C) 0.006 (D) 0.008 (E) 0.010

The following information applies to Questions 24-31. $S = X_1 + \cdots + X_N$ is a collective risk model where:

(i) $f_X(1) = .70$, $f_X(2) = .20$, $f_X(3) = .10$;
(ii) N is a zero modified ETNB distribution with $r = -\frac{1}{2}$, $\beta = 1$ such that $Pr(N = 0) = .20$.

24. Calculate $E[S]$. (nearest .01)

(A) 1.28 (B) 1.30 (C) 1.33 (D) 1.35 (E) 1.38

25. Calculate $Var(S)$. (nearest .01)

(A) 1.36 (B) 1.40 (C) 1.44 (D) 1.48 (E) 1.52

26. Calculate $f_S(2)$. (nearest .01)

(A) .10 (B) .12 (C) .14 (D) .16 (E) .18

27. $E[(S - 1.5)^+] =$ (nearest .01)

(A) .27 (B) .30 (C) .33 (D) .36 (E) .39

For Questions 28-31, use the following material in addition to that given above for Questions 24-31.

(iii) $\widetilde{S} = I_1(X_1) + \cdots + I_1(X_N)$ is aggregate claims when a deductible of 1 applies to each loss.

28. Calculate $E[\widetilde{S}]$. (nearest .01)

(A) .35 (B) .39 (C) .43 (D) .47 (E) .51

29. Calculate $Var(\widetilde{S})$. (nearest .01)

(A) .47 (B) .49 (C) .51 (D) .53 (E) .55

30. Calculate $f_{\widetilde{S}}(0)$. (nearest .01)

(A) .58 (B) .63 (C) .68 (D) .73 (E) .78

31. Calculate $f_{\widetilde{S}}(1)$. (nearest .01)

(A) .14 (B) .15 (C) .16 (D) .17 (E) .18

SOLUTIONS TO UNIT REVIEW QUESTION

1. Since $Pr(80 < S \leq 120) = 0$ we know that $E[I_{100}] = 15$ is obtained by linear interpolation from $E[I_{80}]$ and $E[I_{120}] = 10$. Thus $E[I_{80}] = 20$. Now

$$20 = E[I_{80}] = \sum_{x>80}(x-80)Pr(S=x)$$

$$10 = E[I_{120}] = \sum_{x>120}(x-120)Pr(S=x) = \sum_{x>80}(x-120)Pr(S=x)$$

since there are no new terms in the sum with $Pr(S = x) \neq 0$. Subtracting the two relations gives

$$10 = \sum_{x>80} 40Pr(S=x) = 40Pr(X>80).$$

Hence $Pr(X > 80) = \frac{1}{4}$, $Pr(X \leq 80) = \frac{3}{4}$ ANSWER E

2. In general $E[I_d] = E[X] - d + \sum_{k=0}^{d-1}(d-k)f(k)$ and we are given $E[X] = 4$:

$d = 1,\ E[I_1] = 4 - 1 + 1 \cdot f(0) = 4 - 1 + .05 = 3.05$

$d = 2,\ E[I_2] = 4 - 2 + (2 \cdot f(0) + 1 \cdot f(1)) = 2.16$

$d = 3,\ E[I_3] = 4 - 3 + (3 \cdot f(0) + 2 \cdot f(1) + 1 \cdot f(2)) = 1.52$

Since $E[I_d] = 2$ is obtained by linear interpolation between $E[I_2] = 2.16$ and $E[I_3] = 1.52$ we see that d is $\frac{16}{64}$ of the way from $d = 2$ to $d = 3$, that is, $d = 2.25$, ANSWER D

3. Since I_d is 0 if $X \leq d$ and $X - d$ if $X > d$ (*i.e.*, a function of X),

$$\begin{aligned}
E[I_d] &= \int_0^d 0f(x)\,dx + \int_d^\infty (x-d)f(x)\,dx \\
&= \int_d^\infty (x-d)\beta e^{-\beta x}\,dx \\
&= e^{-\beta d}\int_d^\infty (x-d)\beta e^{-\beta(x-d)}\,dx \\
&= e^{-\beta d}\int_0^\infty y\beta e^{-\beta y}dy \quad (y = x-d) \\
&= \left(e^{-\beta d}\right)\left(\frac{1}{\beta}\right),
\end{aligned}$$

ANSWER A

The last integral is $E[Y]$ where Y is exponential with parameter β. Note that if X is exponential with parameter β then $X - d|_{X \geq d}$ has the same distribution.

4. In the following, $p_A(x)$ and $p_B(x)$ are used as notation for the density of the severity distributions, and $f(x)$ represents the density of S.

Use the following notation

S_A = total adult care time = $X_1 + \cdots + X_{N_A}$, X_i = care time for i^{th} adult

N_A = number of adult patients

S_C = total child care time = $Y_1 + \cdots + Y_{N_C}$, Y_i = care time for i^{th} child

N_C = number of child patients

S = total care time = $S_A + S_C$.

From the theory of sums of compound Poisson distributions S is compound-Poisson with $\lambda = \lambda_A + \lambda_C = 3+2 = 5$ and $p(x)$ is a weighted average of $p_A(x)$ and $p_B(x)$

x	p_A	p_B	$\frac{3}{5}p_A + \frac{2}{5}p_B = p(x)$
1	.4	.9	.6
2	.6	.1	.4

We need to calculate $Pr(\text{office inc.} \leq 800) = Pr(S \leq 4)$ since care costs 200/hr. $Pr(S \leq 4)$ is the sum $f(0) + f(1) \cdots + f(4)$ which we calculate recursively as follows:

$$\lambda_i = \text{exp. no. of claims of amount } i = \lambda p(i)$$

$$\lambda_1 = 5(.6) = 3,\ \lambda_2 = 5(.4) = 2,\ \lambda_3 = \lambda_4 = \cdots = 0$$

recursive relation: $$f(n) = \frac{\lambda_1}{n} f(n-1) + \frac{2\lambda_2}{n} f(n-2) = \frac{3}{n} f(n-1) + \frac{4}{n} f(n-2)$$

Calculation: $$f(0) = Pr(\text{no claims}) = e^{-\lambda} = e^{-5}$$

$$f(1) = 3f(0) = 3e^{-5}$$

$$f(2) = \frac{3}{2}(3e^{-5}) + \frac{4}{2}(e^{-5}) = \frac{13}{2}e^{-5}$$

$$f(3) = \frac{3}{3}\left(\frac{13}{2}e^{-5}\right) + \frac{4}{3}(3e^{-5}) = \frac{63}{6}e^{-5} = \frac{21}{2}e^{-5}$$

$$f(4) = \frac{3}{4}\left(\frac{21}{2}e^{-5}\right) + \frac{4}{4}\left(\frac{13}{2}e^{-5}\right) = \frac{115}{8}e^{-5}$$

$\therefore\ F(4) = f(0) + \cdots + f(4) = e^{-5}(35.375) = .2383,$ **ANSWER A**

5. One could calculate $f(x)$ values recursively or via simple combinatorics as follows:

$S = 3$	Probability
3 claims, all 1	$\left(e^{-1} \cdot \frac{1^3}{3!}\right)((.5)(.5)(.5)) = \frac{e^{-1}}{48}$
2 claims, one 1 and one 2	$\left(e^{-1} \cdot \frac{1^2}{2!}\right)((.5)(.25) + (.25)(.5)) = \frac{e^{-1}}{8}$
1 claim, amount 3	$\left(e^{-1} \cdot \frac{1^1}{1!}\right)(.25) = \frac{e^{-1}}{4}$

$\Rightarrow\ Pr(S{=}3) = e^{-1}\left(\frac{1}{48} + \frac{1}{8} + \frac{1}{4}\right) = .1456,$ **ANSWER B**

6. For aggregate claims S having a compound-Poisson distribution with $\lambda = 2$ we know

$$\frac{Var(S)}{E[S]} = \frac{\lambda E[X^2]}{\lambda E[X]} = \frac{E[X^2]}{E[X]}$$

Now $E[X^k] = E[(e^Y)^k] = E[e^{kY}] = M_Y(k)$.
Since Y is normal with mean 1 and variance 4 we know

$$M_Y(t) = e^{\mu t + \sigma^2 t^2/2} = e^{t+2t^2},$$

so that

$$E[X] = M_Y(1) = e^3, E[X^2] = M_Y(2) = e^{10}$$

and the ratio above is $\frac{e^{10}}{e^3} = e^7$, ANSWER C

7. Since S is discrete with possible values 0, 1, 2, ... it follows that

$$Pr(S \geq 3) = 1 - Pr(S \leq 2) = 1 - f(0) - f(1) - f(2)$$

where $f(x)$ is the density of aggregate claims. The values $f(0) = e^{-.6}$, $f(1) = .12e^{-.6}$ and $f(2) = .1872e^{-.6}$ could be generated by simple combinatorics or the recursive method

$$\lambda_1 = \lambda p(1) = (.6)(.2) = .12, \ \lambda_2 = (.6)(.3) = .18, \ \lambda_3 = (.6)(.5) = .30$$

$$f(x) = \tfrac{1}{x}[1(.12)f(x-1) + 2(.18)f(x-2) + 3(.30)f(x-3)]$$

$$f(0) = Pr(N{=}0) = e^{-\lambda} = e^{-.6}$$

$$f(0) + f(1) + f(2) = 1.3072e^{-.6} = .71896$$

$$Pr(S \geq 3) = 1 - .71896 = .28104,$$ ANSWER E

8. Simple combinatorics works best here. $F^{*4}(6)$ is the probability that a sum of 4 claims is less than or equal to 6. Since claim amounts are 1 or 2 it is simpler to compute the probability of the complementary event that 4 claims sum to 7 or 8. First $f(x)$ is a weighted average of f_A and f_B:

$$\lambda = \lambda_A + \lambda_B = 2, \ f(x) = \tfrac{\lambda_A}{\lambda} f_A(x) + \tfrac{\lambda_B}{\lambda} f_B(x)$$

$$\Rightarrow \qquad f(1) = .75, \ f(2) = .25.$$

$$F^{*4}(6) = 1 - Pr(4 \text{ claims sum to } 7 \text{ or } 8)$$

$$= 1 - \left[\binom{4}{3} f(2)^3 f(1) + \binom{4}{4} f(2)^4\right] = .9492,$$ ANSWER E

9. The portfolio S with profit margin θ (i.e.,

$$E[\text{Profit}] = E[\text{Premium} - S] = E[(1+\theta)E[S] - S] = (1+\theta)E[S] - E[S] = \theta E[S])$$

is split into retained claims, S_{ret}, with profit margin θ' and reinsured claims, S_{reins}, with profit margin ζ:

$$S = S_{ret} + S_{reins} \text{ and } \theta = \underbrace{\frac{E[S_{ret}]}{E[S]}\theta' + \frac{E[S_{reins}]}{E[S]}\zeta}_{\substack{\text{weighted average of profit margins} \\ \text{on the two pieces of } S}} .$$

Here $E[S] = \lambda E[X] = (1)(12) = 12$, $E[S_{reins}] = 8$ and $\theta' = \frac{3}{4}\theta$. Thus $E[S_{ret}] = 4$ and

$$\theta = \frac{4}{12}\left(\frac{3\theta}{4}\right) + \frac{8}{12}(\zeta)$$

resulting in $\zeta = \frac{9}{8}\theta$, ANSWER A

10. The expected value of S is $\lambda E[X] = (1.5)(1f_X(1) + 2f_X(2)) = .2$ so the expected gain before reinsurance is $c - 2$. The reinsurer's expected gain is $\zeta E[I_d]$ (note: same ζ for all possible d due to phrase "uniform relative security loading"). This leaves the insurer with an expected gain on the retained claims portfolio (i.e., after reinsurance) of $c - 2 - \zeta E[I_d]$. From given data

$$d = 3 \qquad c - 2 - \zeta(.339) = .462$$
$$d = 4 \qquad c - 2 - \zeta(.157) = .644,$$

two linear equations in two unknowns resulting in $\zeta = 1$ and $c = 2.801$, ANSWER E

11. In general, when S has possible values 0, 1, 2, ... we know

$$E[I_d] = \underbrace{\sum_{x=d}^{\infty}(x-d)f_S(x)}_{\text{infinite sum}} = E[S] - d + \underbrace{\sum_{x=0}^{d-1}(d-x)f_S(x)}_{\text{finite sum}} .$$

The recursion method for $f_S(x)$ values, $f_S(x) = \frac{1}{x}[1(\lambda_1)f_S(x-1) + \cdots]$, with $\lambda_1 = (2)\left(\frac{1}{2}\right) = 1$, $\lambda_2 = (2)\left(\frac{1}{2}\right) = 1$ produces

$$f_S(0) = e^{-2}, \ f_S(1) = e^{-2}, \ f_S(2) = 1.5e^{-2}.$$

Substituting these values, $d = 3$, and $E[S] = \lambda E[X] = 3$ into the first equation gives $E[I_3] = .8797$, ANSWER D

12. In general we have the recursive relation $f(x) = \dfrac{\left[\sum_{i=1}^{\infty} i\lambda_i f(x-i)\right]}{x}$ where $\lambda_i = \lambda f_X(i)$ is the expected number of claims equal i. Equating coefficients in the given expression for $f(x)$ results in

$$\begin{aligned} .16 &= 1 \cdot \lambda_1 = 1 \cdot \lambda \cdot f_X(1) \\ k &= 2 \cdot \lambda_2 = 2 \cdot \lambda \cdot f_X(2) \\ .72 &= 3 \cdot \lambda_3 = 3 \cdot \lambda \cdot f_X(3)\,. \end{aligned}$$

For a compound Poisson distribution $E[S] = \lambda E[X]$

$$E[X] = \sum_x x f_X(x) = 1 \cdot f_X(1) + 2 \cdot f_X(2) + 3 \cdot f_X(3)\,.$$

Hence $1.68 = E[S] = \lambda(f_X(1) + 2f_X(2) + 3f_X(3)) = .16 + k + .72$, which means $k = .80$. The final result needed is $1 = f_X(1) + f_X(2) + f_X(3) = \frac{.16}{\lambda} + \frac{.80}{2\lambda} + \frac{.72}{3\lambda}$, which has the solution $\lambda = .16 + .40 + .24 = .80$, ANSWER C

13. For a compound Poisson with claim amount variable X

$$\begin{aligned} E[S] &= \lambda E[X] = \lambda\left(\sum i f_X(i)\right) \\ Var(S) &= \lambda E[X^2] = \lambda\left(\sum i^2 f_X(i)\right). \end{aligned}$$

So $E[S] = 56$, $Var(S) = 126$, $\lambda = 29$ means that

$$\frac{56}{29} = f_X(1) + 2f_X(2) + 3f_X(3) \text{ and } \frac{126}{29} = f_X(1) + 4f_X(2) + 9f_X(3).$$

We also know $1 = f_X(1) + f_X(2) + f_X(3)$.

By Cramer's rule

$$f_X(2) = \frac{\det\begin{vmatrix} 1 & \frac{56}{29} & 3 \\ 1 & \frac{126}{29} & 9 \\ 1 & 1 & 1 \end{vmatrix}}{\det\begin{vmatrix} 1 & 2 & 3 \\ 1 & 4 & 9 \\ 1 & 1 & 1 \end{vmatrix}} = \frac{.75862}{2},$$

So $\lambda \cdot f_X(2) = 29\left(\frac{.75862}{2}\right) = 11$ claims of \$2 are expected, ANSWER B

14. Aggregate claims exceeding 100 can happen in three distinct ways corresponding to the number of claims:

$$Pr(S > 100) = \sum_{n=1}^{3} Pr\left(n \text{ claims occur } and \sum_{i=1}^{n} X_i > 100\right)$$

$$= \sum_{n=1}^{3}(n \text{ claims occur } and \underbrace{N(100n = \mu, 9n = \sigma^2)}_{\text{normal variable}} > 100)$$

$$= (.2)Pr(N(\mu{=}100,\ \sigma^2{=}9) > 100) + (.2)Pr(N(\mu{=}200,\ \sigma^2{=}18) > 100) + (.1)Pr(N(\mu{=}300,\ \sigma^2{=}27) > 100)$$

$$= (.2)Pr(Z > 0) + (.2)Pr\left(Z > \frac{-100}{\sqrt{18}}\right) + (.1)Pr\left(Z > \frac{-200}{\sqrt{27}}\right)$$

$$= (.2)\left(\tfrac{1}{2}\right) + (.2)(1) + (.1)(1) \approx .4,$$

approximate since virtually all probability is between ± 3 on the Z-scale

ANSWER C

15. The cost is $S - I_{5000}(S) + 1472$ (*i.e.*, retained claims plus reinsurance costs), so the expected cost is $E[S] + 1472 - E[I_{5000}(S)]$. In general

$$E[I_d(S)] = \sum_{x=d}^{\infty}(x-d)f(x) = \sum_{x=0}^{\infty}(x-d)f(x) - \sum_{x=0}^{d-1}(x-d)f(x) = E[S] - d + \sum_{x=0}^{d-1}(d-x)f(x).$$

Substituting into the above we see that $E[\text{Cost}] = 1472 + 5000 - \sum_{x=0}^{4999}(5000-x)f(x)$. The only possible x values (i.e., $f(x) \neq 0$) less than 4999 are

x	Circumstance	Probability
0	no claims	$\frac{1}{16} = .0625$
2000	1 claim of 2000	$\left(\frac{1}{4}\right)(.4) = .10$
3000	1 claim of 3000	$\left(\frac{1}{4}\right)(.6) = .15$
4000	2 claims of 2000	$\left(\frac{3}{8}\right)(.4)(.4) = .06$.

So $E[\text{Cost}] = 1472 + 5000 + [(5000-0)(.0625) + (5000-2000)(.10) + (5000-3000)(.15) + (5000-4000)(.06)]$

$$= 6472 - 972.50 = 5499.50,$$

ANSWER D

16. The solution here relies on the recursive relation $E[I_d] = E[I_{d-1}] - (1 - F(d-1))$, which can be rewritten as $F(d-1) = 1 + E[I_d] - E[I_{d-1}]$:

$$F(6) = 1 + E[I_7] - E[I_6] = .98$$
$$F(5) = 1 + E[I_6] - E[I_5] = .94$$
$$F(4) = 1 + E[I_5] - E[I_4] = .90$$

Thus the probability that S is 5 or 6, $f(5) + f(6)$, can be calculated as $F(6) - F(4) = .08$,

ANSWER B

17. The graph of reimbursement versus expense looks like

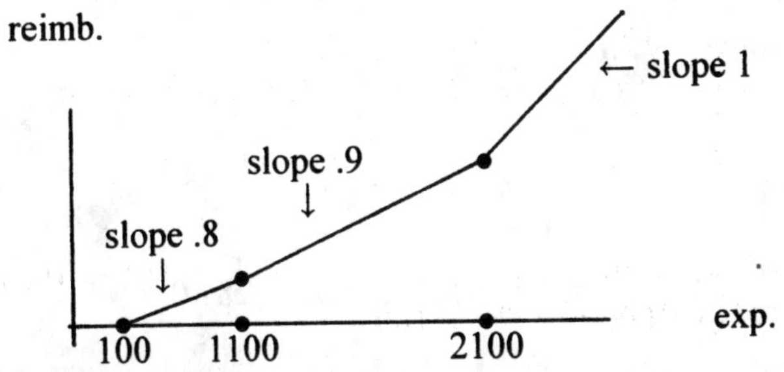

Now $.80I_{100}$ matches this graph up to exp. ≤ 1100. In the next range [1100, 2100] it maintains a slope of .80 so we need to add on $.10I_{1100}$. The combination $.80I_{100} + .10I_{1100}$ matches the graph up to exp. ≤ 2100 and then maintains a slope of .90. So the final correction provided by $.10I_{2100}$ results in ANSWER E.

18. The reimbursement, $.8(I_{50} - I_{250})$ is a function of X having 3 possible values:

$X = x$	$p(x)$	$.8(I_{50} - I_{250})$
0	1/2	$.8(0 - 0) = 0$
100	1/3	$.8(50 - 0) = 40$
300	1/6	$.8(250 - 50) = 160$

The expected reimbursement is $(1/3)40 + (1/6)(160) = 40$, so with a 20% relative security loading the premium is $(1 + .2)(40) = 48$. ANSWER A.

Note: the effect of $I_{50} - I_{250}$ is to cap the reimbursement at 200 which is illustrated in the graph below.

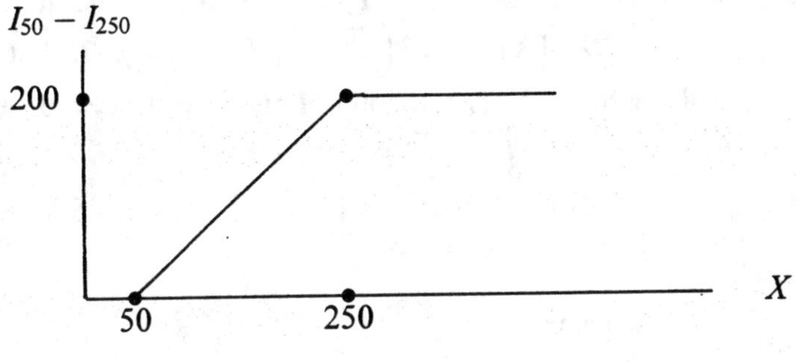

19. If X is uniformly distributed on [0, M], $M > 100$, then

$$E[I_{100}^k(X)] = \int_{100}^{M} (x-100)^k \cdot \frac{1}{M}\,dx = \frac{(M-100)^{k+1}}{(k+1)M}.$$

In 1994, $M = 1000$ so

$$\left.\begin{aligned} E[I_{100}(X)] &= \frac{900^2}{2(1000)} = 405 \\ E[I_{100}^2(X)] &= \frac{900^3}{3(1000)} = 243{,}000 \end{aligned}\right\} Var = 78{,}975, \text{ St. Dev.} = 281.02.$$

In 1995, $M = 1000(1+.05) = 1050$ so

$$\left.\begin{aligned} E[I_{100}(X)] &= \frac{950^2}{2(1050)} = 429.76 \\ E[I_{100}^2(X)] &= \frac{950^3}{3(1050)} = 272{,}182.5 \end{aligned}\right\} Var = 87{,}487, \text{ St. Dev.} = 295.78.$$

So $1 + \frac{\text{Pct. Inc.}}{100} = \frac{295.78}{281.02} = 1.0525.$ ANSWER B

20. Consider the following table:

Loss	Probability	$d = 10$, $max = 125$ Claim: X_1	$d = 0$, $max = 125$ Claim: X_2
30	1/3	20	30
150	1/3	125	125
200	1/3	125	125

Let Y_1 be annual claims against a policy with deductible 10. Y_1 is compound-Poisson with $\lambda = .03$ and severity model X_1, so that $E[Y_1] = \lambda E[X_1] = .03\left(\frac{20+125+125}{3}\right) = 2.7$. Let Y_2 be annual claims against a policy with no deductible. Y_2 is compound-Poisson with $\lambda = .03$ and severity model X_2, so that $E[Y_2] = \lambda \cdot E[X_2] = .03\left(\frac{280}{3}\right) = 2.8$.
With 50 policies of each type we have $E[S] = 50E[Y_1] + 50E[Y_2] = 275$. ANSWER B

21. Since the maximum reinsurance payment is 5, we have

$$\text{Reinsurance Amount} = \left\{\begin{array}{ll} 0 & S \le 20 \\ .80(S-20) & 20 < S \le 26.25 \\ 5 & 26.25 < S \end{array}\right\} = .8[I_{20} - I_{26.25}]$$

Notice that $.80(26.25 - 20) = 5$ (i.e., 26.25 was calculated as $20 + \frac{5}{.80}$). Since $Pr(26 < S < 27) = 0$,

$$E[I_{26.25}] = .75\underbrace{E[I_{26}]}_{2.69} + .25\underbrace{E[I_{27}]}_{2.65} = 2.68.$$

Hence $E[\text{Reinsurance Payment}] = .8(\underbrace{E[I_{20}]}_{3.33} - \underbrace{E[I_{26.25}]}_{2.68}) = .8(.65) = .52.$ ANSWER C

22. Possible S_1 values are 0, 1, 2, 3, ... and possible S_2 values are 0, 3, 6, 7, ... The event $S_1 + S_2 \leq 3$ is the union of the events in the table below where probabilities are determined from

$$\left.\begin{array}{l} f_1(n) = \frac{1}{n}[.75 f_1(n-1) + 1.25 f_1(n-5)] \\ f_2(n) = \frac{1}{n}[1.5 f_2(n-3) + 3.5 f_2(n-7)] \end{array}\right\} \text{Recursion relations}$$

$S_1 = s$	$f_1(s)$	$S_2 = s$	$f_2(s)$	$f_1(s)f_2(s)$
0	e^{-1}	0	e^{-1}	e^{-2}
0	e^{-1}	3	$e^{-1}(.5)$	$.5e^{-2}$
1	$.75e^{-1}$	0	e^{-1}	$.75e^{-2}$
2	$\frac{.75^2}{2}e^{-1}$	0	e^{-1}	$.28125e^{-2}$
3	$\frac{.75^3}{6}e^{-1}$	0	e^{-1}	$.07031e^{-2}$
				Total $= 2.60156e^{-2} = .35208$

ANSWER C

23. $R = R_A + R_B \Rightarrow$ R is compound-Poisson with

$\lambda = \lambda_A + \lambda_B = 7 + 3 = 10$

$X = x$	$.7p_A(x) + .3p_B(x)$
15	.42
25	.52
60	.06

$p(x) = \frac{7}{10}p_A(x) + \frac{3}{10}p_B(x)$

$$\Rightarrow \quad f(0) = e^{-10}, \qquad f(15) = e^{-10}\frac{10!}{1!}(.42), \qquad f(25) = e^{-10}\frac{10!}{1!}(.52),$$

$$f(30) = e^{-10}\frac{10^2}{2!}(.42)^2, \quad f(40) = e^{-10}\frac{10^2}{2!}(2(.42)(.52)), \qquad f(45) = e^{-10}\frac{10^3}{3!}(.42)^3$$

$\Rightarrow \quad Pr(R < 50) = \text{sum of above} = e^{-10}(53.408) = .0024$

ANSWER A

24. From (i) if follows that $E[X] = 1.4$, $E[X^2] = 2.4$ and $Var(X) = .44$. N is a weighted average of a degenerate distribution with all probability at zero, weight $= .20$, and an ETNB distribution with $r = -\frac{1}{2}$, $\beta = 1$, weight $= .80$ (i.e., $N^T = N|_{N>0}$ is ETNB, $r = -\frac{1}{2}$, $\beta = 1$). For N^T we have the following (see Unit III Condensed Review Notes): $p_k^T = Pr(N^T = k)$

$$p_0^T = 0,\ p_1^T = \frac{r\beta}{(1+\beta)^{r+1} - (1+\beta)} = \frac{-.5(1)}{\sqrt{2} - 2} = \frac{1}{4 - 2\sqrt{2}}$$

$$\frac{p_k^T}{p_{k-1}^T} = \frac{\beta}{1+\beta}\left[1 + \frac{r-1}{k}\right] = \frac{1}{2}\left[1 - \frac{3}{2k}\right] \quad k \geq 2$$

$$E[N^T] = \frac{r\beta}{1 - (1+\beta)^{-r}} = \frac{-.5(1)}{1 - \sqrt{2}} = \frac{1}{2\sqrt{2} - 2}$$

$$E[(N^T)^2] = \frac{r\beta(1+\beta+r\beta)}{1 - (1+\beta)^{-r}} = \frac{-.5(2 - .5)}{1 - \sqrt{2}} = \frac{1.5}{2\sqrt{2} - 2}$$

24. (cont.)
With these preliminaries out of the way we can calculate

$$E[S] = E[N]\cdot E[X] = (.20E[0] + .80E[N^T])E[X]$$

$$= \left(0 + .8\left(\frac{1}{2\sqrt{2}-2}\right)\right)1.4 = \frac{1.12}{2\sqrt{2}-2} = 1.352$$ ANSWER D

25. The last item needed to calculate $Var(S)$ is $Var(N)$. For this, we need the second moment:

$$E[N^2] = (.20E[0^2] + .80E[(N^T)^2]) = 0 + .8\left(\frac{1.5}{2\sqrt{2}-2}\right) = 1.449$$

$$\Rightarrow \quad Var(N) = E[N^2] - (E[N])^2 = 1.449 - \left(\frac{.8}{2\sqrt{2}-2}\right)^2 = .516.$$

Hence

$$E[S] = \underbrace{E[N]}_{.966}\underbrace{Var(X)}_{.44} + \underbrace{(E[X])^2}_{1.4^2}\underbrace{Var(N)}_{.516} = 1.436.$$

ANSWER C

26. In general $f_S(0) = P_N(f_X(0)) = P_N(0)$ since $f_X(0) = 0$. This is the same as $Pr(N = 0)$, which is given in (ii) as .20: $f_S(0) = .20$

Now N is an $(a, b, 1)$ distribution with $p_0 = .20$,
$p_1 = (.80)Pr(N^T = 1) = (.80)\left(\frac{1}{4-2\sqrt{2}}\right) = .6828$ (see the solution to Question 24 above), $a = \frac{\beta}{1+\beta} = \frac{1}{2}$, and $b = \frac{\beta(r-1)}{(1+\beta)} = -\frac{3}{4}$. The $(a, b, 1)$ recursion formula for $f_S(k)$ is

$$f_S(k) = \frac{[p_1 - (a+b)p_0]f_X(k) + \sum_{j=1}^{k}\left(a+\frac{bj}{k}\right)f_X(j)f_S(k-j)}{1 - af_X(0)}$$

$$= \frac{.7328f_X(k) + \sum_{j=1}^{k}\left(\frac{1}{2}-\frac{3j}{4k}\right)f_X(j)f_S(k-j)}{1}$$

$$= .7328f_X(k) + \left(\tfrac{1}{2}-\tfrac{3}{4k}\right)(.7)f_S(k-1) + \left(\tfrac{1}{2}-\tfrac{6}{4k}\right)(.2)f_S(k-2) + \left(\tfrac{1}{2}-\tfrac{9}{4k}\right)(.1)f_S(k-3)$$

Thus

$$f_S(1) = .7328\underbrace{f_X(1)}_{.70} + \left(\tfrac{1}{2}-\tfrac{3}{4}\right)(.7)\underbrace{f_S(0)}_{.20} = .4780$$

$$f_S(2) = .7328\underbrace{f_X(2)}_{.20} + \left(\tfrac{1}{2}-\tfrac{3}{8}\right)(.7)\underbrace{f_S(1)}_{.4780} + \left(\tfrac{1}{2}-\tfrac{6}{8}\right)(.2)\underbrace{f_S(0)}_{.20} = .1784$$

ANSWER E

27. $E[(S-0)_+] = E[S] = 1.352$

$$E[(S-1)_+] = E[(S-0)_+] - (1-F_S(0)) = 1.352 - (1-\underbrace{f_S(0)}_{.20}) = .552$$

$$E[(S-2)_+] = E[(S-1)_+] - (1-F_S(1)) = .552 - (1-.20-.4780) = .230$$

Now $X = 1, 2,$ or 3 so $S = 0, 1, 2, \ldots$. Hence $Pr(1 < S < 2) = 0$ and, by linear interpolation,

$$E[(S-1.5)_+] = (.50)E[(S-1)_+] + (.50)E[(S-2)_+] = .5(.552) + .5(.230) = .391$$

ANSWER E

28. $$E[\widetilde{S}] = E[N]E[I_1(X)] = \frac{.8}{(2\sqrt{2}-2)}\underbrace{[0(.7) + 1(.2) + 2(.1)]}_{.4} = .386.$$ ANSWER B

29. $$Var(\widetilde{S}) = \underbrace{E[N]}_{\substack{.966\\\text{(earlier in}\\\text{\#24)}}}\underbrace{Var(I_1(X))}_{.44\text{ (below)}} + \underbrace{(E[I_1(X)])^2}_{\substack{.4^2\\\text{(earlier in}\\\text{\#28)}}}\underbrace{Var(N)}_{\substack{.516\\\text{(earlier in}\\\text{\#25)}}} = .508$$

$$Var(I_1(X)) = (0^2(.7) + (1)^2(.2) + 2^2(.1)) - .4^2 = .44$$ ANSWER C

30. $\widetilde{S} = Y_1 + \cdots + Y_N$ where $Y = I_1(X)$, $f_Y(0) = .70$, $f_Y(1) = .20$, $f_Y(2) = .30$.

In general, $f_{\widetilde{S}}(0) = P_N(f_Y(0)) = P_N(.70)$.

Since N is a 20%/80% weighted average of 0 and

$$N^T(\text{ETNB};\ r = -\tfrac{1}{2}, \beta = 1,\ P_{N^T}(t) = \frac{(1-\beta(t-1))^{-r} - (1+\beta)^{-r}}{1-(1+\beta)^{-r}},$$

we have

$$f_{\widetilde{S}}(0) = P_N(.70) = .20P_0(.70) + .80P_{N^T}(.70) = .20(1) + .80\frac{\sqrt{1.3}-\sqrt{2}}{1-\sqrt{2}} = .729.$$

ANSWER D

31. Since N is $(a,b,1)$ the $(a,b,1)$ recursion formula for $\tilde{S} = Y_1 + \cdots + Y_N$ is

$$f_{\tilde{S}}(k) = \frac{[p_1 - (a+b)p_0]f_Y(k) + \sum_{j=1}^{k}\left(a+\frac{bj}{k}\right) f_Y(j) f_{\tilde{S}}(k-j)}{1 - a f_Y(0)}$$

Recall that $p_0 = Pr(N=0) = .2$,
$p_1 = Pr(N=1) = (.80)Pr(N^T = 1) = .80\left(\frac{1}{4-2\sqrt{2}}\right) = .6828$, $a = \frac{1}{2}$, $b = -\frac{3}{4}$,
$f_Y(0) = .70$, $f_Y(1) = .20$ and $f_Y(2) = .10$. Thus

$$f_{\tilde{S}}(k) = \frac{.7328 f_Y(k) + \sum_{j=1}^{k}\left(\frac{1}{2}-\frac{3j}{4k}\right) f_Y(j) f_{\tilde{S}}(k-j)}{1 - \frac{1}{2}(.70)}$$

With $k = 1$ this results in

$$f_{\tilde{S}}(1) = \frac{.7328(.2) + \left(\frac{1}{2}-\frac{3}{4}\right)(.2) f_{\tilde{S}}(0)}{.65} = .169.$$

ANSWER D.

SECTION IV

STOCHASTIC PROCESS MODELS

INTRODUCTORY NOTE

This section of the manual contains four units. For each unit there is a package of five items:

(1) ***Introductory Notes.*** While not as complete as many textbooks, it is designed to cover all the learning objectives set forth in the SOA - Working Group Report on Course 3.

(2) ***Condensed Review Notes and Advanced Topics.*** These notes constitute a list of the major relations with additional comments on more exotic topics. They should be useful as a reference when solving the Unit Review Questions, and as a final checklist of facts you should be familiar with for the exam.

(3) ***Conceptual Review Test.*** This material should be used in conjunction with reading and rereading the Introductory notes.

(4) ***Computational Review Test.*** These questions are more elementary than the Unit Review Questions and emphasize very basic calculations related to the unit reading.

(5) ***Unit Review Questions.*** Questions in the first three units were constructed by the author to reflect trends in the Course Three Sample Exam. Many questions in Unit Four are from past SOA exams.

UNIT 1: MARKOV CHAINS

A stochastic process is a collection of random variables $\{X(t)\colon t \in T\}$. The idea is to represent a random process as it unfolds over time. $X(t)$ is referred to as the **state of the process** at time t. In most of what follows T is either $\{0, 1, 2, \dots\}$ and we have a **discrete-time** process, or $T = [0, \infty)$ and we have a **continuous-time** process. In the discrete time process it is more common to use X_n rather than $X(n)$ for the state at time n. The **state space** is the set of all possible values of the $X(t)$ as t varies over T.

Examples of discrete time processes are the following:

(1) A coin is flipped repeatedly and X_n denotes the number of heads which occur on the first n flips. $T = \{1, 2, \dots\}$ and the state space is $\{0, 1, 2, \dots\}$.

(2) A player with an initial wealth of $\$m$ (m a whole number) repeatedly plays a game where she either wins \$1 or loses \$1. X_n denotes her wealth after the nth play of the game; $X_0 = m$, $X_1 = m \pm 1$, etc. Here $T = \{0, 1, 2, \dots\}$ and the state space is $\{0, \pm 1, \pm 2, \dots\}$.

(3) Beginning on Jan. 1, 1999, an insurance process begins to generate claims. Let X_n be the total number of claims occurring in the first n years. Then $X_0 = 0$, $X_1 =$ number of claims in 1999, etc.. $T = \{0, 1, 2, \dots\}$ and the state space is $\{0, 1, 2, \dots\}$.

Continuous-time models we will eventually discuss include:

(1) An aggregate claims model as it occurs over time. Consider the insurance process discussed in (3) and let $X(t)$ be the total number of claims occurring in t years where $0 \le t < \infty$ (i.e., $T = [0, \infty)$). Then $\{X(t) | 0 \le t < \infty\}$ is the claims number process. A related process is $\{Y(t) | 0 \le t < \infty\}$ where $Y(t)$ is the total of all claim amounts occurring in the time interval $[0, t]$.

(2) In a Continuing Care Retirement Community residents may be in Independent Living Units (state zero), a Skilled Nursing Facility on a temporary basis (state one), a Skilled Nursing Facility on a permanent basis (state two), or departed (state three). Let $X(t)$ be the state at time t of a randomly selected community member where t is the time measured from entry into the community. Transitions to various states occur over time as in the diagram below.

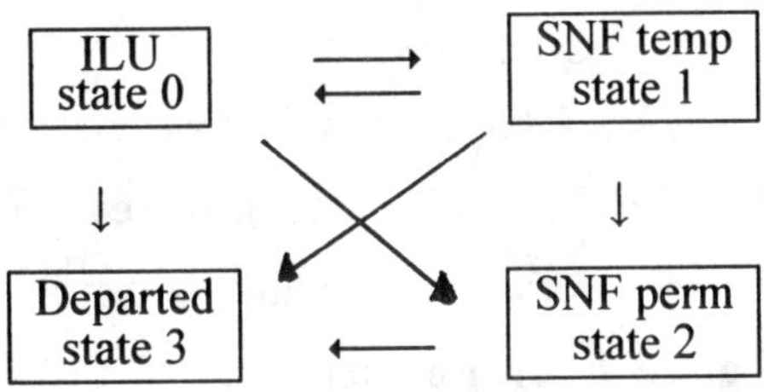

All of the processes we will study are known as Markov chains. If time t is the present, we refer to $[0, t)$ as the past and (t, ∞) as the future. For a Markov chain, the conditional distribution of a future state, given the past states and the present state, is independent of the past and depends only on the present. Furthermore, the conditional distribution of the state at a future time u, given the state at present time t, depends only on $u - t$.

In Unit I we will consider only discrete-time Markov chains with discrete state spaces. The Markovian assumption may be expressed as

$$Pr(X_{n+1} = k | X_n = j, X_{n-1} = j_{n-1}, \ldots, X_0 = j_0) = Pr(X_{n+1} = k | X_n = j) = P_{jk}.$$

The first equality is the idea that the conditional distribution of a future state (time $n+1$), given the present (time n) and the past (time 0, 1, ..., $n-1$), depends only on the present. The second equality says that the distribution of the state at time $n+1$, given the distribution of the state at time n, is the same for all n. If we view $P = [P_{jk}]$ as a matrix, we will eventually see that (Chapman-Kolmogorov equation)

$$Pr(X_{n+m} = k | X_n = j) = P^m_{jk}.$$

where $P^m_{j,k}$ is the (j, k) entry of P^m. Thus the conditional distribution of a state at time $n+m$ given the state at time n depends only on $(m+n) - n = m$ through the matrix P^m. The P_{jk} are known as 1-step transition probabilities whereas the P^m_{jk} are known as m-step transition probabilities.

Discrete-Time Markov Chains With Discrete State Spaces

Suppose the state space of our process is $\{0, 1, 2, \ldots\}$. The states at times n and $n+1$ are related as follows:

$$\underbrace{Pr(X_{n+1} = k)}_{\substack{\text{unconditional} \\ \text{(marginal)}}} = \sum_{j=0}^{\infty} \underbrace{Pr(X_{n+1} = k \text{ and } X_n = j)}_{\text{(joint probability)}}$$

$$= \sum_{j=0}^{\infty} \underbrace{Pr(X_n = j)}_{\text{(marginal)}} \underbrace{Pr(X_{n+1} = k | X_n = j)}_{\text{(conditional)}} = \sum_{j=0}^{\infty} Pr(X_n = j) P_{jk}$$

This equation has a nice Linear Algebra interpretation. If we view the distribution of X_{n+1} as a row vector $\vec{\pi}_{n+1} = (Pr(X_{n+1} = 0), \; Pr(X_{n+1} = 1), \; \ldots)$, then $\vec{\pi}_{n+1} = \vec{\pi}_n P$. By induction $\vec{\pi}_n P^m = \vec{\pi}_{n+1} P^{m-1} = \vec{\pi}_{n+2} P^{m-2} = \cdots = \vec{\pi}_{n+m}$. This means that P^m can be interpreted as giving the conditional distribution of X_{n+m}, given the distribution of X_n, that is,

$$Pr(X_{n+m} = k | X_n = j) = P^m_{j,k} \qquad ((j, k) \text{ entry of the } m^{th} \text{ power of } P)$$

(Chapman-Kolmorgorov Equation)

Example 1 A gambler playing a game either wins \$1 with probability p or loses \$1 with probability $q = 1 - p$. Let X_n be his fortune after n plays. Suppose he quits if his fortune hits 0 or 3. His beginning fortune X_0 is 0, 1, 2 or 3. Then $P_{i,i+1} = p = 1 - P_{i,i-1}$ for $i = 1$ or 2, $P_{00} = 1$, $P_{33} = 1$, and all other $P_{ij} = 0$.

$$P = \begin{bmatrix} 1 & 0 & 0 & 0 \\ 1-p & 0 & p & 0 \\ 0 & 1-p & 0 & p \\ 0 & 0 & 0 & 1 \end{bmatrix}$$

Then

$$P^2 = \begin{bmatrix} 1 & 0 & 0 & 0 \\ 1-p & p(1-p) & 0 & p^2 \\ (1-p)^2 & 0 & p(1-p) & p \\ 0 & 0 & 0 & 1 \end{bmatrix}.$$

Notice that in each row the entries sum to 1. The jth row of P can be interpreted as $(Pr(X_{n+1} = 0|X_n = j), Pr(X_{n+1} = 1|X_n = j), \ldots, Pr(X_{n+1} = 3|X_n = j))$, the distribution of X_{n+1} given that $X_n = j$ (i.e., the distribution of the state at time $n+1$ given that j is the state at time n). The jth row of P^2 can be interpreted as $(Pr(X_{n+2} = 0|X_n = j), \ldots, Pr(X_{n+2} = 3|X_n = j))$, the distribution of X_{n+2} given that $X_n = j$. □

The important point is that a row of P^m can be viewed as a conditional distribution of X_{n+m} given the value of X_n, whereas $\vec{\pi}_{n+m} = \vec{\pi}_n P^m$ is the unconditional distribution at time $n+m$. In Example 1 above, suppose we are given that $X_0 = 2$, then the distribution of X_1, is given by the 3rd row of P

x_1	0	1	2	3
$Pr(X_1 = x_1 \| X_0 = 2)$	0	$1-p$	0	p

On the other hand suppose at time zero we have 50 gamblers in the room and 20 begin with a fortune of 1 and 30 begin with a fortune of 2, that is, $Pr(X_0 = 1) = \frac{20}{50} = .40$, $Pr(X_0 = 2) = \frac{30}{50} = .60$. Then the unconditional distribution of the gamblers fortune at times 1 and 2 are $\underbrace{\underbrace{(0, .40, .60, 0)}_{1\times 4}\underbrace{P}_{4\times 4}}_{1\times 4}$ and $(0, .40, .60, 0)P^2$ respectively. For example, the probability that a gambler in the room has a fortune of 3 at time 2 is

$$(0, .40, .60, 0)\underbrace{\begin{pmatrix} 0 \\ p^2 \\ p \\ 1 \end{pmatrix}}_{\substack{4^{th}\text{ column} \\ \text{of } P^2}} = .40p^2 + .60p.$$

A discrete-time, discrete state space Markov chain can be thought of as a series of nodes – one node for each possible state in the state space. If i and j are possible states (nodes), there is a "path" from i to j if $P_{ij} > 0$ (i.e., there is a positive probability that $X_{n+1} = j$ given that $X_n = i$). It is possible to visit node j at time $n+1$ if you are at node i at time n. You begin at some node at time 0 and make transitions along paths to other nodes as time passes. If you begin at node i at time 0, then P_{ij}^n is the probability you are visiting node j at time n. It is also the probability you are visiting node j at time $m+n$ if you were visiting node i at time m.

Classification of States in a Discrete-Time, Discrete State Space Markov Chain

State j (node j) is said to be **accessible** from state i (node i) if it is possible to go from state i to state j in some time period, that is, $P_{ij}^n > 0$ for some n. A state is always accessible to itself since $P_{ii}^0 = 1$. Two states are said to **communicate** if they are accessible to each other. Communication is an equivalence relation. This follows from the Chapman-Kolgomorov equations since

$$P_{ik}^{m+n} = \sum_{j=0}^{\infty} P_{ij}^m P_{jk}^n \qquad \text{(matrix multiplication).}$$

For if i communicates with j_0 and j_0 communicates with k, there are m and n such that $P_{ij_0}^m > 0$, $P_{j_0k}^n > 0$. By the above $P_{ik}^{m+n} \geq P_{ij_0}^m P_{j_0k}^n > 0$ and it is possible to go from node i to node k in the next $m+n$ transitions.

In example one above, our state space could be represented as.

$$(0) \longleftarrow (1) \rightleftarrows (2) \longrightarrow (3)\ .$$

The states 1 and 2 communicate, but states 0 and 3 communicate only with themselves. So there are three equivalence classes $\{0\}$, $\{1, 2\}$, and $\{3\}$. A chain is called **irreducible** if there is only one class.

Example 2 (Random Walk) Suppose the state space is $\{0, \pm 1, \pm 2, \dots\}$ and $P_{i,i+1} = p = 1 - P_{i,i-1}$ for all i. Thus if you are at node i at time n it is only possible to be at node $i+1$ (one step to the right) or node $i-1$ (one step to the left) at time $n+1$. The state at time n can also be interpreted as a gamblers fortune in a series of plays of a game resulting in winning \$1 with probability p or losing \$1 with probability $1-p$. In this chain

$$\cdots \longleftrightarrow (-n) \longleftrightarrow (-n+1) \longleftrightarrow \cdots \longleftrightarrow (n-1) \longleftrightarrow (n) \longleftrightarrow \cdots$$

there is one class of states since they all communicate with each other. The claim is irreducible. □

Example 3 (Atlantic Hurricanes) Atlantic hurricanes are the ones with potential to make U.S. mainland landfall and cause catastrophic losses to insurers. Suppose hurricane seasons (May-Nov. of a given calendar year) are classified as mild, 0-6 hurricanes, moderate, 7-10 hurricanes, or severe, more than 10 hurricanes. The following table summarizes long term weather history in successive years:

		Probabilities for Next Year			(row)
		mild	moderate	severe	state
one year	mild	.60	.30	.10	0
	moderate	.50	.30	.20	1
	severe	.30	.40	.30	2

Form a 3-state Markov chain[1], {0, 1, 2}, where the 1-step transition probabilities are given by a 3×3 matrix P whose rows are the entries in the table above. All states communicate with each other so there is again one class and the chain is irreducible.

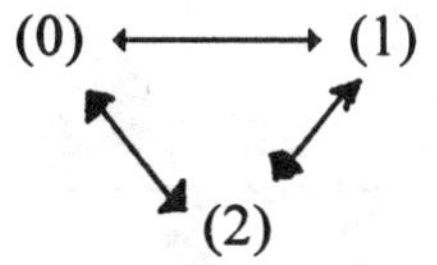

If this season (the present) were moderate, then, under this model, next season would have a 50% chance of being mild, a 30% chance of being moderate, and a 20% chance of being severe (i.e., see row 1 of P). Since

$$P^2 = \begin{bmatrix} .54 & .31 & .15 \\ .51 & .32 & .17 \\ .47 & .33 & .20 \end{bmatrix} \qquad \begin{matrix} \text{row (state)} \\ 0 \\ 1 \\ 2 \end{matrix} \quad ,$$

if this season were moderate, then two seasons from now would have a 17% chance of being severe (i.e., $P^2_{1,2} = .17$, the last entry of P^2 in row 1).

Suppose a forecast for next season made just before the season begins states a 20% chance of being mild, a 70% chance of being moderate and a 10% chance of being severe. Then

$$(.20, .70, .10)\begin{bmatrix} .54 & .31 & .15 \\ .51 & .32 & .17 \\ .47 & .33 & .20 \end{bmatrix} = \vec{\pi}_n P^2 = (.512, .319, .169) = \vec{\pi}_{n+2}$$

can be interpreted as the forecast for two seasons after the upcoming season - 51.2% chance of being mild, a 31.9% chance of being moderate, and a 16.9% chance of being severe. □

[1] One assumes next year's weather is related to this year's, but is independent of previous year's.

Depending on how frequently a state is visited during the process it is classified as recurrent or transient. For state i, let r_i be the probability that the process returns to state i given that it starts in state i. The state is called **recurrent** if $r_i = 1$ and **transient** if $r_i < 1$. As we will see, a recurrent state is visited very frequently (infinitely often) if you begin in the state, whereas a transient state is visited rather infrequently if you begin in it.

To study this notion a bit more carefully, let N_i be the random number of times that state i is visited if you begin in state i (i.e., $X_0 = i$). For a recurrent state N_i is infinite. Since $r_i = 1$ there is an n such that $X_n = i$ (it is certain to return). However, by the Markovian assumption, the process will be "starting over" when it reenters state i, that is, $Y_0 = X_n$, $Y_1 = X_{n+1}$, $Y_2 = X_{n+2}$, ... has the same transition matrix, P, as the original process. Continuing with this argument one sees that i is visited and revisited infinitely often. On the other hand, if state i is transient, then there is a positive probability, $1 - r_i$, that it is not revisited: $1 - r_i = Pr(N_i = 1)$. Given that it has been revisited, there is a probability of $1 - r_i$ it will not be revisited a third time (the process starts over after the first revisiting). Thus

$$Pr(N_i = 2) = \underbrace{Pr(N_i = 2 | N_i \geq 2)}_{\substack{1-r_i \\ \text{(the process starts over} \\ \text{after the first revisit,} \\ \text{and never returns to } i)}} \underbrace{Pr(N_i \geq 2)}_{r_i}.$$

Reasoning in this manner it follows inductively that $Pr(N_i = k) = r_i^{k-1}(1 - r_i)$ (a Geometric distribution[2]), and hence a transient state is visited only a finite number of times. Using a geometric series it is easy to see that $E[N_i] = \frac{1}{1 - r_i}$. Another method of calculating this expected value is provided by the following:

$$\text{let } X_0 = i,\ I_n = \begin{Bmatrix} 1 & X_n = i \\ 0 & X_n \neq i \end{Bmatrix} \qquad \text{(note } I_0 = 1\text{)}$$

$$N_i = I_0 + I_1 + I_2 + \cdots$$

$$\Rightarrow \quad E[N_i] = \sum_{n=0}^{\infty} E[I_n] = \sum_{n=0}^{\infty} (1 \cdot \underset{\substack{\uparrow \\ Pr(X_n = i | X_0 = i)}}{P_{ii}^n} + 0 \cdot (1 - P_{ii}^n)) = \sum_{n=0}^{\infty} P_{ii}^n = 1 + \sum_{n=1}^{\infty} P_{ii}^n$$

---

2 Some authors define Geometric as the number of failures before the first success, others define it as the trial on which the first success occurs (i.e., one greater). Here the latter interpretation is used.

Recurrence versus Transience

Recurrent: $r_i = 1, N_i = \infty, \; E[N_i] = \sum_{n=0}^{\infty} P_{ii}^n = \infty$

Transient: $r_i < 1, \; Pr(N_i = k) = r_i^{k-1}(1 - r_i) \qquad k = 1, 2, \ldots$

$$\frac{1}{1 - r_i} = E[N_i] = \sum_{n=0}^{\infty} P_{ii}^n < \infty$$

In general it is not a simple task to compute r_i or $\sum_{n=0}^{\infty} P_{ii}^n$ and determine whether state i is recurrent (i.e., the series diverges) or transient (the series converges). Before attempting to determine these properties for the states in our previous examples, it is useful to first note that both recurrence and transience are class properties. In other words, if two states i and j communicate ($P_{ij}^n > 0$ and $P_{ji}^m > 0$ for some $n, m > 0$), then they are either both transient or both recurrent. For suppose i is recurrent, then

$$\infty = \sum_{k=0}^{\infty} P_{ii}^k \qquad \Rightarrow \qquad \infty = P_{ji}^m \left[\sum_{k=0}^{\infty} P_{ii}^k \right] P_{ij}^n$$

$$\Rightarrow \quad \infty = \sum_{k=0}^{\infty} P_{ji}^m P_{ii}^k P_{ij}^n = \sum_{k=0}^{\infty} P_{jj}^{m+n+k}$$

$$\Rightarrow \quad \infty = \sum_{k=0}^{\infty} P_{jj}^k \text{ (more positive terms than the above series whose first term is } P_{jj}^{m+n})$$

so j is also recurrent.

In a Markov chain with a finite state-space there must be at least one recurrent state (and hence one class of recurrent states). For if all the states were transient, each would be visited only finitely many times contradicting the fact that infinitely many transitions occur in the chain. This means that in a finite, irreducible Markov chain (finitely many states, all communicating with each other) all states are recurrent. One further idea is noteworthy. It is possible to go from a transient state to a recurrent one, but it is impossible to move from a recurrent state to a transient one. The reasoning is as follows:

Suppose state i is recurrent and state j is transient, and it is possible to move from i to j (i.e., some $P_{ij}^n \neq 0$). Since it is certain that you return to state i given that you start in state i ($r_i = 1$), if it is possible to go from i to j, then it must also be possible to return to i from j. But then i and j communicate and they must both be either recurrent or transient since these are class properties.

Now let's return to Examples 1-3. In both Examples two and three the chain was irreducible (i.e., a single class, all states communicate with each other). In example three (hurricanes) the state space is finite, and a finite Markov chain must have at least one recurrent state. So all 3 states are recurrent. In example two (the random walk) there are infinitely many states in the one class. It can be seen that the states are all recurrent if $p = \frac{1}{2}$ (equal probability of moving left or right) and all states are transient if $p \neq \frac{1}{2}$. The reasoning is as follows:

(i) N_0 is the random number of visits to state 0 given that $X_0 = 0$ (i.e., start in state 0)

(ii) $E[N_0] = \sum_{n=0}^{\infty} P_{00}^n$ is finite (infinite) if state 0 is transient (recurrent)

(iii) P_{00}^n is non-zero only if $n = 2k$ is even and there are k movements to the right and k movements to the left by time n. In this case P_{00}^{2k} is the binomial probability

$$\binom{2k}{k} p^k (1-p)^k = \frac{(k+1)(k+2)\cdots(2k)}{1\cdot 2\cdot \cdots \cdot k} p^k (1-p)^k$$

(iv) Using the ratio test on the series $\sum_{k=0}^{\infty} a_k = \sum_{k=0}^{\infty} \frac{(k+1)(k+2)\cdots(2k)}{1\cdot 2\cdot \cdots \cdot k} p^k (1-p)^k$

we see that the series converges if $1 > \lim_{k\to\infty} \frac{a_{k+1}}{a_k} = \lim_{k\to\infty} p(1-p)\frac{(2k+1)(2k+2)}{(k+1)(k+1)} = p(1-p)4$

(v) This inequality is satisfied if $p \neq \frac{1}{2}$. Thus if $p \neq \frac{1}{2}$, state 0 (and hence each state) is transient.

(vi) If $p = \frac{1}{2}$, then $\lim_{k\to\infty} \frac{a_{k+1}}{a_k} = 1$ and the ratio test is inconclusive. It requires more subtle reasoning, but with $p = \frac{1}{2}$ the series diverges. State (0) is recurrent and hence all states are recurrent.

We can represent the gambling model in example one by the diagram below.

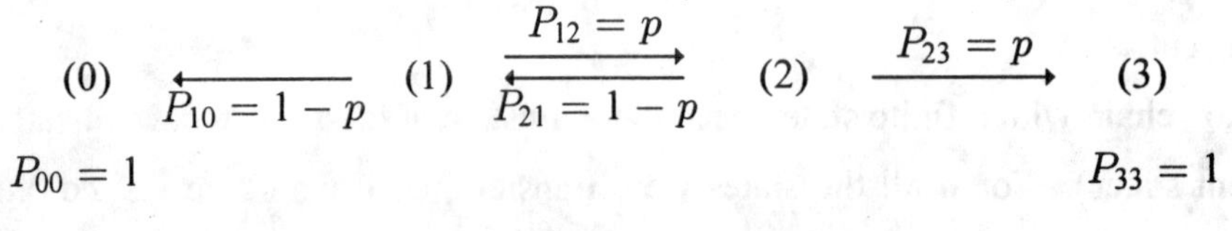

There are three classes, {0}, {1, 2}, {3}. Both 0 and 3 are recurrent states since $P_{00}^k = 1 = P_{33}^k$ means that $E[N_0] = E[N_3] = \sum_{k=0}^{\infty} P_{00}^k = \sum_{k=0}^{\infty} 1 = \infty$. It is also easy to see that r_1, the probability of returning to state 1 given that you start in state 1, is $p(1-p)$ since the only possible way to do this is to move to state 2 on the first transition and then back to state 1 on the next transition. If $0 < p < 1$, then $p(1-p) = r_1 < 1$ and state 1 is transient. Since 1 and 2 communicate it must also follow that state 2 is transient.

Limiting Probabilities in a Discrete-Time, Discrete State Space, Markov Chain

There are two notions of limiting probabilities in a Markov chain. One notion would have the distribution of X_n approaching a limit as $n \to \infty$:

$$\lim_{n\to\infty} Pr(X_n = i) = Pr(X = i)$$

for some random variable X. The idea here is that no matter what initial distribution you begin with, $\vec{\pi}_0 = (Pr(X_0 = 0), Pr(X_0 = 1), \ldots)$, for large n the distribution of X_n is very close to the distribution of X, $\vec{\pi} = (Pr(X = 0), Pr(X = 1), \ldots)$. If this is the case, then

$$\vec{\pi} = \lim_{n\to\infty} \vec{\pi}_n = \lim_{n\to\infty} (\vec{\pi}_{n-1} P) = (\lim_{n\to\infty} \vec{\pi}_{n-1}) P = \vec{\pi}\, P.$$

The distribution of X is called a **steady state** since if X_n has the distribution of X so does X_{n+1}, X_{n+2}, … and so on.

Another idea of a limiting probability is $\lim_{n\to\infty} \frac{N_i(n)}{n}$, where $N_i(n)$ is the number of visits to state i by time n. This is the long-term relatively frequency with which state i is visited. Once we define ergodic states we will return to these limiting ideas.

A state is called **periodic** of period d if beginning in the state at time 0 it is only possible to be in the state at times d, $2d$, $3d$, …. Thus i is period d if $P_{ii}^n = 0$ when n is not divisible by d, and d is the smallest number with this property. If a state does not exhibit periodic behavior it is called **aperiodic**. In example one,

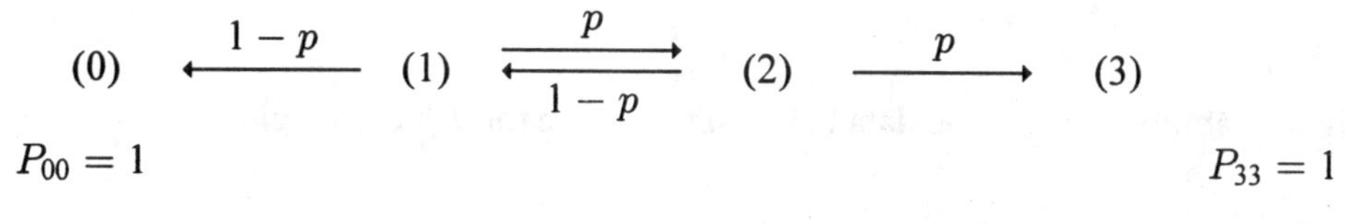

states (1) and (2) have period 2 while states (0) and (3) are aperiodic. Periodicity is a class property. All states in a class have the same period. In example two (the Random Walk) all states are of period 2. In example three (hurricanes) all states are aperiodic.

For a recurrent state i the return to state i is certain (i.e., $r_i = 1$) given that you start in state i. Let T_i be the random number of transitions needed to return to state i given that one begins in state i. If $E[T_i] < \infty$ then i is called **positive recurrent**, whereas if $E[T_i] = \infty$ it is called **null recurrent**. In a finite chain $E[T_i]$ is always finite. Positive recurrence is also a class property. Positive recurrent, aperiodic states are called **ergodic.** The idea is that if $E[T_i] < \infty$ then, starting in state i, the long-term relative frequency of state i is $\frac{1}{E[T_i]}$. If $E[T_i] = 4$, then "on average" you are in state i one out of every four times if you begin in (or ever reach) state i. Without proof we state the following useful result:

Theorem Consider an irreducible (one class), ergodic (all states are aperiodic and positive recurrent) Markov chain with transition probabilities P_{ij}. Then:

(i) $\lim_{n\to\infty} P_{ij}^n$ exists and is independent of i.

(ii) Setting $\vec{\pi} = (\pi_0, \pi_1, \ldots)$ where $\pi_j = \lim_{n\to\infty} P_{ij}^n$, we have $\vec{\pi}P = \vec{\pi}$. In fact π is the unique such row vector (eigenvector for eigenvalue 1) which gives a distribution (i.e., $\sum \pi_i \geq 0$ and $\sum \pi_i = 1$)

(iii) If $N_i(n)$ is the random number of visits to state (i) by time n, then $\lim_{n\to\infty} \frac{N_i(n)}{n}$, the long-term relative frequency of state (i), equals π_i.

(iv) If T_i is the random number of transitions needed to return to state i, given that you begin in state i, then $\pi_i = \frac{1}{E[T_i]}$.

Note: If the aperiodicity condition is dropped then $\lim_{n\to\infty} P_{ij}^n$ may not exist. However, there is still a unique distribution $\vec{\pi}$ such that $\vec{\pi}P = \vec{\pi}$ and π_i is the long-term relative frequency of state i.

The ideas in this result will be illustrated for Example 3 (hurricanes).

States: 0 (mild season), 1 (moderate season), 2 (severe season)

Transition matrix: $(P_{ij}) = \begin{bmatrix} .6 & .3 & .1 \\ .5 & .3 & .2 \\ .3 & .4 & .3 \end{bmatrix}$

There is one class and all states are recurrent and aperiodic. Since the chain is finite, states are positive recurrent. All conditions of the theorem are satisfied.

Limiting probabilities: From the data below one can see the P_{ij}^n converging to π_j.

$$P^2 = \begin{bmatrix} .54 & .31 & .15 \\ .51 & .32 & .17 \\ .47 & .33 & .20 \end{bmatrix}$$

Note how the rows begin to merge to the common $\vec{\pi}$ as n increases.

$$P^4 = \begin{bmatrix} .5202 & .3161 & .1637 \\ .5185 & .3166 & .1649 \\ .5161 & .3173 & .1666 \end{bmatrix}$$

A precise calculation of $\vec{\pi} = (\pi_0, \pi_1, \pi_2)$ can be obtained from the system of 3 linear equations in 3 unknowns given by $\vec{\pi}P = \vec{\pi}$,

$$\begin{aligned}
\pi_0 &= .60\pi_0 + .50\pi_1 + .30\pi_2 \\
\pi_1 &= .30\pi_0 + .30\pi_1 + .40\pi_2 \\
\pi_2 &= .10\pi_0 + .20\pi_1 + .30\pi_2,
\end{aligned}$$

along with the restriction $1 = \pi_0 + \pi_1 + \pi_2$. Using matrix row operations it is easy to see that $\pi_1 = \frac{25}{41}\pi_0$, $\pi_2 = \frac{13}{41}\pi_0$. Setting $\sum \pi_i = 1$ then results in $\pi_0 = \frac{41}{79} \approx .5190$, $\pi_1 = \frac{25}{79} \approx .3165$, and $\pi_2 = \frac{13}{79} \approx .1646$ (compare with the rows of P^4).

Example 4 Consider an irreducible Markov chain with 3 states where in state (1) there are probabilities $P_{12} = P_{10} = .50$. In states (0) or (2) you are certain to move to state (1).

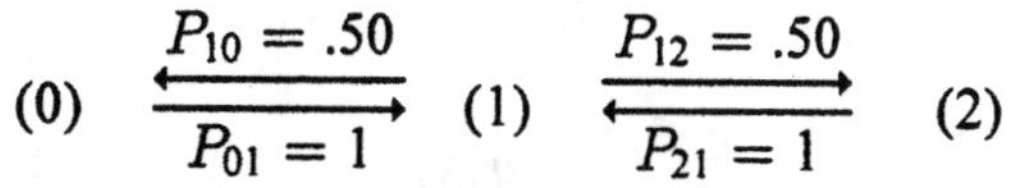

$$P = \begin{bmatrix} 0 & 1 & 0 \\ .5 & 0 & .5 \\ 0 & 1 & 0 \end{bmatrix}, \quad P^2 = \begin{bmatrix} .5 & 0 & .5 \\ 0 & 1 & 0 \\ .5 & 0 & .5 \end{bmatrix}$$

All states have period 2. It is easy to see that $P^{2n+1} = P$ and $P^{2n} = P^2$. Thus $\lim\limits_{n\to\infty} P_{ij}^n$ does not exist. However $\vec{\pi}P = \vec{\pi}$, $\sum \pi_i = 1$ still has the unique solution $\pi_0 = \frac{1}{4}$, $\pi_1 = \frac{1}{2}$, $\pi_2 = \frac{1}{4}$ and the π_i may be viewed as long-term relative frequencies as well as being the unique steady state (i.e., $\vec{\pi}_n = \vec{\pi} \Rightarrow \vec{\pi}_{n+1} = \vec{\pi}_n P = \pi P = \pi$).

Gambler's Ruin

Consider the random walk with state space $\{0, \pm 1, \pm 2, \ldots\}$ and transition probabilities $P_{i,i+1} = p = 1 - P_{i,i-1}$ for all states i. Now insert absorbing barriers at two places. For convenience, states 0 and N.

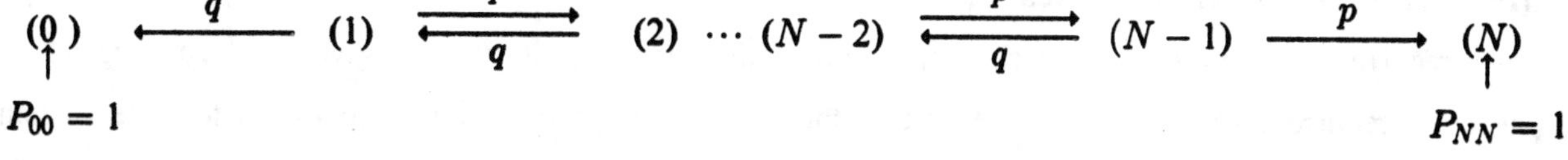

There are now three classes, $\{0\}$, $\{N\}$ and $\{1, 2, \ldots, N-1\}$. The first two classes are recurrent since $P_{00} = 1 = P_{NN}$ means that you are certain to return to one of these states (on the next transition) given that you begin in one of these states. The class $\{1, 2, \ldots, N-1\}$ is transient since it is possible to go from one of these states to either $\{0\}$ or $\{N\}$. Thus, for example, if you begin in state (1), the probability of returning to state 1, r_1, satisfies.

$$1 - r_1 = Pr(\text{never return to state 1} \mid \text{begin in state 1}) \geq Pr(X_1 = 0 | X_0 = 1) = q,$$

hence $r_1 \leq 1 - q$.

Let P_i be the probability that starting in state i you reach state N before reaching state 0. If $Q_i$is the probability of reaching state 0 before state N then $P_i + Q_i = 1$ due to the transience of the class $\{1, 2, \ldots, N-1\}$. Conditioning on the first transition and using the idea that the process starts over after any number of transitions (i.e., the Markovian assumption), it follows that

$$P_i = \underbrace{p \cdot P_{i+1}}_{\substack{\text{first step is to} \\ \text{the right}}} + \underbrace{q \cdot P_{i-1}}_{\substack{\text{first step is to} \\ \text{the left}}},$$

or, equivalently,

$$P_{i+1} - P_i = \tfrac{q}{p}(P_i - P_{i-1}).$$

Since $P_0 = 0$ it follows that

$$P_i = \begin{cases} \dfrac{1 - \left(\frac{q}{p}\right)^i}{1 - \left(\frac{q}{p}\right)^N} & p \neq \frac{1}{2} \quad \text{Note: This ratio is 0/0 if } p = 1/2 \\ \dfrac{i}{N} & p = \frac{1}{2} \quad \text{Note: This is the limit of the ratio above if } \frac{p}{q} \rightarrow 1 \end{cases}$$

The random walk above with barriers at (0) and (N) can also be considered as a model of a gambler beginning with a fortune of i and playing a game repeatedly where he either wins 1 with probability p or loses 1 with probability $q = 1 - p$. He quits when he either goes broke (i.e., hits state (0)) or achieves his goal (i.e., reaches a fortune of N). $1 - P_i$ represents his **probability** of **ruin**.

Mean Time In Transient States

For a recurrent state in a finite Markov chain you will return infinitely often given that you begin in a particular recurrent state. If i is a recurrent state and T_i is the time until you return to state i, then $E[T_i] < \infty$ and the long-term relative frequency of state i given that you start in the class of state i is $\frac{1}{E[T_i]}$. On the other hand, if you begin in a transient state i, let N_i be the **number** of **times** you return to state i. Then $E[N_i] = \frac{1}{1-r_i}$ where r_i is the probability of returning to state i. The long-term relative frequency of state i given that you begin in state i is 0 (since it is visited only finitely many times).

Here we study transient states, numbered for convenience as states (1), (2), ..., (n), and let N_{ij} be the random number of times state j is visited given that you begin in state i where i, j are transient states. Notice that N_i earlier is N_{ii} in this notation. Recalling that it is possible to go from a transient state to a recurrent one, but impossible to achieve the opposite, we arrive at the relation

$$E[N_{ij}] = \delta_{ij} + \sum_k E[N_{ij}|X_1 = k]P_{ik}$$

where $\delta_{ij} = 1$ if $i = j$ and $\delta_{ij} = 0$ otherwise. The δ_{ij} term counts the visit at time zero if states i and j are identical. Clearly $E[N_{ij}|X_1 = k] = E[N_{kj}]$ by the fact that the process starts over at time 1. Furthermore, the sum runs only over k for which state k is transient since otherwise $P_{kj} = 0$ (i.e., it is impossible to go from a recurrent state k to a transient state j). Letting P_T be $(P_{ij})_{1\le i,j\le n}$, the equation above can be written in matrix form as

$$(E[N_{ij}]) = I + P_T(E[N_{ij}]).$$

Hence

$$(E[N_{ij}]) = (I - P_T)^{-1}.$$

Let's return to Example 1, a gambler's ruin model with $N = 3$.

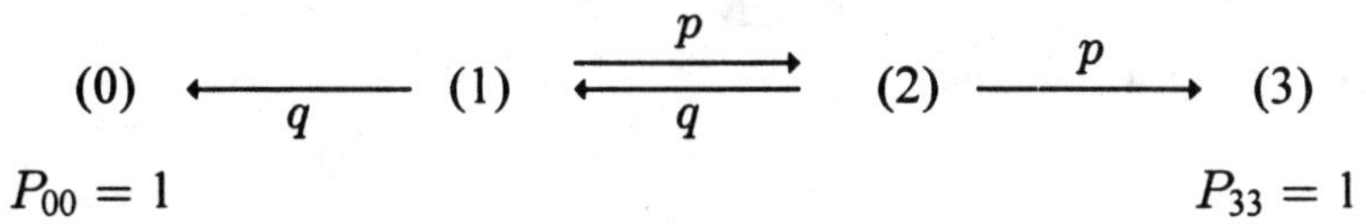

The transient states are $\{1, 2\}$ whereas $\{0\}$ and $\{1\}$ are recurrent classes. From previous results we know

$$P_i = \begin{cases} \dfrac{1-\left(\frac{q}{p}\right)^i}{1-\left(\frac{q}{p}\right)^3} & p \neq \frac{1}{2} \\ \frac{i}{3} & p = \frac{1}{2} \end{cases}$$

where P_i is the probability of reaching a goal of 3 before going broke. Here

$$P_T = \begin{pmatrix} 0 & p \\ 1-p & 0 \end{pmatrix}.$$

Hence, by the above,

$$\begin{bmatrix} E[N_{11}] & E[N_{12}] \\ E[N_{21}] & E[N_{22}] \end{bmatrix} = (I - P_T)^{-1} = \begin{bmatrix} 1 & -p \\ -q & 1 \end{bmatrix}^{-1} = \frac{1}{1-pq}\begin{bmatrix} 1 & p \\ q & 1 \end{bmatrix}.$$

The expected number of visits to state 2 given that you start in state 1, $E[N_{12}]$, can thus be calculated as $\frac{p}{1-pq}$.

For transient states i, j, a related quantity is f_{ij}, the probability state j is ever entered starting from state i. Notice that f_{ii} is what we earlier denoted by r_i, the probability of returning to state i given that you begin in state i. Recall also that $N_{ii} = N_i$ has a geometric distribution with mean $\frac{1}{1-r_i} = \frac{1}{1-f_{ii}}$. Thus $E[N_{ii}] = \frac{1}{1-f_{ii}}$, or equivalently, $r_i = f_{ii} = \frac{E[N_{ii}]-1}{E[N_{ii}]}$. By conditioning on whether state j is ever entered beginning in state i, it is possible to show more generally that

$$f_{ij} = \frac{E[N_{ij}] - \delta_{ij}}{E[N_{jj}]}$$

Example 5 Let $p = q = \frac{1}{2}$ in Example 1 (gambler's ruin with $N = 3$). Calculate

(a) P_1, P_2

(b) $E[N_{ij}]$ for i, j equal 1 or 2

(c) f_{ij} for i, j equal 1 or 2

Solution

(a) With $p = q$ we saw earlier that $P_i = \frac{i}{N}$. Thus $P_1 = \frac{1}{3}$, $P_2 = \frac{2}{3}$.

(b) From work above we see that

$$\begin{bmatrix} E[N_{11}] & E[N_{12}] \\ E[N_{21}] & E[N_{22}] \end{bmatrix} = \frac{1}{1-pq}\begin{bmatrix} 1 & p \\ q & 1 \end{bmatrix} = \begin{bmatrix} \frac{4}{3} & \frac{2}{3} \\ \frac{2}{3} & \frac{4}{3} \end{bmatrix}$$

(c) $$r_1 = f_{11} = \frac{E[N_{11}] - \delta_{1,1}}{E[N_{11}]} = \frac{\frac{4}{3}-1}{\frac{4}{3}} = \frac{1}{4}$$

$$r_2 = f_{22} = \frac{E[N_{22}] - \delta_{2,2}}{E[N_{22}]} = \frac{\frac{4}{3}-1}{\frac{4}{3}} = \frac{1}{4}$$

$$f_{12} = \frac{E[N_{12}] - \delta_{1,2}}{E[N_{22}]} = \frac{\frac{2}{3}-0}{\frac{4}{3}} = \frac{1}{2}$$

$$f_{21} = \frac{E[N_{21}] - \delta_{2,1}}{E[N_{11}]} = \frac{\frac{2}{3}-0}{\frac{4}{3}} = \frac{1}{2}$$

□

CONDENSED REVIEW NOTES AND ADVANCED TOPICS

Stochastic Process

A collection of random variables $\{X(t):\ t \in T\}$. Called **discrete time** if $T = \{0, 1, 2, \dots\}$ (or some other discrete set) or **continuous time** if $T = [0, \infty)$ (or some other interval). $X(t)$ is called the **state** at time t. The **state space** is the set of all possible $X(t)$ values. The process is called a **Markov Chain** if the conditional distribution of a future state given the past states and the present state is independent of the past and depends only on the present. In this unit the process is discrete time and the state space is a subset of $\{0, \pm 1, \pm 2, \dots\}$. We write X_n rather than $X(n)$ for each of these discrete variables. The **Markovian assumption** is written as

$$Pr(X_{n+1} = k | X_n = j, X_{n-1} = j_{n-1}, \dots) = Pr(X_{n+1} = k | X_n = j) = P_{jk}$$

Note: The probability is independent of n so the process "starts over" at any point in time that you wish to throw away the past.

(1) Let $P = [P_{jk}]$ be the matrix of transition probabilities. The jth row[3] is the **conditional distribution** of X_{n+1} given $X_n = j$ (i.e., given you are in state j at time n).

(2) Let $\vec{\pi}_n = (Pr(X_n = 0),\ Pr(X_n = 1),\ \dots)$ be a row vector (1 row matrix) representing the probability distribution at time n, then $\vec{\pi}_{n+1}$, the **unconditional distribution** of X_{n+1}, is given by $\vec{\pi}_{n+1} = \vec{\pi}_n P$ (matrix multiplication).

Note: Being given that $X_n = j$ is the same as computing $\vec{\pi}_{n+1}$ as above using $\vec{\pi}_n = (0, \dots, 0, 1, 0, \dots)$

(3) Chapman-Kolmogorov equations for n-step transition probabilities.

$$Pr(X_{m+n} = k | X_m = j) = P^n_{jk} \qquad ((j, k) \text{ entry of the } n^{th} \text{ power of } P)$$

$$\vec{\pi}_{m+n} = \vec{\pi}_m P^n \qquad \text{(matrix multiplication)}$$

[3] There is a 0th row if 0 is a possible state.

Classification of States

(1) Represent the chain as a series of nodes with a path from node (state) i to node (state) j if $P_{ij} > 0$ (i.e., it is possible that $X_{n+1} = j$ if $X_n = i$).

$$(i) \xrightarrow{P_{ij}} (j)$$

State (j) is **accessible** from state (i) **in one step**.

(2) State (j) is called **accessible** from state (i) if $P_{ij}^n > 0$ for some n (i.e., if $X_m = i$ it is possible that $X_{m+n} = j$ in the sense that this event has positive probability).

(3) Two states are said to **communicate** if they are accessible to one another. Communication is an equivalence relation, so states are separated into groups known as equivalence classes. A chain is **irreducible** if there is just one class (i.e., all states communicate).

(4) Given that the process begins in state (i) (i.e., $X_0 = i$) let r_i be the probability that the process will ever return to state i. A state is called **transient** if $r_i < 1$ and **recurrent** if $r_i = 1$.

(5) For a transient state (i), let N_i be the random number of visits to state (i) (counting the visit at time 0) given that the process begins in state (i) (i.e., $X_0 = i$). N_i has a geometric distribution:

$$Pr(N_i = n) = r_i^{n-1}(1 - r_i)$$

$$E[N_i] = \frac{1}{1 - r_i} = \sum_{n=0}^{\infty} P_{ii}^n < \infty.$$

A transient state is visited only finitely often (rather infrequently in the "long run").

(6) A recurrent state j is visited infinitely often and $E[N_j] = \sum_{n=0}^{\infty} P_{jj}^n = \infty$.

(7) Generally speaking it is difficult to calculate either r_i or $\sum_{n=0}^{\infty} P_{ii}$ as a method of determining whether a state is transient or recurrent. However;

(i) transience and recurrence are class properties (i.e., all states in a class are either transient or recurrent)

(ii) it is impossible to go from a recurrent state to a transient one (the other direction is possible)

(iii) in a finite chain there must be at least one recurrent state (hence in an irreducible, finite chain all states are recurrent).

Limiting Probabilities

1. A state is called **periodic** of period d if $P_{ii}^n = 0$ if n not divisible by d, and d is the smallest such number ($d = 1$ is referred to as **aperiodic**). Starting in state (i), it is only possible to be in state (i) at times $0, d, 2d, \ldots$.
2. Starting in a recurrent state i, let T_i be the random number of transitions until the process returns to state i ($r_i = 1$ so return is certain). If $E[T_i] < \infty$ then the state is called **positive recurrent**. Otherwise, it is called **null recurrent**. In a finite chain a recurrent state is necessarily positive recurrent. Positive recurrence and null recurrence are class properties.
3. Positive recurrent, aperiodic states are called **ergodic**, and other states in the class of an ergodic state are themselves ergodic.

Theorem: Consider an irreducible (one class), ergodic (all states are aperiodic and $E[T_i] < \infty$) Markov chain with transition probabilities P_{ij}. Then:

(i) $\lim_{n\to\infty} P_{ij}^n$ exists and is independent of i, call it π_j. Set $\vec{\pi} = (\pi_0, \pi_1, \ldots)$. Then $\vec{\pi} = \vec{\pi}P$ and $\vec{\pi}$ is called the steady state or stationary state, since if $\vec{\pi}_n = \vec{\pi}$ one also has $\vec{\pi} = \vec{\pi}_{n+1} = \vec{\pi}_{n+2} \cdots$. The distribution $\vec{\pi}$ is the unique solution of $\vec{\pi}P = \vec{\pi}$ (the easiest method of calculation).

(ii) If $N_i(n)$ is the random number of visits to state (i) by time n, then $\lim_{n\to\infty} \frac{N_i(n)}{n}$, the **long-term relative frequency** of state (i), equals $\pi_i = \lim_{n\to\infty} P_{ji}^n$, for all j; and

(iii) If T_i is the random number of transitions needed to return to state i given that $X_0 = i$, then $\pi_i = \frac{1}{E[T_i]}$.

Gambler's Ruin Model

$$(0) \xleftarrow[q]{} (1) \underset{q}{\overset{p}{\rightleftarrows}} (2) \cdots (N-2) \underset{q}{\overset{p}{\rightleftarrows}} (N-1) \xrightarrow{p} (N)$$

$P_{00} = 1$ $\qquad\qquad\qquad\qquad\qquad\qquad$ $P_{NN} = 1$

(1) $\{0\}, \{N\}$ are recurrent classes and $\{1, 2, \ldots, N-1\}$ is a transient class.

(2) Let P_i be the probability of reaching state (N) given that you start in state (i). This is the same as reaching (N) before reaching (0) since (0) and (N) are absorbing states (you can't leave once you arrive).

(3) $$P_i = \begin{cases} \dfrac{1-\left(\frac{q}{p}\right)^i}{1-\left(\frac{q}{p}\right)^N} & p \neq \frac{1}{2} \quad \text{Note: This ratio is 0/0 if } p = 1/2 \\[2ex] \dfrac{i}{N} & p = \frac{1}{2} \quad \text{Note: This is the limit of the ratio above as } \frac{p}{q} \to 1 \end{cases}$$

Note: $1 - P_i$ is the probability of "ruin" given that the initial fortune is i. Ruin means losing your initial fortune.

Mean Time in Transient States

1. N_i is the random number of visits to state i (counting the one at time 0) given that $X_0 = i$ when i is a transient state. For transient states i and j, let N_{ij} be the number of visits to state j given that $X_0 = i$. Then N_i is the same as N_{ii}.

2. If transient states are numbered $1, 2, \ldots, n$ let $P_T = (P_{ij})_{1 \le i,j \le n}$. Then

$$\underset{(n\times n)}{[E[N_{ij}]]} = \underbrace{(\underset{\substack{\uparrow \\ (n\times n) \\ \text{identity}}}{I} - P_T)^{-1}}_{\text{inverse of } (n\times n)}$$

3. For transient states i, j let f_{ij} be the probability of reaching state j given that $X_0 = i$. In this notation f_{ii} is the probability of returning to state i when the process is initially in state i. Earlier this was denoted by r_i. Remember that $E[N_{ii}] = E[N_i] = \dfrac{1}{1-r_i} = \dfrac{1}{1-f_{ii}}$. In general

$$f_{ij} = \frac{E[N_{ij}] - \delta_{ij}}{E[N_{jj}]}, \qquad \delta_{ij} = \begin{cases} 1 & i = j \\ 0 & i \neq j \end{cases}.$$

CONCEPTUAL REVIEW TEST

1. Explain the Markovian assumption for a discrete-time process, $\{X_n: n = 0, 1, 2, \dots\}$, with state space consisting of integers.

2. Describe a random walk.

3. How is the distribution of the state at time n, $\vec{\pi}_n$, related to the distribution at time $m+n$?

4. What is the interpretation of the row of P^4 corresponding to state 2?

5. What does it mean if states i and j communicate with each other?

6. Explain the differences between recurrent and transient classes of states.

7. Given that $X_0 = i$ explain how to calculate the expected value of N_{ij}, the number of visits to state j, in terms of P, P^2, …..

8. Explain why it is impossible to go from a recurrent state, i, to a transient one, j.

9. What is positive recurrent?

10. What can you say about a finite, irreducible, Markov Chain?

11. Explain periodicity and ergodicity.

12. For an irreducible, ergodic Markov chain discuss the idea of a limiting distribution, a steady state (stationary distribution), and the long-term relative frequency of a state.

CONCEPTUAL REVIEW TEST SOLUTIONS

1. The distribution of a future state, X_{n+m}, given the present state, X_n, and past states, $X_0, \ldots, X_{n-1}$, is independent of the past and depends only on the present and m:

$$Pr(X_{n+m} = j | X_n = i, X_{n-1} = i_{n-1}, \ldots) = Pr(X_{n+m} = j | X_n = i) = P_{ij}^m.$$

This means that the process can be viewed as starting over at any time if you forget the past and start the clock over at 0 in the current state.

2. The states are $0, \pm 1, \pm 2, \ldots$, and for each state, i, and you can move either one state to the right or one to the left: $P_{i,i+1} = p = 1 - P_{i,i-1}$.

3. $\vec{\pi}_n P^m = \vec{\pi}_{m+n}$ (matrix multiplication; $\vec{\pi}_n$ is viewed as a 1-row matrix).

4. It gives the conditional distribution of X_{n+4} given that $X_n = 2$.

5. Given that $X_0 = i$ it is possible that $X_n = j$ for some n (i.e., $P_{ij}^n > 0$) and that $X_{n+m} = i$ for some m (i.e., $P_{ji}^m > 0$).

6. Given that the process begins in state i, let r_i be the probability of returning to state i and let N_i be the random number of visits to state i (counting the one at time zero). If $r_i = 1$ state i is recurrent and $N_i = \infty$ (hence $E[N_i] = \infty$), whereas if $r_i < 1$ state i is transient. In the latter case N_i is finite. In fact it has a geometric distribution: $Pr(N_i = n) = r_i^{n-1}(1 - r_i)$ and $E[N_i] = \frac{1}{1 - r_i}$.

7. Let $I_{ij}(n) = \begin{cases} 1 & X_n = j \\ 0 & X_n \neq j \end{cases}$. The probability associated with the value of 1 is P_{ij}^n. Also $I_{ij}(0) = \delta_{ij}$ (1 if $i = j$, zero otherwise) and $N_{ij} = I_{ij}(0) + I_{ij}(1) + \cdots = \delta_{ij} + \sum_{n=1}^{\infty} I_{ij}(n)$. Thus $E[N_{ij}] = \delta_{ij} + \sum_{n=1}^{\infty}[1 \cdot P_{ij}^n + 0 \cdot (1 - P_{ij})^n] = \delta_{ij} + \sum_{n=1}^{\infty} P_{ij}^n$. Notice that N_{ii} is the same as N_i.

Note: If states 0, 1, ..., n are transient and $P_T = (P_{ij})_{0 \le i, j \le n}$ then $\lim_{m\to\infty} P_T^m = 0$. The equation above for the various $E[N_{ij}]$ can be written in matrix form as

$$(E[N_{ij}])_T = I + P_T + P_T^2 + P_T^3 + \cdots.$$

Now $I - P_T^{m+1} = (I - P_T)(I + P_T + \cdots + P_T^m)$. Taking $\lim_{m\to\infty}$ of both sides and using $\lim_{m\to\infty} P_T^m = 0$ (long-term relative frequencies of transient states are zero) results in

$$(E[N_{ij}])_T = I + P_T + P_T^2 + P_T^3 + \cdots = (I - P_T)^{-1}.$$

8. Given that $X_0 = i$ suppose $X_n = j$ for some n. Since you are certain to return to state i it must be possible to go from state j to state i. But then states i and j communicate, hence they must both be transient or recurrent. This contradiction means $X_n = j$ is impossible.
Note: it is possible to go from a transient state to a recurrent one.

9. Given a recurrent state, i, let T_i be the random number of transitions that it takes to return to state i given that $X_0 = i$. $E[T_i] < \infty$ means state i is positive recurrent. If a chain is finite, every recurrent state is positive recurrent.

10. It consists of one class of positive recurrent states.

11. A state i is periodic of period d if d is the smallest positive integer such that $P_{ii}^n = 0$ if n is not divisible by d. A positive recurrent, aperiodic state is ergodic.

12. $\vec{\pi} = (\pi_0, \pi_1, \ldots)$ is called a limiting distribution if $\lim_{n\to\infty} \vec{\pi}_n = \vec{\pi}$ regardless of $\vec{\pi}_0$, the initial distribution. For an irreducible, ergodic Markov chain, $\pi_j = \lim_{n\to\infty} P_{ij}^n$ for all i. It follows that $\vec{\pi} P = \vec{\pi}$. Thus if $\vec{\pi}_n = \pi$, so also is $\vec{\pi}_{n+1} = \vec{\pi}$ – the distribution does not change once it is achieved at some time (stationary). If $N_i(n)$ is the random number of visits to state i by time n, then $\lim_{n\to\infty} \frac{N_i(n)}{n}$ is the "long-term" relative frequency of state i. It also equals π_i and $\pi_i = \frac{1}{E[T_i]}$, where $E[T_i]$ is the expected number of transitions to return to state i given that $X_0 = i$.

COMPUTATIONAL REVIEW TEST

Questions 1 - 5 are concerned with a 3-state Markov chain whose node diagram is given below.

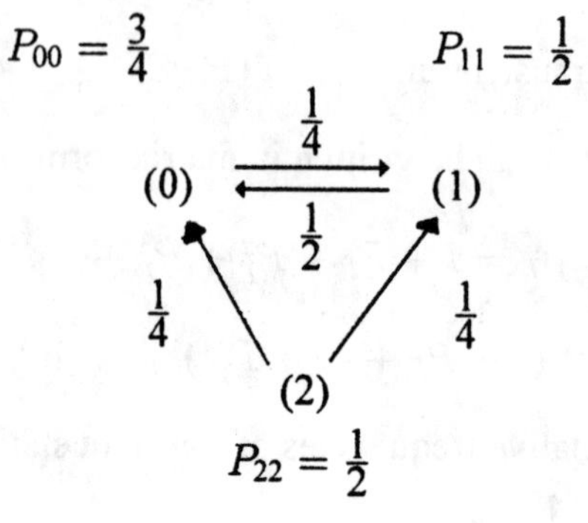

1. What is the matrix $P = (P_{ij})$ of transition probabilities?

2. If $\vec{\pi}_0 = \left(\frac{1}{3}, \frac{1}{3}, \frac{1}{3}\right)$ is the distribution at time 0, what is the distribution of X_2?

3. Given that the state at time 10 is (1) what is the probability that the state at time 12 is (1)?

4. What is $\vec{\pi}_4$ given that $X_2 = 2$?

5. How many classes are there? Which classes are transient, recurrent? For the transient states calculate r_i and $E[N_i]$.

6. If

$$P = \begin{bmatrix} \frac{3}{4} & \frac{1}{4} & 0 \\ 0 & \frac{2}{3} & \frac{1}{3} \\ \frac{1}{2} & 0 & \frac{1}{2} \end{bmatrix}$$

is the matrix of transition probabilities for a Markov chain {0, 1, 2}, classify the states. If there is a limiting distribution calculate it. Calculate $E[T_0]$, $E[T_1]$, $E[T_2]$.

7. Two gamblers, A and B, make a series of $1 wagers where B has a .55 chance of winning and A has a .45 chance of winning on each wager. What is the probability that B wins $10 before A wins $5?

8. Consider a Gambler's Ruin model where $N = 5$ and $p = q = \frac{1}{2}$. You are given that

$$(I - P_T)^{-1} = \begin{bmatrix} 1.6 & 1.2 & .8 & .4 \\ 1.2 & 2.4 & 1.6 & .8 \\ .8 & 1.6 & 2.4 & 1.2 \\ .4 & .8 & 1.2 & 1.6 \end{bmatrix}$$

where $T = \{1, 2, 3, 4\}$ is the set of transient states.

(a) Calculate $E[N_{2,4}]$, the expected number of visits to state 4 given that you begin in state 2.

(b) Calculate $E[N_{2,2}]$ and $E[N_{4,4}]$.

(c) Given that the initial state is 2, what is the probability of eventually reaching state 4?

(d) What is $r_2 = f_{2,2}$ the probability of returning to state 2 given that the process begins in state 2?

COMPUTATIONAL REVIEW TEST SOLUTIONS

1. $$P = \begin{bmatrix} \frac{3}{4} & \frac{1}{4} & 0 \\ \frac{1}{2} & \frac{1}{2} & 0 \\ \frac{1}{4} & \frac{1}{4} & \frac{1}{2} \end{bmatrix}$$

2. $$\vec{\pi}_2 = \vec{\pi}_0 P^2 = \left(\frac{1}{3}, \frac{1}{3}, \frac{1}{3}\right) \begin{bmatrix} .6875 & .3125 & 0 \\ .6250 & .3750 & 0 \\ .4375 & .3125 & .2500 \end{bmatrix} = (.58\bar{3},\ .33\bar{3},\ .08\bar{3}) = \left(\frac{7}{12}, \frac{4}{12}, \frac{1}{12}\right)$$

3. From the Chapman-Kolmogorov equations the probability is P_{11}^2. In the solution above we see that $P_{11}^2 = .375 = \frac{3}{8}$. (Note. Rows are numbered 0, 1, 2.)

4. One can either view $\vec{\pi}_4\big|_{X_2=2}$ as the last row of P^2, (.4375, .3125, .25), or as $(0, 0, 1)P^2$ (matrix mult.).

5. The classes are {0, 1} and {2}. {0, 1} constitutes a finite, irreducible Markov chain by itself since it is impossible to leave this class. Thus both states are recurrent. {2} is transient since once you depart you will never return. For state (2) we have $r_2 = \frac{1}{2}$ and $E[N_2] = \frac{1}{1 - r_2} = 2$.

6.

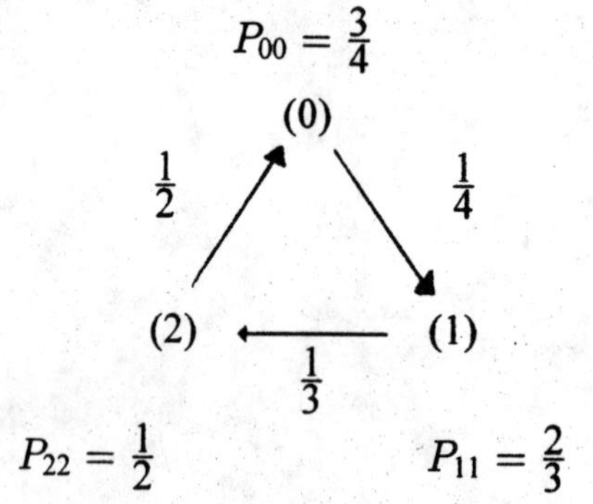

6. (cont.)

There is obviously one class of aperiodic, positive recurrent states (a finite irreducible chain consists of positive recurrent states). If $\vec{\pi}$ denotes the limiting distribution (i.e., $\pi_j = \lim_{n\to\infty} P_{ij}^n$) it is most easily calculated as the only distribution satisfying $\vec{\pi} P = \pi$. Since the transition matrix, P, is given by

$$P = \begin{bmatrix} \frac{3}{4} & \frac{1}{4} & 0 \\ 0 & \frac{2}{3} & \frac{1}{3} \\ \frac{1}{2} & 0 & \frac{1}{2} \end{bmatrix},$$

the corresponding system of equations for $\vec{\pi}$ is:

$$\begin{aligned} \pi_0 &= \tfrac{3}{4}\pi_0 + \tfrac{1}{2}\pi_2 \\ \pi_1 &= \tfrac{1}{4}\pi_0 + \tfrac{2}{3}\pi_1 \\ \pi_2 &= \tfrac{1}{3}\pi_1 + \tfrac{1}{2}\pi_2 \\ 1 &= \pi_0 + \pi_1 + \pi_2 \end{aligned}$$

This results in the unique solution $\pi_0 = \frac{4}{9}$, $\pi_1 = \frac{3}{9}$, and $\pi_2 = \frac{2}{9}$. In general $E[T_i] = \frac{1}{\pi_i}$ so $E[T_0] = \frac{9}{4}$, $E[T_1] = \frac{9}{3} = 3$, $E[T_2] = \frac{9}{2}$.

7. This is the same as the Gambler's Ruin probability where $i = 5$ and $N = 5 + 10 = 15$. The probability sought is

$$P_5 = \frac{1 - \left(\frac{.45}{.55}\right)^5}{1 - \left(\frac{.45}{.55}\right)^{15}} = .6662$$

8. (a) $E[N_{2,4}]$ is the (2, 4) entry of $(I - P_T)^{-1}$, which is .80.

(b) $E[N_{2,2}]$ and $E[N_{4,4}]$ are respectively the (2, 2) entry, 2.4, and the (4, 4) entry, 1.6: so $E[N_{2,2}] = 2.4$, $E[N_{4,4}] = 1.6$

(c) Intuitively $E[N_{2,4}] = f_{2,4}E[N_{4,4}]$. From the above, $f_{2,4} = \frac{.8}{1.6} = \frac{1}{2}$. This probability is the same as in a Gambler's Ruin model with $N = 4$ and $p = q = \frac{1}{2}$. We have seen before that $P_i = \frac{i}{N}$ when $p = q = \frac{1}{2}$. Thus $P_2 = \frac{2}{4}$ checks without above calculation using $E[N_{ij}]$.

(d) Recall the geometric distribution fact

$$\frac{1}{1 - r_2} = E[N_2] = \underbrace{E[N_{22}]}_{\substack{2.4 \text{ in} \\ \text{matrix above}}} = \frac{1}{1 - f_{22}}.\ \text{Thus } r_2 = f_{22} = \frac{7}{12}.$$

UNIT REVIEW QUESTIONS

The following information is to be used for all of the questions. Some additional information will be supplied for Questions 7 - 10.

A 3-state, discrete-time, Markov chain is to be used to model the three conditions of an insured individual:

state 0: alive and active (i.e., not disabled)
state 1: alive but disabled
state 2: dead

Transitions may occur at the end of each year and the matrix of one-step (one-year) transition probabilities is given by

$$P = (P_{ij}) = \begin{bmatrix} .85 & .10 & .05 \\ .15 & .75 & .10 \\ 0 & 0 & 1 \end{bmatrix}$$

1. If an individual is currently alive and active, what is the probability that she will ever become disabled?

   (A) $\frac{1}{3}$ (B) $\frac{1}{2}$ (C) $\frac{2}{3}$ (D) $\frac{3}{4}$ (E) $\frac{5}{6}$

2. If an individual is currently disabled what is the probability that she will ever return to active life?

   (A) .45 (B) .50 (C) .55 (D) .60 (E) .65

3. For an insured individual who is currently active what is the expected number of years until death?

   (A) $11.\overline{1}$ (B) $12.\overline{2}$ (C) $13.\overline{3}$ (D) $14.\overline{4}$ (E) $15.\overline{5}$

4. For an insured individual who is currently disabled what is the expected number of years until death?

   (A) $11.\overline{1}$ (B) $12.\overline{2}$ (C) $13.\overline{3}$ (D) $14.\overline{4}$ (E) $15.\overline{5}$

5. What is the expected length of a period of disablement?

   (A) 1 (B) 2 (C) 3 (D) 4 (E) 5

6. For a currently active insured life what is the expected number of disablements?

   (A) $1.\overline{1}$ (B) $2.\overline{2}$ (C) $3.\overline{3}$ (D) $4.\overline{4}$ (E) $5.\overline{5}$

The following additional information applies to Questions 7-10. A three-year term insurance paying \$1000 at the end of the year of death is issued to a currently active life. The valuation interest rate is $i = .10$. Annual premiums are paid at the start of each policy year.

7. The APV of the death benefit is closest to

(A) 121 (B) 129 (C) 137 (D) 146 (E) 155

8. What is the level annual benefit premium if premiums are waived when the insured is disabled at the time a premium is due?

(A) 54 (B) 58 (C) 62 (D) 66 (E) 70

9. What is the percent decrease in the level annual benefit premium if the disability waiver is removed?

(A) 7.0% (B) 7.4% (C) 7.8% (D) 8.2% (E) 8.6%

10. Assuming a premium waiver is in effect, calculate the benefit reserve at duration one for a life disabled at the end of the first policy year.

(A) 128 (B) 136 (C) 144 (D) 152 (E) 160

SOLUTIONS UNIT REVIEW QUESTIONS

1. Let X_n be the state (i.e., 0, 1, or 2) at time n. If $X_0 = i$ we let f_{ij} be the probability that X_n will eventually take on value j. In this notation the question is asking for f_{01}. Lives may remain in or bounce back and forth between states 0 and 1, but once in state 2 there is no escape. Hence from simple combinatorics

$$f_{01} = \underbrace{.10}_{\substack{\text{reaches}\\\text{state 1}\\\text{at time 1}}} + \underbrace{.85(.10)}_{\substack{\text{reaches}\\\text{state 1}\\\text{at time 2}}} + .85^2(.10) + \cdots = .10\left(\frac{1}{1-.85}\right) = \frac{2}{3} \quad \text{(geometric series)}$$

ANSWER C

Note: Let N_{ij} be the number of visits to state j given that $X_0 = i$. The above result, $f_{01} = \frac{2}{3}$, can also be obtained from the relation between the matrix $(E[N_{ij}])$ $(i, j$ transient states) and the matrix (f_{ij}) (again, one row per transient state): (see the Condensed Review Notes)

$$P_T = (P_{ij}) \qquad i, j \text{ transient}$$

$$(E[N_{ij}]) = (I - P_T)^{-1}$$

$$f_{ij} = \frac{E[N_{ij}] - \delta_{ij}}{E[N_{jj}]}.$$

In this model it can be seen that state 2 (death) is recurrent, whereas states 0 and 1 are transient. From simple combinatorics we have

$$r_0 = f_{00} = Pr(\text{return to state 0 given } X_0 = 0)$$

$$= \underbrace{.85}_{\substack{\text{return}\\\text{at time 1}}} + \underbrace{.10(.15)}_{\substack{\text{return at}\\\text{time 2}}} + \underbrace{(.10)(.75)(.15)}_{\substack{\text{return at}\\\text{time 3}}} + .10(.75)^2(.15) + \cdots$$

$$= .85 + (.10)(.15)\left(\frac{1}{1-.75}\right) = .91$$

and, similarly,

$$r_1 = f_{11} = .75 + .15(.10) + (.15)(.85)(.10) + .15(.85)^2(.10) + \cdots$$

$$= .75 + (.15)(.10)\left(\frac{1}{1-.85}\right) = .85$$

Since r_0, r_1 are less than 1 states 0 and 1 are transient. Hence

$$P_T = \begin{pmatrix} P_{00} & P_{01} \\ P_{10} & P_{11} \end{pmatrix} = \begin{pmatrix} .85 & .10 \\ .15 & .75 \end{pmatrix}$$

1. (cont.) $$\begin{pmatrix} E[N_{00}] & E[N_{01}] \\ E[N_{10}] & E[N_{11}] \end{pmatrix} = (I - P_T)^{-1} = \begin{pmatrix} 11.\bar{1} & 4.\bar{4} \\ 6.\bar{6} & 6.\bar{6} \end{pmatrix}.$$

So

$$r_0 = f_{00} = \frac{E[N_{00}] - 1}{E[N_{00}]} = \frac{11.\bar{1} - 1}{11.\bar{1}} = .91$$
$$f_{01} = \frac{E[N_{01}] - 0}{E[N_{11}]} = \frac{4.\bar{4}}{6.\bar{6}} = \frac{2}{3}$$
$$f_{10} = \frac{E[N_{10}] - 0}{E[N_{00}]} = \frac{6.\bar{6}}{11.\bar{1}} = \frac{3}{5}$$
$$r_1 = f_{11} = \frac{E[N_{11}] - 1}{E[N_{11}]} = \frac{6.\bar{6} - 1}{6.\bar{6}} = .85.$$

2. This is $f_{10} = \frac{3}{5}$. ANSWER D

3. $N_{00} + N_{01}$ is the total number of times an individual currently in state 0 visits either state 0 or state 1 at the start of a year (counting the visit to state 0 at $t = 0$). Since transitions are assumed to occur at year end, this is also the number of years until death. From earlier calculations we have $E[N_{00} + N_{01}] = 11.\bar{1} + 4.\bar{4} = 15.\bar{5}$. ANSWER E

4. $E[N_{10} + N_{11}] = 6.\bar{6} + 6.\bar{6} = 13.\bar{3}$ from earlier results. ANSWER C

5. If $X_0 = 1$, the number of consecutive periods in state 1, S_1, has a Geometric distribution:

$$Pr(S_1 = k) = Pr(X_1 = \cdots = X_{k-1} = 1 | X_0 = 1) = (.75)^{k-1}(.25).$$

Hence $E[S_1] = \frac{1}{.25} = 4$. ANSWER D

6. The total time of disablement is N_{01}. Due to the Markovian assumption

$$N_{01} = \underbrace{S_1}_{\substack{\text{length of 1st} \\ \text{disablement}}} + S_2 + \cdots + S_M$$

where M is the number of disablements and the S_i are independent and identically distributed like S_1. Hence

$$\underbrace{4.\bar{4} = E[N_{01}]}_{\text{earlier calculation}} = \underbrace{E[S_1]}_{\substack{=4 \\ \text{Question 5)}}} E[M] \qquad \text{(standard random sum result)}$$

results in $E[M] = \frac{4.\bar{4}}{4} = 1.\bar{1}$. ANSWER A

7. <u>Time of Death</u> <u>Probability</u>

1 $P_{02} = .05$

2 $P_{02}^2 - P_{02} \cdot P_{22}$ (dead at time 2 but not death at time 1)
$= .1025 - (.05)(1) = .0525$ (see below)

3 $P_{02}^3 - P_{02} \cdot P_{22}^2 - (P_{02}^2 - P_{02} \cdot P_{22})P_{22}$
$= .155375 - (.05)(1)^2 - (.0525) = .052875$ (see below)

$$P = \begin{bmatrix} .85 & .10 & .05 \\ .15 & .75 & .10 \\ 0 & 0 & 1 \end{bmatrix}$$

$$P^2 = (P_{ij}^2) = \begin{bmatrix} .7375 & .1600 & .1025 \\ .2400 & .5775 & .1825 \\ 0 & 0 & 1 \end{bmatrix}$$

$$P^3 = (P_{ij}^3) = \begin{bmatrix} .650875 & .193750 & .155375 \\ .290625 & .457125 & .252250 \\ 0 & 0 & 1 \end{bmatrix}$$

These calculations are more subtle than you might suppose and can also be obtained from tree diagrams. For example:

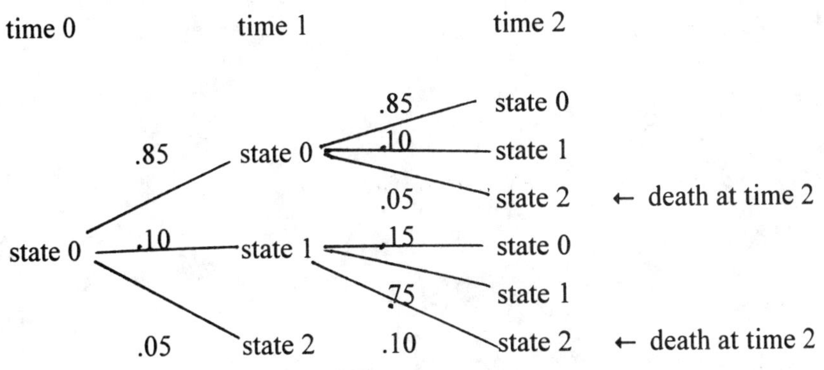

$Pr(\text{death at time 2}) = (.85)(.05) + (.10)(.10) = .0525$

Using the probabilities above and the 3-factor approach to an APV calculation:

$$APV = \left(\frac{1000}{1.1}\right)(.05) + \left(\frac{1000}{1.1^2}\right)(.0525) + \left(\frac{1000}{1.1^3}\right)(.052875) = 128.57$$

ANSWER B

8. The probabilities of payment at times 0, 1, 2 are 1 (i.e., "currently active"), $P_{00} = .85$, and $P_{00}^2 = .7375$. Hence

$$128.57 = APV(\text{Benefit}) = APV(\text{premium}) = P + P(.85)/1.1 + P(.7375)/1.1.^2 = P(2.3822),$$

$P = 53.97$

ANSWER A

9. If the waiver is removed the probability of payment at times 0, 1, and 2 are 1, $P_{00} + P_{01}$, $P_{00}^2 + P_{01}^2$. Thus

$$\begin{aligned}128.57 = APV(\text{Benefit}) &= APV(\text{premium})\\ &= P + P(.85+.10)/1.1 + P(.7375+.1600)/1.1^2 = P(2.6054),\end{aligned}$$

$P = 49.35$. The percent decrease is

$$\frac{53.97 - 49.35}{53.97} \times 100\% = 8.56\%$$

ANSWER E

10.
$$\begin{aligned}APV(\text{future benefit}) &= \frac{1000}{1.1}(P_{12}) + \frac{1000}{1.1^2}(P_{12}^2 - P_{12} \cdot P_{22})\\ &= \left(\frac{1000}{1.1}\right)(.10) + \left(\frac{1000}{1.1^2}\right)(.1825 - .10) = 159.09\end{aligned}$$

$$APV(\text{future premium}) = \underbrace{(53.97)}_{\substack{\text{amount}\\ \text{(Question \#8)}}}\ \underbrace{(1)}_{\text{discount}}\ \underbrace{(0)}_{\text{probability}} \qquad \text{(time 1)}$$

$$+ \underbrace{(53.97)}_{\text{amount}} \underbrace{\left(\frac{1}{1.1}\right)}_{\text{discount}} \underbrace{(.15)}_{\text{probability}=P_{10}} \qquad \text{(time 2)}$$

$$= 7.36$$

$\text{Benefit Reserve}_1 = 159.09 - 7.36 = 151.73$

ANSWER D

UNIT TWO: CONTINUOUS-TIME MARKOV CHAINS WITH DISCRETE STATE SPACES

The setting here is similar to that of Unit One when we studied Markov chains $\{X_n: n = 0, 1, 2, \dots\}$ where the values of X_n were assumed to be integers. Here we consider processes $X(t)$ where $0 \le t < \infty$ and the state at time t, $X(t)$, is an integer. To say that such a process is a continuous-time Markov chain means to assume that

$$Pr(X(s+t) = k|X(s) = j, X(u) = x(u), 0 \le u < s) = Pr(X(s+t) = k|X(s) = j) = P_{jk}(t)$$

for all s, $t \ge 0$. The first equality says that the conditional distribution of a future state at time $t+s$, given the present state at time s and the past states prior to time s, is independent of the past. It depends only on the present (first equality) and the time, t, into the future (second equality - $P_{jk}(t)$ is the same for all s). One can continue to think of the process in terms of a series of nodes (one for each possible state) with transitions from one node to another occurring over time.

If the possible states are 0, 1, 2, ..., we let $\vec{\pi}_t = (Pr(X_t = 0), Pr(X_t = 1), \dots)$ be a row vector giving the probability distribution of $X(t)$, the state at time t. Viewing $(P_{jk}(t))_{0 \le j,k}$ as a matrix, we have

$$\vec{\pi}_{s+t} = \vec{\pi}_s(P_{jk}(t)). \qquad \text{(matrix multiplication)}$$

One can also view the jth row of the **transition probability** matrix, $(P_{jk}(t))$, as the conditional distribution of $X(t)$ given that $X(0) = j$.

In Unit One (discrete time), if the process was in state j at time n, there were probabilities P_{jk} giving the likelihood that the process would be in state k at time $n+1$. P_{jj} could be positive (the process could remain in state j) and $\sum_k P_{jk} = 1$ for all j. In Unit Two (continuous time), if the process is in state j at time s, there is a random waiting time, T_j, until the next **transition** (movement to a **different** node). Associated with this next transition there are probabilities P_{jk} where $P_{jj} = 0$ and $\sum_{k \ne j} P_{jk} = 1$. P_{jk} is the probability the process currently in state j will be in state k at the next transition.

One can think of T_j as the time until decrement (transition) and k as the mode of decrement if the next transition is to state k. In this multiple decrement model, P_{jk} is the marginal probability that k is the mode of decrement. This approach will be discussed later for general Markov chains. We begin with simpler types.

Counting Processes

A process $\{N(t)\colon t \geq 0\}$is called a **counting process** if $N(t)$ represents the number of occurrences over $[0, t]$ of some well-defined random event. $N(0)$ is assumed to be zero.

Example 1

(i) For a certain line of insurance, consider the occurrence of a claim to be the random event. Then $N(t)$ is the random number of claims occurring in the time interval $[0, t]$.

(ii) For a continuing care retirement community, consider the admission of a member to an independent living unit to be the random event. Then $N(t)$ is the random number of entrants admitted to ILU's over the time interval $[0, t]$.

A counting process must satisfy $N(t) \geq 0$, each $N(t)$ is an integer, it must be non-decreasing, and $N(t_2) - N(t_1)$ is the number of random events occurring in $(t_1, t_2]$ if $t_2 > t_1$. The process is said to have **independent increments** if whenever $t_1 < t_2 \leq t_3 < t_4$, then the **process increments** from the disjoint time intervals $(t_1, t_2]$ and (t_3, t_4), $N(t_2) - N(t_1)$ and $N(t_4) - N(t_3)$, are independent random variables. Increments are called **stationary** whenever the distribution of $N(t_2) - N(t_1)$ depends only on $t_2 - t_1$, that is, $N(t_4) - N(t_3)$ has the same distribution as $N(t_2) - N(t_1)$ if $t_4 - t_3 = t_2 - t_1$.

A counting process satisfies the Markovian assumption if it has independent and stationary increments. For if this is the case,

$$\begin{aligned} &Pr(N(s+t) = k \,|\, N(s) = j,\, N(u) = n(u),\, u < s) \\ &\quad = Pr(k - j \text{ occurrences in } (s, s+t] \,|\, j \text{ occurrences in } (0, s]) \\ &\quad = Pr(k - j \text{ occurrences in } (s, s+t]) \qquad \text{(independent increments)} \\ &\quad = Pr(k - j \text{ occurrences in } (0, t]) \qquad \text{(stationary increments)} \\ &\quad = Pr(N(t) = k - j) \qquad \text{(thought of as the transition probability } P_{jk}(t)) \end{aligned}$$

The Poisson Process

A counting process with independent and stationary increments such that $N(t)$ has a Poisson distribution with parameter λt is called a **Poisson process** with **rate** λ. This means that the number of occurrences of the random event in any time interval of length t, $(s, s+t)]$, satisfies

$$Pr(N(s+t) - N(s) = k) = e^{-\lambda t}\frac{(\lambda t)^k}{k!} = Pr(N(t) = k)$$

for $k = 0, 1, 2, \ldots$. In addition, $E[N(t)] = \lambda t$ and $Var(N(t)) = \lambda t$. For any $t > 0$, $\frac{N(t)}{t}$ is the random rate at which events occurred over $(0, t)$ per unit of time. Thus $E[N(t)] = \frac{1}{t}(\lambda t) = \lambda$ is the expected rate at which the random event occurs per unit of time. This explains the idea that λ is the **process rate**.

An equivalent definition of the Poisson process assumes independent increments and that $N(s+t) - N(s)$ has a Poisson-distribution with parameter λt whenever $s,\ t > 0$. The idea that increments are stationary is built into this statement.

Other characterizations of a Poisson process can be given in terms of either the behavior over an infinitesimal time interval $(t,\ t+h]$, where h is a small positive number approaching zero, or the distribution of waiting times between successive occurrences of the random event. Next we consider the infinitesimal approach.

A function $f(h)$ is said to be $0(h)$ if $\lim_{h\to 0}\frac{f(h)}{h} = 0$, that is, if $f(h)$ goes to zero faster than h. If $f(h)$ can be expanded into a convergent power series near 0, this means that

$$f(h) = \sum_{k=0}^{\infty}\frac{f^{(k)}(0)}{k!}h^k = f''(0)\frac{h^2}{2} + f'''(0)\frac{h^3}{6} + \cdots,$$

(Taylor' Theorem)

that is, $f(0) = f'(0) = 0$. For example,

$$f(h) = e^{-\lambda h}\frac{(\lambda h)^1}{1!} - \lambda h = \lambda h(e^{\lambda h} - 1) = \lambda h\left(1 + \frac{(\lambda h)^1}{1!} + \frac{(\lambda h)^2}{2!} + \cdots - 1\right)$$
$$= \lambda^2 h^2 + (\text{higher order terms in } h)$$

is $0(h)$.

A description of the Poisson process in terms of its behavior in **infinitesimal time periods** would assert that $\{N(t) | t \geq 0\}$ has independent and stationary increments, and that

(i) $Pr(N(h) = 1) = \lambda h + 0(h)$, and
(ii) $Pr(N(h) \geq 2) = 0(h)$.

We saw above that a Poisson process satisfies (i). Also, for a Poisson process $N(t)$, it is clear from the following that (ii) is satisfied:

$$\begin{aligned} Pr(N(h) \geq 2) &= e^{-\lambda h}\frac{(\lambda h)^2}{2!} + e^{-\lambda h}\frac{(\lambda h)^3}{3!} + \cdots \\ &= \left(1 + \frac{(\lambda h)^1}{1!} + \frac{(\lambda h)^2}{2!} - \cdots\right)\left(\frac{(\lambda h)^2}{2!} + \frac{(\lambda h)^3}{3!} + \cdots\right) \\ &= \frac{\lambda h^2}{2!} + (\text{higher order terms in } h). \end{aligned}$$

Using (i) and (ii) above, along with an assumption of independent and stationary increments, it is also possible to show that $N(t)$ has a Poisson distribution with parameter λt. The proof is intricate and involves using the assumptions (i), (ii) to derive a differential equation for $P_n(t) = Pr(N(t) = n)$ whose solution is $e^{-\lambda t}\frac{(\lambda t)^n}{n!}$. In the infinitesimal description above, one could drop the assumption of stationary increments and build this into modified infinitesimal assumptions

(i)′ $Pr(N(t+h) - N(t) = 1) = \lambda h + 0(h)$, and
(ii)′ $Pr(N(t+h) - N(t) \geq 2) = 0(h)$.

for all t.

Finally, we consider an equivalent description of a Poisson process in terms of the waiting times between occurrences of the random events being counted. Let $0 < T_1 < T_2 < \cdots$ be the random times of the first, second, ... occurrences of the random event. $W_1 = T_1$, $W_2 = T_2 - T_1$, $W_3 = T_3 - T_2$, ... are called the **waiting times (interarrival** times). For a Poisson process it is possible to show that the W_i's are independent exponential distributions with parameter λ. For example, the survival function of W_1 is

$$Pr(W_1 > t) = Pr(\text{no occurrences in } (0, t]) = Pr(N(t) = 0) = e^{-\lambda t}\frac{(\lambda t)^0}{0!} = e^{-\lambda t}.$$

Thus the probability density function of W_1 is $-\frac{d(e^{-\lambda t})}{dt} = \lambda e^{-\lambda t}$, the exponential density with parameter λ. The fact that all of the W_i are independent and exponentially distributed follows from the assumptions of independent and stationary increments. Conversely, it is also possible to show for a counting process with independent and identically distributed exponential waiting times between occurrences, that process increments are independent and stationary Poisson distributions.

Example 2 Let $N(t)$ be a Poisson process with rate $\lambda = 3$.

(i) What is the probability of 4 occurrences of the random event in the time interval (2.5, 4]?

(ii) What is the probability that $T_2 > 5$ given that $N(4) = 1$?

(iii) What is the distribution of T_n?

(iv) What is the expected time of occurrence of the 5th event?

Solution

(i) $N(4) - N(2.5)$ has a Poisson distribution with parameter $\lambda(4 - 2.5) = 3(1.5) = 4.5$. So the probability of 4 occurrence is $e^{-4.5}\frac{(4.5)^4}{4!}$.

(ii) If $T_2 > 5$ and $N(4) = 1$, there was one occurrence in $(0, 4]$ and no occurrence in $(4, 5]$. Thus

$$\begin{aligned} Pr(T_2 > 5|N(4) = 1) &= Pr(\text{no occurrences in } (4,\, 5]\big|\text{one occurrence in } (0,\, 4)) \\ &= Pr(\text{no occurrences in } (4,\, 5]) \qquad \text{(independent increment)} \\ &= Pr(\text{no occurrence in } (0,\, 1]) \qquad \text{(stationary increment)} \\ &= e^{-\lambda(1)} = e^{-3}. \end{aligned}$$

(iii) In general, if $Y_1, \ldots, Y_n$ are independent Gamma[4] distributions with parameters α_i, β, then $\sum Y_i$ is a Gamma distribution with parameters $\alpha = \sum \alpha_i$, β. This follows since

$$M_{\sum Y_i}(t) = \prod_{i=1}^{n} M_{Y_i}(t) = \prod_{i=1}^{n} \left(1 - \frac{t}{\beta}\right)^{-\alpha_i} = \left(1 - \frac{t}{\beta}\right)^{-\sum \alpha_i},$$

which is the generating function of a Gamma distribution with parameters $\alpha = \sum \alpha_i$, β. So $W_1 + \cdots + W_n = T_n$ is a Gamma variable with $\alpha = n$, $\beta = \lambda = 3$ since each W_i is exponential with parameter $\lambda = 3$ (i.e., Gamma with $\alpha = 1$ and $\beta = \lambda = 3$).

(iv) $E[T_5] = 5E[W] = \frac{5}{\lambda} = \frac{5}{3}$. □

Due to the **memoryless property** of exponential distributions (i.e., W exponential with parameter $\lambda \;\Rightarrow\; W - w_0\big|_{W>w_0}$ is exponential with parameter λ), or equivalently, the Markovian assumption, a Poisson process starts itself over at any time t. That is, if $M(t) = N(t+t_0) - N(t_0)$ for $t > 0$, then $\{M(t)\colon\, t > 0\}$ is also a Poisson process with rate λ.

If one thinks of a Poisson process in terms of transitions between nodes over time, the nodes (possible states) are (0), (1), (2), ... and it is only possible to go from node (n) to $(n+1)$. That is, $P_{n,n+1} = 1$. The waiting time at node (n) until the transition to node $(n+1)$ is the waiting time W_{n+1} until $(n+1)^{st}$ the occurrence of the event being counted. We saw earlier that the waiting times are independent exponentials with parameter λ. Furthermore, for a Poisson process with rate λ,

$$\begin{aligned} P_{jk}(t) &= Pr(X(s+t) = k|X(s) = j) \\ &= Pr(k - j \text{ occurrences in } (s,\, s+t]\big|j \text{ ocurrences in } (0,\, s]) \\ &= Pr(k - j \text{ occurrences in } (s,\, s+t]) \\ &= e^{-\lambda t}\frac{(\lambda t)^{k-j}}{(k-j)!} \qquad \text{for } k \geq j, \end{aligned}$$

since the number of occurrences has a Poisson distribution with parameter λt.

---

[4] $f(x) = \left(\frac{\beta^{\alpha}}{\Gamma(\alpha)}\right) x^{\alpha-1} e^{-\beta x}$

Separation of a Poisson Process Into Independent Poisson Processes

Recall an idea developed earlier in Section Three, Aggregate Loss Models. Suppose N has a Poisson distribution with parameter λ. Assume N is the random number of occurrences of some event in a given time period. Suppose the events can be split into two categories, C_1 and C_2, and suppose p_i is the probability that the event falls in category C_i ($p_1 + p_2 = 1$). If N_i is the random number of occurrences of events in C_i, we saw that

(i) $N = N_1 + N_2$,
(ii) N_i is Poisson with parameter λp_i, and
(iii) N_1 and N_2 are independent.

Now suppose $\{N(t)|0 \le t < \infty\}$ is a Poisson process with rate λ and events may be categorized as above. If we let $N_i(t)$ be the random number of occurrences of events in Category C_i over the time interval [0, t], then it is easy to see that $\{N_1(t)|0 \le t < \infty\}$ and $\{N_2(t)|0 \le t < \infty\}$ are independent Poisson processes with respective rates λp_1, λp_2. The waiting time between events in category i is thus exponential with mean $\frac{1}{\lambda p_i}$. See Unit Three of Section Three for more details and meaningful examples of categorizing claims, the event being counted.

Example 3 Let $\{N_1(t)|0 \le t < \infty\}$ and $\{N_2(t)|0 \le t < \infty\}$ be independent Poisson processes with respective rates λ_1, λ_2. For non-negative integers n and m, what is the probability that n events in the first process occur before m events in the second process?

Solution Let $T_i^{(j)}$ be the time of occurrence of the ith event in process j where $j = 1$ or 2. The waiting times, $W_i^{(j)}$ are independent exponentials with parameters λ_j. Suppose $W^{(1)}$ and $W^{(2)}$ are independent exponentials with parameters λ_1 and λ_2. Then

$$
\begin{aligned}
Pr(W^{(1)} < W^{(2)}) &= \int_{t_1=0}^{\infty}\int_{t_2=t_1}^{\infty} \underbrace{\lambda_1 e^{-\lambda_1 t_1} \cdot \lambda_2 e^{-\lambda_2 t_2}}_{\text{joint density}} dt_2 dt_1 \\
&= \int_{t_1=0}^{\infty} \lambda_1 e^{-\lambda_1 t_1} (-e^{-\lambda_2 t_2}\Big|_{t_2=t_1}^{\infty}) dt_1 \\
&= \int_{t_1=0}^{\infty} \lambda_1 e^{-(\lambda_1+\lambda_2)t_1}\, dt_1 \\
&= \frac{-\lambda_1}{\lambda_1+\lambda_2} e^{-(\lambda_1+\lambda_2)t_1}\Big|_{t_1=0}^{\infty} = \frac{\lambda_1}{\lambda_1+\lambda_2}.
\end{aligned}
$$

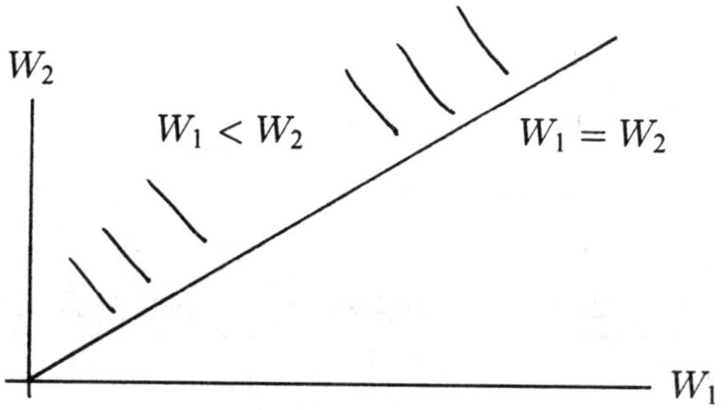

The above calculation is the first step in our solution. It is the probability that the first event occurring in either process is from the first process. After the first event of either process, consider the wait until the next event of either process. The probability that the next event is from the ith process is again $\frac{\lambda_i}{\lambda_1 + \lambda_2}$, as above, due to the independence of the waiting times $W^{(1)}$, $W^{(2)}$, and the memoryless property of exponential distributions.

This reasoning indicates that each event which occurs from the combined processes is from the ith process with probability $\frac{\lambda_i}{\lambda_1 + \lambda_2}$. So the probability that n events of process one occur before m events of process two is the same as the probability that n "successes" occur before m "failures" in a sequence of Bernoulli trials where $p = \frac{\lambda_1}{\lambda_1 + \lambda_2}$, $q = \frac{\lambda_2}{\lambda_1 + \lambda_2}$. This probability is given by

$$\sum_{k=n}^{n+m-1} \binom{n+m-1}{k} \left(\frac{\lambda_1}{\lambda_1 + \lambda_2}\right)^k \left(\frac{\lambda_2}{\lambda_1 + \lambda_2}\right)^{m+n-1-k},$$

the probability of n, $n+1$, $\ldots$, $n+m-1$ successes in $n+m-1$ trials. Notice that the event of interest must occur in $n+m-1$ trials. The sum above is over the breakdown of the sequences of $n+m-1$ trials which result in n or more successes. □

Conditional Distribution of the Arrival Times in a Poisson Process

Let $\{N(t) | 0 \leq t < \infty\}$ be a Poisson process. Suppose you are given that $N(t) = n$, that is, n occurrences of the random event took place during the time interval $[0, t]$. Given this information, what is the joint distribution of the times, $T_1, T_2, \ldots, T_n$, that the events occurred? Recall that $W_1 = T_1$, $W_2 = T_2 - T_1$, $W_n = T_n - T_{n-1}$, the waiting times between successive occurrence, are independent exponentials with parameter λ ($f_{W_i}(t) = \lambda e^{-\lambda t}$). So consider the conditional joint probability

$$Pr(T_1 = t_1, T_2 = t_2, \ldots, T_n = t_n | N(t) = n)$$

$$= \frac{Pr(T_1 = t_1, \ldots, T_n = t_n, N(t) = n)}{Pr(N(t) = n)}$$

$$= \frac{Pr(W_1 = t_1, W_2 = t_2 - t_1, \ldots, W_n = t_n - t_{n-1}, W_{n+1} > t - t_n)}{Pr(N(t) = n)}$$

$$= \frac{(\lambda e^{-\lambda t_1})(\lambda e^{-\lambda(t_2-t_1)})\cdots(\lambda e^{-\lambda(t_n-t_{n-1})})(e^{-\lambda(t-t_n)})}{[e^{-\lambda t}\frac{(\lambda t)^n}{n!}]} = \frac{n!}{t^n}$$

after cancellation. This is the same as the distribution of the order statistics for a sample of size n from a uniform distribution on $[0, t]$.

Thus, if one randomly selects one of the T_i and calls this T, then T is uniformly distributed on [0, t]. If one randomly selects a pair of the T_i they are independent and uniformly distributed on [0, t].

The Non-Homogenous Poisson Process

In the Poisson process described above we saw that $Pr(1 \text{ event in } (t, t+h]) = \lambda h + 0(h)$. That is, the approximate probability of a single event occurring in any interval $(t, t+h]$ is λh for all times t. One way to expand this model to situations where the rate of occurrence of the event of interest is time dependent, is to replace λ by a positive-valued **(intensity)** function $\lambda(t)$ for $t > 0$. This is the idea of a **non-homogeneous Poisson process.** In the infinitesimal approach this means that one assumes for $\{N(t) | 0 \leq t < \infty\}$

(i) $N(0) = 0$,

(ii) Independent increments,

(iii) $Pr(1 \text{ occurrence in } (t, t+h]) = \lambda(t)h + 0(h)$, and

(iv) $Pr(2 \text{ or more occurrences in } (t, t+h]) = 0(h)$.

In this non-homogeneous model, let $m(t) = \int_0^t \lambda(s)\,ds$ be the **cumulative intensity function.** It then follows from a differential equation derived from (i) - (iv) above, that the process increment, $N(t+s) - N(s)$ is Poisson with parameter $m(t+s) - m(s)$. Notice that if $\lambda(t) = \lambda$ then $m(t) = \int_0^t \lambda\,ds = \lambda t$, hence $m(t+s) - m(s) = \lambda t$ and $N(t+s) - N(s)$ is Poisson with parameter λt as we saw in the earlier treatment of the homogeneous Poisson process.

More General Continuous-Time Markov Chains With Discrete State Spaces

We continue with the theory of a general continuous-time Markov chain $\{X(t):0 \leq t\}$ where the possible values (states) are 0, 1, 2, ... Recall from our earlier discussion the definition of the **transition probability function**

$$P_{jk}(t) = Pr(X(s+t) = k|X(s) = j),$$

the probability that the process is in state k at time $s+t$ given that it was in state j at time s. Over the next few sections we will discuss the calculation of these functions and the idea of a limiting distribution $\vec{\pi} = (\pi_0, \pi_1, \ldots)$ where

$$1 = \sum \pi_i, \ \pi_i \geq 0, \text{ and}$$

$$\pi_k = \lim_{t \to \infty} P_{jk}(t) \text{ for all } j.$$

If such a limiting distribution exists, the distribution of $X(t)$ converges to it as t approaches ∞ regardless of the distribution at time 0.

For the Poisson process we just finished discussing, we knew that $P_{ij}(t) = e^{-\lambda t}\dfrac{(\lambda t)^{j-i}}{(j-i)!}$ if $j \geq i$ due to the way the process was defined. $N(s+t) - N(s)$ was defined to have a Poisson distribution with parameter λt. Hence

$$\begin{aligned} P_{ij}(t) &= Pr(N(s+t) = j \,|\, N(s) = i) \\ &= Pr(N(s+t) - N(s) = j - i \,|\, N(s) = i) \\ &= Pr(N(s+t) - N(s) = j - i) \qquad \text{(independent increments)} \\ &= e^{-\lambda t}\frac{(\lambda t)^{j-i}}{(j-i)!} \end{aligned}$$

Other continuous-time Markov chains are defined in such a way that the distribution of $X(s+t)\big|_{X(s)}$ is not directly given. Calculation of the $P_{ij}(t)$ becomes a much more difficult problem.

Before discussing the calculation of the $P_{jk}(t)$ and limiting distributions, it is essential to discuss the mechanism by which a continuous-time Markov chain makes the transition from a current state (node) to the next state. In a discrete-time process there were probabilities P_{jk} giving the likelihood that the process would be in state k at time $n+1$ given that it were in state j at time n. P_{jj} could be positive and $\sum_k P_{jk} = 1$. In contrast, for a continuous-time process currently in state j, $X(t) = j$, there is a random waiting time, T_j, until the next transition. Associated with this next transition[5] are probabilities P_{jk}, the probability that the process is next in state k, satisfying

[5] a visit to a state different from the current one

$$P_{jj} = 0, \ \sum_{k \neq j} P_{jk} = 1.$$

This mechanism is most easily discussed in the context of a multiple decrement model. T_j is the time until decrement (transition from state j) and $K_j = k$ is the mode of decrement if the process is next in state k. P_{jk} is the marginal probability that k is the mode of decrement.

Due to the Markovian assumption, the forces of decrement (transition intensity functions) in state j are constant. Let λ_{jk} be the constant **transition intensity function** from state j to state k. If $\lambda_{jk} > 0$ it is possible to make a transition from state j to state k. Define $\lambda_j = \sum_{k \neq j} \lambda_{jk}$ to be the total force of decrement. Then T_j has an exponential distribution with parameter λ_j and $\dfrac{\lambda_{j\ell}}{\sum_{k \neq j} \lambda_{jk}} = P_{j\ell}$ is the marginal probability that ℓ is the mode of decrement (i.e., next state visited). Thus, if $X(s) = j$, then $e^{-\lambda_j t} \lambda_{jk}\, dt$ is approximately the probability that the next transition occurs in the time interval $(s{+}t,\ s{+}t{+}dt]$ and is to the state k. An illustrative example using the multiple decrement notation of Section Two (Contingent Payment Models) follows.

Example 4 Suppose T is the time until decrement and there are two modes of decrement with constant forces $\lambda^{(i)}(t) = \lambda_i$. Let k be the mode of decrement.

(i) What is the distribution of T?

(ii) What is the distribution of K?

Solution

(i) Let $\lambda = \lambda^{(\tau)}(t) = \lambda^{(1)}(t) + \lambda^{(2)}(t) = \lambda_1 + \lambda_2$ be the total force of decrement. The survival function of T is given by

$$s_T(t) = {}_t p_0^{(\tau)} = Pr(T > t) = e^{-\int_0^t \lambda^{(\tau)}(s) ds} = e^{-\int_0^t \lambda\, ds} = e^{-\lambda t}.$$

Thus $f_T(t) = -\frac{d}{dt}(s_T(t)) = \lambda e^{-\lambda t}$, an exponential density with parameter $\lambda = \lambda_1 + \lambda_2$.

(ii)
$$Pr(K = 1) = {}_\infty q_0^{(1)} = \int_{t=0}^{\infty} {}_t p_0^{(\tau)} \lambda^{(1)}(t)\, dt$$
$$= \int_{t=0}^{\infty} e^{-\lambda t} \cdot \lambda_1 dt$$
$$= \frac{-\lambda_1}{\lambda} e^{-\lambda t} \Big|_{t=0}^{\infty} = 0 - \left(\frac{-\lambda_1}{\lambda}\right)(1) = \frac{\lambda_1}{\lambda} = \frac{\lambda_1}{\lambda_1 + \lambda_2}$$

Similarly $Pr(K = 2) = \dfrac{\lambda_2}{\lambda_1 + \lambda_2}$ □

As a result of the preceding discussion, it is clear that one could completely describe a continuous-time, discrete Markov chain by giving the constant transition intensity functions λ_{jk} for each state j.

Example 5

(i) Suppose the possible states are 0, 1, 2 and that for each state j it is only possible to move to state $j+1$ at the next transition. Suppose $\lambda_{j,j+1} = \lambda$ for all j and $\lambda_{j,k} = 0$ if $k \neq j+1$. Then T_j is exponentially distributed with parameter λ and $P_{j,j+1} = \frac{\lambda_{j,j+1}}{\sum_{k\neq j} \lambda_{jk}} = \frac{\lambda_{j,j+1}}{\lambda_{j,j+1}} = 1$. In this case we have described the Poisson process with rate λ. Recall the description of this process in terms of exponential waiting times between the occurrences of events being counted.

(ii) A variation on the Poisson process is called a **pure birth process**. For each state 0, 1, 2, ..., it is assumed that $P_{j,j+1} = 1$ (it is only possible to move from state j to state $j+1$ at the next transition). Unlike the Poisson process, however, $\lambda_{j,j+1}$ is allowed to vary with j. In this pure birth process it is common to use λ_j in place of the more cumbersome $\lambda_{j,j+1}$. Such a model could be used to describe the progression of a disease from one stage to the next where no reversal of stages is possible. State n would correspond to death if $\lambda_n = \lambda_{n,n+1} = 0$. With this assumption, once $X(s) = n$ it follows that $X(t) = n$ for all $t > s$. (When you're dead, you are dead forever after!) Panjer's AIDS progression model is of this type. The waiting time from state j to state $j+1$ is exponentially distributed with mean $\frac{1}{\lambda_j}$. Notice that as λ_j approaches 0, $\frac{1}{\lambda_j}$ approaches ∞. This is the idea that $\lambda_n = 0$ if stage n is death.

(iii) Another variation used in population models as well as queuing theory is a **birth-death process**. In state 0 it is only possible to go to state 1, so $P_{01} = 1$ and $\lambda_{0j} = 0$ unless $j = 1$. For any state $n > 0$ it is possible to move only to states $n+1$ (next transition is a "birth") or $n-1$ (next transition is a death). Only $\lambda_{n,n+1}$ and $\lambda_{n,n-1}$ are non-zero. The standard notation is $\lambda_{n,n+1} = \lambda_n$ and $\lambda_{n,n-1} = \mu_n$. Hence, $P_{n,n+1} + P_{n,n-1} = 1$ and, since $P_{j\ell} = \frac{\lambda_{j\ell}}{\sum_{k\neq j} \lambda_{jk}}$,

$$P_{n,n+1} = \frac{\lambda_{n,n+1}}{\lambda_{n,n-1} + \lambda_{n,n+1}} = \frac{\lambda_n}{\mu_n + \lambda_n}$$

$$P_{n,n-1} = \frac{\lambda_{n,n-1}}{\lambda_{n,n-1} + \lambda_{n,n+1}} = \frac{\mu_n}{\mu_n + \lambda_n}.$$

The waiting time in state n until the next transition, T_n, is exponentially distributed with parameter $\sum_{k\neq n} \lambda_{nk} = \lambda_{n,n+1} + \lambda_{n,n-1} = \lambda_n + \mu_n$. □

Properties of The Transition Probability Functions $P_{jk}(t)$

Many of the properties of these functions are best understood in a matrix algebra context. For example, if $\vec{\pi}_t = (Pr(X(t)=0),\ Pr(X(t)=1),\ \ldots)$ is a row vector giving the probability distribution of $X(t)$, then $\vec{\pi}_{t+s} = \vec{\pi}_s \cdot (P_{jk}(t))$ (matrix multiplication).

In discrete-time Markov chains we saw in Unit One that $P^n_{jk} = Pr(X_n = k | X_0 = j)$ is the same as the j,k entry of the matrix $(P_{jk})^n$ (Chapman-Kolmogorov equations). The analogous idea with continuous-time processes is

$$\vec{\pi}_{t+s} = \vec{\pi}_0 \cdot (P_{jk}(s+t)) = \vec{\pi}_s \cdot (P_{jk}(t)) = [\vec{\pi}_0 \cdot (P_{jk}(s))](P_{jk}(t)),$$

that is,

$$(P_{jk}(s+t)) = (P_{jk}(s))(P_{jk}(t)),$$

where the two matrices on the right are multiplied in the usual fashion.

The next step is to see how the $P_{jk}(t)$ can be determined from the constant transition intensity functions λ_{jk}. Calculus of matrix functions together with matrix algebra give a nice theoretical description of how to calculate the $P_{jk}(t)$. It is useful to understand why this is no easy task. The event $\{X(t) = k | X(0) = j\}$ is rather complex. In between times 0 and t the process could visit an unlimited chain of other states. So trying to decompose the event into simpler events is not a useful approach.

If $(f_{jk}(t))$ is a square matrix of functions of t, one can define the derivative matrix, $(f_{jk}(t))'$, as

$$\lim_{\Delta t \to 0} \frac{(f_{jk}(t+\Delta t) - f_{jk}(t))}{\Delta t} \quad \text{(matrix subtraction in numerator, then divide each entry by } \Delta t\text{)}.$$

The limit of a matrix is a matrix of limits, so that $(f_{jk}(t))' = (f'_{jk}(t))$. Recall that if $f'(x) = k \cdot f(x)$ and $f(0) = 1$, then $f(x) = e^{kx} = 1 + kx + \frac{(kx)^2}{2!} + \cdots$. With matrix calculus, if $(f_{jk}(t))' = (f_{jk}(t))(a_{jk})$, and $(f_{jk}(0)) = I$, then $(f_{jk}(t)) = exp(t(a_{jk})) = I + t(a_{jk}) + \frac{t^2}{2}(a_{jk})^2 + \cdots$ where I is the identity matrix of the same size as $(f_{jk}(t))$.

From the Chapman-Kolmogorov equations

$$\begin{aligned}(P'_{jk}(t)) &= \lim_{\Delta t \to 0} \frac{(P_{jk}(t+\Delta t)) - (P_{jk}(t))}{\Delta t} \\ &= \lim_{\Delta t \to 0} \frac{(P_{jk}(t))(P_{jk}(\Delta t)) - (P_{jk}(t))}{\Delta t} = (P_{jk}(t)) \lim_{\Delta t \to 0} \left[\frac{(P_{jk}(\Delta t)) - I}{\Delta t}\right]\end{aligned}$$

Now $(P_{jk}(\Delta t)) = Pr(X(\Delta t) = k | X(0) = j) \approx \lambda_{jk}(\Delta t)$ if $j \neq k$. So, since $1 = \sum_k P_{jk}(\Delta t)$, it follows that $P_{jj}(\Delta t) = 1 - \sum_{k \neq j} P_{jk}(\Delta t) = 1 - \sum_{k \neq j} \lambda_{jk}(\Delta t) = 1 - (\sum_{k \neq j} \lambda_{jk})(\Delta t) = 1 - \lambda_j(\Delta t)$, where $\lambda_j = \sum_{k \neq j} \lambda_{jk}$ is the total force of transition (decrement) in state j. Hence,

$$\frac{P_{jk}(\Delta t)-I}{\Delta t}=\frac{\begin{pmatrix}1-\lambda_0(\Delta t) & \lambda_{01}(\Delta t) & \cdots\\ \lambda_{10}(\Delta t) & 1-\lambda_1(\Delta t) & \cdots\\ \vdots & & \end{pmatrix}-\begin{pmatrix}1 & 0 & \cdots\\ 0 & 1 & \\ \vdots & & \end{pmatrix}}{\Delta t}=\begin{pmatrix}-\lambda_0 & \lambda_{01} & \lambda_{02} & \cdots\\ \lambda_{10} & -\lambda_1 & \lambda_{12} & \cdots\\ \vdots & & & \end{pmatrix}.$$

Call this last matrix Λ. Substituting Λ into the derivative calculation above, we see that

$$(P_{jk}(t))' = (P_{jk}(t))\Lambda \qquad \text{(matrix multiplication)},$$

hence $(P_{jk}(t)) = exp(t\Lambda) = I + t\Lambda + \frac{t^2\Lambda^2}{2!} + \cdots$, since $P_{jk}(0) = I$. If one equates the $(jk)^{th}$ entry of each side of the matrix differential equation $(P'_{jk}(t)) = (P_{jk}(t))\Lambda$, the resulting equation is

$$P'_{jk}(t) = \underbrace{\sum_{\ell} P_{j\ell}(t)\Lambda_{\ell k}}_{\text{(matrix mult. def.)}} = \sum_{\ell\neq k} P_{j\ell}(t)\lambda_{\ell k} - \lambda_k P_{jk}(t),$$

which is known as the **Kolmogorov Forward Equation**. In some cases this can also be used to solve for the Transition Probability functions. Both methods are contrasted in the following example to illustrate the ideas, the notation, and the difficulty in computing the $P_{jk}(t)$.

Example 6 Consider a continuous-time Markov chain with 2 states denoted by 0 ("up") and 1 ("down"). Calculate $P_{00}(t)$, $P_{01}(t)$, $P_{10}(t)$, and $P_{11}(t)$ from the constant transition intensity functions λ_{01} and λ_{10}.

Solution

(i) Method 1: Kolmogorov Forward Equations

In this 2-state model the total forces of transition are $\lambda_0 = \sum_{j\neq 0}\lambda_{0j} = \lambda_{01}$ and $\lambda_1 = \sum_{j\neq 1}\lambda_{1j} = \lambda_{10}$.

The Kolmogorov Forward equation for $P'_{00}(t)$ is

$$P'_{00}(t) = P_{01}(t)\lambda_{10} - \lambda_0 P_{00}(t) = P_{01}(t)\lambda_1 - \lambda_0 P_{00}(t) = (1-P_{00}(t))\lambda_1 - \lambda_0 P_{00}(t).$$

The final step uses the idea that $\sum_k P_{jk}(t) = 1$ since the process in certain to be in some state at time t given that it is in state j at time 0. This equation can then be rearranged to give.

$$P'_{00}(t) = -(\lambda_0+\lambda_1)P_{00}(t) + \lambda_1$$

$$\left[P_{00}(t) - \frac{\lambda_1}{\lambda_0+\lambda_1}\right]' = -(\lambda_0+\lambda_1)\left[P_{00}(t) - \frac{\lambda_1}{\lambda_0-\lambda_1}\right]$$

Now set $f(t) = P_{00}(t) - \frac{\lambda_1}{\lambda_0 + \lambda_1}$. From the above $f'(t) = -(\lambda_0+\lambda_1)f(t)$ and $f(0) = P_{00}(0) - \frac{\lambda_1}{\lambda_0 + \lambda_1} = 1 - \frac{\lambda_1}{\lambda_0 + \lambda_1} = \frac{\lambda_0}{\lambda_0 + \lambda_1}$. Hence $f(t) = \frac{\lambda_0}{\lambda_0 + \lambda_1}e^{-(\lambda_0+\lambda_1)t}$. Finally, $P_{00}(t) = f(t) + \frac{\lambda_1}{\lambda_0 + \lambda_1} = \frac{\lambda_0}{\lambda_0 + \lambda_1}e^{-(\lambda_0+\lambda_1)t} + \frac{\lambda_1}{\lambda_0 + \lambda_1}$. Hence $P_{01}(t) = 1 - P_{00}(t) = \frac{\lambda_0}{\lambda_0 + \lambda_1} - \frac{\lambda_0}{\lambda_0 + \lambda_1}e^{-(\lambda_0+\lambda_1)t}$. Similar forms for $P_{10}(t)$ and $P_{11}(t)$ can be obtained in the same way. These relations are summarized below.

<u>2-States/Up-Down</u>

$$P_{00}(t) = \frac{\lambda_0}{\lambda_0 + \lambda_1}e^{-(\lambda_0+\lambda_1)t} + \frac{\lambda_1}{\lambda_0 + \lambda_1}$$

$$P_{01}(t) = \frac{\lambda_0}{\lambda_0 + \lambda_1} - \frac{\lambda_0}{\lambda_0 + \lambda_1}e^{-(\lambda_0+\lambda_1)t}$$

$$P_{10}(t) = \frac{\lambda_1}{\lambda_0 + \lambda_1} - \frac{\lambda_1}{\lambda_0 + \lambda_1}e^{-(\lambda_0+\lambda_1)t}$$

$$P_{11}(t) = \frac{\lambda_1}{\lambda_0 + \lambda_1}e^{-(\lambda_0+\lambda_1)t} + \frac{\lambda_0}{\lambda_0 + \lambda_1}$$

For example, if $\lambda_0 = .2$ and $\lambda_1 = .6$

$$P_{00}(t) = \tfrac{1}{4}e^{-.8t} + \tfrac{3}{4}, \qquad P_{01}(t) = \tfrac{1}{4} - \tfrac{1}{4}e^{-.8t},$$

$$P_{10}(t) = \tfrac{-3}{4}e^{-.8t} + \tfrac{3}{4}, \qquad P_{11}(t) = \tfrac{3}{4}e^{-.8t} + \tfrac{1}{4}.$$

(ii) Method 2: The Matrix Equation $(P_{jk}(t)) = exp(t\Lambda)$
In this simple 2-state model, Λ is the 2×2 matrix

$$\Lambda = \begin{pmatrix} -\lambda_0 & \lambda_0 \\ \lambda_1 & -\lambda_1 \end{pmatrix}.$$

Thus

$$\begin{pmatrix} P_{00}(t) & P_{01}(t) \\ P_{10}(t) & P_{11}(t) \end{pmatrix} = exp(t\Lambda) = \begin{pmatrix} 1 & 0 \\ 0 & 1 \end{pmatrix} + t\begin{pmatrix} -\lambda_0 & \lambda_0 \\ \lambda_1 & -\lambda_1 \end{pmatrix} + \frac{t^2}{2}\begin{pmatrix} -\lambda_0 & \lambda_0 \\ \lambda_1 & -\lambda_1 \end{pmatrix}^2 + \cdots.$$

It takes some severe matrix algebra to go from this identity to the explicit forms obtained in Method 1 for the $P_{jk}(t)$, but it is easy to see they agree in a numerical example. Let $\lambda_0 = .20$, $\lambda_1 = .60$ and set $t = 2$. Then $P_{00}(2) = \frac{1}{4}e^{-1.6} + \frac{3}{4} = .80047$, $P_{01}(2) = \frac{1}{4} - \frac{1}{4}e^{-1.6} = .19953$, $P_{10}(2) = \frac{-3}{4}e^{-1.6} + \frac{3}{4} = .59858$, $P_{11}(2) = \frac{3}{4}e^{-1.6} + \frac{1}{4} = .40142$. On the other hand, using the matrix method

$$\begin{pmatrix} P_{00}(2) & P_{01}(2) \\ P_{10}(2) & P_{11}(2) \end{pmatrix} = exp\left(2\begin{pmatrix} -.20 & .20 \\ .60 & -.60 \end{pmatrix}\right) = \begin{pmatrix} .80047 & .19953 \\ .59858 & .40142 \end{pmatrix}$$

Obtained via TI-85 calculator.

□

A final comment here is worth making. With a decent computation device (computer/calculator capable of matrix algebra), the matrix approach to calculating $(P_{jk}(t_0))$ for some particular time t_0 is straightforward and easy. To find explicit forms for the $P_{jk}(t)$ for a general t is difficult with either the matrix approach or the Kolmogorov Forward equation. In the Condensed Review Notes at the end of this unit we illustrate $P_{ij}(t)$ calculations for a pure-birth process by a recursive method. One can also use $(P_{jk}(t)) = exp(t\Lambda)$ when Λ can be diagonalized from its eigenvalues. (Illustrated later.)

Limiting Probabilities

The theory here follows the pattern seen with discrete-time Markov chains. Suppose for all states i that $\lim_{t\to\infty} P_{ij}(t)$ exists and is independent of i, that is $\lim_{t\to\infty} P_{ij}(t) = \pi_j$. Then $\vec{\pi} = (\pi_0, \pi_1, \ldots)$ is called the **limiting distribution**. This distribution is **stationary** in the sense that if $Pr(X(t) = j) = \pi_j$, then $Pr(X(t+s) = j) = \pi_j$ for all s. In other words, if $\vec{\pi}$ gives the distribution of the state at time t, the $\vec{\pi}$ is also the distribution of the state at any time after t. In matrix notation, one has $\vec{\pi}(P_{ij}(t)) = \vec{\pi}$. Sufficient conditions for the limiting distribution to exist are:

(i) All states must communicate, that is, beginning in state j there is a positive probability of eventually reaching state k after (perhaps) many transitions; and

(ii) For each state k, the expected time to return to state k, given that $X(0) = k$, is finite (i.e., positive recurrence).

When such a limiting distribution exists (i.e., $\pi_j = \lim_{t\to\infty} P_{ij}(t)$ for all i), it follows from

$$(P'_{jk}(t)) = (P_{jk}(t))\Lambda \quad \text{(matrix mult.)}$$

that $\vec{\pi}\Lambda = (0, \ldots, 0)$. In fact, $\vec{\pi}$ is the unique solution of this system of linear equations such that $\pi_j > 0$, $1 = \sum \pi_j$. The two state up-down model of Example 6 will be used to illustrate these ideas.

Example 7 Find the limiting distribution for a 2-state, continuous-time Markov chain where $\lambda_0 = \lambda_{01}$ and $\lambda_1 = \lambda_{10}$ are the only positive transition intensities.

Solution

Method 1: We saw the following in the solution to Example 6:

$$P_{00}(t) = \frac{\lambda_0}{\lambda_0 + \lambda_1} e^{-(\lambda_0+\lambda_1)t} + \frac{\lambda_1}{\lambda_0 + \lambda_1}$$

$$P_{01}(t) = \frac{\lambda_0}{\lambda_0 + \lambda_1} - \frac{\lambda_0}{\lambda_0 + \lambda_1} e^{-(\lambda_0+\lambda_1)t}$$

$$P_{10}(t) = \frac{\lambda_1}{\lambda_0 + \lambda_1} - \frac{\lambda_1}{\lambda_0 + \lambda_1} e^{-(\lambda_0+\lambda_1)t}$$

$$P_{11}(t) = \frac{\lambda_1}{\lambda_0 + \lambda_1} e^{-(\lambda_0+\lambda_1)t} + \frac{\lambda_0}{\lambda_0 + \lambda_1}$$

This two-state chain is irreducible (all states communicate) and positive recurrent (due to a finite number of states). Thus the limiting distribution must exist, and, from the explicit $P_{ij}(t)$ description above, it follows that

$$\lim_{t\to\infty} P_{00}(t) = \frac{\lambda_1}{\lambda_0 + \lambda_1} = \pi_0$$

$$\lim_{t\to\infty} P_{01}(t) = \frac{\lambda_0}{\lambda_0 + \lambda_1} = \pi_1$$

$$\lim_{t\to\infty} P_{10}(t) = \frac{\lambda_1}{\lambda_0 + \lambda_1} = \pi_0$$

$$\lim_{t\to\infty} P_{11}(t) = \frac{\lambda_0}{\lambda_0 + \lambda_1} = \pi_1$$

since $\lim_{t\to\infty} e^{-at} = 0$ when $a > 0$. These relations can be summarized by $\lim_{t\to\infty} P_{ij}(t) = \pi_j$.

Method 2: If one cannot find explicit forms for the $P_{ij}(t)$ as above, one can still find $\vec{\pi}$ by solving the linear system $\vec{\pi}\Lambda = (0, 0)$ subject to the restriction $\pi_0 + \pi_1 = 1$. In this 2-state model Λ is given by

$$\Lambda = \begin{pmatrix} -\lambda_0 & \lambda_0 \\ \lambda_1 & -\lambda_1 \end{pmatrix}.$$

We must thus solve

$$\pi_0(-\lambda_0) + \pi_1(\lambda_1) = 0$$

$$\pi_0(\lambda_0) + \pi_1(-\lambda_1) = 0$$

subject to $\pi_0 + \pi_1 = 1$. Notice that the equations are redundant (dependent). From the first equation it follows that $\pi_1 = \frac{\lambda_0}{\lambda_1}\pi_0$. Thus $1 = \pi_0 + \pi_1 = \pi_0 + \frac{\lambda_0}{\lambda_1}\pi_0$ results in $\pi_0 = \frac{\lambda_1}{\lambda_0 + \lambda_1}$, $\pi_1 = 1 - \pi_0 = \frac{\lambda_0}{\lambda_0 + \lambda_1}$.

Other Approximation Methods:

Since $(P_{ij}(t)) = exp(t\Lambda)$, one might calculate $exp(t\Lambda)$ for some large t (large enough to allow many expected transitions to have occurred by this time). For example, if $\lambda_0 = .20$ and $\lambda_1 = .60$ the expected waiting times in states 0 and 1 are $5 = \frac{1}{.20}$ and $\frac{5}{3} = \frac{1}{.60}$. The expected time for one "round trip" is thus $5 + \frac{5}{3} = \frac{20}{3}$. If $t = 10\left(\frac{20}{3}\right) \approx 67$, there would be 10 expected round trips. Using a TI-85 calculator,

$$exp\left(67\begin{pmatrix} -.20 & .20 \\ .60 & -.60 \end{pmatrix}\right) = \begin{pmatrix} .750000 & .250000 \\ .750000 & .250000 \end{pmatrix}.$$

Each row is the limiting distribution $\pi_0 = \frac{\lambda_1}{\lambda_0 + \lambda_1} = \frac{.60}{.80} = .75$ and $\pi_1 = \frac{\lambda_0}{\lambda_0 + \lambda_1} = \frac{.20}{.80} = .25$ (to six decimal places). □

Another equivalent version of limiting probabilities is based on the question: What is the **long-term relative frequency** of state k? With $X(0) = j$ and for any k and $t > 0$, consider

$$\frac{(\text{time in state } k \text{ during } [0, t])}{t},$$

the proportion of the time interval $[0, t]$ spent in state k for one possible history of the process. Now take a limit as $t \to \infty$. This limit should also be π_k. Consider this idea in the context of the 2-state model of Examples 6 and 7.

Suppose $X(0) = 0$. There is a series of transitions $0 \to 1$, $1 \to 0$, $0 \to 1$, ... with waiting times $T_{0,1}$, $T_{1,1}$, $T_{0,2}$, where $T_{i,j}$ is the time in state i until the jth transition from this state. All $T_{0,j}$ are exponentially distributed with mean $\frac{1}{\lambda_0}$, and all $T_{1,j}$ are exponentially distributed with mean $\frac{1}{\lambda_1}$. If $t = T_{0,1} + T_{1,1} + \cdots + T_{1,n}$ (n round trips by time t) then the proportion of time spent in state 0 is

$$\frac{T_{0,1} + \cdots + T_{0,n}}{T_{0,1} + T_{1,1} + \cdots + T_{1,n}}.$$

Now divide top and bottom by n and recall that the sample mean converges in probability to the population mean as the sample size goes to infinity. Thus the numerator converges to $\frac{1}{\lambda_0}$, and the denominator to $\frac{1}{\lambda_0} + \frac{1}{\lambda_1}$. The ratio converges in probability to

$$\frac{\left(\frac{1}{\lambda_0}\right)}{\left(\frac{1}{\lambda_0} + \frac{1}{\lambda_1}\right)} = \frac{\lambda_1}{\lambda_0 + \lambda_1},$$

which we saw in Example 7 to be π_0.

Diagonalizing Λ to Compute $(P_{ij}(t)) = exp(t\Lambda)$

If B is a diagonal matrix (all off-diagonal entries zero),

$$B = \begin{pmatrix} b_1 & & \\ & b_2 & \\ & & \ddots \end{pmatrix},$$

then

$$exp(tB) = \begin{pmatrix} e^{tb_1} & & \\ & e^{tb_2} & \\ & & \ddots \end{pmatrix}$$

is also a diagonal matrix. Now, if one can find an invertible matrix A such that $A^{-1}\Lambda A$ is diagonal (i.e., find the eigenvalues of Λ), say B, then $\Lambda = ABA^{-1}$ and

$$exp(t\Lambda) = exp(A(tB)A^{-1}) = A\,exp(tB)A^{-1}$$

since $(A(tB)A^{-1})^n = A(tB)A^{-1} \cdot A(tB)A^{-1} \cdots A(tB)A^{-1} = A(tB)^n A^{-1}$. With this trick one can calculate explicit $P_{ij}(t)$ formulas such as we derived in Example 6 from the Kolgomorov forward equation.

For example, consider again the 2-state Markov chain with $\lambda_0 = .20$, $\lambda_1 = .60$. The eigenvalues of

$$\Lambda = \begin{pmatrix} -.20 & .20 \\ .60 & -.60 \end{pmatrix}$$

are 0 and $-.80$ and the eigenvectors are $(1, 1)$ and $(1, -3)$. Now form A by putting the eigenvectors down the columns:

$$A = \begin{pmatrix} 1 & 1 \\ 1 & -3 \end{pmatrix}.$$

It is easily checked that A^{-1} is given by

$$\mathrm{A}^{-1} = -\frac{1}{4}\begin{pmatrix} -3 & -1 \\ -1 & 1 \end{pmatrix},$$

and

$$\mathrm{A}^{-1}\Lambda\mathrm{A} = \begin{pmatrix} 0 & 0 \\ 0 & -.80 \end{pmatrix}.$$

Hence

$$\begin{aligned}
(P_{ij}(t)) &= \mathrm{A}\cdot exp\left(t\begin{pmatrix} 0 & 0 \\ 0 & -.80 \end{pmatrix}\right)\mathrm{A}^{-1} \\
&= \mathrm{A}\cdot exp\left(\begin{pmatrix} 0 & 0 \\ 0 & -.80t \end{pmatrix}\right)\mathrm{A}^{-1} \\
&= \mathrm{A}\begin{pmatrix} 1 & 0 \\ 0 & e^{-.8t} \end{pmatrix}\mathrm{A}^{-1} \\
&= \begin{pmatrix} 1 & 1 \\ 1 & -3 \end{pmatrix}\begin{pmatrix} 1 & 0 \\ 0 & e^{-.8t} \end{pmatrix}\begin{pmatrix} \frac{3}{4} & \frac{1}{4} \\ \frac{1}{4} & -\frac{1}{4} \end{pmatrix} \\
&= \begin{pmatrix} \frac{3}{4}+\frac{1}{4}e^{-.8t} & \frac{1}{4}-\frac{1}{4}e^{-.8t} \\ \frac{3}{4}-\frac{3}{4}e^{-.8t} & \frac{1}{4}+\frac{3}{4}e^{-.8t} \end{pmatrix}
\end{aligned}$$

as we saw in Example 6.

An Example of Cash Flow Analysis Connected With a Continuous-Time Markov Chain

Suppose a machine is either up (operating) or down (not operating). While it is up suppose it produces a continuous income stream of A/year. While it is down it requires a continuous service labor cost of B/year. In addition, each time it goes down, a cost of C is incurred for parts needed to repair the machine. Suppose the process can be viewed as the 2-state Markov chain of Examples 6 and 7 where 0 is the "up" state.

Example 8 At a force of interest of δ, calculate the following for a machine currently up:

(i) The actuarial present value of the costs of being down (i.e., $A + B$/year continuously while down; lost income and service labor costs).

(ii) The actuarial present value of the costs of going down (i.e., C at each "breakdown"; the cost of parts).

Solution

(i) The costs of **being** down are like a continuous life annuity. The APV is given by the integral

$$\int_{t=0}^{\infty} \underbrace{(A+B)\,dt}_{\substack{\text{amount during}\\ [t,t+dt] \text{ if down}}} \cdot \underbrace{e^{-\delta t}}_{\text{discount}} \cdot \underbrace{P_{01}(t)}_{\substack{\text{probability}\\ \text{of being down}}} = (A+B)\int_{t=0}^{\infty} e^{-\delta t} \underbrace{\left[\frac{\lambda_0}{\lambda_0+\lambda_1} - \frac{\lambda_0}{\lambda_0+\lambda_1} e^{-(\lambda_0+\lambda_1)t}\right]}_{P_{01}(t),\ \text{Example 6}} dt$$

$$= (A+B)\left[\frac{\lambda_0}{\lambda_0+\lambda_1}\right]\left[\frac{1}{\delta} - \frac{1}{\lambda_0+\lambda_1+\delta}\right]$$

(ii) The costs of **going** down are similar to those incurred in life insurance – triggered by the transition from state 0 ("living") to state 1 ("dead"). If the machine is currently up, then $P_{00}(t)\lambda_{01}\,dt$ is approximately the probability of going down in the instant $[t, t+dt]$. So the APV of going-down costs is

$$\int_{t=0}^{\infty} \underbrace{C}_{\substack{\text{amount per}\\ \text{breakdown}}} \cdot \underbrace{e^{-\delta t}}_{\text{discount}} \cdot \underbrace{P_{00}(t)\lambda_{01}\,dt}_{\substack{\text{probability of going}\\ \text{down in } [t,t+dt]}}$$

where λ_{01}, the force of transition from up to down, was written as λ_0, in Examples 6 and 7. This integral becomes.

$$(C\lambda_0)\int_{t=0}^{\infty} e^{-\delta t} \cdot \underbrace{\left[\frac{\lambda_0}{\lambda_0+\lambda_1} e^{-(\lambda_0+\lambda_1)t} + \frac{\lambda_1}{\lambda_0+\lambda_1}\right]}_{P_{00}(t),\ \text{Example 6}} dt$$

$$= (C\lambda_0)\left[\frac{\lambda_0}{\lambda_0+\lambda_1} \cdot \frac{1}{\delta+\lambda_0+\lambda_1} + \frac{\lambda_1}{\lambda_0+\lambda_1} \cdot \frac{1}{\delta}\right] \quad \square$$

Note: Jones uses similar techniques in his model of Continuing Care Retirement Communities to analyze the cost of services provided to members of the community. See the example at the end of the Condensed Review Notes for this Unit.

CONDENSED REVIEW NOTES AND ADVANCED TOPICS

Continuous-Time Markov Chains

$\{X(t)|0 \leq t < \infty\}$ is assumed to be a collection of discrete random variables with values (states) in the state-space $\{0, 1, 2, \ldots\}$. The process is said to be in state j at time if $X(t) = j$. It is called a **time-homogeneous Markov chain** if for all s, t

$$Pr(X(s+t) = k \big| X(s) = j, X(u) = x(u), 0 \leq u < s) = Pr(X(s+t) = k \big| X(s) = j) = P_{jk}(t)$$

$\vec{\pi}_t = (Pr(X_t = 0), Pr(X_t = 1), \ldots)$ (row vector = distribution at time t)

$\underbrace{\vec{\pi}_{s+t}}_{1\times n} = \underbrace{\vec{\pi}_s}_{1\times n} \underbrace{(P_{jk}(t))}_{n\times n}$ (matrix multiplication with n states)

$(P_{jk}(t))$ **transition probability matrix** (j^{th} row gives the conditional distribution of $X(t)$ given $X(0) = j$)

Counting Processes

$N(t)$ is the number of occurrences over the time interval $[0, t]$ of some well-defined random event (e.g. a claim occurs against a portfolio of policies).

Properties:

(i) $N(0) = 0$, $N(t) \geq 0$, $N(t)$ integral

(ii) $N(t_2) - N(t_1)$ is the number of events occurring in $(t_1, t_2]$ if $t_1 < t_2$

(iii) **Increments** are **independent** if $N(t_2) - N(t_1)$ and $N(t_4) - N(t_3)$ are independent whenever $t_1 < t_2 \leq t_3 < t_4$

(iv) **Increments** are **stationary** if $N(t_2) - N(t_1)$ has the same distribution as $N(t_4) - N(t_3)$ whenever $t_2 - t_1 = t_4 - t_3$.

A counting process with independent and stationary increments is a time-homogeneous Markov chain.

The Poisson Process (Special Counting Process)

1. A counting process with independent and stationary increments such that $N(t)$ is Poisson with parameter λt is said to be a **Poisson process** with **rate** λ. (λ occurrences of the random event are expected per unit of time).

Properties:

(i) $E[N(t)] = \lambda t, Var(N(t)) = \lambda t$

(ii) $P_{jk}(t) = Pr(N(s+t) = k \mid N(s) = j)$

$$= Pr(N(s+t) - N(s) = k - j \mid N(s) = j)$$

$$= Pr(N(s+t) - N(s) = k - j) \qquad \text{(independent increments)}$$

$$= e^{-\lambda t}\frac{(\lambda t)^{k-j}}{(k-j)!} \qquad \text{if } k \geq j$$

2. The Poisson Process can also be characterized by assuming independence of increments and that $N(t_2) - N(t_1)$ is Poisson with parameter $\lambda(t_2 - t_1)$ if $t_2 > t_1$.

3. **Infinitesimal Characterization.** A function $f(h)$ is said to be $0(h)$ if $\lim_{h \to 0} \frac{f(h)}{h} = 0$, that is $f(h)$ goes to zero faster than h. If $f(h)$ has a convergent power series near 0 this means that $f(0) = f'(0) = 0$, $f(h) = f''(0)\frac{h^2}{2!} +$ (higher order terms).

$\{N(t) | t \geq 0\}$ is a Poisson process if it has independent and stationary increments and, in addition,

(i) $Pr(N(h) = 1) = \lambda h + 0(h)$, and

(ii) $Pr(N(h) \geq 2) = 0(h)$.

Note: The assumption of stationarity could be dropped if $N(h)$ is replaced in (i) and (ii) by $N(t+h) - N(t)$ and (i) and (ii) hold for all t.

4. **Waiting Time Characterization.** Let $0 < T_1 < T_2 <$ be the random times of the first, second, ... occurrences of the event being counted. Set $W_1 = T_1$, $W_i = T_i - T_{i-1}$ for $i > 1$. The W_i are **waiting times (interarrival times).** For a Poisson process the W_i are independent and identically distributed as exponentials with parameter λ: $f_W(t) = \lambda e^{-\lambda t}$, $E[W] = \frac{1}{\lambda}$, $Var(W) = \frac{1}{\lambda^2}$.

Conversely, if a counting process has waiting times with the properties above, then it is a Poisson process with rate λ.

Note: The distribution of $T_n = W_1 + \cdots + W_n$ is a Gamma[6] distribution with $\alpha = n, \beta = \lambda$. So $E[T_n] = \frac{\alpha}{\beta} = \frac{n}{\lambda}$, $Var(T_n) = \frac{\alpha}{\beta^2} = \frac{n}{\lambda^2}$.

[6] $f(x) = \left(\frac{\beta^\alpha}{\Gamma(\alpha)}\right)x^{\alpha-1}e^{-\beta x}$

5. **Separation of a Poisson Process Into Independent Poisson Processes.** Suppose the events can be split into two categories, C_1 and C_2 (e.g. claims $\le a$ and claims $> a$). Let p_i be the probability an event falls in category C_i. Let $N_i(t)$ be the number of category C_i events occurring in $[0, t]$. Then

(i) $N(t) = N_1(t) + N_2(t)$

(ii) $N_1(t)$, $N_2(t)$ are independent.

(iii) $\{N_i(t) | 0 \le t < \infty\}$ is a Poisson process with rate $\lambda_i = \lambda p_i$.

(iv) The probability that n events of category 1 occur before m events of category 2 is

$$\sum_{k=n}^{n+m-1} \binom{n+m-1}{k} \left(\frac{\lambda_1}{\lambda_1+\lambda_2}\right)^k \left(\frac{\lambda_2}{\lambda_1+\lambda_2}\right)^{m+n-1-k}.$$

6. **Conditional Distribution of the Arrival Times in a Poisson Process**

$Pr(T_1 = t_1,\, T_2 = t_2,\, \ldots,\, T_n = t_n | N(t) = n) = \frac{n!}{t^n}$, which is the same joint distribution as the order statistics for a sample of size n from a uniform distribution on $[0, t]$.

7. **The Non-Homogeneous Poisson Process**

$\{N(t) | 0 \le t < \infty\}$ is assumed to satisfy:

(i) $N(0) = 0$,

(ii) Independent increments,

(iii) $Pr(1 \text{ occurrence in } (t, t{+}h]) = \lambda(t)h + 0(h)$, and

(iv) $Pr(2 \text{ or more occurrences in } (t, t{+}h]) = 0(h)$.

Let $m(t) = \int_0^t \lambda(s)\, ds$. Then $N(t{+}s) - N(s)$ is Poisson with parameter $m(t{+}s) - m(s)$. If $\lambda(t) = \lambda$ for all t this is the Poisson process with rate λ.

More General Continuous-Time Markov Chains With Discrete State Space

1. **Transition From One State to Another**. If a process is currently (time s) in a state j, that is $X(s) = j$, there is a random waiting time, T_j, until transition to the next state. Associated with this next transition are probabilities P_{jk}, the probability that the process is next in state k, satisfying $P_{jj} = 0$ and $1 = \sum_{k \ne j} P_{jk}$.

2. **The Multiple Decrement Model of Transition Between States.** T_j is the time until decrement (transition) and $K_j = k$ is the mode of decrement if the next transition is to state k.

(i) λ_{jk} denotes the constant **transition intensity function** from state j to state k. It is constant due to the Markovian assumption. Set $\lambda_j = \sum_{k \neq j} \lambda_{jk}$, the total force of transition.

(ii) T_j is exponentially distributed with parameter λ_j (mean $= \frac{1}{\lambda_j}$, variance $= \frac{1}{\lambda_j^2}$)

(iii) Given that $X(s) = j$, $e^{-\lambda_j t}\lambda_{jk}\,dt$ is approximately the probability that the next transition is to state k and it occurs in the time interval $(s+t, s+t+dt]$. (i.e., $e^{-\lambda_j t}\lambda_{jk}$ is the joint density of the time until transition, T_j, and the mode of transition, K_j)

(iv) P_{jk}, the probability that the process is in state k at the next transition, given it is currently in state j, is the marginal probability that k is the mode of transition. Due to constant forces

$$P_{jk} = Pr(K_j = k) = {}_{\infty}q_0^{(k)} = \frac{\lambda_{jk}}{\sum_{k \neq j} \lambda_{jk}} = \frac{\lambda_{jk}}{\lambda_j}$$

3. **Properties of the Transition Probability Functions $P_{jk}(t)$.** When we write $(P_{jk}(t))$ we think of arranging these functions in a square matrix. (See notes under the earlier heading Continuous-Time Markov Chains with which this summary began).

(i) **Chapman-Kolmogorov equations**

$$(P_{jk}(s))(P_{jk}(t)) = (P_{jk}(s+t))$$

equivalently,

$$P_{jk}(s+t) = \sum_{\ell} P_{j\ell}(s) P_{\ell k}(t)$$

(ii) **Relation With the Transition Intensity Functions**

Let Λ be the square matrix given by

$$\begin{pmatrix} -\lambda_0 & \lambda_{01} & \lambda_{02} & \cdots \\ \lambda_{10} & -\lambda_1 & \lambda_{12} & \cdots \\ \vdots & & & \end{pmatrix}$$

where $\lambda_j = \sum_{k \neq j} \lambda_{jk}$ (all rows sum to 0).

Then

$$(P_{jk}(t))' = (P_{jk}(t))\Lambda \quad \text{(matrix multiplication)},$$

$$(P_{jk}(0)) = I. \quad \text{(identity matrix)}$$

so

$$(P_{jk}(t)) = exp(t\Lambda) = I + t\Lambda + \frac{t^2\Lambda^2}{2!} + \cdots,$$

Equating the $(j,k)^{th}$ entry of both sides of the matrix differential equation above results in

$$P'_{jk}(t) = \sum_{\ell \neq k} P_{j\ell}(t)\lambda_{lk} - \lambda_k P_{jk}(t),$$

which is known as **Kolmogorov's Forward Equation.** **Kolmogorov's Backward Equation** states

$$P'_{jk}(t) = \sum_{\ell \neq j} \lambda_{j\ell} P_{\ell k}(t) - \lambda_j P_{jk}(t),$$

These systems of differential equations can be solved simultaneously (if you are lucky) to obtain concrete expressions for the $P_{jk}(t)$ (See Examples 6 and 7 in the reading) as an alternative to the matrix solution $(P_{jk}(t)) = exp(t\Lambda)$.

4. **Limiting Probabilities**

(i) If all states communicate (beginning in any state j there is a positive probability of reaching state k for any k), and if for each k the expected time to return to state k, given that $X(0) = k$, is finite, then $\lim_{t\to\infty} P_{ij}(t)$ exists and is independent of i. Set $\pi_j = \lim_{t\to\infty} P_{ij}(t)$, $\vec{\pi} = (\pi_0, \pi_1, \ldots)$. $\vec{\pi}$ is called the **limiting distribution**. Regardless of the distribution of $X(0)$, $\vec{\pi}_t = \vec{\pi}_0(P_{jk}(t))$ approaches $\vec{\pi}$ as $t \to \infty$. The distribution is **stationary** in the sense that if $\vec{\pi}_t = \vec{\pi}$ then $\vec{\pi}_{t+s} = \vec{\pi}$ for all $s > 0$. $\vec{\pi}$ is the unique solution of $\vec{\pi} = \vec{\pi}(P_{jk}(t))$ subject to $1 = \pi_0 + \pi_1 + \cdots$. $\vec{\pi}$ may be obtained as the unique solution of the linear system (matrix equation)

$$\vec{\pi} \cdot \Lambda = (0, 0. \ldots) \qquad \text{(rate into a state = rate out in a steady state)}$$

subject to $1 = \pi_0 + \pi_1 + \cdots$.

(ii) If $X(0) = j$, for any k and $t > 0$ consider

$$\frac{(\text{time in state } k \text{ during } [0,t]}{t},$$

the fraction of the time interval $[0,t]$ spent in state k. As $t \to \infty$ this ratio converges in probability to π_k. The limit of this ratio is called the **long-term relative frequency** of state k.

5. **Diagonalizing Λ to find $[P_{jk}(t)]$.**

(i) If $B = \begin{pmatrix} b_1 & 0 & \cdots \\ 0 & b_2 & \\ \vdots & & \ddots \end{pmatrix}$ then $exp(tB) = \begin{pmatrix} e^{tb_1} & 0 & \cdots \\ 0 & e^{tb_2} & \\ \vdots & & \ddots \end{pmatrix}$.

(ii) If Λ has distinct eigenvalues $b_0, b_1, \ldots$ and A is formed by putting corresponding eigenvectors down the columns, then $A^{-1}\Lambda A = B$ and

$$(P_{jk}(t)) = exp(t\Lambda) = A\,exp(tB)A^{-1}$$

A Two-State Markov Chain Example

1. States 0 and 1 are called "up" and "down" respectively.

2. $\lambda_{01}, \lambda_{10}$ are the forces of transition and $\lambda_0 = \lambda_{01}, \lambda_1 = \lambda_{10}$ are the total forces. Thus

$$\Lambda = \begin{pmatrix} -\lambda_0 & \lambda_0 \\ \lambda_1 & -\lambda_1 \end{pmatrix}.$$

3. $$P_{00}(t) = \frac{\lambda_0}{\lambda_0+\lambda_1}e^{-(\lambda_0+\lambda_1)t} + \frac{\lambda_1}{\lambda_0+\lambda_1} \xrightarrow{\text{(as } t\to\infty)} \frac{\lambda_1}{\lambda_0+\lambda_1}$$

$$P_{01}(t) = \frac{\lambda_0}{\lambda_0+\lambda_1} - \frac{\lambda_0}{\lambda_0+\lambda_1}e^{-(\lambda_0+\lambda_1)t} \longrightarrow \frac{\lambda_0}{\lambda_0+\lambda_1}$$

$$P_{10}(t) = \frac{\lambda_1}{\lambda_0+\lambda_1} - \frac{\lambda_1}{\lambda_0+\lambda_1}e^{-(\lambda_0+\lambda_1)t} \longrightarrow \frac{\lambda_1}{\lambda_0+\lambda_1}$$

$$P_{11}(t) = \frac{\lambda_1}{\lambda_0+\lambda_1}e^{-(\lambda_0+\lambda_1)t} + \frac{\lambda_0}{\lambda_0+\lambda_1} \longrightarrow \frac{\lambda_0}{\lambda_0+\lambda_1}$$

4. Limiting distribution: $\pi_0 = \frac{\lambda_1}{\lambda_0+\lambda_1}, \; \pi_1 = \frac{\lambda_0}{\lambda_0+\lambda_1}$

5. Suppose the state is currently up. The APV of B/yr continuously (t in years) while the state is down is

$$\int_{t=0}^{\infty} \underbrace{B\,dt}_{\substack{\text{Amount}\\ \text{in } [t,\,t+dt]}} \cdot \underbrace{e^{-\delta t}}_{\text{discount}} \cdot \underbrace{P_{01}(t)}_{\substack{\text{probability}\\ \text{down at time } t}} \qquad \text{(Cost of being down)}$$

Suppose a cost of C is incurred each time there is a transition from up to down. The APV of these cost is

$$\int_{t=0}^{\infty} \underbrace{C}_{\substack{\text{amount per}\\\text{breakdown}}} \cdot \underbrace{e^{-\delta t}}_{\text{discount}} \cdot \underbrace{P_{00}(t)\lambda_{01}\,dt}_{\substack{\text{probability of going}\\\text{down in } [t,t+dt]}} . \qquad \text{(Cost of going down)}$$

Suppose an income of I/yr is continuously earned while up. The APV of these earnings is

$$\int_{t=0}^{\infty} \underbrace{I\,dt}_{\substack{\text{Amount}\\\text{in } [t,t+dt]}} \cdot \underbrace{e^{-\delta t}}_{\text{discount}} \cdot \underbrace{P_{00}(t)}_{\substack{\text{probability of}\\\text{being up at time } t}} .$$

Pure Birth Processes

1. The states are 0, 1, 2, ... and it is only possible to make a transition from state i to state $i+1$. So $P_{i,i+1} = 1$, $\lambda_j = \lambda_{j,j+1}$ is the total force of transition. T_j, the time in state j, is exponentially distributed with parameter λ_j with $E[T_j] = \frac{1}{\lambda_j}$, $Var(T_j) = \frac{1}{\lambda_j^2}$. Because it is only possible to move forward in the chain over time, it follows that $T_i + T_{i+1} + \cdots + T_{j-1}$ is the time it takes to move from state i to state j when $j > i$. Due to independence, the expected value and variance of this time are $\sum_{k=i}^{j-1} \frac{1}{\lambda_k}$, $\sum_{k=i}^{j-1} \frac{1}{\lambda_k^2}$. The Poisson process with rate λ is the special case where all $\lambda_j = \lambda$.

2. **Recursive Calculation of $P_{ij}(t)$ with $j > i$.**
Note first that $P_{ii}(t)$ is just the survival function $e^{-\lambda_i t}$ of the waiting time, T_i, until transition. Suppose$P_{ii}(t)$, $P_{i,i+1}(t)$, ..., $P_{i,j-1}$ have been calculated. Then $P_{i,j}(t)$ can be calculated via

$$P_{i,j}(t) = \int_{s=0}^{t} \underbrace{P_{i,j-1}(s)}_{\substack{\text{in state } j-1\\\text{at time } s}} \cdot \underbrace{\lambda_{j-1}\,ds}_{\substack{\text{transition to}\\\text{state } j \text{ during}\\ [s,\, s+ds]}} \cdot \underbrace{e^{-\lambda_j(t-s)}}_{\substack{\text{remains in state}\\ j \text{ from time } s\\\text{to time } t}}$$

$$= \lambda_{j-1} e^{-\lambda_j t} \int_{s=0}^{t} P_{i,j-1}(s) e^{\lambda_j s}\,ds \ \text{ if } j > i.$$

Example

$$P_{0,1}(t) = \lambda_0 e^{-\lambda_1 t} \int_{s=0}^{t} e^{-\lambda_0 s} e^{\lambda_1 s}\, ds = \begin{cases} \dfrac{\lambda_0}{\lambda_1 - \lambda_0}[e^{-\lambda_0 t} - e^{-\lambda_1 t}] & \lambda_1 \neq \lambda_0 \\ \lambda t e^{-\lambda t} & \lambda = \lambda_1 = \lambda_0 \end{cases}$$

Note: When $\lambda = \lambda_i = \lambda_{i+1} = \ldots = \lambda_{j-1}$, then $T_i + \cdots + T_{j-1}$ is a Gamma distribution with $\alpha = j - i$ (number of transitions to go from state i to state j) and $\beta = \lambda$. A special case of this is seen in the example above when $\lambda_1 = \lambda_0 = \lambda$.

3. $P_{ij}(t)\lambda_j\, dt$ is approximately the probability that the state at time t is j (given that the state at time 0 is i) and the transition to state j+1 occurs in the next instant. This is also $f_{T_i+\cdots+T_j}(t)dt$. In other words, $P_{ij}(t)\lambda_j$ is the density function of $T_i + \cdots + T_j$, whereas $P_{ij}(t)$ is the survival function.

4. In a pure birth process all states are transient and the process tends to infinity as $t \to \infty$. There is no limiting distribution, but studying $(T_0 + T_1 + \cdots + T_j)$-type variables can help understand how swiftly the process tends to infinity.

5. **Panjer's Aids Progression Model**. There are six states:

   0 At Risk

   1 HIV positive, no symptoms

   2 LAS

   3 ARC

   4 AIDS

   5 Death

   No reversal of progress is assumed to be possible. This can thus be viewed as a modified pure birth process with state 5 as an absorbing state. The theory of sums $T_i + \cdots + T_j$ developed above will still apply.

Birth/Death Processes

1. The states are 0, 1, 2, ... and it is only possible to go from state 0 to state 1 or from state i to states $i+1$ or $i-1$ if $i \geq 1$. Thus $P_{01} = 1$ and $P_{i,i-1} + P_{i,i+1} = 1$ if $i \geq 1$. The notational standards earlier established are adjusted here as follows:

earlier standard	Birth/Death Model Notation	
$\lambda_{i,i+1}$	λ_i	
$\lambda_{i,i-1}$	μ_i	$(\mu_0 = 0)$
$\lambda_i = \lambda_{i,i+1} + \lambda_{i,i-1}$	$\lambda_i + \mu_i$	(λ_0 in state 0)

The waiting time in state i, T_i, is exponentially distributed with parameter $\lambda_i + \mu_i$, and the transition probabilities are $P_{i,i+1} = \frac{\lambda_i}{\lambda_i + \mu_i}$, $P_{i,i-1} = \frac{\mu_i}{\lambda_i + \mu_i}$ as we saw in our earlier multiple decrement model of transition to the next state.

2. The question as to whether the process is ergodic and has a limiting distribution comes down to a subtle calculation measuring the relative sizes of the λ_i and μ_{i+1}. If $\sum_{n=1}^{\infty} \left(\frac{\lambda_0 \cdots \lambda_{n-1}}{\mu_1 \cdots \mu_n} \right) < \infty$, the chain is ergodic and the limiting distribution $\vec{\pi} = (\pi_0, \pi_1, \ldots)$ can be calculated via the following:

$$\pi_0 = \frac{1}{1 + \sum_{n=1}^{\infty} \left(\frac{\lambda_0 \cdots \lambda_{n-1}}{\mu_1 \cdots \mu_n} \right)}$$

$$\pi_{j+1} = \frac{\lambda_j}{\mu_{j+1}} \pi_j \text{ for } j \geq 0.$$

The ratio test would imply convergence of the series if $\lim_{n \to \infty} \frac{\lambda_n}{\mu_{n+1}} < 1$ or divergence if $\lim_{n \to \infty} \frac{\lambda_n}{\mu_{n+1}} > 1$.

3. Let $T_{i,i+1}$ denote the random time it takes to reach state $i+1$ from state i. (Note: The process may move backward for a while before moving forward. Thus if $i > 0$, $T_{i,i+1}$ is not the same as T_i, the time in state i until the next transition.) By a conditioning argument on the next transition, and using the double expectation theorem, recursive calculations of $E[T_{i,i+1}]$, $Var(T_{i,i+1})$ are possible via

$$E[T_{i,i+1}] = \frac{1}{\lambda_i} + \frac{\mu_i}{\lambda_i} E[T_{i-1,i}] \qquad i \geq 1$$

$$Var(T_{i,i+1}) = \frac{1}{\lambda_i(\lambda_i+\mu_i)} + \frac{\mu_i}{\lambda_i} Var(T_{i-1,i}) + \frac{\mu_i}{\mu_i+\lambda_i}(E[T_{i-1,i}]+E[T_{i,i+1}])^2.$$

In state 0 it is true that $T_{0,1} = T_0$ since the next transition must be to state 1. Hence

$$E[T_{0,1}] = E[T_0] = \frac{1}{\lambda_0}$$

$$Var(T_{0,1}) = Var(T_0) = \frac{1}{\lambda_0^2},$$

can be used to start the recursion.

The Continuing Care Retirement Community Model

1. In a Continuing Care Retirement Community residents may be in Independent Living Units (ILU - state 0), a Skilled Nursing Facility on a Temporary Basis (SNFT - state 1), a Skilled Nursing Facility on a Permanent Basis (SNFP - state 2), or departed (D - state 3). Transitions occur over time as in the diagram below.

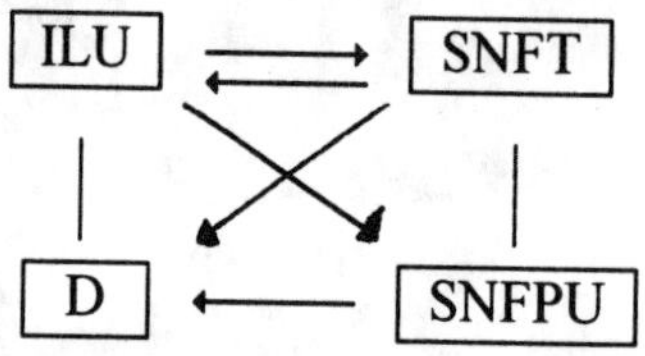

Suppose these transitions are modeled by a continuous-time, Markov chain with non-zero transition intensities as follows:

$\lambda_{01} = .20,\quad \lambda_{02} = .10,\quad \lambda_{03} = .10 \quad\Rightarrow\quad \lambda_0 = .40$

$\lambda_{10} = .40,\quad \lambda_{12} = .10,\quad \lambda_{13} = .10 \quad\Rightarrow\quad \lambda_1 = .60$

$\lambda_{23} = 1 \quad\Rightarrow\quad \lambda_2 = 1$

$\lambda_{33} = 0 \quad\Rightarrow\quad \lambda_3 = 0$ (state 3 is absorbing)

2. In the notation of Unit Two we have

$$\Lambda = \begin{bmatrix} -.40 & .20 & .10 & .10 \\ .40 & -.60 & .10 & .10 \\ 0 & 0 & -1.00 & 1.00 \\ 0 & 0 & 0 & 0 \end{bmatrix}.$$

Some of the following results were obtained with the help of a TI-85 calculator:

(i)

eigenvalue	eigenvector
−.20	[1, 1, 0, 0]
−.80	[−1, 2, 0, 0]
−1	[−1, −1, 8,0]
0	[1, 1, 1, 1]

(ii) The matrix A is formed by putting eigenvectors down the columns:

$$A = \begin{bmatrix} 1 & -1 & -1 & 1 \\ 1 & 2 & -1 & 1 \\ 0 & 0 & 8 & 1 \\ 0 & 0 & 0 & 1 \end{bmatrix}$$

$$A^{-1} = \frac{1}{24}\begin{bmatrix} 16 & 8 & 3 & -27 \\ -8 & 8 & 0 & 0 \\ 0 & 0 & 3 & -3 \\ 0 & 0 & 0 & 24 \end{bmatrix}$$

$$B = A^{-1}\Lambda A = \begin{bmatrix} -.2 & 0 & 0 & 0 \\ 0 & -.8 & 0 & 0 \\ 0 & 0 & -1 & 0 \\ 0 & 0 & 0 & 0 \end{bmatrix}$$

(iii) Using these results and the relation

$$(P_{jk}(t)) = exp(t\Lambda) = \mathrm{A}exp(tB)\mathrm{A}^{-1}$$

results in

$$\left.\begin{aligned} P_{00}(t) &= \tfrac{2}{3}e^{-.2t} + \tfrac{1}{3}e^{-.8t} \\ P_{01}(t) &= \tfrac{1}{3}e^{-.2t} - \tfrac{1}{3}e^{-.8t} \\ P_{02}(t) &= \tfrac{1}{8}e^{-.2t} - \tfrac{1}{8}e^{-t} \\ P_{03}(t) &= \tfrac{-9}{8}e^{-.2t} + \tfrac{1}{8}e^{-t} + 1 \end{aligned}\right\} \quad \text{State 0 Transition Probability Functions}$$

$$\left.\begin{aligned} P_{10}(t) &= \tfrac{2}{3}e^{-.2t} - \tfrac{2}{3}e^{-.8t} \\ P_{11}(t) &= \tfrac{1}{3}e^{-.2t} + \tfrac{2}{3}e^{-.8t} \\ P_{12}(t) &= \tfrac{1}{8}e^{-.2t} - \tfrac{1}{8}e^{-t} \\ P_{13}(t) &= \tfrac{-9}{8}e^{-.2t} + \tfrac{1}{8}e^{-t} + 1 \end{aligned}\right\} \quad \text{State 1 Transition Probability Functions}$$

$$\left.\begin{aligned} P_{22}(t) &= e^{-t} \\ P_{23}(t) &= -e^{-t} + 1 \end{aligned}\right\} \quad \text{State 2 Transition Probability Functions}$$

$$P_{33}(t) = 1 \quad \} \quad \text{State 3 Transition Probability Function}$$

(iv) Illustrative APV calculations:

(a) For a current ILU resident, calculate the APV of $\$C$/year paid continuously while the resident is in the skilled nursing facility.

Solution: $$APV = \int_{t=0}^{\infty} \underbrace{C\,dt}_{\substack{\text{Amount} \\ \text{in } [t,\,t+dt]}} \cdot \underbrace{e^{-\delta t}}_{\text{Discount}} \cdot \underbrace{(P_{01}(t) + P_{02}(t))}_{\substack{\text{Prob. that the current} \\ \text{ILU resident is in the} \\ \text{SNF at time } t}}$$

(b) For a current ILU resident, calculate the APV of $\$B$ paid each time he enters the SNF on either a permanent or temporary basis.

Solution: $$APV = \int_{t=0}^{\infty} \underbrace{B}_{\text{Amount}} \cdot \underbrace{e^{-\delta t}}_{\text{Discount}} \cdot [\underbrace{P_{00}(t)(\lambda_{01}+\lambda_{02})\,dt}_{\substack{\text{Prob. that a current} \\ \text{ILU resident enters the} \\ \text{SNF during } [t,\,t+dt]}}]$$

CONCEPTUAL REVIEW TEST

1. What is necessary for a continuous-time Process $\{X(t)|0 \leq t < \infty\}$ to be a Markov chain?

2. If $X(0) = i$ (i.e., distribution of $\vec{\pi}_0$ is $(0, \ldots, 0, \underset{\substack{\uparrow \\ \text{state } i}}{1}, 0, \ldots)$) how is $\vec{\pi}_t$ determined from the transition Probability matrix?

3. What properties must $\{N(t)|0 \leq t < \infty\}$ have to be a counting process? Explain the ideas of independent and stationary increments.

4. Define a Poisson process in terms of the following:
   (i) A counting process,
   (ii) An infinitesimal approach,
   (iii) In terms of waiting times, and
   (iv) As a pure birth process.

5. Describe the non-homogeneous Poisson process.

6. Describe the multiple decrement model of transition from one state to the next for a general continuous-time Markov chain with states $0, 1, 2, \ldots$.

7. Describe how the $P_{jk}(t)$ can be calculated from the transition intensity matrix Λ or the Kolmogorov Forward Equations.

8. If all states communicate and are positive recurrent describe the limiting distribution. How is it calculated? Explain stationarity. Explain the idea of long-term relative frequency of a state. How can $\vec{\pi}$ be computed without knowing the $P_{jk}(t)$?

CONCEPTUAL REVIEW TEST SOLUTIONS

1. The conditional distribution of a future state given the present state and past states is independent of the past and depends on the present and time into the future.

$$Pr(\underbrace{X(s+t)=k}_{\text{future}} \,|\, \underbrace{X(s)=j}_{\text{present}},\ \underbrace{X(u)=x(u)}_{\text{past}},\ 0 \le u < s)$$

$$= Pr(X(s+t)=k|X(s)=j)$$

$$= \underbrace{Pr(X(s)=k|X(0)=j)}_{P_{jk}(t)}$$

for all $s, t > 0$.

2. $\vec{\pi}_i$ is the ith row of $(P_{jk}(t))$ (beware: there is a 0th row). In other words

$$\vec{\pi}_i = (0, \ldots, 0, 1, 0, \ldots)\,(P_{jk}(t)) = (P_{i0}(t), P_{i1}(t), \ldots)$$

3. $N(t)$ is the number of occurrences in $(0, t]$ of some random event. Hence $N(0) = 0$, $N(t)$ is non-decreasing, integral, and $N(t_2) - N(t_1)$ is the number of occurrences in $(t_1, t_2]$. If $t_1 < t_2 \le t_3 < t_4$ the process increments are called independent if $N(t_4) - N(t_3)$ and $N(t_2) - N(t_1)$ are independent random variables. Increments are called stationary if $N(t+s) - N(s)$ has the same distribution as $N(t)$ for all s.

Note: A counting process with independent and stationary increments satisfies the Markovian assumption.

4. (i) A counting process with independent and stationary increments such that $N(t)$ has a Poisson distribution with parameter λt is called a Poisson process with rate λ.

(ii) A counting process with independent and stationary increments and such that $Pr(N(h) = 1) = \lambda h + 0(h)$, $Pr(N(h) \ge 2) = 0(h)$ is a Poisson Process.

(iii) If $T_1 < T_2 < \cdots$ are the times of occurrence in a counting process, $W_1 = T_1$, $W_2 = T_2 - T_1$, ... are called waiting times. If the W_i are independent and identically distributed exponentials with parameter λ, then the process is Poisson.

(iv) For a pure birth process if $\lambda_n = \lambda$ for $n = 0, 1, \ldots$ then the process is Poisson.

5. A counting process $\{N(t)|0 \leq t < \infty\}$ is a non-homogeneous Poisson process if there is a function $\lambda(t) \geq 0$ such that:

(i) $N(0) = 0$,

(ii) Increments are independent, and

(iii) $Pr(N(t+h) - N(t) = 1) = \lambda(t)h + 0(h)$, and

(iv) $Pr(N(t+h) - N(t) \geq 2) = 0(h)$ for all t.

Setting $m(t) = \int_0^t \lambda(s)\,ds$, it follows that the process increment $N(s+t) - N(s)$ is Poisson with parameter $m(s+t) - m(s)$.

6. There are constant forces of transition from state j to state k (if $k \neq j$) denoted by λ_{jk}. The total force of transition in state j is $\lambda_j = \sum_{k \neq j} \lambda_{jk}$. The time in state k until decrement (transition to the next state), T_k, is exponentially distributed with parameter λ_j. The mode of decrement is k if the next transition is to state k. Due to constant forces, P_{jk}, the probability that the process is next in state k, is the marginal probability ${}_{\infty}q_0^{(k)} = \frac{\lambda_{jk}}{\lambda_j}$ of the mode of decrement. The joint density of T_j, K_j is $e^{-\lambda_j t} \cdot \lambda_{jk}$.

7. Λ is defined by

$$\begin{pmatrix} -\lambda_0 & \lambda_{01} & \lambda_{02} & \cdots \\ \lambda_{10} & -\lambda_1 & \lambda_{12} & \cdots \\ \vdots & & & \end{pmatrix}.$$

From the Markov assumption and the Chapman-Kolmogorov equations it follows that

(*) $(P_{jk}(t))' = (P_{jk}(t))\Lambda$.

Since $(P_{jk}(0)) = I$, it follows that

$$(P_{jk}(t)) = exp(t\Lambda) = I + t\Lambda + \frac{t^2\Lambda^2}{2!} + \cdots,$$

Equating $(j, k)^{th}$ entries on both sides of (*) above gives,

$$P'_{jk}(t) = \sum_{\ell \neq k} P_{j\ell}(t)\lambda_{\ell k} - \lambda_k P_{jk}(t),$$

Kolmogorov's Forward equation.

8. $\pi_k = \lim_{t\to\infty} P_{jk}(t)$ for all j is the probability assigned to state k. If $\vec{\pi} = (\pi_0, \pi_1, \ldots)$ then $\vec{\pi}(P_{jk}(t)) = \vec{\pi}$ for all $t > 0$. Thus if $\vec{\pi}_s = \vec{\pi}$ it follows that $\vec{\pi}_{s+t} = \vec{\pi}$ for all $t \geq 0$. The distribution of the state does not change (i.e., is stationary) once it reaches $\vec{\pi}$. Starting in any state i the relative frequency of state k over $[0, t]$ is the fraction of this time interval spent in state k. The limit as $t \to \infty$ (i.e., the "long-term" relative frequency) is the value $\pi_k = \lim_{t\to\infty} P_{jk}(t)$ when this limit exists. The distribution $\vec{\pi}$ can be computed as the unique solution of the linear system

$$(\pi_0, \pi_1, \ldots)\Lambda = (0, 0, \ldots)$$

subject to $\pi_0 + \pi_1 + \cdots = 1$.

COMPUTATIONAL REVIEW TEST

1. For a Poisson process the expected waiting time between events is .10 years.
   (i) What is the probability that 10 or fewer events occur during a 2-year time span?
   (ii) What is the probability that the waiting time between 2 consecutive events is at least .2 years?
   (iii) If $N(2) = 20$ what is the probability that exactly 10 events occur during $(0, 1]$?

2. A group of insureds experience losses X which are uniformly distributed on $(0, 100]$. The number of losses by time t, $N(t)$ is assumed to follow a Poisson process with $\lambda = 5$. A claim results if the loss exceeds the deductible of 20.
   (i) How many claims are expected by time $t = 2$?
   (ii) What is the expected time between claims?
   (iii) What is the expected retained loss for the group for any 4-year period?
   (iv) What is the probability that 10 (partially) covered losses occur before 2 uncovered losses?

3. For a non-homogeneous Poisson process the intensity function is given by

$$\lambda(t) = \begin{cases} 10 & \text{if } t \text{ is in } (0, \frac{1}{2}], (1, \frac{3}{2}], \ldots \\ 2 & \text{if } t \text{ is in } (\frac{1}{2}, 1], (\frac{3}{2}, 2], \ldots \end{cases}.$$

   (i) How many occurrences are expected in the time period $(0, 1]$? During $(0, \frac{3}{2}]$?
   (ii) If $T_{10} = .45$ is given, calculate the probability that $T_{11} > .75$.

4. For a certain continuous-time Markov chain it is given that for state j that $\lambda_{j,j+1} = .04$, $\lambda_{j,j+2} = .02$, and $\lambda_{jk} = 0$ for all other $k \neq j$. T_j is the time in state j. Calculate:
   (i) The expected time until transition.
   (ii) The probability that $T_j > 5$.
   (iii) The probability that the next transition is to state $j+2$ (i.e., $P_{j,j+2}$).

5. For a pure birth process with $\lambda_0 = 1$, $\lambda_1 = 2$ and $\lambda_2 = 3$ calculate $P_{00}(t)$, $P_{01}(t)$, $P_{02}(t)$. Calculate the expected value, variance, and density function of the time from state zero to state 2.

6. Consider the pure birth process in Problem 5. Suppose $\delta = .05$. Suppose an individual is currently in state 0.

(i) Calculate the APV of a continuous annuity of c/yr while in state 1.

(ii) Calculate the APV of the cost of transition to state 1 if a cost of b in incurred at the time of transition.

7. For a Markov chain with states 0, 1, 2 the only non-zero transition intensities are $\lambda_{0,1} = 1$, $\lambda_{1,0} = \lambda_{1,2} = .5$, and $\lambda_{2,0} = .75$. Notice that all states communicate and the state space is finite (ergodic), so a limiting distribution exists.

(i) Calculate $(P_{jk}(1))$, $(P_{jk}(5))$. (You will need a calculation device for e^A where A is a 3×3 matrix.

(ii) Calculate the limiting distribution.

COMPUTATIONAL REVIEW TEST SOLUTIONS

1. Since W is exponential with parameter λ, $\frac{1}{\lambda} = E[W] = .10$. So $\lambda = 10$.

(i) $N(2)$ is Poisson with parameter $2\lambda = 20$. Hence $Pr(N(2) \leq 10) = \sum_{k=0}^{10} e^{-20} \frac{20^k}{k!}$

(ii) $Pr(W > .20) = s_W(2) = e^{-\lambda(.2)} = e^{-2} = .1353$.

(iii) Method 1

$$Pr(N(1) = 10 | N(2) = 20) = \frac{Pr(N(1) = 10 \text{ and } N(2) = 20)}{Pr(N(2) = 20)}$$

$$= \frac{Pr(10 \text{ events in } (0,1] \text{ and } 10 \text{ events in } (1,2])}{e^{-2\lambda}\frac{(2\lambda)^{20}}{20!}}$$

$$= \frac{Pr(10 \text{ events in } (0,1])Pr(10 \text{ events in } (1,2])}{e^{-\lambda}\frac{(2\lambda)^{20}}{20!}} \quad \textbf{(independent increments)}$$

$$= \frac{e^{-\lambda}\frac{\lambda^{10}}{10!} \cdot e^{-\lambda}\frac{\lambda^{10}}{10!}}{e^{-2\lambda}\frac{(2\lambda)^{20}}{20!}} = \frac{20!}{10!10!}\left(\frac{1}{2}\right)^{20}$$

Method 2 Given that $N(2) = 20$, the 20 (unordered) claim arrival times are **uniformly** distributed on $(0, 2]$. The probability that one observation, T, from $T \sim U(0, 20)$ **falls in** $(0, 1]$ is $\frac{1}{2}$. So the probability that exactly 10 of the observations fall in $(0, 1]$ is the **Binomial** probability $\binom{20}{10}\left(\frac{1}{2}\right)^{10}\left(1-\frac{1}{2}\right)^{10} = \frac{20!}{10!10!}\left(\frac{1}{2}\right)^{20}$.

2. Let $N_1(t)$ be the number of losses less than 20 during $(0, t]$ and let $N_2(t)$ be the number **greater** than or equal to 20. $Pr(X < 20) = \int_0^{20} \frac{1}{100}\, dt = .20$. Hence $N(t) = N_1(t) + N_2(t)$, **the** $N_i(t)$ **are** independent Poisson processes, and $\lambda_1 = \lambda \cdot Pr(X < 20) = 5(.20) = 1$,
$\lambda_2 = \lambda \cdot Pr(X \geq 20) = 5(.8) = 4$.

(i) $N_2(t)$ is the number of claims in $(0, t]$. Hence $N_2(2)$ is Poisson with parameter $2\lambda_2 = \mathbf{8}$. Thus $E[N_2(2)] = 8$.

(ii) The waiting times connected with $N_2(t)$ (i.e., time between claims) are **exponentially** distributed with parameter λ_2. Thus $E[W_2] = \frac{1}{\lambda_2} = \frac{1}{4} = .25$ yrs.

(iii) The number of retained losses in $(0,4]$ is $N(4)$. Its expected value is $4\lambda = 20$. The model for a retained loss is $Y = X \wedge 20$; $E[Y] = \int_0^{20} x(.01)\,dx + \int_{20}^{100} 20(.01)dx = 18$. The total of retained losses is $Y_{Agg} = Y_1 + \cdots + Y_N$. Thus $E[Y_{Agg}] = E[N]E[Y] = 360$.

(iv) The probability that 10 partially covered losses occur before 2 uncovered losses is the same as the probability of 10 successes before 2 failures in a sequence of Bernoulli trials where $p = .80$ and $q = .20$. This probability is given by,

$$\sum_{k=10}^{11} \binom{11}{k} (.80)^k (.20)^{11-k} = \binom{11}{10} (.80)^{10} (.20) + \binom{11}{11} (.80)^{11},$$

the probability of 10 or 11 successes in 11 trials. Notice that either 10 successes or 2 failures must occur by the 11th trial.

3. (i) $m(1) = \int_0^1 \lambda(t)\,dt = \int_0^{\frac{1}{2}} 10\,dt + \int_{\frac{1}{2}}^1 2\,dt = \frac{10}{2} + \frac{2}{2} = 6$

$m(\frac{3}{2}) = \int_0^{\frac{3}{2}} \lambda(t)\,dt = m(1) + \int_1^{\frac{3}{2}} 10\,dt = 6 + 5 = 11$

$N(t)$ is distributed as Poisson with parameter $m(t) = \int_0^t \lambda(s)\,ds$. Hence $m(t)$ occurrences are expected in $(0, t]$.

(ii) The hazard rate for W_{11} is $h(t) = \lambda(t_{10} + t)$ for $t > 0$. Here $t_{10} = .45$. Now

$$\begin{aligned} Pr(T_{11} > .75 | T_{10} = .45) &= Pr(W_{11} > .30) \\ &= s_{W_{11}}(.30) \\ &= exp\left(-\int_0^{.30} h(t)\right) dt \\ &= exp\left(-\int_0^{.05} 10\,dt - \int_{.05}^{.30} 2\,dt\right) = exp(-1) = .368. \end{aligned}$$

This probability could also have been calculated as

$$\begin{aligned} &Pr(N(.75) = 10 | N(.45) = 10) \\ &\qquad = Pr(N(.75) - N(.45) = 0 | N(.45) = 10) = Pr(N(.75) - N(.45) = 0) \end{aligned}$$

due to the independence of increments. The variable $N(.75) - N(.45)$ is Poisson with parameter $m(.75) - m(.45) = \int_{.45}^{.50} 10\,dt + \int_{.50}^{.75} 2\,dt = 1$. The probability that a Poisson-1 variable is zero is $e^{-1}\frac{1^0}{0!} = e^{-1}$!

4. (i) T_j is exponentially distributed with parameter $\lambda_j = \sum_{k \neq j} \lambda_{jk} = .04 + .02 = .06$. Thus $E[T_j] = \frac{1}{.06}$.

(ii) $Pr(T_j > 5) = s_{T_j}(5) = e^{-\lambda_j(5)} = e^{-.30}$.

(iii) $P_{j,j+2} = \frac{\lambda_{j,j+2}}{\lambda_j} = \frac{.02}{.06} = \frac{1}{3}$.

5. Let $T_0, T_1, \ldots$ be the random time in states $0, 1, \ldots$. Transition is certain to go from state j to state j+1 and the T_j are independent exponentials with parameters $\lambda_0, \lambda_1, \ldots$ respectively. Thus $T_0 + T_1$ is the time from state 0 to state 2. Its moments are

$$E[T_0 + T_1] = \frac{1}{\lambda_0} + \frac{1}{\lambda_1} = \frac{1}{1} + \frac{1}{2} = 1.5$$

$$Var[T_0 + T_1] = \frac{1}{\lambda_0^2} + \frac{1}{\lambda_1^2} = \frac{1}{1} + \frac{1}{4} = 1.25$$

The density of $T_0 + T_1$ is $P_{01}(t)\lambda_1$.

Now $P_{00}(t) = Pr(T_0 > t) = e^{-\lambda_0 t} = e^{-t}$ since it is only possible to go from state 0 to state 1. If s is the time of transition from state 0 to state 1 then

$$P_{01}(t) = \int_0^t P_{00}(s)\lambda_0 e^{-\lambda_1(t-s)}\, ds = \int_0^t e^{-s} \cdot 1 \cdot e^{-2(t-s)}\, ds$$
$$= e^{-2t} \int_0^t e^s\, ds = e^{-2t}(e^t - 1) = e^{-t} - e^{-2t}.$$

Similarly

$$P_{02}(t) = \int_0^t P_{01}(s)\lambda_1 e^{-\lambda_2(t-s)}\, ds = \int_0^t (e^{-s} - e^{-2s})2 \cdot e^{-3(t-s)}\, ds$$
$$= 2e^{-3t} \int_0^t e^{2s} - e^s\, ds$$
$$= 2e^{-3t}(\tfrac{1}{2}(e^{2t} - 1) - (e^t - 1)) = e^{-t} - 2e^{-2t} + e^{-3t}.$$

Finally the density of $T_0 + T_1$ is $P_{01}(t)\lambda_1 = (e^{-t} - e^{-2t})2$.

Check: $2\int_0^\infty (e^{-t} - e^{-2t})\, dt = 2\left(\frac{1}{1} - \frac{1}{2}\right) = 1!$

6. (i)

$$APV = \int_{t=0}^{\infty} \underbrace{c\,dt}_{\substack{\text{Amount}\\ \text{in } [t,t+dt]}} \cdot \underbrace{e^{-\delta t}}_{\text{discount}} \cdot \underbrace{P_{01}(t)}_{\substack{\text{probability in}\\ \text{state 1}}}$$

$$= \int_{t=0}^{\infty} c \cdot e^{-.05t}(e^{-t} - e^{-2t})\,dt = c\left[\frac{1}{1.05} - \frac{1}{2.05}\right] = .46436c$$

(ii)

$$APV = \int_{t=0}^{\infty} \underbrace{b}_{\text{amount}} \cdot \underbrace{e^{-\delta t}}_{\text{discount}} \cdot \underbrace{P_{00}(t)\lambda_0\,dt}_{\substack{\text{probability transition}\\ \text{to state 1 occurs in } [t,t+dt]}}$$

$$= \int_{t=0}^{\infty} b \cdot e^{-.05t}(e^{-t} \cdot 1)\,dt = \frac{b}{1.05} = .9524b$$

7. (i) The transition intensity matrix is $\Lambda = \begin{pmatrix} -1 & 1 & 0 \\ .5 & -1 & .5 \\ .75 & 0 & -.75 \end{pmatrix}$

Using a TI-85 and the relation $(P_{jk}(t)) = exp(t\Lambda)$ gives

$$((P_{jk}(1)) \approx \begin{pmatrix} .4896 & .4056 & .1048 \\ .2814 & .4896 & .2290 \\ .3435 & .1573 & .4992 \end{pmatrix} \text{ and } ((P_{jk}(5)) \approx \begin{pmatrix} .3745 & .3765 & .2489 \\ .3750 & .3745 & .2505 \\ .3758 & .3734 & .2508 \end{pmatrix},$$

which could also be calculated as $(P_{jk}(1))^5$ due to the Chapman-Kolmogorov equations. Notice how the rows of $(P_{jk}(5))$ are nearly identical. They are getting close to the limiting distribution.

(ii) Without explicit formulas for $P_{jk}(t)$, one must calculate $\pi_k = \lim\limits_{t\to\infty} P_{jk}(t)$ (all j) from the constrained homogeneous linear system $\vec{\pi} \cdot \Lambda = (0, 0, 0)$:

$$\begin{aligned} -\pi_0 \;+\; .5\pi_1 \;+\; .75\pi_2 &= 0 \\ \pi_0 \;-\; \pi_1 \qquad\qquad &= 0 \\ .5\pi_1 \;-\; .75\pi_2 &= 0 \\ \textstyle\sum \pi_i = 1 \qquad \text{(constraint)} & \end{aligned}$$

It is clear from the 2nd and 3rd equations that $\pi_1 = \pi_0$, $\pi_2 = \frac{2}{3}\pi_1 = \frac{2}{3}\pi_0$. Hence, from the constraint $1 = \pi_0 + \pi_1 + \pi_2 = \pi_0(1{+}1{+}\frac{2}{3})$, it follows that $\pi_0 = \frac{3}{8}$, $\pi_1 = \pi_0 = \frac{3}{8}$, $\pi_2 = \frac{2}{3}\pi_0 = \frac{2}{8}$. Compare this result with the rows of $(P_{jk}(5)$ in part (i).

UNIT REVIEW QUESTIONS

The following information is to be used for Questions 1 -11. Some additional information will be supplied for Questions 8-11. (Note: These questions are continuous-time analogues of the discrete-time model employed in the Unit One review questions)

A 3-state, continuous-time, Markov chain is to be used to model the three conditions of an insured individual:

state 0: alive and active (i.e. not disabled)
state 1: alive but disabled
sate 2: dead

The transition intensity functions are

$$\lambda_{01} = .05 = \lambda_{02}$$
$$\lambda_{10} = .35, \ \lambda_{12} = .05$$
$$\lambda_{20} = \lambda_{21} = 0 \qquad \text{(once in state 2 there is no additional transition).}$$

You are also given:

(i) $$\Lambda = \begin{bmatrix} -.10 & .05 & .05 \\ .35 & -.40 & .05 \\ 0 & 0 & 0 \end{bmatrix};$$

(ii) the eigenvalues of Λ are 0, $-.05$ and $-.45$ and the corresponding eigenvectors are

$$\begin{bmatrix} 1 \\ 1 \\ 1 \end{bmatrix}, \begin{bmatrix} 1 \\ 1 \\ 0 \end{bmatrix}, \begin{bmatrix} 1 \\ -7 \\ 0 \end{bmatrix};$$

(iii) the inverse of $A = \begin{pmatrix} 1 & 1 & 1 \\ 1 & 1 & -7 \\ 1 & 0 & 0 \end{pmatrix}$

is

$$\begin{pmatrix} 0 & 0 & 1 \\ \frac{7}{8} & \frac{1}{8} & -1 \\ \frac{1}{8} & -\frac{1}{8} & 0 \end{pmatrix}.$$

1. For a life currently active what is the probability that it is still surviving in t years?

(A) $\frac{7}{8}e^{-.05t} + \frac{1}{8}e^{-.45t}$ (B) $\frac{7}{8}e^{-.05t} - \frac{1}{8}e^{-.45t}$ (C) $e^{-.05t}$

(D) $e^{-.45t}$ (E) $\frac{1}{2}(e^{-.05t} + e^{-.45t})$

2. If an insured individual is currently alive and active what is the probability that she will ever become disabled?

(A) .50 (B) .60 (C) .75 (D) .80 (E) 1

3. If an insured individual is currently disabled what is the probability that she will ever return to active life?

(A) $\frac{1}{2}$ (B) $\frac{2}{3}$ (C) $\frac{3}{4}$ (D) $\frac{4}{5}$ (E) $\frac{7}{8}$

4. For an insured individual who is currently active what is the expected number of years until death?

(A) 20 (B) 22 (C) 25 (D) 30 (E) 45

5. What is the expected length of a period of disablement?

(A) 2.0 (B) 2.5 (C) 4 (D) 10 (E) 20

6. For a currently active insured life what is the expected time of disablement during her future lifetime?

(A) $1.\bar{1}$ (B) $2.\bar{2}$ (C) $3.\bar{3}$ (D) $4.\bar{4}$ (E) $5.\bar{5}$

7. For a currently active insured life what is the expected number of disablements during her future lifetime?

(A) $\frac{5}{6}$ (B) $\frac{7}{8}$ (C) $\frac{8}{9}$ (D) 1 (E) $\frac{11}{9}$

The following additional information applies to Questions 8-11.

A three-year term insurance paying $1000 at death is issued to a currently active life. The valuation force of interest is $\delta = .10$. Annual premiums are paid continuously.

8. The APV of the death benefit is closest to

(A) 100 (B) 107 (C) 114 (D) 121 (E) 130

9. What is the level annual benefit premium if premiums are waived when the insured is disabled? (nearest dollar)

(A) 45 (B) 47 (C) 49 (D) 51 (E) 53

10. What is the percent decrease in the level annual benefit premium if the disability waiver is removed?

(A) 4.7% (B) 4.9% (C) 5.1% (D) 5.3% (E) 5.5%

11. Assuming a premium waiver for disability is in effect, calculate the benefit reserve at duration one for a life currently disabled. (Nearest dollar)

(A) 60 (B) 63 (C) 66 (D) 69 (E) 72

SOLUTIONS TO UNIT REVIEW QUESTIONS

1. The probability sought is $P_{00}(t) + P_{01}(t) = 1 - P_{02}(t)$. From the given eigenvalues and eigenvectors one can calculate

$$(P_{ij}(t)) = exp(t\Lambda) = \mathrm{A}exp(tB)\mathrm{A}^{-1}$$

where

$$B = \begin{pmatrix} 0 & 0 & 0 \\ 0 & -.05 & 0 \\ 0 & 0 & -.45 \end{pmatrix}$$

(see the Unit Condensed Review Notes). Using the given information and these relations it follows that

$$(P_{ij}(t)) = \begin{pmatrix} \frac{7}{8}e^{-.05t} + \frac{1}{8}e^{-.45t} & \frac{1}{8}e^{-.05t} - \frac{1}{8}e^{-.45t} & 1 - e^{-.05t} \\ \frac{7}{8}e^{-.05t} - \frac{7}{8}e^{-.45t} & \frac{1}{8}e^{-.05t} + \frac{7}{8}e^{-.45t} & 1 - e^{-.05t} \\ 0 & 0 & 1 \end{pmatrix}$$

Thus $P_{00}(t) + P_{01}(t) = e^{-.05t}$ ANSWER C

2. The question asks for P_{01}, the probability that the next transition to state 1, since once she visits state 2 (death) she cannot become disabled. In general $P_{ij} = \frac{\lambda_{ij}}{\sum_{k \neq i} \lambda_{ik}}$. Here

$$P_{01} = \frac{\lambda_{01}}{\lambda_{01} + \lambda_{02}} = \frac{.05}{.05 + .05} = \frac{1}{2}.$$ ANSWER A

3. As in Question 2, $P_{10} = \frac{\lambda_{10}}{\lambda_{10} + \lambda_{12}} = \frac{.35}{.35 + .05} = \frac{7}{8}.$ ANSWER E

4. In the same manner that one can see $\overset{\circ}{e}_x = \int_0^{\omega-x} {}_tp_x\,dt$ in Life Contingencies, one can see that the expected time here is

$$\int_0^\infty \underbrace{(P_{00}(t)+P_{01}(t))}_{\text{Prob. alive at time } t} \underbrace{dt}_{\substack{\text{fraction of}\\ \text{year in } [t,t+dt]}} = \int_0^\infty \left(\tfrac{7}{8}e^{-.05t}+\tfrac{1}{8}e^{-.45t}\right)+\left(\tfrac{1}{8}e^{-.05t}-\tfrac{1}{8}e^{-.45t}\right)dt$$

$$= \int_0^\infty e^{-.05t}\,dt = \frac{1}{.05} = 20$$

ANSWER A

5. T_1, the time in state 1, is exponential with mean $\frac{1}{\lambda_1}$ where $\lambda_1 = \lambda_{10}+\lambda_{12} = .35+.04 = .40$: $\frac{1}{.40} = 2.5$

ANSWER B

6. The expected time is

$$\int_0^\infty \underbrace{P_{01}(t)}_{\substack{\text{Prob. disabled}\\ \text{at time } t}} \underbrace{dt}_{\substack{\text{fraction of}\\ \text{a year}}} = \int_0^\infty \tfrac{1}{8}e^{-.05t}-\tfrac{1}{8}e^{-.45t}\,dt = \tfrac{1}{8}\left(\tfrac{1}{.05}-\tfrac{1}{.45}\right) = 2.\bar{2}.$$

ANSWER B

7. The total time of disablement, T, is a random sum of M (the number of disablements) independent times distributed like T_1, the time of a single disablement. Thus

$$\underbrace{2.\bar{2} = E[T]}_{\text{Question 6}} = E[M]\cdot \underbrace{E[T_1]}_{\substack{=2.5\\ \text{Question 5}}},$$

hence $E[M] = \frac{2.\bar{2}}{2.5} = \frac{8}{9}$.

ANSWER C

8. For a currently active individual the time until death variable, T, has a density function $f(t)$ satisfying

$$\underbrace{f(t)\,dt}_{\substack{\text{approx. prob.}\\ \text{that death}\\ \text{occurs in } [t,t+dt]}} = \underbrace{P_{00}(t)}_{\substack{\text{alive and}\\ \text{active at}\\ \text{time } t}} \underbrace{\lambda_{02}\,dt}_{\substack{\text{dies in}\\ \text{next}\\ \text{instant}}} + \underbrace{P_{01}(t)}_{\substack{\text{disabled \&}\\ \text{active at}\\ \text{time } t}} \underbrace{\lambda_{12}\,dt}_{\substack{\text{dies in}\\ \text{next}\\ \text{instant}}}$$

$$= \left[\left(\tfrac{7}{8}e^{-.05t}+\tfrac{1}{8}e^{-.45t}\right)(.05)+\left(\tfrac{1}{8}e^{-.05t}-\tfrac{1}{8}e^{-.05t}\right)(.05)\right]dt$$

$$= [.05e^{-.05t}]dt$$

Thus

$$APV = \int_0^3 \underbrace{1000}_{\text{amount}}\cdot \underbrace{e^{-.10t}}_{\text{discount}}\cdot \underbrace{.05e^{-.05t}\,dt}_{\text{probability}} = 1000(.05)\left[\frac{1-e^{-.45}}{.15}\right] = 120.79$$

ANSWER D

9. The APV of $\$P$/yr continuously while the individual is in state 0 is

$$\int_0^3 \underbrace{P\,dt}_{\substack{\text{Amt. in}\\ [t,t+dt]}} \cdot \underbrace{P_{00}(t)}_{\text{Prob.}} \cdot \underbrace{e^{-\delta t}}_{\text{disc.}} = P\int_0^3 \left[\tfrac{7}{8}e^{-.05t}+\tfrac{1}{8}e^{-.45t}\right]e^{-.10t}\,dt$$

$$= P\left[\left(\tfrac{7}{8}\right)\left(\frac{1-e^{-.45}}{.15}\right)+\left(\tfrac{1}{8}\right)\left(\frac{1-e^{-1.65}}{.55}\right)\right] = 2.2975P.$$

Setting $2.2975P$ equal to 120.79 (Question 8 - the APV of benefits), results in $P = 52.58$.

ANSWER E

10. If the waiver is removed then the APV of P/yr continuously while alive (i.e., in state 0 or state 1) is

$$\int_0^3 \underbrace{P\,dt}_{\text{Amt.}} \cdot \underbrace{(P_{00}(t)+P_{01}(t))}_{\text{Prob.}} \cdot \underbrace{e^{-\delta t}}_{\text{discount}} = P\int_0^3 e^{-.05t}e^{-.10t}\,dt$$

$$= P\left(\frac{1-e^{-.45}}{.15}\right) = 2.4158P.$$

Thus $2.4158P = 120.79$ implies $P = 50.00$. The percent decrease is $\dfrac{52.58-50.00}{52.58}\times 100\% = 4.9\%$.

ANSWER B

11. For a life in state 1 at duration 1

$$APV_{t=1}(\text{fut ben}) = \int_0^2 \underbrace{1000}_{\text{Amount}} \cdot \underbrace{e^{-.10t}}_{\text{Discount}} \cdot \underbrace{[P_{10}(t)\lambda_{02}+P_{11}(t)\lambda_{12}]dt}_{\substack{\text{Probability}=.05e^{-.05t}\\ \text{(see Question One solution above)}}}$$

$$= 50\left[\frac{1-e^{-.30}}{.15}\right] = 86.39$$

$$APV_{t=1}(\text{fut prem}) = \int_0^2 \underbrace{P\,dt}_{\text{Amount}} \cdot \underbrace{e^{-\delta t}}_{\text{Discount}} \cdot \underbrace{P_{10}(t)}_{\substack{\text{Probability}\\ \text{in state 0 at}\\ \text{time } t}}$$

$$= \underbrace{52.58}_{(\#9)}\int_0^2 e^{-.10t}\left[\tfrac{7}{8}e^{-.05t}-\tfrac{7}{8}e^{-.45t}\right]dt$$

$$= (52.58)\left(\tfrac{7}{8}\left(\frac{1-e^{-.30}}{.15}\right)-\tfrac{7}{8}\left(\frac{1-e^{-1.1}}{.55}\right)\right) = 23.69$$

Reserve $= 86.39 - 23.69 = 62.70$.

ANSWER B

UNIT THREE: BROWNIAN MOTION

In the preceding Units we studied discrete-time and continuous-time stochastic processes where the state space was assumed to be 0, 1, 2, ... (discrete). Graphs of a possible history of these processes over time might look like the figures below.

Discrete-Time

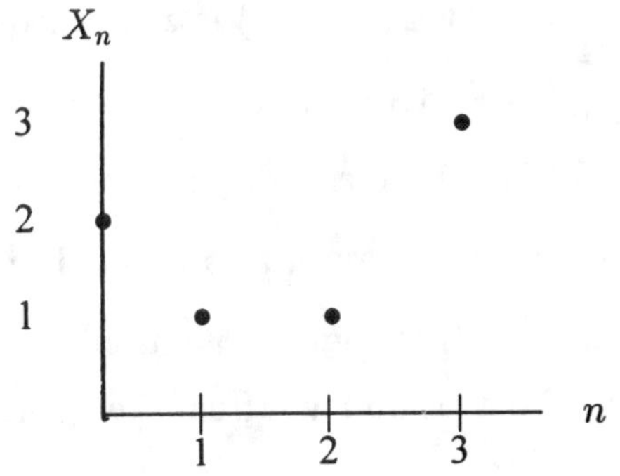

Continuous-Time
(Poisson-Process)

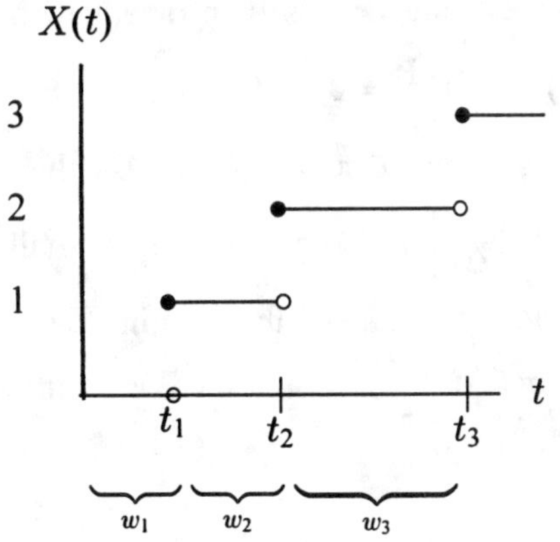

t_i = time of ith occurrence
w_i = i^{th} waiting time

In this Unit we introduce special types of continuous-time processes where the state-space is a continuum.

These processes, Brownian motion, Brownian motion with drift, and Geometric Brownian motion, can be used to model the variation in the price of a stock over time and to price an option on a stock.

Brownian Motion

A continuous-time process $\{X(t)|0 \leq t < \infty\}$ is called a **Brownian motion process** if

(i) $X(0) = 0$,

(ii) increments are independent and stationary, and

(iii) $X(t)$ is normal with mean 0 and variance $\sigma^2 t$.

To gain an intuitive understanding it is useful to see how such a process arises as a limit of a random walk.

Suppose X_1, X_2, ... are independent and identically distributed like X where $Pr(X = -1) = \frac{1}{2} = Pr(X = 1)$. Let $Y_0 = 0$ and $Y_n = X_1 + \cdots + X_n$ for $n \geq 1$. The process Y_0, Y_1,

... is a random walk. If $Y_n = k$, the state at time n is k, the state at time $n+1$ is either $k-1$ or $k+1$, each with probability of $\frac{1}{2}$ (i.e., $P_{n,n+1} = \frac{1}{2} = P_{n,n-1}$). Now let $\Delta x = \sigma\sqrt{\Delta t}$ where Δt is a small increment in time and Δx is the length of a small step taken to the left or right if X is replaced by $(\Delta x)X$. Consider the process $\{X(t) | 0 \le t < \infty\}$ given by

$$X(t) = (\Delta x)X_1 + \cdots + (\Delta x)X_{\left[\frac{t}{\Delta t}\right]} = (\Delta x)\left(\sum_{i=1}^{\left[\frac{t}{\Delta t}\right]} X_i\right)$$

where $\left[\frac{t}{\Delta t}\right]$ is the greatest integer less than or equal to $\frac{t}{\Delta t}$. Notice that $E[X(t)]$ is zero since each $E[X_i] = E[X] = (-1)\frac{1}{2} + (1)\frac{1}{2} = 0$, and $Var(X(t)) = (\Delta x)^2\left[\frac{t}{\Delta t}\right]Var(X) = (\Delta x)^2\left[\frac{t}{\Delta t}\right] \cdot 1$ $= \sigma^2\Delta t\left[\frac{t}{\Delta t}\right]$ after substituting $\Delta x = \sigma\sqrt{\Delta t}$. By the Central Limit Theorem $X(t)$ is approximately normal in distribution if $\left[\frac{t}{\Delta t}\right]$ is large (i.e., Δt is small). Letting Δt approach zero results in $\left[\frac{t}{\Delta t}\right]$ approaching infinity. Hence as $\Delta t \to 0$, the limiting distribution of $X(t)$ is normal with mean zero and variance equal to $\lim_{\Delta t \to 0} \sigma^2(\Delta t)\left[\frac{t}{\Delta t}\right] = \sigma^2 t$. The limit comes about as follows from the "pinching theorem":

$$\frac{t}{\Delta t} - 1 < \left[\frac{t}{\Delta t}\right] \le \frac{t}{\Delta t} \quad \Rightarrow \quad \sigma^2(t - (\Delta t)) < \sigma^2(\Delta t)\left[\frac{t}{\Delta t}\right] \le \sigma^2 t$$

$$\Rightarrow \quad \sigma^2(t - 0) \le \lim_{\Delta t \to 0} \sigma^2(\Delta t)\left[\frac{t}{\Delta t}\right] \le \sigma^2 t.$$

If one plotted $X(t)$ versus time (after the limit $\Delta t \to 0$ as has been applied), one would see very rapid up and down "wiggles" of small magnitude. Each step is $\pm\,\Delta x$ during a time period Δt. So the "speed" of the motion is $\frac{\Delta x}{\Delta t} = \frac{\sigma\sqrt{\Delta t}}{\Delta t} = \frac{\sigma}{\sqrt{\Delta t}}$, which goes to infinity as Δt goes to zero.

The distribution of $X(t+\Delta t) - X(t)$ is the same as that of $X(\Delta t)$ (stationary increments) which is normal with mean 0 and variance $\sigma^2(\Delta t)$. It is highly probable (about .999) then that $X(t+\Delta t) - X(t)$ falls in the range $0 \pm 3(\sigma\sqrt{\Delta t})$ (mean plus or minus 3 deviations). As Δt goes to zero the width of this interval goes to zero. This suggests that $\lim_{\Delta t \to 0} X(t+\Delta t) - X(t) = 0$, that is, that $X(t)$ is continuous in t. While this is true (with probability one), a precise proof is quite complicated. The rapid up and down wiggling of the $X(t)$ versus t graph suggests it is nowhere differentiable, that is, $\lim_{\Delta t \to 0} \frac{X(t+\Delta t) - X(t)}{\Delta t}$ does not exist. The main evidence in support of this idea is that the distribution of $\frac{1}{\Delta t}(X(t+\Delta t) - X(t))$ is normal with mean $\frac{0}{\Delta t}$ and variance $\frac{\sigma^2(\Delta t)}{(\Delta t)^2} = \frac{\sigma^2}{\Delta t}$. As Δt goes to zero, the variance goes to infinity. Thus the difference quotient is not highly likely to be near some number $X'(t)$.

If $\{X(t)|0 \le t < \infty\}$ is a Brownian motion process with variance parameter σ^2, $\{Y(t) = \frac{1}{\sigma}X(t)\text{: } 0 \le t < \infty\}$ is a Brownian motion with variance parameter 1. It is called **standard Brownian** motion. $Y(t)$ is normal with mean 0 and variance equal to $\frac{1}{\sigma^2}(\sigma^2 t) = t$. The **density function** of $Y(t)$,

$$f_{Y(t)}(y) = \frac{1}{\sqrt{2\pi t}} e^{-\frac{y^2}{2t}}, \ -\infty < y < \infty$$

could be denoted more compactly by $f_t(y)$.

To obtain the joint density of $Y(t_1)$, $Y(t_2)$, ..., $Y(t_n)$ for $t_1 < t_2 < \cdots < t_n$, notice that $\{Y(t_i) = y_i\}$ is equivalent to $Y(t_1) = y_1$, $Y(t_2) - Y(t_1) = y_2 - y_1$, ..., $Y(t_n) - Y(t_{n-1}) = y_n - y_{n-1}$. Hence the joint density is

$$f(y_1, \ldots, y_n) = f_{t_1}(y_1) f_{t_2 - t_1}(y_2 - y_1) \cdots f_{t_n - t_{n-1}}(y_n - y_{n-1}) \qquad \text{(independent increments)}$$

$$= \frac{exp\left[-\frac{1}{2}\left(\frac{y_1^2}{t_1} + \frac{(y_2-y_1)^2}{t_2-t_1} + \cdots + \frac{(y_n-y_{n-1})^2}{t_n-t_{n-1}}\right)\right]}{(2\pi)^{n/2}[t_1(t_2-t_1)\cdots(t_n-t_{n-1})]^{1/2}}.$$

The probabilities of events regarding $Y(t_1)$, $Y(t_2)$, ..., $Y(t_n)$ can thus be obtained. For example, from the above with $n = 2$ it can be shown that $Y(t_1)|_{Y(t_2)}$ is normal with mean $\frac{t_1}{t_2} \cdot Y(t_2)$ and variance $\frac{t_1}{t_2}(t_2 - t_1)$. The algebra involved is rather formidable. However, employing the double expectation theorem, one can witness the consistency of these results with $Y(t_1) \sim N(0, t_1)$ (notation: $Y(t_1)$ is normal with mean 0 and variance t_1):

$$E[Y(t_1)] = E[E[Y(t_1)|Y(t_2)]] = E\left[\frac{t_1}{t_2} \cdot Y(t_2)\right] = \frac{t_1}{t_2} \cdot 0 = 0$$

$$Var(Y(t_1)) = E[Var(Y(t_1)|Y(t_2))] + Var(E[Y(t_1)|Y(t_2)])$$
$$= E\left[\frac{t_1}{t_2}(t_2 - t_1)\right] + Var\left(\frac{t_1}{t_2} \cdot Y(t_2)\right)$$
$$= \frac{t_1}{t_2}(t_2 - t_1) + \left(\frac{t_1}{t_2}\right)^2 \cdot t_2 = t_1 - \frac{t_1^2}{t_2} + \frac{t_1^2}{t_2} = t_1.$$

Example 1 Suppose $\{X(t)|0 \le t < \infty\}$ is a Brownian motion process with variance parameter σ^2. Calculate the following in terms of $\phi(x)$, the standard normal distribution function.

(i) $Pr(X(2) > X(1)|X(1) = x_1)$

(ii) $Pr(X(2) \le 2\sigma|X(1) = \sigma)$

(iii) $Pr(X(1) \le 2\sigma|X(2) = \sigma)$

Solution

(i) Due to independent increments

$$Pr(X(2) > X(1)|X(1) = x_1) = Pr(X(2) - X(1) > 0|X(1) = x_1)$$
$$= Pr(X(2) - X(1) > 0) = \frac{1}{2}$$

since $X(2) - X(1)$ is normal with mean 0 and variance $(2-1)\sigma^2$.

(ii) $Pr(X(2) \leq 2\sigma|X(1) = \sigma) = Pr(X(2) - X(1) \leq \sigma|X(1) = \sigma)$
$= Pr(X(2) - X(1) \leq \sigma)$

due to independent increments. Now $X(2) - X(1)$ is normal with mean zero and variance $(2-1)\sigma^2$ so the probability is $\phi\left(\frac{\sigma-0}{\sigma}\right) = \phi(1)$.

(iii) $Pr(X(1) \leq 2\sigma|X(2) = \sigma) = Pr(Y(1) \leq 2|Y(2) = 1)$ where $Y(t) = \frac{1}{\sigma}X(t)$ is standard Brownian motion. Now $Y(1)|Y(2) = 1$ is normal with mean $\frac{t_1}{t_2}y_2 = \frac{1}{2} \cdot 1$ and variance $\frac{t_1}{t_2}(t_2 - t_1) = \frac{1}{2}(2 - 1) = \frac{1}{2}$. Hence,

$$Pr(Y(1) \leq 2|Y(2) = 1) = Pr\left(N\left(\frac{1}{2}, \frac{1}{2}\right) \leq 2\right) = \phi\left(\frac{2 - \frac{1}{2}}{\sqrt{\frac{1}{2}}}\right) \approx \phi(2.12).$$

Hitting Times

Suppose that $\{Y(t)|0 \leq t < \infty\}$ is a standard Brownian motion process. Thus $E[Y(t)] = 0$, $Var(Y(t)) = \sigma^2 t = 1 \cdot t$ and $f_{Y(t)}(y) = \frac{1}{\sqrt{2\pi t}}e^{-y^2/2t} = f_t(y)$ for $-\infty < y < \infty$. For a fixed positive value y_0 define T_{y_0} to be the random time until the process first reaches the value y_0. Since $Pr(Y(t) \geq y_0) = Pr\left(N(0,\ 1) \geq \frac{y_0 - 0}{\sqrt{t}}\right) = 1 - \phi\left(\frac{y_0}{\sqrt{t}}\right)$ approaches .50 as t goes to infinity, eventually the process is beyond y_0 about 50% of the time. Thus it is certain to have reached y_0 eventually. The distribution function of the **hitting time variable** T_{y_0} can be obtained as follows:

(i) $Pr(Y(t) \geq y_0) = Pr(Y(t) \geq y_0|T_{y_0} \leq t)Pr(T_{y_0} \leq t) + Pr(Y(t) \geq y_0|T_{y_0} > t)Pr(T_{y_0} > t)$

(ii) $Pr(Y(t) \geq y_0|T_{y_0} \leq t) = Pr(Y(t) \geq y_0|Y(s) = y_0$, some $s \leq t)$
$= Pr(Y(t) - Y(s) \geq y_0 - y_0 = 0|Y(s) = y_0) = .50$

(independent increments and $Y(t) - Y(s) \sim N(0, t-s)$)

(iii) $Pr(Y(t) \geq y_0|T_{y_0} > t) = 0$ since $Y(t)$ is continuous in t and has not reached y_0 by time t. That is $Y(0) = 0$, $Y(s) < y_0$ for all $s \leq t$.

(iv) Substituting (ii) and (iii) into (i) gives

$$F_{T_{y_0}}(t) = Pr(T_{y_0} \leq t) = 2Pr(Y(t) \geq y_0) = 2Pr\left(N(0,1) \geq \frac{y_0}{\sqrt{t}}\right) = 2\left(1 - \phi\left(\frac{y_0}{\sqrt{t}}\right)\right)$$

With the relation in (iv) and a table of $\phi(y)$ values one can easily approximate probabilities concerning hitting times. While the Standard Brownian motion process is certain to reach any value y_0, it does so at a leisurely pace. It can be shown that $E[T_{y_0}] = \infty$. (It comes down to the fact that $\int_0^\infty u^{-3/2}\,du = \infty$.)

Example 2 Calculate the following hitting-time probabilities and percentiles:

(i) $Pr(T_1 \leq 1)$;

(ii) The median of T_1; and

(iii) The 90th percentile of T_1.

Solution

(i) $Pr(T_1 \leq 1) = 2\left(1 - \phi\left(\frac{1}{\sqrt{1}}\right)\right) \approx 2[1 - .8413] = .3174.$

(ii) $.5 = Pr(T_1 \leq m) = 2\left(1 - \phi\left(\frac{1}{\sqrt{m}}\right)\right) \quad \Rightarrow \quad .75 = \phi\left(\frac{1}{\sqrt{m}}\right)$

$\Rightarrow \quad \frac{1}{\sqrt{m}} \approx .675 \quad (N(0,1)$ table interpolation)

$\Rightarrow \quad m \approx 2.193$

(iii) $.90 = Pr(T_1 \leq p) = 2\left(1 - \phi\left(\frac{1}{\sqrt{p}}\right)\right)$

$\Rightarrow \quad .55 = \phi\left(\frac{1}{\sqrt{p}}\right) \quad \Rightarrow \quad \frac{1}{\sqrt{p}} \approx .1258$ ($N(0,1)$ table interpolation)

$\Rightarrow \quad p \approx 63.166.$

Note: The calculation in (iii) corroborates the result mentioned earlier that $E[T_1] = \infty$. There is a 10% chance that $Y(t)$ will not hit 1 by time 63.166! □

The expression $F_{T_{y_0}}(t) = 2\left(1 - \phi\left(\frac{y_0}{\sqrt{t}}\right)\right)$ was derived for $y_0 > 0$. From the symmetry about 0 of a $N(0, \sigma^2)$ distribution it follows that

$$F_{T_{y_0}}(t) = 2\left(1 - \phi\left(\frac{|y_0|}{\sqrt{t}}\right)\right)$$

for any y_0.

Consider next the probability that a standard Brownian motion process hits $a > 0$ before hitting $b < 0$, that is,

$$Pr(T_a < T_b).$$

To calculate this probability from a joint density of T_a and T_b is a formidable challenge. However, we have seen the probability that a random walk starting at 0 and taking unit steps reaches $A > 0$ before reaching $-B < 0$ is $\frac{B}{A+B}$. Thus, viewing standard Brownian motion as a limit of a random walk with step $\Delta x = \sigma(\Delta t)^{1/2} = 1 \cdot (\Delta t)^{1/2}$, it follows that

$$Pr(T_a < T_b) = \lim_{\Delta t \to 0} \frac{\left[\frac{-b}{\Delta x}\right]}{\left[\frac{-b}{\Delta x}\right] + \left[\frac{a}{\Delta x}\right]} = \frac{|b|}{|b| + a}$$

since $\Delta x \to 0$ as $\Delta t \to 0$.

The Maximum Process Value Over $[0, t]$

Suppose again that $\{Y(t) | 0 \leq t < \infty\}$ is a standard Brownian Motion process. Define M_t to be the maximum value of $Y(s)$ for $0 \leq s \leq t$. The survival function of M_t can be computed as follows for $m > 0$:

$$Pr(M_t \geq m) \;=\; \underbrace{Pr(T_m \leq t)}_{\text{(Continuity of } Y(t) \text{ in } t)} \;=\; 2\left(1 - \phi\left(\frac{m}{\sqrt{t}}\right)\right)$$

Since the right-hand side is continuous in m we see that $Pr(M_t > m) = Pr(M_t \geq m)$. One can use the above relation to calculate $E[M_t]$ and probabilities concerning M_t.

From the above it follows that $Pr(M_t \leq m) = 1 - 2\left(1 - \phi\left(\frac{m}{\sqrt{t}}\right)\right)$, hence the density function of M_t is given by

$$f_{M_t}(m) = 2\phi'\left(\frac{m}{\sqrt{t}}\right) \cdot \frac{1}{\sqrt{t}} = \frac{2}{\sqrt{t}} \cdot \frac{1}{\sqrt{2\pi}} e^{-\frac{1}{2}\left(\frac{m}{\sqrt{t}}\right)^2}, \quad m \geq 0$$

Thus

$$E[M_t] = \int_0^\infty m \cdot \frac{2}{\sqrt{t}} \cdot \frac{1}{\sqrt{2\pi}} e^{-\frac{m^2}{2t}}\, dm.$$

Substituting $u = m^2$, $du = 2m\, dm$ converts the above integral to

$$E[M_t] = \frac{1}{\sqrt{2\pi t}} \int_0^\infty e^{-\frac{u}{2t}}\, du = \frac{1}{\sqrt{2\pi t}} \cdot 2t = \sqrt{\frac{2t}{\pi}}.$$

Example 3 Suppose $\{X(t)|0 \leq t < \infty\}$ is a Brownian motion process with $\sigma^2 = 4$. Calculate the following:

(i) The probability that the maximum value of $X(t)$ for $0 \leq t \leq 1$ exceeds 2;

(ii) The median value of $\max_{0 \leq t \leq 1} X(t)$; and

(iii) The mean value of $\max_{0 \leq t \leq 1} X(t)$;

Solution

(i) Set $Y(t) = \frac{1}{\sigma}X(t) = \frac{1}{2}X(t)$. Then $\{Y(t)|0 \leq t < \infty\}$ is a standard Brownian motion process. Thus

$$Pr(\max_{0 \leq t \leq 1} X(t) > 2) = Pr(\max_{0 \leq t \leq 1} Y(t) \geq 1) = Pr(M_1 \geq 1) = 2\left(1 - \phi\left(\frac{1}{\sqrt{1}}\right)\right) \approx \underbrace{.3174}_{(\phi(x)\text{ table})}$$

(ii)

$$.50 = Pr(\max_{0 \leq t \leq 1} X(t) \geq m) = Pr(\max_{0 \leq t \leq 1} Y(t) \geq \tfrac{m}{2}) = Pr(M_1 \geq \tfrac{m}{2}) = 2\left(1 - \phi\left(\frac{m/2}{\sqrt{1}}\right)\right)$$

$$\Rightarrow \quad \phi\left(\tfrac{m}{2}\right) = .75 \quad \Rightarrow \quad \tfrac{m}{2} \approx .675 \quad \Rightarrow \quad m \approx 1.35$$

(iii)

$$E[\max_{0 \leq t \leq 1} X(t)] = E[\max_{0 \leq t \leq 1} 2Y(t)] = 2E[\max_{0 \leq t \leq 1} Y(t)] = 2E[M_1] = 2\sqrt{\frac{2(1)}{\pi}} \approx 1.596$$

Brownian Motion With Drift

If $\{Y(t)|0 \leq t < \infty\}$ is a standard Brownian motion process, then set $X(t) = ut + \sigma Y(t)$. The process $\{X(t)|0 \leq t < \infty\}$ is called a **Brownian motion process** with **drift coefficient** μ and **variance parameter** σ^2. Since

(i) $Y(0) = 0$,

(ii) $\{Y(t)|0 \leq t < \infty\}$ has independent and stationary increments, and

(iii) $Y(t) \sim N(0, t)$,

it follows easily that

(i) $X(0) = 0$,

(ii) $\{X(t)\}$ has independent and stationary increments, and

(iii) $X(t) \sim N(\mu t, \sigma^2 t)$,

Geometric Brownian Motion

Let $Z(t) = e^{X(t)}$ where $\{X(t)|0 \leq t < \infty\}$ is the Brownian motion with drift process described immediately above. Notice that $Z(t_2)/Z(t_1) = e^{X(t_2)-X(t_1)}$. The important properties of this process are:

(i) $Z(0) = 1$;

(ii) If $t_1 < t_2 \leq t_3 < t_4$ then $Z(t_2)/Z(t_1)$ and $Z(t_4)/Z(t_3)$ are independent; and

(iii) If $t_2 - t_1 = t = t_4 - t_3$, the ratios are identically distributed lognormal variables $Z(t) = e^{X(t)}$ where $X(t) \sim N(\mu t, \sigma^2 t)$.

Geometric Brownian motion can be used as a model of the variation over time of the price of a stock if one assumes for each unit time period that the distribution of the ending value over the beginning value is the same lognormal distribution. Suppose a stock currently sells for P_0 and set $P(t) = P_0 Z(t)$. Then,

$$\frac{P(n)}{P(n-1)} = \frac{P_0 Z(n)}{P_0 Z(n-1)} = e^{X(n)-X(n-1)},$$

which has the same distribution as $e^{X(1)}$, a lognormal with $X(1) \sim N(\mu, \sigma^2)$.

Example 4 Suppose a stock currently sells for 100 and that the price process $\{P(t) = 100Z(t)|0 \leq t < \infty\}$ is modeled by a multiple of a geometric Brownian motion where the drift parameter is $\mu = .02$ and the variance parameter is $\sigma^2 = .02$. At a force of interest of $\delta = .02$ the present value of the price at time t is $e^{-\delta t}P(t)$. Calculate the following:

(i) $E[P(1)]$, $Var(P(1))$ and $Pr(P(1) > e^{.03}(100))$;

(ii) The probability that the maximum present value of the price over [0, 1] exceeds $100e^{.01}$;

(iii) The probability that the present value of the price hits $100e^{.04}$ before time 5; and

(iv) The probability that the present value of the price hits $100e^{.02}$ before it hits $100e^{-.01}$.

Solution If $X \sim N(\mu, \sigma^2)$, then $Z = e^X$ is lognormal and $E[Z^k] = E[e^{kX}] = M_X(k) = e^{\mu k + \sigma^2 k^2/2}$. As a result

$$E[Z] = e^{\mu + \sigma^2/2}$$
$$Var(Z) = e^{2\mu + \sigma^2}(e^{\sigma^2} - 1)$$

(i) $P(1) = 100Z(1)$, so $E[P(1)] = 100E[Z(1)]$ and $Var(P(1)) = 10{,}000Var(Z(1))$. Now $Z(1)$ is lognormal with $\mu = .02$, $\sigma^2 = .02$, so by the above

$$E[Z(1)] = e^{.02+.02/2} = e^{.03} = 1.0305$$

$$Var(Z(1)) = e^{2(.02)+.02}(e^{.02} - 1) = .0215$$

$$E[P(1)] = 100(1.0305) = 103.05$$

$$V(P(1)) = 10{,}000(.0215) = 214.51.$$

Furthermore,

$$\begin{aligned} Pr(P(1) > e^{.03}(100)) &= Pr(Z(1) > e^{.03}) \\ &= Pr(e^{X(1)} > e^{.03}) \\ &= Pr(X(1) > .03) \\ &= Pr(N(0,1) > \frac{.03 - .02}{\sqrt{.02}}) \\ &= 1 - \phi(.0707) = 1 - .5282 = .4718. \end{aligned}$$

(ii)

$$\begin{aligned} \underset{0 \le t \le 1}{Max}\, P(t)e^{-\delta t} &= 100 \underset{0 \le t \le 1}{Max}\, e^{X(t)}e^{-.02t} \\ &= 100 \underset{0 \le t \le 1}{Max}\, e^{.02t + \sqrt{.02}Y(t)} \cdot e^{-.02t} \qquad (Y(t) \sim N(0,t)) \\ &= 100 \underset{0 \le t \le 1}{Max}\, e^{\sqrt{.02}Y(t)} \\ &= 100 exp[\sqrt{.02} \underset{0 \le t \le 1}{Max}\, Y(t)]. \end{aligned}$$

Hence, the probability sought is

$$Pr(\underset{0 \le t \le 1}{Max}\, Y(t) > \frac{.01}{\sqrt{.02}}) = 2\left[1 - \phi\left(\frac{\frac{.01}{\sqrt{.02}}}{\sqrt{1}}\right)\right] = 2[1 - \phi(.0707)] = .9436.$$

(iii) $Pr(e^{-.02t}P(t)$ hits $100e^{.04}$ before $t = 5)$

$$\begin{aligned} &= Pr(100e^{-.02t}e^{X(t)} \text{ hits } 100e^{.04} \text{ before } t = 5) \\ &= Pr(100e^{-.02t}e^{.02t + \sqrt{.02}Y(t)} \text{ hits } 100e^{.04} \text{ before } t = 5) \\ &= Pr(Y(t) \text{ hits } \frac{.04}{\sqrt{.02}} \text{ before } t = 5) \\ &= Pr(T_{.2828} \le 5) = 2\left[1 - \phi\left(\frac{.2828}{\sqrt{5}}\right)\right] \\ &\approx 2(1 - \phi(.1265)) = 2(1 - .5503) \approx .899. \end{aligned}$$

(iv) Again, the present value of the price is $e^{-.02t}P(t) = e^{-.02t}(100)e^{.02t + \sqrt{.02}Y(t)} = 100e^{\sqrt{.02}Y(t)}$ where $Y(t) = N(0,t)$. So the probability sought is the probability that a standard Brownian motion process hits $\frac{.02}{\sqrt{.02}}$ before it hits $-\frac{.01}{\sqrt{.02}}$. We saw earlier that this is given by $\frac{|-\frac{1}{2}|}{|-\frac{1}{2}| + 1} = \frac{1}{3}$.

□

We continue the development of the stock price model $P(t) = P_0 Z(t)$ where $\{Z(t)|0 \le t < 0\}$ is Brownian motion with drift coefficient μ and variance parameter σ^2 and P_0 is the time 0 price. Thus $P(t) = P_0 e^{\mu t + \sigma Y(t)}$ where $Y(t)$ is standard Brownian motion (i.e., $E[Y(t)] = 0$, $Var(Y(t)) = t$). At a force of interest δ, $e^{-\delta t} P(t) = P_0 e^{(\mu-\delta)t + \sigma Y(t)}$ is the present value of the price at time 0.

Suppose $0 < s < t$ and view time s as the present. Suppose a share of the stock is purchased for the given $P(s)$ value and is to be sold in $t - s$ years for the random price $P(t)$. The random present value at time s of the sale price is $e^{-\delta(t-s)} P(t)$. The actuarial present value of the sale price at time s is

$$\begin{aligned} E[e^{-\delta(t-s)} P(t) | P(s)] &= E[e^{-\delta(t-s)} P(s) \cdot P(t)/P(s) | P(s)] \\ &= P(s) e^{-\delta(t-s)} E[P(t)/P(s) | P(s)] \\ &= P(s) e^{-\delta(t-s)} E\left[\frac{P_0 e^{\mu t + \sigma Y(t)}}{P_0 e^{\mu s + \sigma Y(s)}} \middle| Y(s) \right] \\ &= P(s) e^{-\delta(t-s)} E[e^{\mu(t-s)} e^{\sigma(Y(t)-Y(s))} | Y(s)] \\ &= P(s) e^{-(\delta-\mu)(t-s)} E[e^{\sigma Y(t-s)}] \end{aligned}$$

where the last step is due to independent and stationary increments in the standard Brownian motion process. Recall that $Y(t-s) \sim N(0, t-s)$. Hence, its moment generating function is $M_{Y(t-s)}(u) = e^{0u + (t-s)u^2/2}$. Thus in the final line of the series of equations above we have

$$E[e^{\sigma Y(t-s)}] = M_{Y(t-s)}(\sigma) = e^{(t-s)\sigma^2/2}.$$

Substituting this result into the above gives us the expression

$$E[e^{-\delta(t-s)} P(t) | P(s)] = P(s) e^{-(\delta-\mu)(t-s)} e^{(t-s)\sigma^2/2} = P(s) e^{(\mu + \sigma^2/2 - \delta)(t-s)}.$$

for the actuarial present value at time s of the time t sale price. If μ and σ^2 are chosen so that $\mu + \sigma^2/2 - \delta = 0$, then $P(s)$ equals the actuarial present value at time s of the time t price. As such, the actuarial present value of the profit on this transaction (buy at time s, sell at time t) is zero.

An Arbitrage Example

Suppose a gambling game has outcomes denoted 1, 2, ..., n and wagers can be made on any of the outcomes. Wager i is a bet that the outcome is i. Suppose for a unit bet on wager i you win $W_i + 1$ if i is the outcome. The **return** on this unit bet, winnings minus the unit bet, is given by

$$R_i = \begin{cases} (W_i + 1) - 1 & \text{outcome } i \\ 0 - 1 & \text{not the outcome } i \end{cases}.$$

A betting scheme is a vector $(x_1, x_2, \ldots, x_n)$ where x_i is bet on wager i for each $i = 1, \ldots, n$. If $x_i < 0$ you are accepting the bet rather than placing the bet. The total return on this betting scheme is $R = \sum_{i=1}^{n} x_i R_i$ since R_i is the return on a unit bet on wager i.

Now consider $1 - \sum_{i=1}^{n} (1 + W_i)^{-1}$. If this difference is zero, then there is a probability distribution on the outcomes, $Pr(\text{outcome } i) = \frac{1}{1 + W_i}$, such that the expected return on every betting scheme is zero. (Notice that the difference above being zero is equivalent to saying that the outcome probabilities sum to 1!). Here's why:

(i) $$E[R_i] = W_i Pr(\text{outcome } i) - 1 Pr(\text{outcome} \neq i)$$
$$= W_i \cdot \frac{1}{1+W_i} - 1 \sum_{j \neq i} \frac{1}{1+W_j}$$
$$= \frac{W_i + 1}{1+W_i} - \sum_{j} \frac{1}{1+W_j} \qquad \text{(add in and subtract out } \frac{1}{W_i + 1}\text{)}$$
$$= 1 - 1 = 0$$

(ii) $$E[R] = E[\sum x_i R_i] = \sum x_i E[R_i] = \sum x_i \cdot 0 = 0.$$

If $\theta = 1 - \sum_{i=1}^{n} (1 + W_i)^{-1} \neq 0$, set $x_i = \frac{1}{(1 + W_i) \cdot \theta}$ and consider the betting scheme $(x_1, \ldots, x_n)$. The return on this scheme is $R = \sum x_i R_i$. The following shows that $R = 1$ for every possible outcome j:

$$R(j) = \sum_{i=1}^{n} x_i R_i(j) = x_j R_j(j) + \sum_{i \neq j} x_i R_i(j)$$
$$= \frac{1}{(1+W_j) \cdot \theta} \cdot W_j + \sum_{i \neq j} \frac{1}{(1+W_i) \cdot \theta} \cdot (-1)$$
$$= \frac{W_j}{(1+W_j) \cdot \theta} + \frac{1}{(1+W_j) \cdot \theta} - \sum_{i=1}^{n} \frac{1}{(1+W_i) \cdot \theta}$$
$$= \frac{1}{\theta} - \frac{1}{\theta} \underbrace{\left(\sum_{i=1}^{n} \frac{1}{(1+W_i)} \right)}_{1-\theta}$$
$$= \frac{1}{\theta} - \frac{1-\theta}{\theta} = \frac{\theta}{\theta} = 1.$$

This illustrates a betting scheme with a sure (certain) return of 1. So, regardless of the probability distribution of outcomes, unlimited, sure profits can be earned. This is the idea of an **arbitrage**, a risk-less sure win.

We have seen in this simple betting model that there is either a probability distribution on the outcomes such that all wagers have an expected return of zero, or else there is a risk-less sure win (arbitrage).

The Black-Scholes Option Pricing Formula

Consider the process $P(t) = P_0 Z(t)$ modeling the future variation in the price of a stock currently ($t = 0$) selling for P_0 per share. $Z(t) = e^{\mu t + \sigma Y(t)}$ is geometric Brownian motion with drift and $Y(t)$ is standard Brownian motion. Consider the following universe of wagers on the future price of this stock:

(I) Purchase a share at time $s > 0$ for the given $P(s)$ value, and then sell it at time $t > s$ for the random future $P(t)$ value; and

(II) Purchase at time 0 for a price $C(t, P_1)$ the option to buy a share at time t for price P_1.

Assuming that the arbitrage theorem of the preceding section can be applied here, there are two alternatives. Either there is a probability distribution on outcomes (i.e., future prices of the stock share) such that all wagers have an expected return of zero, or there is an arbitrage possibility (risk-less sure win). If δ is the force of interest used to compute present values, we saw earlier that the actuarial present value of the profit (return) on wager (I) (buy at time s, sell at time t) is zero for all s and t if $\mu + \sigma^2/2 = \delta$. So choosing a μ, σ^2 combination to satisfy this relation gives a probability distribution of future stock prices (i.e., geometric Brownian motion) such that the expected return on wager (I) is zero. Thus if we use this probability distribution to price the option wagers (II) (i.e., determine $C(t, P_1)$ such that the expected return is zero), there is no arbitrage possible in this universe of wagers.

The random present value at time 0 of the wager (II) return is

$$e^{-\delta t}(P(t) - P_1)^+ - C(t, P_1)$$

where $(P(t) - P_1)^+$ means $P(t) - P_1$ if $P(t) > P_1$, and zero otherwise. If $P(t)$ exceeds P_1, the option would be exercised. A share is bought at the price P_1 from the seller of the option and sold immediately at the market price $P(t)$ for a gain of $P(t) - P_1$. Setting the actuarial present value of this return equal to zero results in the option price relation

$$C(t, P_1) = E[e^{-\delta t}(P(t) - P_1)^+].$$

With considerable effort the right hand side of this relation can be expressed as

$$C(t, P_1) = e^{-\delta t}\left[P_0 e^{\mu t+\sigma^2 t/2}\phi(\sigma\sqrt{t}+b) - P_1\phi(b)\right] = P_0\phi(\sigma\sqrt{t}+b) - (e^{-\delta t}P_1)\phi(b)$$

where

$$\mu+\sigma^2/2 = \delta$$

ϕ is the $N(0, 1)$ distribution function, and

$$b = \frac{\delta t - \sigma^2 t/2 - ln(P_1/P_0)}{\sigma\sqrt{t}}.$$

Notice that the price, $C(t, P_1)$, depends on P_0, P_1, δ, t and σ^2, but not on the drift coefficient μ. Recall that μ and σ^2 were chosen to satisfy $\mu+\sigma^2/2 = \delta$ (one equation, two unknowns). So it is natural to take σ^2 to be estimated value of the variance parameter under the assumption of geometric Brownian motion, and then pick the irrelevant μ to satisfy $\mu = \delta-\sigma^2/2$. When this is done the option pricing formula above is known as the Black-Scholes option pricing formula.

Example 5 Suppose $P(t) = P_0 Z(t) = P_0 e^{\mu t+\sigma Y(t)}$ is a geometric Brownian motion model of the price process of a stock. Suppose $P_0 = 100$, $\delta = .05$, $\sigma^2 = .02$. Use the Black-Scholes option pricing formula to calculate $C(1, 105)$ and $C(1, 110)$.

Solution Note that $\mu = \delta-\sigma^2/2 = .04$, but we don't need to know this. The first value we need to calculate is

$$b = \frac{\delta t - \sigma^2 t/2 - ln(P_1/P_0)}{\sigma\sqrt{t}} = \begin{cases} \dfrac{.04 - ln(105/100)}{\sqrt{.02}} & P_1 = 105 \\ \dfrac{.04 - ln(110/100)}{\sqrt{.02}} & P_1 = 110 \end{cases} = \begin{cases} -.062156 & P_1 = 105 \\ -.391102 & P_1 = 110 \end{cases}$$

Then

$$C(1, 105) = 100\underbrace{\phi(\sqrt{.02} - .062156)}_{.531589} - e^{-.05}(105)\underbrace{\phi(-.062156)}_{.475220} = 5.69$$

$$C(1, 110) = 100\underbrace{\phi(\sqrt{.02} - .391102)}_{.401417} - e^{-.05}(110)\underbrace{\phi(-.391102)}_{.347861} = 3.74$$

CONDENSED REVIEW NOTES AND ADVANCED TOPICS

Brownian Motion

1. $\{X(t)|0 \le t < \infty\}$ is called a **Brownian motion process** with variance parameter σ^2 if
   (i) $X(0) = 0$,
   (ii) increments are independent and stationary, and
   (iii) $X(t) \sim N(0, \sigma^2 t)$ (normal with mean 0 and variance $\sigma^2 t$)

2. Properties
   (i) $X(t)$ is continuous in t with probability one.
   (ii) $Y(t) = \frac{1}{\sigma}X(t)$ is called **standard Brownian motion.**
   $Y(t) \sim N(0, t)$
   $f_t(y) = f_{Y(t)}(y) = \frac{1}{\sqrt{2\pi t}}e^{-\frac{y^2}{2t}}, \ -\infty < y < \infty$
   (iii) If $\{Y(t)|0 \le t < \infty\}$ is **standard Brownian motion** then the **joint density** of $Y(t_1)$, $Y(t_2), \ldots, Y(t_n)$ for $t_1 < t_2 < \cdots < t_n$ is

$$f(y_1, \ldots, y_n) = \frac{exp\left[-\frac{1}{2}\left(\frac{y_1^2}{t_1} + \frac{(y_2-y_1)^2}{t_2-t_1} + \cdots + \frac{(y_n-y_{n-1})^2}{t_n-t_{n-1}}\right)\right]}{(2\pi)^{n/2}[t_1(t_2-t_1)\cdots(t_n-t_{n-1})]^{1/2}}.$$

   (iv) $Y(t_1)|_{Y(t_2)}$ is normal with mean $\frac{t_1}{t_2} \cdot Y(t_2)$ and variance $\frac{t_1}{t_2}(t_2 - t_1)$.

Hitting Times With Standard Brownian Motion

Suppose $\{Y(t)|0 \le t < \infty\}$ is standard Brownian motion. For any $y_0 \ne 0$ let T_{y_0} be the random time until the process first reaches y_0.

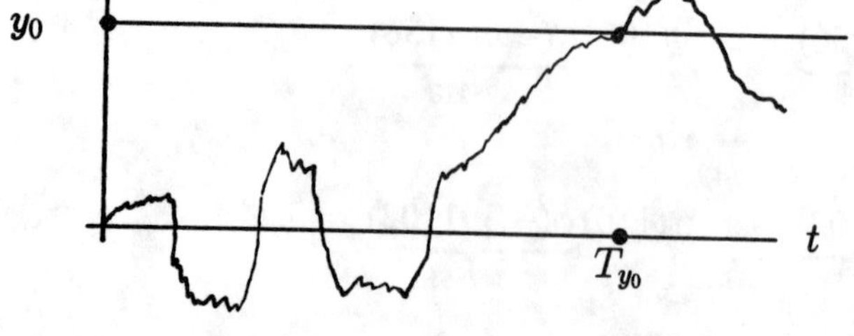

Then the distribution function is given by

$$F_{T_{y_0}}(t) = Pr(T_{y_0} \le t) = 2\left(1 - \phi\left(\frac{|y_0|}{\sqrt{t}}\right)\right)$$

where ϕ is the $N(0,1)$ distribution function.

$E[T_{y_0}]$ is always infinite. The probability that the process hits $a > 0$ before it hits $b < 0$ is $\frac{|b|}{|b| + a}$.

Maximum Process Value Over [0, t] With Standard Brownian Motion

Let $M_t = \underset{s \in [0,t]}{max} Y(s);$. The survival function of M_t is given by

$$Pr(M_t > m) = Pr(M_t \ge m) = Pr(T_m \le t) = \left(1 - \phi\left(\frac{m}{\sqrt{t}}\right)\right).$$

The density function and expected value are

$$f_{M_t}(m) = \sqrt{\frac{2}{\pi t}} e^{-m^2/2t} \qquad 0 \le m < \infty$$

$$E[M_t] = \sqrt{\frac{2t}{\pi}}$$

Brownian Motion With Drift

If $\{Y(t)\}$ is standard Brownian motion and $X(t) = \mu t + \sigma Y(t)$, then $\{X(t)\}$ is a **Brownian motion process** with **drift coefficient** μ and **variance parameter** σ^2.

(i) $X(0) = 0$,

(ii) $\{X(t) | 0 \le t < \infty\}$ has independent and stationary increments, and

(iii) $X(t) \sim N(\mu t, \sigma^2 t)$

Geometric Brownian Motion

Let $Z(t) = e^{X(t)}$ where $\{X(t)\}$ is Brownian motion with drift. Notice that $Z(t_2)/Z(t_1) = e^{X(t_2)-X(t_1)}$.

(i) $Z(0) = 1$.

(ii) If $t_1 < t_2 \le t_3 < t_4$ then $Z(t_2)/Z(t_1)$ and $Z(t_4)/Z(t_3)$ are independent and identically distributed as lognormals $Z(t) = e^{X(t)}$ if $t = t_2 - t_1 = t_4 - t_3$.

(iii) $Z(t) = e^{X(t)}$ is lognormal. Since $M_{X(t)}(s) = e^{(\mu t)s+(\sigma^2 t)s^2/2}$ $(X(t) \sim N(\mu t, \sigma^2 t))$ if follow that

$$E[Z(t)^k] = E[e^{X(t)k}] = M_{X(t)}(k) = e^{\mu tk+\sigma^2 tk^2/2}$$

For example, $$E[Z(1)] = e^{\mu+\sigma^2/2}$$

$$Var(Z(1)) = e^{2\mu+2\sigma^2} - (e^{\mu+\sigma^2/2})^2 = e^{2\mu+\sigma^2}(e^{\sigma^2} - 1).$$

Modeling a Stock Price Process With Geometric Brownian Motion

Suppose a share of a certain stock is currently (i.e., $t = 0$) selling for P_0. Set $P(t) = P_0 Z(t) = P_0 e^{\mu t+\sigma Y(t)}$ where $Z(t)$ is geometric Brownian motion and $Y(t)$ is standard Brownian motion. $\{P(t) | 0 \le t < \infty\}$ is called a **price process model**. Notice that $P(1)/P(0)$, $P(2)/P(1)$, ... are independent and identically distributed as lognormal with mean $e^{\mu+\sigma^2/2}$ and variance $e^{2\mu+\sigma^2}(e^{\sigma^2}-1)$.

At a force of interest δ the random present value at time s of the time t sale price, $P(t)$, is $e^{-\delta(t-s)}P(t)$. Also,

$$E[e^{-\delta(t-s)}P(t) | P(s)] = P(s)e^{-(\delta-\mu)(t-s)}E[e^{\sigma(Y(t-s))}]$$

$$= P(s)e^{-(\delta-\mu)(t-s)}e^{(t-s)\sigma^2/2}$$

$$= P(s)e^{(\mu+\sigma^2/2-\delta)(t-s)}.$$

So, if μ and δ are chosen to satisfy $\mu+\sigma^2/2 = \delta$,

$$E[e^{-\delta(t-s)}P(t) | P(s)] = P(s).$$

Suppose a share is purchased at time s for the given $P(s)$ observed at time s, and is to be sold at time $t > s$ for the value $P(t)$ (random). Then, if $\mu+\sigma^2/2 = \delta$, the expected (actuarial) present value of the gain on this process is 0. σ^2 should be estimated for the process from data on the price of a share at regular intervals and then μ should be chosen to satisfy $\mu = \delta - \sigma^2/2$. This is roughly saying that δ is the expected yield rate on the transaction.

A Simple Arbitrage Example

Outcomes of a gambling game are denoted $\{1, 2, \ldots, n\}$. Wager i is a bet that i is the outcome. For a unit bet on Wager i let R_i = (winnings) – (bet) be the return. Then

$$R_i = \begin{cases} (W_i+1) - 1 & \text{outcome } i \\ 0 - 1 & \text{not the outcome } i \end{cases}$$

if $W_i + 1$ is the amount won on the unit bet if i is the outcome. A betting scheme is a vector $(x_1, \ldots, x_n)$ where x_i is bet on wager i. The return on this scheme is $R = \sum_{i=1}^{n} x_i R_i$.

1. If $1 - \sum_{i=1}^{n}(1+W_i)^{-1} = 0$ there is a probability distribution on the set of outcomes, $Pr(i) = \frac{1}{W_i + 1}$, such that the expected return on every betting scheme is zero.

2. If $\theta = 1 - \sum_{i=1}^{n}(1+W_i)^{-1} \neq 0$, set $x_i = \frac{1}{\theta(1+W_i)}$. Then the return on the betting scheme $(x_1, \ldots, x_n)$ is 1 regardless of the outcome. Unlimited, risk-less profits are possible (an arbitrage).

The Black-Scholes Option Pricing Formula

Consider $P(t) = P_0 Z(t) = P_0 e^{\mu t + \sigma Y(t)}$ as a stock price process where $Z(t)$ is geometric Brownian motion. Consider the following universe of bets on the future price of this stock:

I. Purchase a share at time s for the given $P(s)$ observed at time s, then sell it at time t for the random $P(t)$ value.

II. Purchase at time 0 for $C(t, P_1)$ the option to buy a share at time t for P_1.

If δ is the force of interest and if μ and σ^2 are chosen to satisfy $\mu + \sigma^2/2 = \delta$, we saw earlier that the actuarial present value of the return on Wager(I) was zero, this is,

$$P(s) = E[e^{-\delta(t-s)} P(t) | P(s)].$$

Thus, if we use the probability distribution of future prices given by Geometric Brownian motion with the μ and σ^2 satisfying $\mu+\sigma^2/2 = \delta$ to price the option, Wager II, there is no possible arbitrage in this universe of bets. That is, determine $C(t, P_1)$ such that $0 = E[e^{-\delta t}(P(t) - P_1)^+ - C(t, P_1)]$. This results in the **Black-Scholes option price** formula

$$C(t, P_1) = E[e^{-\delta t}(P(t) - P_1)^+] = P_0\phi(\sigma\sqrt{t}+b) - e^{-\delta t}P_1\phi(b)$$

where

$$b = \frac{\delta t - \sigma^2 t/2 - ln(P_1/P_0)}{\sigma\sqrt{t}}, \quad \mu+\sigma^2/2 = \delta.$$

CONCEPTUAL REVIEW TEST

1. If $\{X(t)|0 \leq t < \infty\}$ is a Brownian motion process with variance parameter σ^2, what are $E[X(2)]$, $Var(X(2))$ and $Pr(X(2) > 4\sigma)$?

2. Define a standard Brownian motion process and how Brownian motion with drift and geometric Brownian motion are defined in terms of it.

3. If $\{Z(t)\}$ is geometric Brownian motion with drift parameter $\mu = .04$ and $\sigma^2 = .0001$, what is the distribution of $Z(4)/Z(1)$?

4. If $\{X(t)|0 \leq t < \infty\}$ is a Brownian motion process with drift parameter μ and variance parameter σ^2, what is the distribution of $X\left(\frac{1}{2}\right)$ given that $X(1) = \mu + .1\sigma$?

5. If $\{X(t)|0 \leq t < \infty\}$ is a Brownian motion process with variance parameter $\sigma^2 = 2$, express the probability that $X(t)$ does not hit 4 by time 10 in terms of the standard normal distribution function.

6. If $X(t)$ is as in Question 5 above, express the probability that the $\max X(t)$ value on $[0, 10]$ exceeds 4 in terms of the standard normal distribution function.

7. If $\{Z(t)|0 \leq t < \infty\}$ is a geometric Brownian motion process with drift coefficient μ and variance parameter σ^2, consider $P(t) = P_0 Z(t)$ as a model of the future price of a stock currently selling for P_0. What is the distribution of $P(n)/P(n-1)$?

CONCEPTUAL REVIEW TEST SOLUTIONS

1. $X(t) \sim N(0, \sigma^2 t)$ so $X(2) \sim N(0, 2\sigma^2)$. Thus $E[X(2)] = 0$, $Var(X(2)) = 2\sigma^2$ and $Pr(X(2) > 4\sigma) = Pr\left(N(0,1) > \frac{4\sigma - 0}{\sqrt{2\sigma^2}}\right) = 1 - \phi\left(\frac{4}{\sqrt{2}}\right)$.

2. $\{Y(t) | 0 \le t < \infty\}$ is called standard Brownian motion if

   (i) $Y(0) = 0$,

   (ii) increments are stationary and independent, and

   (iii) $Y(t) \sim N(0, t)$.

   If $X(t) = \mu t + \sigma Y(t)$, $Z = e^{X(t)} = e^{\mu t + \sigma Y(t)}$, then $\{X(t) | 0 \le t < \infty\}$ and $\{Z(t) | 0 \le t < \infty\}$ are called Brownian motion with drift and geometric Brownian motion respectively.

3. $Z(t_2)/Z(t_1) = e^{\mu t_2 + \sigma Y(t_2) - (\mu t_1 + \sigma Y(t_1))} = e^{\mu(t_2 - t_1) + \sigma(Y(t_2) - Y(t_1))}$. The distribution of $Y(t_2) - Y(t_1)$ is $N(0, t_2 - t_1)$, hence the exponent above is $N(\mu(t_2 - t_1), \sigma^2(t_2 - t_1))$. With $t_1 = 1$, $t_2 = 4$ we thus have the exponent is $N(.04(4-1), .0001(4-1)) = N(.12, .0003)$. Thus $Z(4)/Z(1)$ is lognormal with mean $e^{.12 + .0003/2} = e^{.12015}$ and variance $e^{2(.12015)}(e^{.0003} - 1)$.

4. $X(t) = \mu t + \sigma Y(t)$ where $Y(t) \sim N(0, t)$. If we are given that $X(1) = \mu + .1\sigma$ it is the same as being given that $Y(1) = .10$. The conditional distribution of $Y(t_1)$ given that $Y(t_2) = y_2$ $(t_1 < t_2)$ is normal with mean $\frac{t_1}{t_2} \cdot (y_2)$ and variance $\frac{t_1}{t_2}(t_2 - t_1)$. Thus $Y\left(\frac{1}{2}\right)\Big|_{Y(1) = .10}$ is normal with mean $\frac{1}{2}(.10)$ and variance $\frac{1}{2}\left(1 - \frac{1}{2}\right) = \frac{1}{4}$. Since

$$X\left(\tfrac{1}{2}\right)\Big|_{Y(1)=.10} = \mu \cdot \tfrac{1}{2} + \sigma Y\left(\tfrac{1}{2}\right)\Big|_{Y(1)=.10}$$

   we have $X\left(\frac{1}{2}\right)\Big|_{Y(1)=.10} = \frac{\mu}{2} + \sigma N(.05, .25) = N\left(\frac{\mu}{2}\right) + .05\sigma, .25\sigma^2)$.

5. If $Y(t) = \frac{1}{\sigma}X(t)$ then $\{Y(t)\}$ is a standard Brownian motion process and we are seeking the probability that $Y(t)$ does not hit $\frac{1}{\sigma}4 = \frac{4}{\sqrt{2}}$ by time 10. Since

   $Pr(T_{y_0} \le t) = 2\left(1 - \phi\left(\frac{|y_0|}{\sqrt{t}}\right)\right)$ we have

$$Pr(T_{4/\sqrt{2}} > 10) = 1 - 2\left(1 - \phi\left(\frac{4/\sqrt{2}}{\sqrt{10}}\right)\right) = 2\phi\left(\frac{4}{\sqrt{20}}\right) - 1.$$

6. As above, this is the probability that the $Y(t) = \frac{1}{\sqrt{2}}X(t)$ max on $[0, 10]$ exceeds $\frac{4}{\sqrt{2}}$. Since $Pr(\max_{[0,t]} Y(s) > m) = 2\left[1 - \phi\left(\frac{m}{\sqrt{t}}\right)\right]$, the probability sought is $2\left[1 - \phi\left(\frac{4/\sqrt{2}}{\sqrt{10}}\right)\right] = 2 - 2\phi\left(\frac{4}{\sqrt{20}}\right)$.

7. $Z(t) = e^{\mu t + \sigma Y(t)}$ where $\{Y(t)\}$ is standard Brownian motion. Hence $P(n)/P(n-1) = P_0 e^{\mu n + \sigma Y(n)}/P_0 e^{\mu(n-1)+\sigma Y(n-1)} = e^{\mu + \sigma[Y(n) - Y(n-1)]}$. Since standard Brownian motion has stationary increments, $Y(n) - Y(n-1) \sim Y(1) = N(0, 1)$. Thus $P(n)/P(n-1) \sim e^{\mu + \sigma N(0,1)} \sim e^{N(\mu, \sigma^2)}$. So $P(n)/P(n-1)$ is lognormal with mean $e^{\mu + \sigma^2/2}$ and variance $e^{2\mu + \sigma^2}(e^{\sigma^2} - 1)$.

COMPUTATIONAL REVIEW TEST

1. Suppose $\{X(t)\}$ is a Brownian motion process with variance parameter $\sigma^2 = 4$. Express the following in terms of $\phi(\;)$, the $N(0,1)$ distribution function:
   (i) $Pr(X(2) \leq 1)$;
   (ii) $Pr\left(X(1) \leq 1 \middle| X(2) = \frac{1}{2}\right)$; and
   (iii) $Pr(X(4) - X(2) > 1 | X(2) = \frac{1}{2})$.

2. If T_{y_0} is the time until a standard Brownian motion process hits y_0 calculate the following probabilities and percentiles:
   (i) $Pr(T_2 \leq 8)$;
   (ii) The median of T_2; and
   (iii) The 99th percentile of T_2.

3. Suppose $\{X(t) | 0 \leq t < \infty\}$ is a Brownian motion process with $\sigma^2 = 9$. Calculate the following:
   (i) $Pr(\underset{[0,2]}{max} X(t) \leq 4)$;
   (ii) The median value, m, of $\underset{[0,2]}{max} X(t)$; and
   (iii) The mean value of $\underset{[0,2]}{max} X(t)$.

4. $P(t) = 20Z(t)$, where $\{Z(t)\}$ is a Brownian motion with drift process, is used as a model of the random future price of a stock currently selling at 20. It is estimated that $\sigma^2 = .01$. Present values are calculated at a force of interest of $\delta = .05$. The drift coefficient μ is chosen so that $P(s) = E[e^{-\delta(t-s)}P(t) | P(s)]$, that is, such that the actuarial present value of the profit on a buy at time s, sell at time t transaction is zero.
   (i) What is μ?
   (ii) What is the distribution of $P(2)$? What are its mean and variance?
   (iii) Use the Black-Scholes formula to price an option to buy a share at 22 at time $t = 2$.

5. A gambling game has outcomes 1, 2, 3. A unit bet that the outcome is i will pay 2, 3 or 4 respectively if $i = 1, 2, 3$. Is an arbitrage possible? If not, explain why. If it is, illustrate a betting scheme with a certain return of 10.

COMPUTATIONAL REVIEW TEST SOLUTIONS

1. (i) Since $X(t) \sim N(0, \sigma^2 t)$,
$Pr(X(2) \leq 1) = Pr\left(N(0,1) \leq \frac{1-0}{\sqrt{\sigma^2 \cdot 2}} = \frac{1}{\sqrt{8}}\right) = \phi\left(\frac{1}{\sqrt{8}}\right)$.

(ii) Set $Y(t) = \frac{1}{\sigma}X(t)$. $Pr(X(1) \leq 1 | X(2) = \frac{1}{2}) = Pr(Y(1) \leq \frac{1}{\sqrt{4}} \cdot 1 | Y(2) = \frac{1}{\sqrt{4}}\frac{1}{2})$. In general, $Y(t_1)|_{Y(t_2)}$ is normal with mean $\frac{t_1}{t_2} \cdot Y(t_2)$ and variance $\frac{t_1}{t_2}(t_2 - t_1)$ if $t_1 < t_2$. So $Y(1)|_{Y(2)=\frac{1}{4}}$ is normal with mean $\frac{1}{2}\left(\frac{1}{4}\right)$ and variance $\frac{1}{2}(2-1) = \frac{1}{2}$. Hence
$Pr\left(Y(1) \leq \frac{1}{\sqrt{4}} | Y(2) = \frac{1}{4}\right) = Pr\left(N\left(\frac{1}{8}, \frac{1}{2}\right) \leq \frac{1}{\sqrt{4}}\right) = \phi\left(\left(\frac{1}{\sqrt{4}} - \frac{1}{8}\right)/\sqrt{\frac{1}{2}}\right)$.

(iii) $X(4) - X(2)$ is independent of $X(2)$ and has the same distribution as
$X(4-2) = N(0, \sigma^2 \cdot 2) = N(0, 8)$. So
$Pr(X(4) - X(2) > 1 | X(2) = \frac{1}{2}) = Pr(X(2) > 1) = Pr(N(0,8) > 1) = \phi\left(\frac{1}{\sqrt{8}}\right)$

2. (i) $Pr(T_2 \leq 8) = 2\left[1 - \phi\left(\frac{2}{\sqrt{8}}\right)\right] = 2[1 - .7602] = .480$

(ii) $.50 = Pr(T_2 \leq m) = 2\left[1 - \phi\left(\frac{2}{\sqrt{m}}\right)\right] \Rightarrow \phi\left(\frac{2}{\sqrt{m}}\right) = .75$

$\Rightarrow \frac{2}{\sqrt{m}} = .675$ (the 75th percentile of $N(0,1)$) $\Rightarrow m = 8.78$

(iii) $.99 = Pr(T_2 \leq p) = 2\left[1 - \phi\left(\frac{2}{\sqrt{p}}\right)\right] \Rightarrow .505 = \phi\left(\frac{2}{\sqrt{p}}\right)$

$\Rightarrow \frac{2}{\sqrt{p}} \approx .0126 \Rightarrow p \approx 25{,}200!$

3. (i) Set $Y(t) = \frac{1}{\sigma}X(t) = \frac{1}{3}X(t)$. Then $\{Y(t)\}$ is a standard Brownian motion process. Thus

$$\begin{aligned} Pr(\max_{[0,2]} X(t) \leq 4) &= Pr(\max_{[0,2]} Y(t) \leq \tfrac{4}{3}) \\ &= 1 - Pr(\max_{[0,2]} Y(t) > \tfrac{4}{3}) \\ &= 1 - 2\left[1 - \phi\left(\frac{4/3}{\sqrt{2}}\right)\right] \\ &= 2\phi\left(\frac{4}{3\sqrt{2}}\right) - 1 = .654. \end{aligned}$$

(ii) $.50 = Pr(\underset{[0,2]}{maxX(t)} > m) = Pr\left(\underset{[0,2]}{maxY(t)} > \frac{m}{3}\right) = 2\left[1 - \phi\left(\frac{m/3}{\sqrt{2}}\right)\right]$

$$\Rightarrow \phi\left(\frac{m}{3\sqrt{2}}\right) = .75 \Rightarrow \frac{m}{3\sqrt{2}} = .675$$

$$\Rightarrow m = 2.86.$$

(iii) $E[\underset{[0,2]}{maxX(t)}] = E[\underset{[0,2]}{max}\,3Y(t)] = 3E[\underset{[0,2]}{maxY(t)}] = 3\sqrt{\frac{2(2)}{\pi}} = 3.39.$

4. (i) μ must satisfy $\mu+\sigma^2/2 = \delta$: $\mu = \delta - \sigma^2/2 = .05 - .005 = .045.$

(ii) $P(2) = 20Z(2)$ and $Z(t) = e^{\mu t+\sigma Y(t)}$ where $Y(t) \sim N(0,t)$. Thus $\mu t+\sigma Y(t) \sim N(\mu t, \sigma^2 t)$. Thus $P(2) = 20Z(2) = e^{ln20}Z(2) = e^{ln(20)+N(.045(2),\,.01(2))} = e^{N(.09+ln20,\,.02)}$ has a lognormal distribution. If $Z = e^{N(\mu,\sigma^2)}$ then $E[Z] = e^{\mu+\sigma^2/2} = e^{.09+ln20+.01} = 22.10$ and $Var(Z) = e^{2\mu+\sigma^2}(e^{\sigma^2}-1) = (22.10)^2(e^{\sigma^2}-1) = (22.10)^2(e^{.02}-1) = 9.87.$

(iii) We first need to calculate

$$b = \frac{\delta t - \sigma^2 t/2 - ln(P_1/P_0)}{\sigma\sqrt{t}} = \frac{.05(2) - .01(2)/2 - ln(22/20)}{.1\sqrt{2}} = -.0375.$$

Then

$$C(2,22) = P_0\phi(\sigma\sqrt{t}+b) - (e^{-\delta t}P_1)\phi(b)$$

$$= 20\phi(.10\sqrt{2} - .0375) - (e^{-.10}22)\phi(-.0375)$$

$$= 20\underbrace{\phi(.104)}_{.5414} - 19.91\underbrace{\phi(-.0375)}_{.485}$$

$$= 1.17.$$

5. $W_1+1 = 2,\ W_2+1 = 3,\ W_3+1 = 4$ so $\sum_{i=1}^{3}\frac{1}{1+W_i} = \frac{1}{2}+\frac{1}{3}+\frac{1}{4} = \frac{13}{12} \neq 1$. Hence, an arbitrage is possible since no probability distribution on $\{1, 2, 3\}$ will result in an expected return of 0 on all wagers. Now set $\theta = 1 - \sum_{i=1}^{3}\frac{1}{1+W_i} = -\frac{1}{12}$ and let $x_i = \frac{1}{(1+W_i)\theta}$; $x_1 = -\frac{12}{2}$, $x_2 = -\frac{12}{3}$, $x_3 = -\frac{12}{4}$. Then a betting scheme of (x_1, x_2, x_3) has a certain return of 1. Hence $\left(-\frac{120}{2}, -\frac{120}{3}, -\frac{120}{4}\right)$ has a certain return of 10. For example, the total return if the outcome is 1 is calculated as.

$$\underbrace{-\tfrac{120}{2}(W_1+1) - \tfrac{120}{3}(0) - \tfrac{120}{4}(0)}_{\text{total winnings}} - \underbrace{\left(-\tfrac{120}{2} - \tfrac{120}{3} - \tfrac{120}{4}\right)}_{\text{total wage}}$$

$$= -120 - 0 - 0 + (60+40+30) = 10.$$

UNIT REVIEW QUESTIONS

In the following $\phi(x)$ denotes the distribution function of the Standard Normal Distribution.

For Questions 1 and 2 $\{X(t)|0 \leq t < \infty\}$ is a Brownian motion process with variance parameter $\sigma^2 = 4$.

1. Which of the following is equal to $Pr(-\sigma \leq X(2) \leq 2\sigma | X(1) = \sigma)$?

(A) $\phi(1) - \phi(-1)$ (B) $\phi(1) - \phi(-2)$ (C) $\phi(2) - \phi(-1)$ (D) $\phi(2) - \phi(1)$ (E) $\phi(2) - \phi(-2)$

2. Which of the following is equal to $Pr(-\sigma \leq X(1) \leq 2\sigma) | X(2) = \sigma)$?

(A) $\phi(2) - \phi(-1.5)$ (B) $\phi(2) - \phi(-1)$ (C) $\phi(2.5\sqrt{2}) - \phi(\sqrt{2})$ (D) $\phi(3) - \phi(-3)$ (E) $\phi(1.5\sqrt{2}) - \phi(-1.5\sqrt{2})$

For Questions 3-10 use a Geometric Brownian Motion model with $\mu = 0$, $\sigma^2 = .09$ to model the ratio $P(t)/20$, where $P(t)$ is the price at time t for a share of a stock currently selling at 20.

3. Calculate the probability that the price hits $20e^{.15}$ by time 2.

(A) $1 - \phi\left(\frac{1}{2\sqrt{2}}\right)$ (B) $2\left(1 - \phi\left(\frac{1}{2\sqrt{2}}\right)\right)$ (C) $2\left(1 - \phi\left(\frac{2}{\sqrt{2}}\right)\right)$ (D) $2\phi\left(\frac{1}{2\sqrt{2}}\right) - 1$ (E) $2\phi\left(\frac{2}{\sqrt{2}}\right) - 1$

4. Calculate the median time that is required for the price to hit $20e^{.15}$.

(A) .40 (B) .55 (C) .70 (D) .85 (E) 1.00

5. Calculate the probability that the maximum price over the time interval $[0, 2]$ exceeds $20e^{.30}$.

(A) $1 - \phi\left(\frac{1}{\sqrt{2}}\right)$ (B) $2\left(1 - \phi\left(\frac{1}{\sqrt{2}}\right)\right)$ (C) $2\phi\left(\frac{1}{\sqrt{2}}\right) - 1$ (D) $2\phi\left(\sqrt{2}\right) - 1$ (E) $2\phi\left(\frac{\sqrt{2}}{2}\right) - 1$

6. Calculate the median value of the maximum price of the stock over the time interval $[0, 2]$.

(A) 20.60 (B) 22.10 (C) 23.40 (D) 25.00 (E) 26.60

7. What is the expected value of the price of a share of this stock at time $t = 2$?

(A) 21.70 (B) 21.90 (C) 22.10 (D) 22.30 (E) 22.50

8. Calculate the variance in the price of a share of this stock at time $t = 2$.

(A) 80.7 (B) 87.8 (C) 94.4 (D) 101.2 (E) 108.4

9. What is the probability that the stock increases by more than 20% in a two-year period?

(A) .25 (B) .29 (C) .33 (D) .37 (E) .41

10. Calculate the expected time that is takes from time $t = 0$ for the price of the stock to double.

(A) 1.67 (B) 1.94 (C) 2.31 (D) 7.70 (E) Does not exist

SOLUTIONS TO UNIT REVIEW QUESTIONS

1. $X(t) \sim N(0, \sigma^2 t) = N(0, 4t)$, so $X(2) - X(1) \sim X(2-1) = N(0, 4)$. Hence

$$Pr(-\sigma \leq X(2) \leq 2\sigma | X(1) = \sigma)$$
$$= Pr(-2\sigma \leq X(2) - X(1) \leq \sigma | X(1) = \sigma)$$
$$= Pr(-2(2) \leq N(0,4) \leq 2) \quad \text{(independent increments)}$$
$$= Pr\left(\frac{-4}{\sqrt{4}} \leq N(0,1) \leq \frac{2}{\sqrt{4}}\right)$$
$$= \phi(1) - \phi(-2)$$

ANSWER B

2. $Y(t) = \frac{1}{\sigma}X(t) = \frac{1}{2}X(t)$ is Standard Brownian Motion. Recall that if $t_1 < t_2$ we have $Y(t_1)|Y(t_2)$ is Normal with mean $\frac{t_1}{t_2}Y(t_2)$ and variance $\frac{t_1}{t_2}(t_2 - t_1)$. Now

$$Pr(-\sigma \leq X(1) \leq 2\sigma | X(2) = \sigma) = Pr\left(\frac{-2}{2} \leq Y(1) \leq \frac{2(2)}{2} | Y(2) = \frac{2}{2}\right)$$
$$= Pr(-1 \leq Y(1) \leq 2 | Y(2) = 1)$$
$$= Pr\left(-1 \leq N\left(\frac{1}{2}(1), \frac{1}{2}(2-1)\right) \leq 2\right)$$
$$= Pr\left(\frac{-1-\frac{1}{2}}{\sqrt{\frac{1}{2}}} \leq N(0,1) \leq \frac{2-\frac{1}{2}}{\sqrt{\frac{1}{2}}}\right)$$
$$= \phi(1.5\sqrt{2}) - \phi(-1.5\sqrt{2}).$$

ANSWER E

3. $P(t) = 20Z(t)$, $Z(t) = e^{\mu t + \sigma Y(t)} = e^{.3Y(t)}$ where $Y(t) \sim N(0, t)$. So

$$Pr(\text{Price hits } 20e^{.15} \text{ by } t = 2)$$
$$= Pr\left(Y(t)) \text{ hits } \frac{1}{2} \text{ by } t = 2\right) = Pr(T_{1/2} \leq 2) = 2\left(1 - \phi\left(\frac{1/2}{\sqrt{2}}\right)\right).$$

ANSWER B

4. The time for the price to hit $20e^{.15}$ is the time for $Y(t)$ to hit $\frac{1}{2}$, that is, the hitting time variable $T_{1/2}$. The question seeks the median of $T_{1/2}$. Now

$$Pr(T_{1/2} \le t) = 2\left(1 - \phi\left(\frac{1/2}{\sqrt{t}}\right)\right) = .5$$

means that $.75 = \phi\left(\frac{1/2}{\sqrt{t}}\right)$. The 75th percentile of the standard normal distribution is $\approx .675$. Thus $\frac{1/2}{\sqrt{t}} = .675$ and the median is $t = \left(\frac{.5}{.675}\right)^2 = .55$. ANSWER B

5. Since $P(t) = 20e^{.3Y(t)}$ the price exceeds $20e^{.3}$ over the time interval $[0,2]$ if $Y(t) = N(0,t)$ exceeds 1 over this time interval. Thus

$Pr(\text{max price over } [0,2] \text{ exceeds } 20e^{.3})$

$$= Pr(\max_{0 \le t \le 2} Y(t) \ge 1) = Pr(M_2 \ge 1) = 2\left(1 - \phi\left(\frac{1}{\sqrt{2}}\right)\right)$$ ANSWER B

6. $P(t) = 20e^{.3Y(t)}$. Because $e^{.3x}$ is an increasing function of x it follows that $\underset{[0,2]}{\text{Max}}\, P(t) = 20exp(.3\underset{[0,2]}{\text{Max}} Y(t))$. Due to this increasing relation between the two random maximums it follows that $\text{Median}(\underset{[0,2]}{\text{Max}}\, P(t)) = 20exp(.3\text{Median}(\underset{[0,2]}{\text{Max}}\, Y(t)))$. Hence we can concentrate on the median value of $\underset{[0,2]}{\text{Max}}\, Y(t) = M_2$ (see Condensed Review Notes). The survival function of M_2 is $Pr(M_2 > m) = 2\left(1 - \phi\left(\frac{m}{\sqrt{2}}\right)\right)$, so the median value is the solution m of the equation

$$.5 = 2\left(1 - \phi\left(\frac{m}{\sqrt{2}}\right)\right),$$

that is, $\phi\left(\frac{m}{\sqrt{2}}\right) = .75$. From the $N(0,1)$ table it follows that $\frac{m}{\sqrt{2}} = .675$, hence the median of M_2 is $\sqrt{2}(.675)$. Returning to our earlier discussion, the median of $\underset{[0,2]}{\text{Max}}\, P(t) = 20e^{.3(\sqrt{2}(.675))} = 26.63$. ANSWER E.

7 & 8. $P(2) = 20e^{.3Y(2)}$ where $Y(2) \sim N(0,2)$. Hence $Z(2) = e^{.3Y(2)}$ is lognormal in distribution. Since $.3Y(2) \sim N(0, (.3)^2 2) = N(0, .18)$ it follows from the lognormal relations

$$Z = e^{N(\mu, \sigma^2)} \quad \Rightarrow \quad E[Z] = e^{\mu + \sigma^2/2}$$
$$Var(Z) = e^{2\mu + \sigma^2}(e^{\sigma^2} - 1)$$

that

$$E[Z(2)] = e^{0 + .18/2} = e^{.09} = 1.0942$$
$$Var(Z(2)) = e^{2(0) + .18}(e^{.18} - 1) = .2361.$$

From $P(2) = 20Z(2)$ if follows that

$$E[P(2)] = 20E[Z(2)] = 21.88 \text{ (Answer B, Question 7)}$$
$$Var(P(2)) = 20^2 Var(Z(2)) = 94.44. \text{ (Answer C, Question 8)}.$$

9. $P(t+2)/P(t) = 20e^{.3Y(t+2)}/20e^{.3Y(t)} = e^{.3[Y(t+2)-Y(t)]}$, which has the same distribution as the lognormal variable $e^{.3Y(2)}$. Now
$Pr(P(t+2)/P(t) > 1.20) = Pr(e^{.3Y(2)} > 1.20) = Pr\left(Y(2) > \frac{ln(1.20)}{.30} = .6077\right)$. Since
$Y(2) \sim N(0,2)$ we have $Pr(Y(2) > .6077) = Pr\left(N(0,1) > \frac{.6077-0}{\sqrt{2}} = .4297\right) \approx .334.$

ANSWER C

10. $P(t) = 20e^{.3Y(t)}$ first hits 40 when $Y(t)$ first hits $\frac{ln(2)}{.3} = y_0$. However $E[T_{y_0}]$, an expected hitting time for Standard Brownian motion, is always infinite.

ANSWER E

UNIT FOUR: RUIN MODELS

Introduction

The models discussed here concern the long-term operation of a line of business. They attempt to measure the risk. At time $t = 0$ initial capital u is available to begin the operation. Premium will be assumed to arrive continuously at a rate of c per year. (t is in years). Suppose $N(t)$ claims occur in the time period $(0, t]$ of amounts $X_1, X_2, \ldots, X_{N(t)}$. Then aggregate claims over $(0, t]$, $S(t)$, is modeled by the random sum $X_1 + X_2 + \cdots + X_{N(t)}$. The **surplus** at time t, $U(t)$, is then defined as

$$U(t) = \underbrace{u + ct}_{\substack{\text{available} \\ \text{by time } t}} - \underbrace{S(t)}_{\substack{\text{needed} \\ \text{by time } t}} .$$

$\{N(t)\}$, $\{S(t)\}$, and $\{U(t)\}$ are continuous-time stochastic processes. By restricting t values to 0, 1, 2, ... we could regard these processes as discrete-time processes. There are four factors driving the surplus process:

(i) u, initial surplus (non-random);

(ii) c, annual premium rate (non-random);

(iii) $\{N(t)\}$, claim frequency process; and

(iv) a model for claim amounts (severity).

With discrete-time and continuous-time models we make various assumptions about these factors and try to compute things such as the distribution of $U(t)$ or the chance that $U(t)$ ever becomes negative (the **probability** of **ruin**, a measure of risk in the operation).

We begin with some simple ad-hoc models using first principles calculations and then proceed to discrete-time and continuous-time models where more assumptions regarding the driving factors lead to greater understanding of the surplus process models.

Some Simple Examples of Surplus Models and Ruin Calculations

Suppose initial surplus is $u = 2$ and premium arrives at a rate of $c = 3$/year. Suppose there is exactly one claim, X, that will eventually occur. Assume that the time until it occurs, T, and X are discrete random variables whose distributions are given below:

T	$Prob$
2	.20
5	.80

X	$Prob$
4	.90
15	.10

(assumed to be independent)

The only interesting times to study surplus are at times 2 and 5 when the claim might occur. In between these times the surplus increases continuously with a slope of 3: $U(t) = 2 + 3t - S(t)$ where

$$S(t) = \begin{cases} X & T \leq t \\ 0 & T > t \end{cases}.$$

<u>Possible Pictures</u>

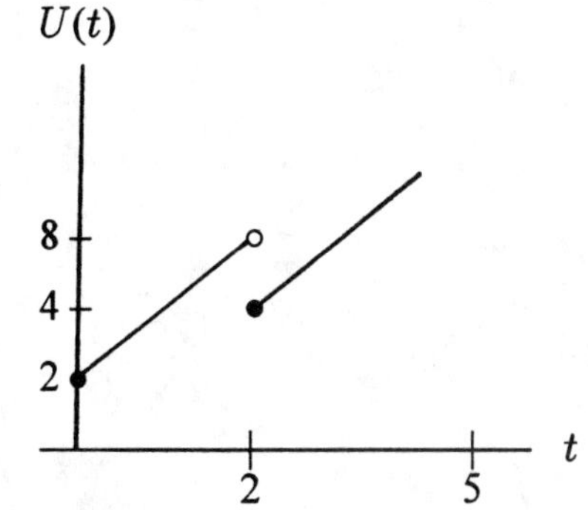

$T = 2, X = 4$

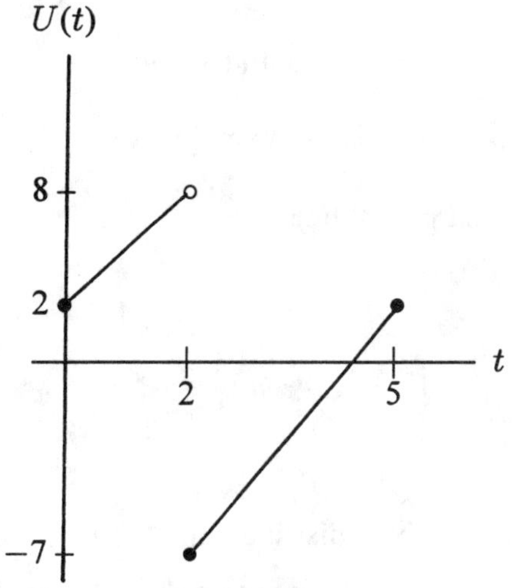

$T = 2, X = 15$

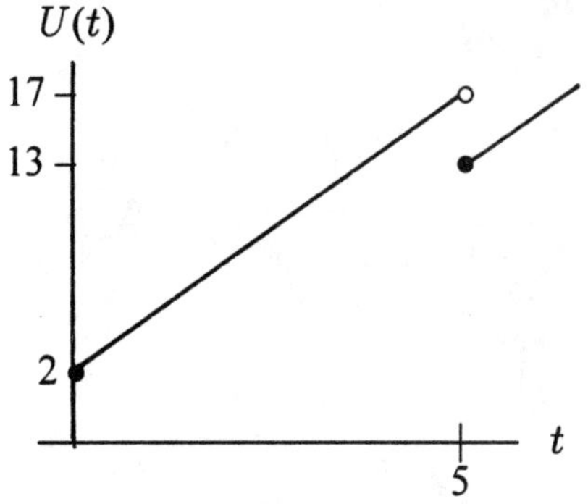

$T = 5, X = 4$

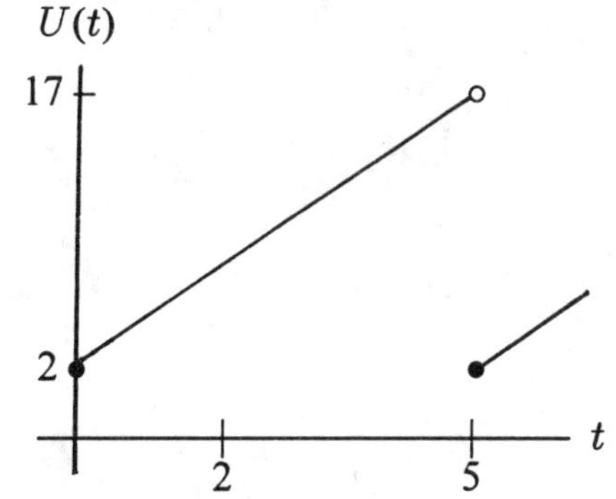

$T = 5, X = 15$

From the pictures we can see that the distributions of $U(2)$ and $U(5)$ are as in the tables below.

$U(2)$	$Prob.$	
4	(.2)(.9)	$T = 2$
−7	(.2)(.1)	$T = 2$
8	.80	$T = 5$

$U(5)$	$Prob.$	$Event$
13	.90	$X = 4$
2	.10	$X = 15$

Also,

$$Prob.(Ruin) = Pr(T = 2 \text{ and } X = 15) = Pr(T = 2)Pr(X = 15) = (.2)(.1) = .02.$$

(independence)

As a variation on this discrete model consider the following continuous model:

$u = 2,\ c = 3$

T = time until the one claim, X, occurs = exponential ($\beta = .2$)

X = Uniform on [5, 20]

Consider the surplus at time $t = 4$:

	Event	Probability
$U(4) = 14$	$T > 4$	$e^{-\beta(4)} = e^{-.8}$
$U(4) = 14 - X$	$T \leq 4$	$1 - e^{-\beta(4)} = 1 - e^{-.8}$

So $U(4)$ has a mixed distribution: the discrete part is a point mass of $e^{-.8}$ at a value of 14 and the continuous part, $14 - X$, is uniformly distributed on $[-6, 9]$. Thus

$$E[U(4)] = 14(e^{-.8}) + \left(\frac{-6+9}{2}\right)(1 - e^{-.8}) = 7.12.$$

The probability of ruin is $Pr(\underbrace{2+3T}_{\text{available}} < \underbrace{X}_{\text{needed}})$.

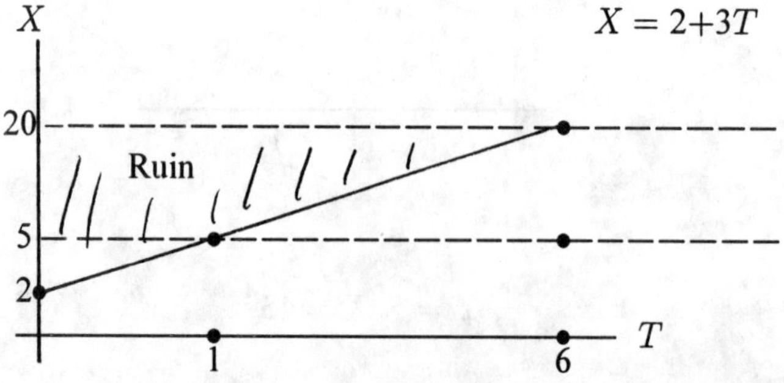

Assuming T and X are independent the joint density is

$$f_{T,X}(t,x) = (.2e^{-.2t})\left(\tfrac{1}{15}\right) \quad t > 0,\ 5 \le x \le 20$$

Thus

$$\begin{aligned} Pr(Ruin) = Pr(2{+}3T < X) &= \int_{t=0}^{1}\int_{x=5}^{20} \tfrac{.20}{15} e^{-.2t} dx\, dt \\ &\quad + \int_{t=1}^{6}\int_{x=2+3t}^{20} \tfrac{.20}{15} e^{-.2t} dx\, dt \qquad \text{(see picture above)} \\ &= \int_0^1 .2e^{-.2t} dt + \int_1^6 \tfrac{.20}{15} e^{-.2t}(20{-}2{-}3t) dt \\ &= 1 - e^{-.2} + \int_1^6 \tfrac{18}{15}(.2)e^{-.2t} dt - \int_1^6 \tfrac{.20}{5} te^{-.2t} dt \\ &= 1 - e^{-.2} + \tfrac{6}{5}[e2^{-.2} {-} e^{-1.2}] + \tfrac{.2}{5}\left[\left(\tfrac{t}{.2} + \tfrac{1}{.2^2}\right)e^{-.2t}\right]_{t=1}^{6} \\ &= .1813 + .6210 - .3198 = .4825. \end{aligned}$$

A Continuous-Time Surplus Model With Aggregate Claims Modeled as a Compound-Sum

Claims of random amounts $X_1, X_2, \cdots$ arrive at random times $T_1 < T_2 < \cdots$, and are assumed to be independent and identically distributed like a claim amount model X. At time zero initial capital u is available to begin operation. Premium is assumed to arrive continuously at the rate of c per year. For any time t (in years), $N(t)$ denotes the number of claims arriving prior to time t, and $S(t)$ denotes the total of these claims. The financial position at any point in time, t, is measured by the surplus, $U(t)$, defined as

$$\underbrace{U(t)}_{\text{surplus}} = \underbrace{u{+}ct}_{\substack{\text{funds available} \\ \text{prior to time } t}} - \underbrace{S(t)}_{\substack{\text{funds needed} \\ \text{prior to time } t}},$$

the excess of funds available over those needed. If $U(t)$ is positive the business is "in the black" at time t, and, if it is negative, then the business is "in the red." If $U(t)$ ever becomes negative then **ruin** is said to occur. This is a random event depending on the random arrival times and claim amounts. The probability of ruin occurring is thus a measure of risk in the long-term operation. If there is reasonable initial capital and ample premium (e.g., if premium per year "safely" exceeds expected annual claims) ruin should be unlikely to occur. The main result of this unit is a concrete expression for the probability of ruin in terms of initial capital, the annual premium rate, and parameters of the claim number and claim amount models.

The following example will be used to illustrate some of the above ideas and several new ones which play key roles in the development of a formula for the probability of ruin. Suppose that for times $t \le 7$ the history of claims is given by the table below:

Claim Number $= i$	1	2	3	4	5
Arrival Time $= T_i$	.5	2	2.75	4	6
Amount $= X_i$	2.5	10	7	4	12

Assume that $u = 5$ is available as initial capital and $c = 4$ per year in premium arrives continuously. In this case, $S(t)$, the total of all claims occurring in the time period $[0,t]$, is given by:

$$S(t) = \begin{cases} 0 & 0 \le t < T_1 = .5 \\ X_1 = 2.5 & T_1 \le t < T_2 = 2 \\ X_1 + X_2 = 12.5 & T_2 \le t < T_3 = 2.75 \\ X_1 + X_2 + X_3 = 19.5 & T_3 \le t < T_4 = 4 \\ X_1 + \cdots + X_4 = 23.5 & T_4 \le t < T_5 = 6 \\ X_1 + \cdots + X_5 = 35.5 & T_5 \le t \le 7 \end{cases}$$

Graph Of Aggregate Claims Versus Time

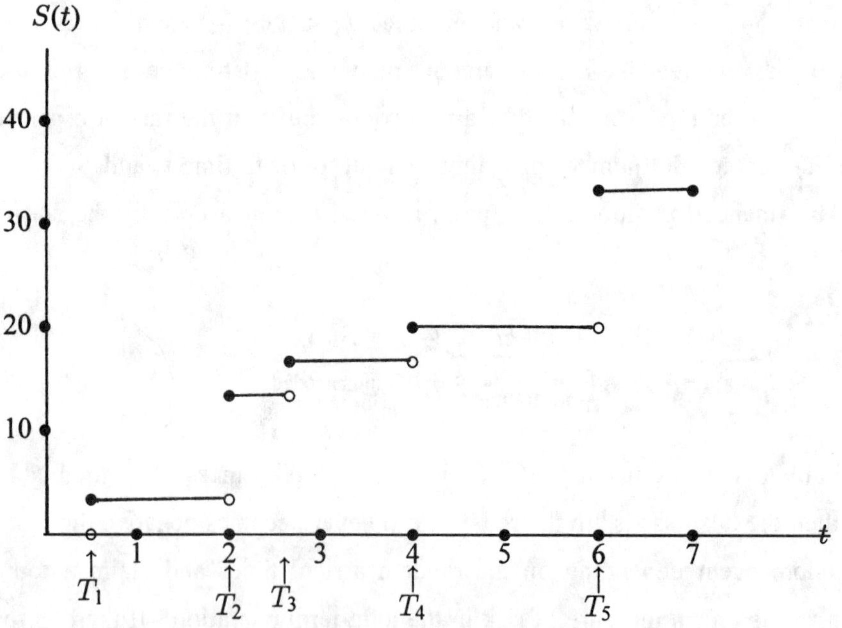

The graph depicts one possible history of the claims process over the short term. It is a right continuous step-function. Jump discontinuities occur at the claim arrival times with the claim amount as the height of the jump. The horizontal length of the "steps" corresponds to the waiting time between consecutive claim arrivals: $W_1 = T_1$, $W_2 = T_2 - T_1, \cdots$, and so on.

Surplus as a function of time, $U(t)$, is given by $U(t) = u{+}ct - S(t) = 5 + 4t - S(t)$. As a result of the above description of $S(t)$ we have the following:

$$U(t) = \begin{cases} 5 + 4t & 0 \le t < .5 = T_1 \\ 5 + 4t - 2.5 & .5 \le t < 2 = T_2 \\ 5 + 4t - 12.5 & 2 \le t < 2.75 = T_3 \\ 5 + 4t - 19.5 & 2.75 \le t < 4 = T_4 \\ 5 + 4t - 23.5 & 4 \le t < 6 = T_5 \\ 5 + 4t - 35.5 & 6 \le t \le 7 \end{cases}$$

Graph Of Surplus Versus Time

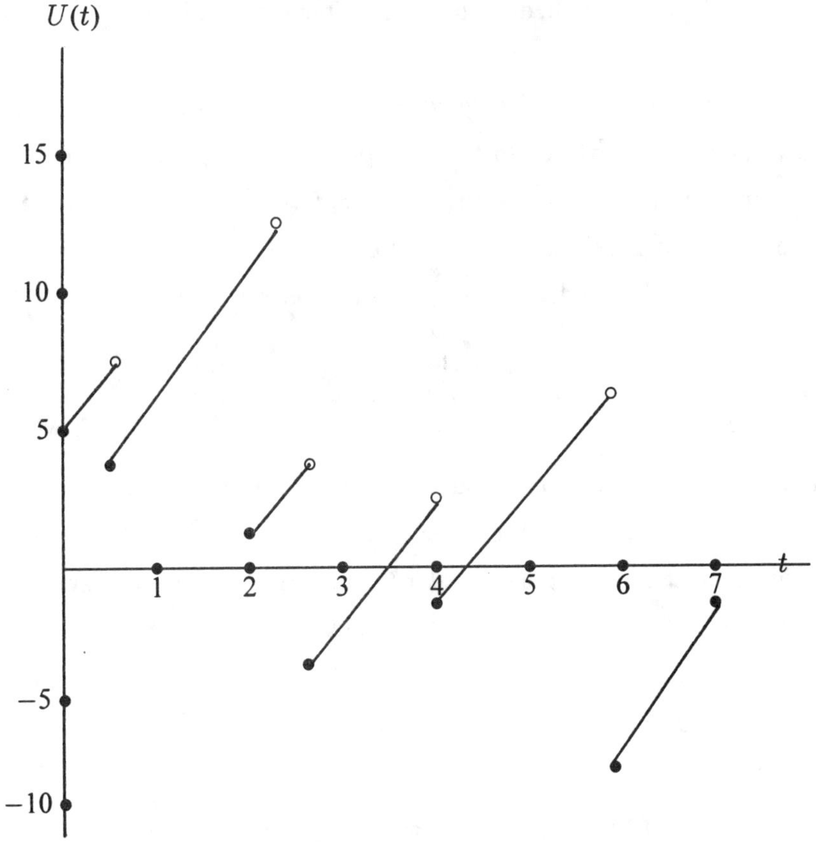

It is clear from the graph that ruin occurs at time 2.75 with the arrival of the third claim. This is the first instant at which surplus is negative. The downward trend of the surplus values at claim arrival times suggests a precarious business: expected claims per year seem to exceed annual premium, driving the business into the red. Perhaps this could have been avoided, even for the long term, with a sufficiently large annual premium and initial capital.

Closely related to the calculation of the probability of ruin is the maximal aggregate loss, L, defined as

$$L = \max_{0 \le t} \{ \underbrace{S(t)}_{\substack{\text{needed} \\ \text{over } [0,t]}} - \underbrace{c \cdot t}_{\substack{\text{collected} \\ \text{over } [0,t]}} \} = \text{largest loss over all possible } [0,t].$$

Notice that $S(0) - c \cdot 0 = 0 - 0 = 0$ so that $L \geq 0$. The event $L \leq u$ is the same as saying ruin does not occur. If $\psi(u)$ denotes the probability of ruin as a function of initial capital, u, then

$$\begin{aligned} 1 - \psi(u) &= Pr(\text{ruin does not occur}) \\ &= Pr(\text{largest loss does not exceed initial capital}) \\ &= Pr(L \leq u) = F_L(u) \quad \text{(distribution function).} \end{aligned}$$

So finding an expression for $\psi(u)$ is clearly tied to understanding the distribution of the maximal aggregate loss, L.

In the graph of surplus, $U(t)$, the maximal aggregate loss is the vertical drop from the initial point $(0, U(0))$ to the lowest point on the graph. In the example above suppose that for $t > 7$ claim experience is such that the graph never drops below the point $(6, U(6) = -6.5)$. Then the maximal aggregate loss is the vertical distance from (0,5) to (6,–6.5), or $L = 5 - (-6.5) = 11.5$.

The distribution of L can be studied by decomposing it into a random sum

$$L = L_1 + \cdots + L_N$$

where N is the random number of "record lows" on the surplus graph and L_i is the vertical drop from the $(i-1)^{st}$ record low to the ith one. In the example above new record lows are set with the arrival of the 1st, 2nd, 3rd and 5th claims. Notice that between the 3rd and 5th claim arrival times the graph stays above its low point at $T_3 = 2.75$, $U(T_3) = -3.5$. Thus $N = 4$ and the values of $L_1, \cdots, L_4$ are computed as

T = time of record low	0	$T_1 = .5$	$T_2 = 2$	$T_3 = 2.75$	$T_5 = 6$
$U(t)$ = record low	5	4.5	.5	−3.5	−6.5
Amount of Drop		$L_1 = .5$	$L_2 = 4$	$L_3 = 4$	$L_4 = 3$

Notice that $L_1 + \cdots + L_4 = 11.5$, the maximal aggregate loss.

Now that most of the major ideas and terminology have been introduced, we can return to the beginning and start filling in some of the details.

The Compound-Poisson Surplus Process

In the discussion to follow we make frequent use of ideas already developed in earlier sections of this manual. The reader may need to review the following:

(i) Compound sums - Section Three, Unit One

(ii) Poisson distributions - Section Three, Unit Three

(iii) The Compound-Poisson distribution - Section Three, Unit Four

(iv) The Poisson process - Section Four, Unit Two

Some of the facts from these earlier sections are derived once again in the reading here to reinforce understanding.

Without rather strong assumptions about the process generating the claims it is impossible to develop much concrete theory. Here we assume that claims are generated by a Poisson process. The term "process" is used in a technical sense to describe a series of random variables generated over time. It concerns both the frequency with which the claims occur and the amounts occurring. The first assumption is that $N(t)$, the random number of claims occurring in the time interval [0,t], is Poisson with parameter λt. This simply says λ claims per year are expected. So (λt) claims are expected in t years. It follows that the random number of claims in any t year period (e.g., [2.5,2.5+t]) is Poisson with parameter λt. Also, increments in this counting process are independent when the time intervals are disjoint.

From the claim arrival times $T_1 < T_2 < \cdots$ we can compute the waiting times between consecutive claims:

$$W_1 = T_1, W_2 = T_2 - T_1, W_3 = T_3 - T_2, \cdots.$$

It follows from the Poisson-process assumptions that these waiting times are independent and identically distributed like an exponential variable with parameter[7] λ. Here is how the argument goes for $T_1 = W_1$:

$$\begin{aligned} Pr(W_1 > w) &= Pr(\text{no claims in time interval } [0,w]) \\ &= Pr(\text{Poisson } (\lambda w) \text{ variable is zero}) \\ &= e^{-\lambda w} \, . \, \frac{(\lambda w)^0}{0!} \qquad \text{(Poisson } (\lambda w) \text{ density at zero)} \\ &= e^{-\lambda w} \, . \end{aligned}$$

[7] $f(x) = \lambda e^{-\lambda x}$

Thus $1 - F_{W_1}(w) = Pr(W_1 > w) = e^{-\lambda w}$. Differentiating with respect to w leads to $f_{W_1}(w) = \lambda e^{-\lambda w}$, the exponential density with parameter λ. There is at least a little bit about this which is intuitive. Suppose $\lambda = 5$, that is 5 claims are expected in a year. Then the expected waiting time between claims, $\frac{1}{\lambda}$ for an exponential λ variable, is $\frac{1}{5}^{th}$ of a year.

The other facet of this process is the claim amount model, X, generating a series of claims X_1, $X_2, \cdots$ at the random arrival times $T_1, T_2, \cdots$. For any time period [0,t], $X_1, X_2, \cdots, X_{N(t)}$ and $N(t)$ are assumed to be independent, and all the X_i are distributed like X. Thus we can form the random sum

$$\underbrace{S(t)}_{\substack{\text{aggregate}\\ \text{claims over}\\ [0,t]}} = X_1 + X_2 + \cdots + X_{\underbrace{N(t)}_{\substack{\text{number}\\ \text{of claims}\\ \text{in } [0,t]}}}$$

modeling aggregate claims over [0,t]. Since $N(t)$ is Poisson (λt), we know that $S(t)$ is a compound-Poisson distribution. Bringing to bear the compound-Poisson theory, we see

$$E[S(t)] = (\lambda t)E[X],$$

and

$$Var(S(t)) = (\lambda t)E[X^2].$$

The assumptions also guarantee that the process increment $S(t+s) - S(s)$, aggregate claims over the t-year period $[s,s+t]$, is a compound-Poisson variable with parameter λt. Furthermore, if $t_1 < t_2 \leq t_3 < t_4$ then the process increments $S(t_4) - S(t_3)$ and $S(t_2) - S(t_1)$ are independent.

Finally, we can form the random surplus $U(t) = u + ct - S(t)$ at time t. We again assume that u is the initial capital and c per year in premium arrives continuously. We can now begin to gain a little appreciation of the risk in the operation. The expected surplus as a function of t, $E[U(t)]$, is linear in t,

$$\begin{aligned} E[U(t)] &= E[\underbrace{u+ct}_{\text{non-random}} - \underbrace{S(t)}_{\text{random}}] \\ &= u + ct - E[S(t)] = u + ct - (\lambda t)E[X] \\ &= u + (\underbrace{c - \lambda \cdot E[X]}_{\substack{\text{slope } = \text{ excess of}\\ \text{annual premium}\\ \text{over expected}\\ \text{annual claims}}})t. \end{aligned}$$

Remember that $\lambda \cdot E[X]$ is the expected value of $S(1)$, aggregate claims over a 1-year period. If premium per year "safely" exceeds expected annual claims, *i.e.*, if $c - \lambda E[X]$ is "sufficiently" large and positive, then

$$\lim_{t\to\infty} E[U(t)] \;=\; \lim_{t\to\infty}\Big(u + \underbrace{(c-\lambda E[X])}_{\text{positive}}t\Big) \;=\; +\infty.$$

Thus, "in the long run," the business is solid. Nevertheless, in the short term, there is a chance that a few early-arriving, large claims might temporarily push you into the red. Ruin can still occur, but $\psi(u)$, the probability of ruin, should be low. It should be a decreasing function of the slope $c - \lambda \cdot E[X]$ (greater expected annual profit should reduce risk) and a decreasing function of u (greater initial capital is a larger safety margin).

When the slope $c - \lambda E[X]$ is positive, the safety margin is typically measured by the relative security loading, θ, where

$$1+\theta \;=\; \frac{c}{\lambda \cdot E[X]} \;=\; \frac{\text{annual premium}}{\text{expected annual claims}}$$

or

$$\theta \;=\; \frac{\text{expected annual profit}}{\text{expected annual claims}}\,.$$

In case the slope $c - \lambda E[X] < 0$ you would have $\lim_{t\to\infty} E[U(t)] \;=\; -\infty$ and ruin is certain (i.e., $\psi(u) = 1$). It is also true that ruin is certain when the slope is zero, although this is not quite as intuitively clear. In the next few sections we will gradually obtain sharper conclusions about $\psi(u)$ in terms of initial capital, annual premium, claim frequency and claim amounts. We say this to remind you that a lot more than u goes into the determination of the probability of ruin. The traditional notation tends to obscure this fact.

A Closer Look at the Maximal Aggregate Loss as a Random Sum in the Compound Poisson Surplus Model

Let's return to the maximal aggregate loss, L, and go into a little more detail under the assumption that the aggregate claims process is a compound-Poisson process. The starting point is the decomposition of L into a random sum via the "record lows" on the graph of surplus, $U(t)$, versus time. We described L geometrically as the vertical drop from the initial point $(0,u)$ to the lowest point on the graph. If surplus never drops below the initial surplus, there is never a loss over any time period $[0,t]$, so that $L = 0$. If it does ever drop below u, there may be several record lows before it bottoms out when the maximal aggregate loss is encountered. In the graph below we have depicted a possible surplus history where there are three record lows which occur with the arrival of the 2nd, 4th and 5th claims.

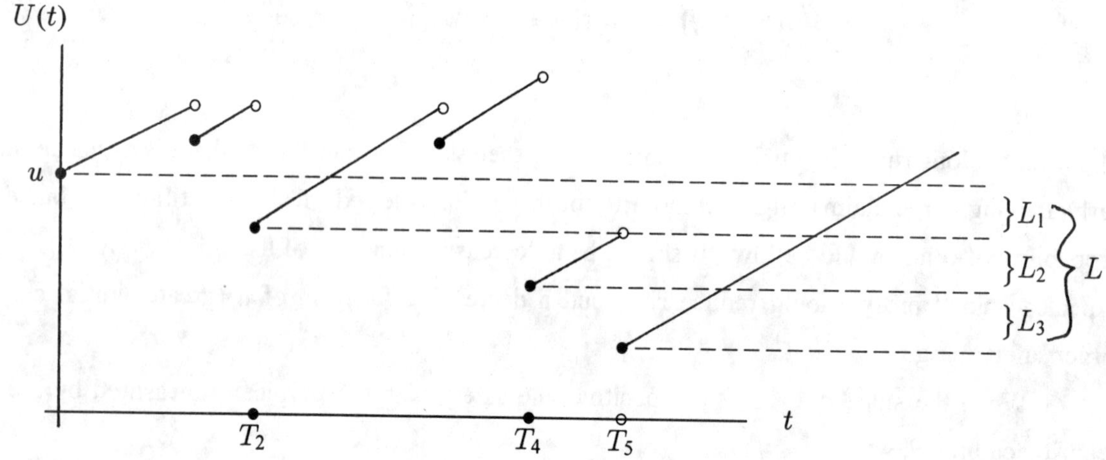

Here we would have $L = L_1 + L_2 + L_3$ and $N = 3$ record lows. Each L_i is the vertical drop between consecutive record lows. There is a loss of $\$L$ over this time period of operations.

In general there are a random number, N, of record lows and $L = L_1 + \cdots + L_N$. Consider L_1. It can be described as the loss at the first instant that surplus drops below its initial level, given that this happens. If you consider just the premium coming in and the sequence of claims coming in, and forget about the initial capital u (i.e., pretend that you have zero initial capital), then at the instant of the record low we could instead view the situation as ruin occurring. L_1 would then be the loss at the time of ruin with no initial capital, given that ruin occurred. By a similar mental device one can reason that $L_2, L_3 \cdots, L_N$ may also be viewed in this same way. Each time a record low occurs, forget the past.[8] Pretend as though you are starting fresh with zero initial capital. The sequence of premiums and claims that resulted in the next record low can be viewed as triggering another ruin with no initial capital. The drop between the record lows, an L_i, can be viewed as the loss at time of ruin with no initial capital, given that this happens. It follows from the Poisson process assumptions that $L_1, L_2, \cdots L_N$ and N are independent. So in summary, the $L_1, \ldots, L_N$ are independent and identically distributed like L_1.

Next we need to give precise descriptions of L_1 and N distributions. The first result says that L_1 is closely related to the claim amount variable X. We will employ the conventions that $p(x)$, $P(x)$ stand for its density and distribution functions respectively:

$$f_{L_1}(y) = \frac{1}{p_1}[1 - P(y)], \qquad p_1 = E[X].$$

This result is not terribly intuitive and difficult to prove. There are, however, several claim amount distributions where L_1 is reasonably simple.

---

[8] In a Markov chain, the process starts over at any given time (memoryless).

Example 1 Show that if X is exponential with mean $1/\beta$, then L_1 is also the same exponential distribution. Show that if $X = x_0$ is constant, then L_1 is uniform over the interval form 0 to x_0.

Solution

(1) $p(y) = \beta e^{-\beta y}$ means $P(y) = \int_0^y \beta e^{-\beta x} dx = -e^{-\beta x}\Big|_0^y = 1-e^{-\beta y}$.

Hence, since $p_1 = E[X] = \frac{1}{\beta}$,

$$f_{L_1}(y) = \frac{1}{p_1}[1-P(y)] = \frac{1}{(1/\beta)}[1-(1-e^{-\beta y})] = \beta e^{-\beta y}.$$

(2) If $X = x_0$ then

$$P(y) = Pr(X \le y) = \begin{cases} 0 & y < x_0 \\ 1 & y \ge x_0 \end{cases},$$

and $p_1 = E[X] = x_0$. So

$$1 - P(y) = \begin{cases} 1 & y < x_0 \\ 0 & y \ge x_0 \end{cases},$$

which means

$$f_{L_1}(y) = \frac{1}{x_0}[1-P(y)] = \begin{cases} \frac{1}{x_0} & y < x_0 \\ 0 & y \ge x_0 \end{cases}.$$

All of the above is based on $y \ge 0$. So we conclude L_1 is uniform on $[0,x_0]$. □

Now let's consider N, the number of record lows. As we saw in the discussion about the L_i having the same distribution as L_1, each record low is like a ruin with no initial capital. What's going on here can be viewed as a sequence of Bernoulli trials. With each trial we begin observing just after a record low to see if ruin occurs. The trial is a "failure" if ruin occurs and q, the probability of failure, is $\psi(0)$, the probability of ruin with no initial capital. When a "success" finally occurs, we have seen N failures corresponding to the N record lows. Thus N is a Geometric variable with $p = 1-\psi(0)$. Now, what about $\psi(0)$?

It is remarkable that the simple formula $\psi(0) = \frac{1}{1+\theta}$ follows from the Poisson-process assumptions. Proof of this fact is again extremely complicated. It is intuitive, however, that as θ goes up, risk should go down. Furthermore, as θ goes up the fraction $\frac{1}{1+\theta}$ goes down in a relatively simple manner.

The final results we wish to include here are rather explicit equations for the moment generating functions of L_1 and L:

$$M_{L_1}(t) = \frac{M_X(t)-1}{p_1 t}, \quad p_1 = E[X]$$

$$M_L(t) = \frac{\theta p_1 t}{1+(1+\theta)p_1 t - M_X(t)}.$$

The first of these generating functions can be used along with power series tricks to calculate moments of L_1. This is an alternate method to using the L_1 density given earlier in terms of $P(x)$:

$$M_X(t) = 1 + E[X]\cdot t + E[X^2]\cdot \frac{t^2}{2!} + E[X^3]\cdot \frac{t^3}{3!} + \cdots.$$

$$\Rightarrow \quad M_{L_1}(t) = \frac{M_X(t)-1}{p_1 t} = \frac{E[X]\cdot t + E[X^2]\cdot \frac{t^2}{2!} + \cdots}{E[X]\cdot t}$$

$$= 1 + \frac{E[X^2]}{2E[X]}\cdot t + \frac{E[X^3]}{3E[X]}\cdot \frac{t^2}{2!} + \cdots.$$

$$\Rightarrow \quad E[L_1] = M'_{L_1}(0) = \frac{E[X^2]}{2E[X]} \qquad \text{(coefficient of } t\text{)}$$

$$E[L_1^2] = M''_{L_1}(0) = \frac{E[X^3]}{3E[X]} \qquad \left(\text{coefficient of } \tfrac{t^2}{2!}\right)$$

Derivation of the $M_{L_1}(t)$ formula above is very complex, but it follows from results on random sums, and the random sum decomposition $L = L_1 + \cdots + L_N$, that

$$M_L(t) = M_N\left(\ln M_{L_1}(t)\right).$$

Furthermore, N is geometric so that $M_N(t)$ has a known form. All of this plus the form of $M_{L_1}(t)$ given above leads to the form of $M_L(t)$ given above after a few algebraic steps. The form of $M_L(t)$ given above can be used to obtain L moments. An alternative way to get these moments is the theory of random sums:

$$L = L_1 + \cdots + L_N, \quad \text{all } L_i \sim L_1, \ N \text{ geometric}$$

$$\Rightarrow E[L] = E[N]\cdot E[L_1]$$

$$Var(L) = E[N]\cdot Var(L_1) + (E[L_1])^2 \cdot Var(N)$$

where moments of L_1 are obtained from moments of X

$$E[L_1] = \frac{E[X^2]}{2E[X]}$$

$$Var(L_1) = E[L_1^2] - (E[L_1])^2 = \frac{E[X^3]}{3E[X]} - \left(\frac{E[X^2]}{2E[X]}\right)^2$$

and moments of N are obtained from the Negative Binomial formulas with $r=1$, $p=1-\psi(0)$, $q=\psi(0)=\frac{1}{1+\theta}$

$$E[N] = \frac{rq}{p} = \frac{\psi(0)}{1-\psi(0)} = \frac{1}{\theta}$$

$$Var(N) = \frac{rq}{p^2} = \frac{E[N]}{p} = \frac{1+\theta}{\theta^2}.$$

It is highly unsatisfying to give so many deep and technical results without a single derivation or much in the way of intuitive explanation. We've simply attempted to describe the important ideas and have avoided getting bogged down in technical proofs. None of the proofs tend to enhance your understanding.

Example 2 Suppose we have a compound-Poisson claims process with $\lambda = 4$ expected claims per year. Assume that all claims are 5 and that $c = 25$ per year in premium arrives continuously. Calculate θ, $\psi(0)$, the expected value and variance of L_1, the expected number of record lows, and the expected value and variance of the maximal aggregate loss.

Solution

(1) $1+\theta = \frac{c}{\lambda \cdot E[X]} = \frac{25}{20} = 1.25$ since $X = x_0 = 5$.

Thus $\theta = .25$.

(2) $\psi(0) = \frac{1}{1+\theta} = \frac{1}{1.25} = .80.$

(3) We have seen in example 1 that L_1 is uniform over the interval [0,5]. Thus

$$E[L_1] = \frac{5}{2}, Var(L_1) = \frac{5^2}{12} = \frac{(\text{length})^2}{12}.$$

An alternate way of finding these numbers is

$$E[L_1] = \frac{E[X^2]}{2E[X]} = \frac{E[5^2]}{2E[5]} = \frac{25}{10} = \frac{5}{2}$$

$$Var(L_1) = \frac{E[X^3]}{3E[X]} - (E[L_1])^2 = \frac{5^3}{15} - \left(\frac{5}{2}\right)^2 = \frac{5^2}{12}.$$

(4) The expected number of record lows was seen to be

$$E[N] = \frac{1}{\theta} = \frac{1}{.25} = 4$$

and its variance was

$$Var(N) = \frac{1+\theta}{\theta^2} = \frac{1.25}{.25^2} = 20.$$

(5) For the maximal aggregate loss we have

$$E[L] = E[N]\cdot E[L_1] = (4)\left(\tfrac{5}{2}\right) = 10$$

$$Var(L) = E[N]\cdot Var(L_1) + (E[L_1])^2\cdot Var(N)$$
$$= (4)\left(\tfrac{5^2}{12}\right) + \left(\tfrac{5}{2}\right)^2(20) = \tfrac{400}{3}.$$

These same results can be coaxed out of

$$M_L(t) = \frac{\theta p_1 t}{1+(1+\theta)p_1 t - M_X(t)} = \frac{(.25)(5)t}{1+(1.25)(5)t - e^{5t}} = \frac{1.25t}{1+6.25t - e^{5t}},$$

although it takes considerably more effort. Notice that $X = x_0 = 5$ means

$$M_X(t) = E[e^{tX}] = E[e^{5t}] = e^{5t}.$$

□

The Adjustment Coefficient and the Probability of Ruin in the Compound-Poisson Surplus Model

The adjustment coefficient, R, appears in a significant way in formulas for the probability of ruin. Unfortunately there is no intuition for the manner in which it is defined. So we will concentrate on describing concepts and important results. Reinsurance schemes tend to "adjust" R upward, which results in $\psi(u)$ being lowered.

The technical definition of R for a Poisson claims process is as the unique, non-zero solution of

$$\lambda + cR = \lambda\cdot M_X(R).$$

An equivalent form of this equation is obtained in dividing by λ and replacing $\frac{c}{\lambda}$ by

$$\frac{c}{\lambda} = \frac{c}{\lambda p_1}\cdot p_1 = (1+\theta)p_1 \quad \text{(note: } p_1 = E[X]).$$

So R is also the unique, non-zero solution of the equation

$$1 + (1+\theta)p_1 R = M_X(R).$$

Example 3 If X is exponential with mean $\frac{1}{\beta}$ find a closed form expression for R.

Solution $M_X(t) = \frac{\beta}{\beta - t}$ so the equation is

$$1 + (1+\theta)\frac{1}{\beta}R = \frac{\beta}{\beta - R}.$$

Multiplying through by $\beta - R$ yields a quadratic equation

$$\beta - R + \frac{1+\theta}{\beta} R(\beta - R) = \beta$$

$$\Rightarrow \quad R\left(\frac{1+\theta}{\beta}(\beta - R) - 1\right) = 0$$

$$\Rightarrow \quad R = 0 \text{ or } R = \frac{\theta\beta}{1+\theta}$$

The unique non-zero solution is $R = \frac{\theta\beta}{1+\theta}$.

Note: This is the only X distribution for which a nice formula for R exists. For any other distribution, finding R would typically require numerical, approximation methods. This is also the only case when $\psi(u)$ has a closed form that's usable. □

Although is not generally possible to obtain a closed form expression for R, the following estimate is always available:

$$1 + (1+\theta)E[X]R = M_X(R) = 1 + E[X]R + \frac{1}{2!}E[X^2]R^2 + \underbrace{\cdots}_{\text{positive terms}} > 1 + E[X]R + \frac{1}{2}E[X^2]R^2$$

$$\Rightarrow \quad \theta E[X]R > \frac{1}{2}E[X^2]R^2$$

$$\Rightarrow \quad \frac{2\theta E[X]}{E[X^2]} > R$$

Note: Since $E[L] = E[N]E[L_1] = \left(\frac{1}{\theta}\right)\frac{E[X^2]}{2E[X]}$, the upper bound for R derived above is the same as $\frac{1}{E[L]}$, the reciprocal expected maximal loss!

The connection of R with the probability of ruin with initial capital u, $\psi(u)$, is via the relation

$$\psi(u) = \frac{e^{-Ru}}{E\left[e^{-RU(T)}\middle| T < \infty\right]}$$

where T is the time of ruin given that ruin occurs (*i.e.*, given $T < \infty$). The denominator is a type of moment generating function. $U(T)$ is the (negative) surplus at the time of ruin if ruin occurs, so $-RU(T) > 0$ and the denominator is bigger than 1. This leads to the relation

$$\psi(u) < e^{-Ru},$$

and the upper bound e^{-Ru} goes down as R increases. This would seem to indicate that increasing the adjustment coefficient will decrease the probability of ruin.

In the case that m is the maximum possible claim amount (i.e., $Pr(X \leq m) = 1$ and m is as small as possible), it is also possible to find a lower bound for the probability of ruin, $e^{-R(u+m)}$. Hence

$$\underbrace{e^{-R(u+m)}}_{\text{lower bound}} < \psi(u) < \underbrace{e^{-Ru}}_{\text{upper bound}} .$$

In the case that **claim amounts**, X, are **exponentially distributed** ($p(x) = \beta e^{-\beta x}$) the $\psi(u)$ formula above reduces to

$$\psi(u) = \frac{1}{1+\theta}e^{-Ru}, \ R = \frac{\theta\beta}{1+\theta}.$$

This is the only situation where a closed form expression is possible.

One other method to approximate $\psi(u)$ has yet to be exploited. We know that $\psi(u) = 1 - F_L(u)$ where $L = L_1 + \cdots + L_N$ is the maximal aggregate loss. We have seen that the L_i are independent and identically distributed like L_1, and the L_1 distribution can be obtained via $f_{L_1}(y) = \frac{1}{E[X]}[1 - F_X(y)]$ from the claim amount distribution. Furthermore, N is a geometric variable with $p = \frac{\theta}{1+\theta}$, $q = \frac{1}{1+\theta}$. In Section Three of this manual it was shown that N is an $(a, b, 0)$ distribution. This idea together with $L = L_1 + \cdots + L_N$ could be used to recursively calculate $f_L(0)$, $f_L(1)$, if possible L_1 values were 0, 1, 2, ... Thus if L_1 is discretized (see Section Three, Unit Four), then approximate values of $\psi(u) = 1 - F_L(u)$ can be obtained recursively. An example of these ideas is illustrated next.

An Example of Recursive Approximations of the Probability of Ruin in the Compound Poisson Surplus Model

Consider a compound-Poisson surplus model where $\lambda = 5$, $\theta = .25$ and the distribution of claim amount is given by $p(1) = .70$, $p(2) = .30$. Then the density function of L_1 is given by

$$f_{L_1}(y) = \frac{1}{E[X]}[1 - F_X(y)], \qquad 0 \leq y \leq 2$$

$$= \left(\frac{1}{1.3}\right)\begin{cases} 1 & 0 \leq y < 1 \\ .30 & 1 \leq y < 2 \\ 0 & 2 \leq y \end{cases}$$

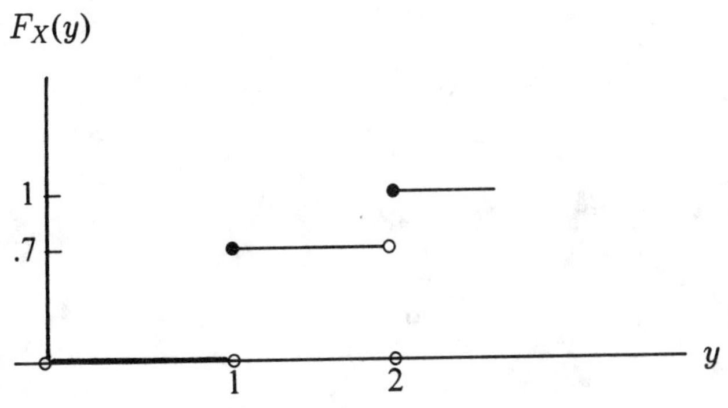

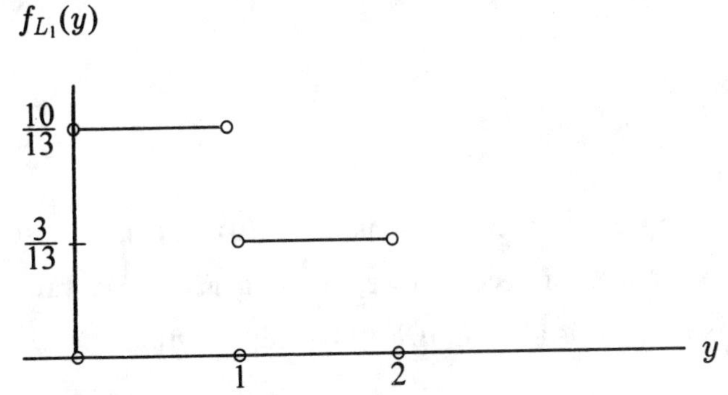

Suppose we use local moment matching (Section Three, Unit Four) to discretize L_1. We use a span of $h = 1$ and seek to preserve

$$E[L_1] = \int_0^2 y \cdot f_{L_1}(y)\,dy = \int_0^1 y \cdot \tfrac{10}{13}\,dy + \int_1^2 y \cdot \tfrac{3}{13}\,dy = \tfrac{1}{2} \cdot \tfrac{10}{13} + \tfrac{3}{2} \cdot \tfrac{3}{13} = \tfrac{19}{26}.$$

(Note: This value could also have been obtained without the L_1 – density via $E[L_1] = \frac{E[X^2]}{2 \cdot E[X]} = \frac{.19}{2(.13)}$.) Point masses m_0^i, m_1^i are assigned at points i, $i+1$ as indicated in the diagram and calculations below.

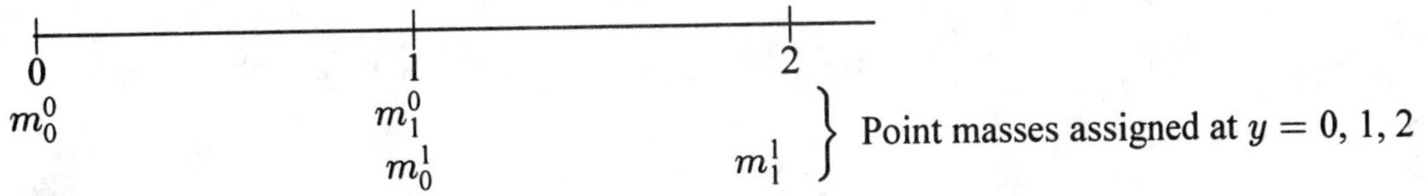

Total: $\frac{10}{26}$ $\left(\frac{10}{26} + \frac{3}{26}\right)$ $\frac{3}{26}$

Calculation of m_0^0, m_1^0 and m_0^1, m_1^1

$$\left\{\begin{array}{l} m_0^0 + m_1^0 = Pr(0 \le L_1 \le 1) = \frac{10}{13} \\ 0 \cdot m_0^0 + 1 \cdot m_1^0 = \int_0^1 y \cdot f_{L_1}(y)\,dy = \frac{1}{2} \cdot \frac{10}{13} \\ m_0^1 + m_1^1 = Pr(1 \le L_1 \le 2) = \frac{3}{13} \\ 1 \cdot m_0^1 + 2 \cdot m_1^1 = \int_1^2 y \cdot f_{L_1}(y)\,dy = \frac{3}{2} \cdot \frac{3}{13} \end{array}\right. \qquad \begin{array}{l} m_1^0 = \frac{5}{13} = \frac{10}{26} \\ m_0^0 = \frac{5}{13} = \frac{10}{26} \\ m_1^1 = \frac{9}{26} - \frac{3}{13} = \frac{3}{26} \\ m_0^1 = \frac{3}{13} - \frac{3}{26} = \frac{3}{26} \end{array}$$

Check: $\quad E[L_1^{disc}] = \frac{10}{26} \cdot 0 + 1 \cdot \frac{13}{26} + 2 \cdot \frac{3}{26} = \frac{19}{26}.$

L_1^{disc}	$Prob.$
0	$\frac{10}{26}$
1	$\frac{13}{26}$
2	$\frac{3}{26}$

We can now move to the recursive approximate calculations of $f_L(0)$, $f_L(1)$, ... based on the discretization of L_1 obtained above. The number of record lows, N, is a geometric variable with $q = \psi(0) = \frac{1}{1+\theta} = \frac{1}{1.25} = .80$, $p = \frac{\theta}{1+\theta} = .20$. It is also an $(a, b, 0)$ type distribution:

$$a + \frac{b}{k} = \frac{Pr(N = k)}{Pr(N = k-1)} = \frac{q^k p}{q^{k-1} p} = q \qquad \Rightarrow \qquad a = q = .80,\ b = 0.$$

Since $L = L_1 + \cdots + L_N$ we can approximate the L distribution in replacing the precise L_1 distribution by the discretized version above and then using the $(a, b, 0)$ recursion formula. The details are given below.

$(a, b, 0)$ Recursion: $\quad f_L(k) = \frac{1}{1 - a f_{L_1}(0)} \sum_{j=1}^{k} \left(a + \frac{bj}{k}\right) f_{L_1}(j) f_L(k-j)$

Starting Value:

$$\begin{aligned} f_L(0) &= P_N(f_{L_1}(0)) && \text{(Probability generating function)} \\ &= \left(1 - \tfrac{q}{p}(f_{L_1}(0) - 1)\right)^{-1} && \text{(Geometric distribution fact)} \\ &= \left(1 - 4\left(\tfrac{10}{26} - 1\right)\right)^{-1} \\ &= \tfrac{26}{90} = .2889 && \text{(approximate value based on } L_1^{disc}\text{)} \end{aligned}$$

Using $a = q = .80$, $f_{L_1}(0) = \frac{10}{26}$, $b = 0$, $k = 2$, the precise recursion relation is

$$f_L(k) = \frac{26}{18}[.80 f_{L_1}(1) f_L(k-1) + .80 f_{L_1}(2) f_L(k-2)] = \frac{20.8}{18}\left[\frac{13}{26} f_L(k-1) + \frac{3}{26} f_L(k-2)\right]$$

Hence

$$f_L(1) \approx \frac{20.8}{18}\left[\frac{13}{26}\cdot\underbrace{\frac{26}{90}}_{f_L(0)}\right] = .1669$$

$$f_L(2) \approx \frac{20.8}{18}\left[\frac{13}{26}(.1669) + \frac{3}{26}(.2889)\right] = .1350$$

$$f_L(3) \approx \frac{20.8}{18}\left[\frac{13}{26}(.1350) + \frac{3}{26}(.1669)\right] = .1002$$

$$f_L(4) \approx \frac{20.8}{18}\left[\frac{13}{26}(.1002) + \frac{3}{26}(.1350)\right] = .0759$$

Summary

	u	0	1	2	3	4
Approximate values based on L_1^{disc} above	$f_L(u)$	.2889	.1669	.1350	.1002	.0759
	$F_L(u)$	.2889	.4558	.5908	.6910	.7669
	$\psi(u)$	.7111	.5442	.4092	.3090	.2331

Note: We know $\psi(0)$ is precisely $\frac{1}{1+\theta} = \frac{1}{1.25} = .80$. To obtain better accuracy in the approximations above it is necessary to shrink the span (i.e., put in more subintervals and point masses) in the discretization of L_1.

An Example of a Probability of Ruin Calculation in the Compound-Poisson Surplus Model when Claim Amounts are Distributed as a Mixture of Exponentials

We mentioned earlier that when X has an exponential density[9] with parameter β that $R = \frac{\theta\beta}{1+\theta}$ and $\psi(u) = \frac{1}{1+\theta}e^{-Ru}$. Similar expressions for $\psi(u)$ can be obtained with considerable algebraic effort when X is a mixture of exponential densities. Suppose $p(x) = \sum_{i=1}^{n} A_i(\beta_i e^{-\beta_i x})$ where $A_1 + \cdots + A_n = 1$ and the weights A_i are positive. Then

$$M_X(t) = \sum_{i=1}^{n} A_i M_{X_i}(t) = \sum_{i=1}^{n} A_i\left(\frac{\beta_i}{\beta_i - t}\right).$$

Using the fact that L has a point mass of $1 - \psi(0) = \frac{\theta}{1+\theta}$ at zero (i.e., if ruin does not occur with $u = 0$ then L is zero), and the form

---

9 $f(x) = \beta e^{-\beta x}$

$$M_L(t) = \frac{\theta p_1 t}{1+(1+\theta)p_1 t - M_X(t)} = \underbrace{\frac{\theta}{1+\theta}\cdot 1}_{\substack{\text{Generating}\\ \text{function of}\\ \text{the discrete}\\ \text{part of } L}} + \frac{1}{1+\theta}\cdot \underbrace{\left[\frac{\theta[M_X(t)-1]}{1+(1+\theta)p_1 t - M_X(t)}\right]}_{\substack{\text{Generating function}\\ \text{of the cont. part of } L}}$$

of its generating function, it follows that

$$\underbrace{\int_0^\infty e^{ut}(-\psi'(u))du}_{\substack{\text{Def. of gen. fcn.}\\ \text{of the cont. part}}} = \frac{\theta[M_X(t)-1]}{1+(1+\theta)p_1 t - M_X(t)}\cdot\frac{1}{1+\theta}.$$

With $M_X(t) = \sum_{i=1}^n A_i\left(\frac{\beta_i}{\beta_i - t}\right)$ the right-hand side above can be written in a partial fraction expansion (massive amounts of algebra required)

$$\sum_{i=1}^n \frac{C_i r_i}{r_i - t}.$$

The only function $\psi(u)$ satisfying $\psi(\infty) = 1 - F(\infty) = 1 - 1 = 0$ and

$$\int_0^\infty e^{ut}(-\psi'(u))du = \sum_{i=1}^n \frac{C_i r_i}{r_i - t}.$$

is

$$\psi(u) = \sum_{i=1}^n C_i e^{-r_i u}.$$

The difficulty in employing this method is the algebra needed to obtain the partial fraction expansion

$$\frac{1}{1+\theta}\cdot\frac{\theta[M_X(t)-1]}{1+(1+\theta)p_1 t - M_X(t)} = \sum_{i=1}^n \frac{C_i r_i}{r_i - t}$$

when $M_X(t) = \sum_{i=1}^n A_i\left(\frac{\beta_i}{\beta_i - t}\right)$.

When $n = 1$ (hence $A_1 = 1$, $M_X(t) = \frac{\beta_1}{\beta_1 - t}$) this method reproduces the earlier result $\psi(u) = \frac{1}{1+\theta}e^{-Ru}$, $R = \frac{\theta\beta}{1+\theta}$. Even with $n = 2$ the algebra to calculate C_1, C_2, r_1, r_2 is considerable:

$$\frac{1}{1+\theta}\cdot\frac{\theta[M_X(t)-1]}{1+(1+\theta)p_1 t - M_X(t)} = \frac{C_1 r_1}{r_1 - t} + \frac{C_2 r_2}{r_2 - t},$$

$$M_X(t) = A_1\left(\frac{\beta_1}{\beta_1 - t}\right) + A_2\left(\frac{\beta_2}{\beta_2 - t}\right)$$

$$\Rightarrow \quad \psi(u) = C_1 e^{-r_1 u} + C_2 e^{-r_2 u}.$$

One could employ the following techniques in place of the partial fraction expansion algebra:

(1) $\frac{1}{1+\theta} = \psi(0) = C_1 e^{-r_1 0} + C_2 e^{-r_2 0} = C_1 + C_2$

(2) The partial fraction expression has asymptotes at $t = r_1,\ r_2$, hence these are zeros of the denominator on the left hand side. So

$$1 + (1+\theta)p_1 r_i = M_X(r_i) = A_1\left(\frac{\beta_1}{\beta_1 - r_i}\right) + A_2\left(\frac{\beta_2}{\beta_2 - r_i}\right)$$

(Note: In a multiple choice question one could determine r_1, r_2 values by elimination.)

(3) Once r_1 and r_2 values are determined, use $\frac{1}{1+\theta} = \psi(0) = C_1 + C_2$ and one other linear equation in C_1, C_2. A convenient additional equation is obtained by differentiating both sides of

$$\frac{\theta}{1+\theta} \cdot \frac{M_X(t) - 1}{1 + (1+\theta)p_1 t - M_X(t)} = \frac{C_1 r_1}{r_1 - t} + \frac{C_2 r_2}{r_2 - t}$$

and plugging in $t = 0$. This results in $E[N]E[L_1] = E[L] = \frac{C_1 r_1}{(r_1 - 0)^2} + \frac{C_2 r_2}{(r_2 - 0)^2}$, or equivalently

$$\frac{1}{\theta} \cdot \frac{E[X^2]}{2(E[X])} = \frac{C_1}{r_1} + \frac{C_2}{r^2}.$$

(4) If $r_1 < r_2$ and $\beta_1 < \beta_2$ then $0 < r_1 < \beta_1 < r_2 < \beta_2$. A picture illustrating this size relation is given in the next example. In this case $R = r_1$ and $M_X(t)$ diverges if $t \geq \beta_1$.

Example 3 For a continuous time, Compound-Poisson surplus process suppose that

(i) X, the claim amount model, is a 50/50 mixture of exponential distributions with $\beta_1 = 2$, $\beta_2 = 4$,

(ii) $\theta = \frac{7}{9}$

Obtain a closed form expression for $\psi(u)$.

Solution We are given that $M_X(t) = \frac{1}{2} \cdot \frac{2}{2-t} + \frac{1}{2} \cdot \frac{4}{4-t}$, hence $E[X] = \frac{1}{2} \cdot \frac{1}{2} + \frac{1}{2} \cdot \frac{1}{4} = \frac{3}{8}$, $E[X^2] = \frac{1}{2} \cdot \frac{2}{(2)^2} + \frac{1}{2} \cdot \frac{2}{(4)^2} = \frac{5}{16}$ ($E[X^2] = \frac{2}{\beta^2}$ if X is exponential with parameter β). It then follows that $E[L] = E[N]E[L_1] = \frac{1}{\theta} \cdot \frac{E[X^2]}{2E[X]} = \frac{9}{7} \cdot \frac{5/16}{3/4} = \frac{15}{28}$. The first step in the algorithm described above is to calculate r_1, r_2 as zeros of $1 + (1+\theta)E[X]t = M_X(t)$ which specializes here to the following:

$$1 + \frac{16}{9} \cdot \frac{3}{8}t = \frac{1}{2} \cdot \frac{2}{2-t} + \frac{1}{2} \cdot \frac{4}{4-t} \quad \Rightarrow \quad 1 + \frac{2}{3}t = \frac{1}{2-t} + \frac{2}{4-t}$$

Putting the fractions over a common denominator and cross-multiplying results in the equivalent quadratic equation $2t^2 - 9t + 7 = 0$: $r_i = \frac{9 \pm \sqrt{81-56}}{4} = \frac{9 \pm 5}{4}$, $r = 1$, $r_2 = \frac{7}{2}$.

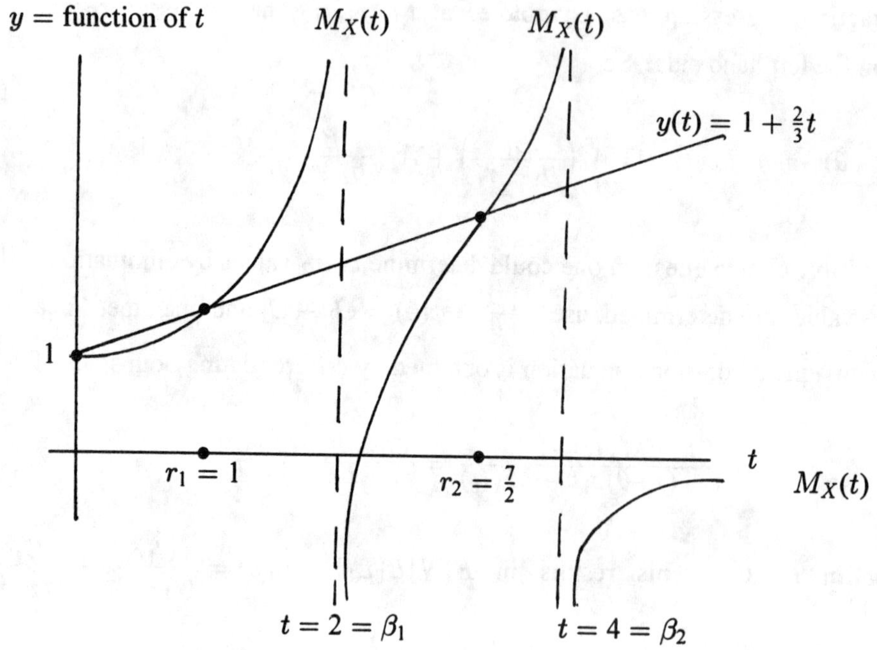

Note: Here $R = r_1 = 1$ and $M_X(t)$ is divergent if $t \geq 2 = \beta_1$. So the graph we are calling $M_X(t)$ in the picture is really the graph of the partial fraction expansion which is defined at $t \neq 2, 4$.

We know now that $\psi(u) = C_1 e^{-1(u)} + C_2 e^{-7/2(u)}$ where C_1 and C_2 satisfy the pair of linear equations below:

$$\psi(0) = C_1 + C_2, \quad E[L] = \frac{C_1}{r_1} + \frac{C_2}{r_2}$$

$$\Rightarrow \quad \frac{9}{16} = C_1 + C_2, \ \frac{15}{28} = \frac{C_1}{1} + \frac{C_2}{(7/2)}$$

$$\Rightarrow \quad C_1 = \frac{42}{80}, \ C_2 = \frac{3}{80}.$$

Hence

$$\psi(u) = \frac{42}{80}e^{-u} + \frac{3}{80}e^{-(7/2)u}. \qquad \square$$

Reinsurance and the Probability of Ruin

The discussion here concerns a long-term compound-Poisson process generating aggregate claims $S(t)$ over a t-year period. Here we will conform with the notation and assumptions of the preceding discussion: λ is the Poisson parameter, c per year in premium is paid continuously, and X is the claim amount model. Recall that the probability of ruin with initial capital u is

$$\psi(u) < e^{-Ru}$$

where R is the adjustment coefficient. We want to consider here a long-term reinsurance scheme based on reinsuring a piece of each individual claim. (Stop-loss reinsurance was based on aggregate claims.) We will see that the adjustment coefficient of the retained claims portfolio, R', is "adjusted" upward, i.e., $R' > R$ so that $e^{-R'u} < e^{-Ru}$ and the probability of ruin is forced downward. Here is the standard notation:

$h(X) =$ reinsured amount $< X$

$X - h(X) =$ retained claim amount

$c =$ annual premium $= (1+\theta)\lambda \cdot E[X]$

$c_h =$ annual reinsurance premium $= (1+\xi)\lambda \cdot E[h(X)]$

$\theta =$ insurer's relative security

$\xi =$ reinsurer's relative security

$c - c_h =$ retained premium

$\lambda + cR = \lambda M_X(R)$ (original portfolio)

$\lambda + (c - c_h)R' = \lambda M_{X-h(X)}(R')$ (retained portfolio)

In certain cases we can develop a close relation of R' to R, which illustrates quite clearly how R' behaves. When both the insurer and reinsurer have the same security loading (*i.e.*, the highly unlikely situation $\theta = \xi$), R' tends to increase as the degree of reinsurance increases. However, if $\xi > \theta$, then R' increases as the degree of reinsurance approaches a critical point and then decreases as the degree passes the critical point. These ideas will be evident in the examples to follow. Both concern **proportional reinsurance** where $h(X) = \alpha X$. (With $\alpha = .25$ one has 25% of each claim being ceded and 75% being retained.)

Example 4 Suppose $h(X) = \alpha X$ and $\theta = \xi$. Show that

$$R' = \frac{R}{(1-\alpha)}.$$

Solution In the retained claim process, $(1-\alpha)X$ is retained from each claim and λ is the expected number of retained claims per year[10]. Retained annual premium is

$$\begin{aligned} c - c_h &= (1+\theta)\lambda \cdot E[X] - (1+\xi)\lambda \cdot E[\alpha X] \\ &= (1+\theta) \cdot \lambda \cdot E[X] \cdot (1-\alpha) \quad (\text{since } \theta = \xi) \\ &= c \cdot (1-\alpha) \quad (\text{same fraction of premium and claims retained}) \end{aligned}$$

Also $X - h(X) = (1-\alpha)X$ so that the equation for R' is:

$$\begin{aligned} \lambda + (c-c_h)R' &= \lambda M_{X-h(X)}(R') \\ \Rightarrow \lambda + (c(1-\alpha))R' &= \lambda M_{(1-\alpha)X}(R') \\ \Rightarrow \lambda + c((1-\alpha)R') &= \lambda M_X\,((1-\alpha)R') \end{aligned}$$

Now R is the unique positive solution of $\lambda + cR = \lambda M_X(R)$, so it is clear from the last equation that $(1-\alpha)R' = R$, or equivalently, $R' = R/(1-\alpha)$. As α increases more of each claim is reinsured, $(1-\alpha)$ decreases, and R' increases. For example, if 20% of each claim is ceded then $R' = 1.25\,R$. □

Example 5 Suppose $h(X) = \alpha X$ and X is exponentially distributed with parameter β. What is the relation of R' to R?

Solution If X is exponential with parameter β it is easy to show that $(1-\alpha)X$, the retained claim amount, is exponential with parameter $\beta' = \beta/(1-\alpha)$. Exponential claim amounts is the one situation where there is a nice formula for the adjustment coefficient: $R = \theta\beta/(1+\theta)$. Since retained claims are also exponential we have

$$R' = \frac{\theta'\beta'}{1+\theta'} = \frac{\theta'\beta}{(1-\alpha)(1+\theta')},$$

where θ' is the relative security in the portfolio of retained claims. If both loading factors are equal, $\theta = \xi$, then $\theta' = \theta$ and again $R' = R/(1-\alpha)$. However, if $\xi > \theta$ then $\theta' < \theta$ and the relation is not so simple. □

With proportional reinsurance we have

---

10 i.e., retained aggregate claims has a compound-Poisson distribution with parameter λ

$$\theta' = \frac{\theta E[X] - \xi E[h(X)]}{E[X] - E[h(X)]}$$

$$= \frac{\theta E[X] - \xi E[(\alpha X)]}{E[X] - E[\alpha X]}$$

$$= \frac{\theta - \xi\alpha}{1-\alpha} = \begin{cases} \theta & \text{if } \xi = \theta \\ < \theta & \text{if } \xi > \theta \end{cases}$$

Suppose we have exponential claims, $\theta = .25$ and $\xi = .50$. Without reinsurance we have an adjustment coefficient

$$R = \frac{\theta\beta}{1+\theta} = \frac{.25\beta}{1.25} = \frac{\beta}{5}.$$

If proportional reinsurance with $\alpha = .10$ is elected, then

$$\theta' = \frac{.25 - (.50)(.10)}{1 - .10} = \frac{.20}{.90}, \quad R' = \frac{\theta'\beta'}{1+\theta'} = \frac{2}{11}\left(\frac{\beta}{.9}\right) = \frac{\beta}{4.95},$$

which says $R' > R$ and reinsurance has increased security by increasing the adjustment coefficient.

However if proportional reinsurance with $\alpha = .20$ is elected then

$$\theta' = \frac{.25 - (.50)(.20)}{1 - .20} = \frac{.15}{.80}, \quad R' = \frac{\theta'\beta'}{1+\theta'} = \frac{3}{19}\left(\frac{\beta}{.8}\right) = \frac{\beta}{5.0\overline{6}},$$

which says $R' < R$. In this case we have exceeded a critical degree of reinsurance. Security will further diminish as α increases (i.e., as the degree of reinsurance increases).

A Discrete-Time Surplus Process Model

Let $U(n) = u + cn - S(n)$ be the surplus at time n for $n = 0, 1, 2, \ldots$ where u is the initial surplus, c is the annual premium rate, and $S(n)$ is aggregate claims over the time period $(0, n]$. Furthermore we assume that $S(n) = W_1 + \cdots + W_n$ where the W_i are independent and identically distributed like W, the **annual claim model**. The **annual gain** is $G = c - W$ and surplus can be rewritten as

$$U(n) = u + (c - W_1) + \cdots + (c - W_n) = u + G_1 + \cdots + G_{n-1} + G_n = U(n-1) + G_n.$$

(nice relation for recursive calculation of the distribution of $U(n)$)

As with the continuous-time, compound-Poisson surplus process model, we will mainly be concerned with the adjustment coefficient and calculation of the probability of ruin. Many results are similar to those described earlier.

Ruin is said to occur at time n if $U(n) < 0$ and $U(j) \geq 0$ for $j = 0, 1, \ldots, n-1$. $\widetilde{T}$ is used for the time of ruin with the understanding $\widetilde{T} = \infty$ if ruin does not occur. Thus $\widetilde{T}|_{\widetilde{T}<\infty}$ is the time of ruin given that ruin occurs. We use $\widetilde{\psi}(u)$ to denote the probability of ruin with initial capital u, that is, $\widetilde{\psi}(u) = Pr(\widetilde{T} < \infty)$. The **adjustment coefficient**, $\widetilde{R}$, is defined as the positive solution of

$$M_W(\widetilde{R}) = e^{c\widetilde{R}},$$

or equivalently

$$M_G(-\widetilde{R}) = 1.$$

This follows since $M_G(t) = M_{c-W}(t) = E[e^{(c-W)t}] = E[e^{ct}e^{W(-t)}] = e^{ct}M_W(-t)$.
$(1 = M_G(-\widetilde{R}) = e^{-c\widetilde{R}}M_W(-(-\widetilde{R})) \quad \Leftrightarrow \quad e^{c\widetilde{R}} = M_W(\widetilde{R}).)$

This definition looks quite different than the one given for the compound-Poisson, continuous-time surplus process. However, suppose $W = X_1 + \cdots + X_N$, annual claims, is a compound-Poisson distribution with

(i) $N \sim$ Poisson-λ, λ claims expected per year,

(ii) $X_1, \ldots X_N$ independent and identically distributed like X, the claim amount model.

Then $S(n)$ is compound-Poisson with parameter $n\lambda$ and claim amount model X. Now the moment generating function of such a compound-Poisson distribution is
$M_W(t) = M_N(lnM_X(t)) = e^{\lambda(exp(lnM_X(t))-1)} = e^{\lambda[M_X(t)-1]}$. Hence $\widetilde{R}$ is the unique positive solution of

$$e^{c\widetilde{R}} = M_W(\widetilde{R}) = e^{\lambda[M_X(\widetilde{R})-1]}.$$

Taking logs of both sides and rearranging we find

$$\lambda + c\widetilde{R} = M_X(\widetilde{R}),$$

the same relation used in the continuous-time, compound-Poisson surplus process model to define R. So in the compound-Poisson models of surplus, $\widetilde{R}$ (discrete time) and R (continuous time) are identical.

In the discrete time surplus model described here, suppose W, the annual claim model, is normal with mean μ and variance σ^2; hence $M_W(t) = e^{\mu t + \sigma^2 t^2/2}$. In this case $\widetilde{R}$ is the unique positive solution of

$$e^{c\widetilde{R}} = M_W(\widetilde{R}) = e^{\mu\widetilde{R} + \sigma^2\widetilde{R}^2/2},$$

or, after taking logs of both sides and canceling one power of $\widetilde{R}$,

$$\widetilde{R} = \frac{2(c-\mu)}{\sigma^2} \qquad \text{(Adjustment coefficient when } W = N(\mu, \sigma^2)\text{)}.$$

This is the only case when a closed form expression for $\widetilde{R}$ is possible. In general, consider the relation

$$c\widetilde{R} = ln(e^{c\widetilde{R}}) = lnM_W(\widetilde{R}).$$

If $R(t) = lnM_W(t)$ it is known that $R(0) = 0$, $R'(0) = E[W]$, $R''(0) = Var(W)$ and $R'''(0)$ is the third central moment of W. This means that the power series expansion of $R(t)$ about the origin looks like

$$lnM_W(t) = R(t) = 0 + E[W]t + Var(W)t^2/2 + E[(W-E(W))^3]t^3/6 + \cdots.$$

This leads to the approximate calculation of $\widetilde{R}$ from

$$c\widetilde{R} = ln(e^{c\widetilde{R}}) = ln(M_W(\widetilde{R})) \approx E[W]\widetilde{R} + Var(W)\widetilde{R}^2/2,$$

(use up to 2nd order terms in the series)

that is

$$\text{(general approximation)} \qquad \widetilde{R} \approx \frac{2(c - E[W])}{Var(W)}.$$

[Note. We saw above that this is exact when $W \sim N(\mu, \sigma^2)$]

In the case that W is compound-Poisson then $\widetilde{R} = R$ and any continuous-time method of approximating R could be used to approximate $\widetilde{R}$. For example, $E[W] = \lambda \cdot E[X]$, $c = (1+\theta)E[W]$, $Var(W) = \lambda E[X^2]$, and with the above approximation

$$\text{(compound-Poisson approximation)} \qquad \begin{aligned}\widetilde{R} &= \frac{2(c - E[W])}{Var(W)} \\ &= \frac{2((1+\theta)E[W] - E[W])}{Var(W)} \\ &= \frac{2\theta E[W]}{Var(W)} = \frac{2\theta\lambda E[X]}{\lambda E[X^2]} = \frac{2\theta E[X]}{E[X^2]}.\end{aligned}$$

The connection of $\widetilde{R}$ with the probability of ruin, $\widetilde{\psi}(u)$, is via

$$\widetilde{\psi}(u) = \frac{e^{-\widetilde{R}u}}{E[e^{-R\widetilde{U}(\widetilde{T})}|\widetilde{T} < \infty]}.$$

The denominator is the moment generating function of the negative surplus at the time of ruin, given that ruin occurs. This denominator satisfies

$$1 \leq \text{Denominator } \leq e^{\tilde{R}m}$$

if m is the maximal possible annual claim amount. This leads to the following bounds on $\tilde{\psi}(u)$:

$$e^{-\tilde{R}(u+m)} < \tilde{\psi}(u) < e^{-\tilde{R}u} \qquad \text{where } Pr(W \leq m) = 1$$

In addition to these analytic results concerning $\tilde{R}$ and $\tilde{\psi}(u)$, there is a simple recursive method of sneaking up on $\tilde{\psi}(u)$ when W, annual claims, is discrete. Let $\tilde{\psi}(u, n)$ be the probability of ruin by time n. Then

$$\tilde{\psi}(u, 1) \leq \tilde{\psi}(u, 2) \leq \cdots \leq \tilde{\psi}(u)$$

with $\lim\limits_{n\to\infty} \tilde{\psi}(u, n) = \tilde{\psi}(u)$. This recursive method will be illustrated in the following example.

Example 6 Suppose $U(n) = 1 + 1.5n - S(n)$ where $u = 1$ is the initial surplus, $c = 1.5$ is the annual premium rate, and $S(n) = W_1 + \cdots + W_n$ is aggregate claims over $[0, n]$. Suppose the distribution of W is given by

$W = w$	0	1	2	3
$Pr(W = w)$	.40	.30	.20	.10

Calculate $\tilde{\psi}(1, 1)$, $\tilde{\psi}(1, 2)$, $\tilde{\psi}(1, 3)$ ... recursively.

Solution The idea is to use the relation

$$U(n) = u + (c-W_1) + \cdots + (c-W_n) = u + G_1 + \cdots + G_n = U(n-1) + G_n.$$

The distribution of $G = c - W = 1.5 - W$ is

G	1.5	.5	$-.5$	-1.5
$Prob$	.40	.30	.20	.10

The distribution of $U(1) = 1 + G$ is thus

$U(1)$	$Prob.$
2.5	.40
1.5	.30
.50	.20
$-.5$	.10

G_2	$Prob.$
1.5	.40
.5	.30
$-.5$	.20
-1.5	.10

From the $U(1)$ distribution we see that ruin at time 1 is equivalent to $U(1) = -.5$. Hence $\widetilde{\psi}(1,1) = .10$

Now

$$\widetilde{\psi}(1,2) = Pr(\text{ruin at time } 1) + Pr(\{\text{ruin at time } 2\} \cap \{\text{no ruin at time } 1\})$$

(to avoid double counting). Thus, in developing the distribution of $U(2)$ as the convolution of the distributions of $U(1)$ and G_2, we **ignore the case $U(1) = -.50$ where ruin already occurred at time one**.

	$U(2)$	$Probability$		$U(1)$, G_2 combinations
	4	(.4)(.4)	= .16	(2.5, 1.5)
	3	(.3)(.4) + (.4)(.3)	= .24	(1.5, 1.5), (2.5, .5)
	2	(.4)(.2) + (.3)(.3) + (.2)(.4)	= .25	(2.5, −.5), (1.5, .5), (.5, 1.5)
	1	(.4)(.1) + (.3)(.2) + (.2)(.3)	= .16	(2.5, −1.5), (1.5, −.5), (.5, .5)
	0	(.3)(.1) + (.2)(.2)	= .07	(1.5, −1.5), (.5, −.5)
(omit in $U(3)$)	−1	(.2)(.1)	= .02	(.5, −1.5)

Total $= .90 = 1 - \psi(1,1)$

Hence $\psi(1,2) = .10 + Pr(\{\text{ruin at time } 2\} \cap \{\text{no ruin at time } 1\}) = .10 + .02 = .12$

To calculate $Pr(\{\text{ruin at time } 3\} \cap \{\text{no ruin at } 1,2\})$ we convolute the non-negative portion of $U(2)$ above with G_3. The only new combinations giving ruin at time 3 with no ruin at time 1 or 2 are listed below:

$U(2)$	$Prob.$	$G(3)$	$Prob.$	$Prob.\,Product$
1	.16	−1.5	.10	.016
0	.07	−1.5	.10	.007
0	.07	−.5	.20	.014
				Total .037

Hence $\psi(1,3) = .10 + .02 + .037 = .157$. □

CONDENSED REVIEW NOTES AND ADVANCED TOPICS

I. THE COLLECTIVE RISK MODEL OVER AN EXTENDED PERIOD

$$\underbrace{S(t)}_{\substack{\text{aggregate}\\ \text{claims}\\ \text{over}[0,t]}} = \underbrace{X_1}_{\substack{\text{first}\\ \text{claim}\\ \text{amount}}} + \underbrace{X_2}_{\substack{\text{second}\\ \text{claim}\\ \text{amount}}} + \cdots + X_{\underset{\substack{\uparrow\\ \text{number of claims}\\ \text{occurring in } [0,t]}}{N(t)}}$$

1. Assumptions for Compound Poisson Process

(a) $X_1, X_2, \ldots$ independent and identically distributed like X; $p(x)$ and $P(x)$ are the density and distribution functions of X, and $p_k = E[X^k]$ is the kth moment.

(b) $N(t)$ is distributed as Poisson λt; t is in years, so this means λ claims per year are expected.

(c) $X_1, \cdots, X_{N(t)}$, $N(t)$ are independent.

(d) Same applies to the events in any time period $(s,t]$; $N(t) - N(s)$ is Poisson $\lambda(t-s)$, the number of claims, and $S(t) - S(s)$ represents aggregate claims.

2. Consequences

(a) $S(t)$ is compound Poisson with parameter λt

(b) $$E[S(t)] = \underbrace{E[N(t)]}_{\substack{\text{expected}\\ \text{number of}\\ \text{claims}}} \cdot \underbrace{E[X]}_{\substack{\text{expected}\\ \text{claim}\\ \text{amount}}} = \underbrace{(\lambda t) \cdot p_1}_{\substack{\text{linear}\\ \text{in } t}}$$

(c) $$\begin{aligned} Var(S(t)) &= Var(X) \cdot E[N(t)] + (E[X])^2 \cdot Var(N(t)) \\ &= (p_2 - p_1^2) \cdot \lambda t + p_1^2 \cdot \lambda t = p_2 \cdot \lambda t \end{aligned}$$

3. Surplus

(a) $$\underbrace{U(t)}_{\substack{\text{surplus}\\ \text{at time } t}} = \underbrace{u + ct}_{\substack{\text{available}\\ \text{over } [0,t]}} - \underbrace{S(t)}_{\substack{\text{needed}\\ \text{over } [0,t]}}$$

$u =$ initial capital

$c =$ premium per year, arriving continuously

(b) Graphs

Aggregate Claims Versus Time

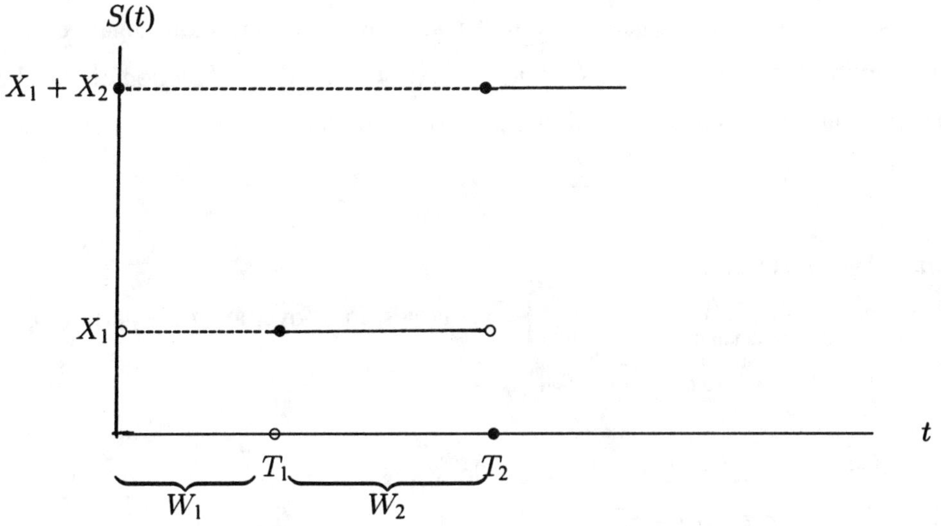

$T_i =$ arrival time of ith claim

$W_i =$ waiting time between $(i-1)^{st}$ and i^{th} claims; independent and identically distributed exponential variables; $f_W(w) = \lambda e^{-\lambda w}$, $w > 0$, $E[W] = \frac{1}{\lambda}$, $Var(W) = \frac{1}{\lambda^2}$.

The graph is a step function with jumps at claim arrival times corresponding to claim amount and lengths of steps corresponding to waiting times.

Surplus Versus Time

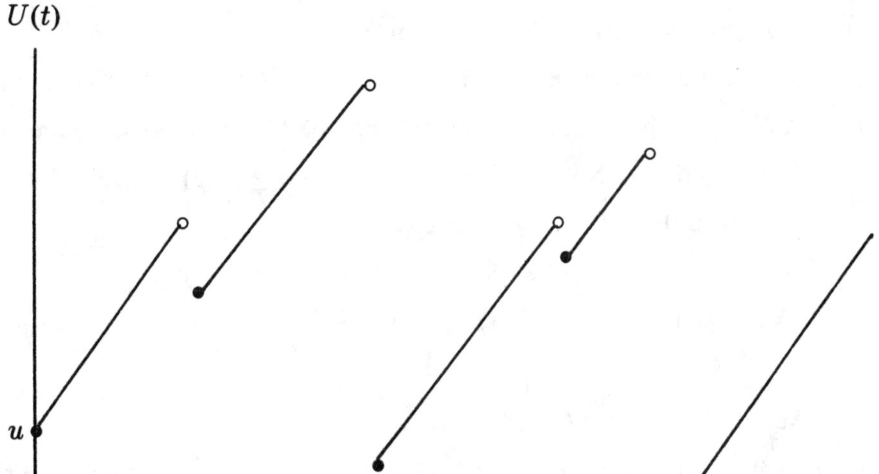

Slope $= c =$ annual premium rate

drop at time $T_i =$ arriving claim amount X_i

(c) Ruin

Ruin is said to occur if surplus ever becomes negative, a random event. If it ever happens, the time of ruin, T, is defined as the first instant at which surplus is negative. In the graph above ruin does occur at $T = T_4$. $\psi(u) = Pr(\text{ruin occurs})$ as a function of initial capital. It depends on initial capital, annual premium rate, and the distributions of claim number and claim amount.

4. Maximal Aggregate Loss

(a) $$L = \max_{t \geq 0} \left\{ \underset{\substack{\text{amount} \\ \text{paid out} \\ \text{over } [0,t]}}{S(t)} - \underset{\substack{\text{premium} \\ \text{collected} \\ \text{over } [0,t]}}{ct} \right\} = \text{largest loss* over any time period } [0, t]$$

*initial capital is not considered in profit/loss

Note: $L \geq 0$ since $S(0) - c \cdot 0 = 0$

(b) The Relation of $\psi(u)$ to the Distribution of L

$$\begin{aligned} 1 - \psi(u) &= Pr(\text{ruin does not occur given initial capital } u) \\ &= Pr(U(t) \geq 0 \text{ for all } t) \\ &= Pr(u + ct - S(t) \geq 0 \text{ for all } t) \\ &= Pr(u \geq S(t) - ct \text{ for all } t) \\ &= Pr(u \geq \max_t \{S(t) - ct\}) \\ &= Pr(u \geq L) = F_L(u), \text{ the distribution function of maximal aggregate loss} \end{aligned}$$

(c) Maximal Aggregate Loss as a Random Sum

(i) A record low for surplus is said to occur at time t if $U(t) < U(s)$ for all $s \leq t$.

(ii) Let $N =$ number of record lows and suppose $t_1 < t_2 < \cdots < t_N$ are the times at which they occur. Note: N can be zero if $U(t) \geq U(0) = u$ for all t.

(iii) Then $u = U(0) > U(t_1) > \cdots > U(t_N)$:

$L = u - U(t_N) = u - (u + ct_N - S(t_N)) = S(t_N) - ct_N$, and

$$L = u - U(t_N) = \underset{\underset{L_1}{\uparrow}}{(u - U(t_1))} + \underset{\underset{L_2}{\uparrow}}{(U(t_1) - U(t_2))} + \cdots + \underset{\underset{L_N}{\uparrow}}{(U(t_{N-1}) - U(t_N))}$$

where $L_i =$ loss over $(t_{i-1}, t_i]$

(iv) t_i is the first time t after time t_{i-1} such that a loss occurs over $(t_{i-1}, t]$ if such a loss occurs

(d) First Surplus Below the Initial Level

(i) If N = number of record lows is ≥ 1, then t_1 is the first time that surplus is below the initial level u. Let Y = surplus at time t_1 *given that* $N \geq 1$. Then

$$Y = \text{initial surplus} - (\text{loss over } (0,t_1]) = u - L_1,$$

and for a Compound Poisson process

$Pr(u - y - dy \leq Y \leq u - y$ ***and*** surplus falls below u)

$$= Pr(y \leq L_1 \leq y + dy \textbf{ and } \text{surplus falls below } u)$$

$$= \tfrac{\lambda}{c}[1 - P(y)]\,dy,$$

where $P(y)$ is the d.f. of claim amount.

Since $\psi(0) = \frac{1}{1+\theta} = \frac{\lambda p_1}{c} = Pr(\text{surplus falls below } u)$, the *density* of L_1 is

$$f(y) = \frac{c}{\lambda p_1} \cdot \frac{\lambda}{c}[1 - P(y)] = \frac{1}{p_1}[1 - P(y)]$$

(ii) L_1 can also be described as the loss at time of ruin with no initial capital, given that ruin occurs, since

$$L_1 = u - U(t_1) = u - (u + ct_1 - S(t_1)) = S(t_1) - ct_1$$

(iii) View all claims after time t_1 as a sequence of observations of the original experiment and assume no initial capital. Then if $N \geq 2$, t_2 is the time of ruin for this sequence since it is the first time after t_1 such that a loss occurs for $(t_1, t_2]$. This implies L_2 is distributed as L_1. Similarly all L_i are distributed as L_1.

(iv) $\underset{\substack{\text{maximal}\\\text{aggregate}\\\text{loss}}}{L} = L_1 + \cdots + L_N$

$L_1, \ldots, L_N$ independent and identically distributed like L_1.

N geometrically distributed with $Pr(N = n) = (\psi(0))^n(1 - \psi(0))$, where $\psi(0)$ is the probability of ruin with no initial capital.

(v) Distribution of L_1 in special cases

Exponential claim amount density $\Rightarrow$ L_1 has the identical exponential density.

Constant claim amount x_0 $\Rightarrow$ L_1 is uniform over the interval $[0, x_0]$

(Both are easily derived from $f_{L_1}(y) = \frac{1}{p_1}[1 - P(y)]$)

II. SUMMARY OF IMPORTANT FACTS ABOUT THE DISTRIBUTIONS OF L_1, N, AND L FOR THE COMPOUND POISSON SURPLUS PROCESS

1. The L_1 Distribution

density $$f_{L_1}(y) = \frac{1}{p_1}[1 - P(y)] \quad y \geq 0$$

where p_1 is the expected claim amount, $E[X]$, and $P(y)$ is the distribution function of X

moments $$\left.\begin{aligned} E[L_1] &= \frac{p_2}{2p_1} \\ E[L_1^2] &= \frac{p_3}{3p_1} \end{aligned}\right\}$$ ($p_k = E[X^k]$) easier than integrating with the density above

moment gen. function $$M_{L_1}(t) = \frac{M_X(t) - 1}{p_1 t} = \frac{(1 + p_1 t + p_2 \frac{t^2}{2} + \cdots) - 1}{p_1 t}$$

$$= 1 + \left(\frac{p_2}{2p_1}\right) t + \left(\frac{p_3}{3p_1}\right) t^2/2 + \cdots$$

2. The N Distribution

N has a geometric distribution where q is the probability of ruin with no initial capital, $\psi(0) = \frac{1}{1+\theta}$, and $p = \frac{\theta}{1+\theta}$

density $$f_N(n) = q^n p = \left(\frac{1}{1+\theta}\right)^n \left(\frac{\theta}{1+\theta}\right) \quad n = 0, 1, 2, \ldots$$

moments $$E[N] = \frac{q}{p} = \frac{1}{\theta}$$
$$Var(N) = \frac{q}{p^2} = \frac{1+\theta}{\theta^2}$$

moment gen. function $$M_N(t) = \frac{p}{1 - qe^t}$$

3. The L Distribution

$$L = L_1 + L_2 + \cdots + L_N \quad \text{where} \begin{cases} L_i \sim L_1 \\ N \text{ is geometric} \end{cases}$$

moments $\quad E[L] = E[N] \cdot E[L_1] \quad$ (random sum)

$$Var(L) = E[N] \cdot Var(L_1) + (E[L_1])^2 Var(N)$$

(Use 1. and 2. above with these random sum results.)

moment gen. function $\quad M_L(t) = M_N(lnM_{L_1}(t)) = \dfrac{\theta p_1 t}{1 + (1{+}\theta)p_1 t - M_X(t)}$

distribution function $\quad F_L(u) = Pr(L \leq u) = 1 - \psi(u)$

III. THE PROBABILITY OF RUIN

1. Expected Surplus as a Function of Time

$$\begin{aligned} E[U(t)] &= E[u + ct - S(t)] \\ &= E\underbrace{[u+ct]}_{\text{constant}} - E\underbrace{[S(t)]}_{\text{random}} \\ &= u + ct - (\lambda t)(p_1) \qquad p_1 = E[X] \\ &= u + (c - \lambda p_1)t, \text{ which is linear in } t \\ Var(U(t)) &= Var(u + ct - S(t)) \\ &= Var(S(t)) = (\lambda t)(p_2) \qquad p_2 = E[X^2] \qquad \text{(see I.2.c. above)} \end{aligned}$$

$$\begin{pmatrix} \text{Expected Surplus} \\ \text{Plus or Minus} \\ \text{2 Deviations} \end{pmatrix}(t) = u + (c - \lambda p_1)t \pm 2\sqrt{\lambda p_2 t}$$

(a) Case (i): $c - \lambda p_1$ = negative, or expected annual claims exceed annual premium

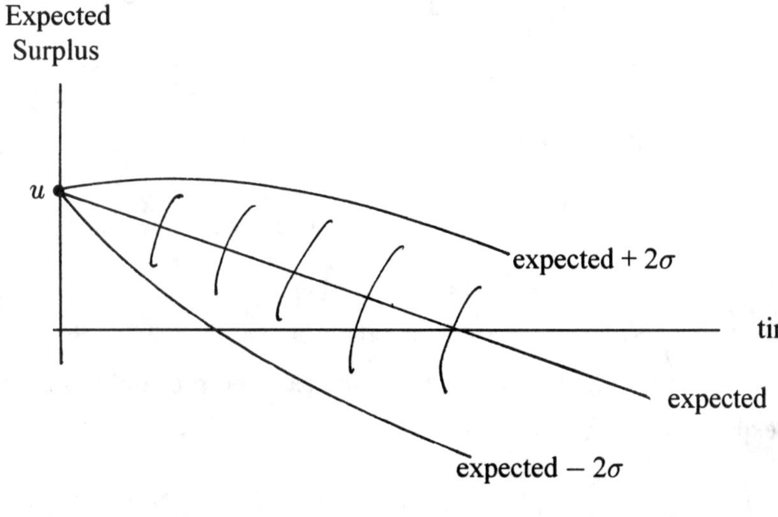

In this case $\psi(u) = 1$ for all u. Ruin is certain. Chebychev says actual surplus $U(t)$ is likely to be within several deviations of expected, and eventually (expected + 2σ) falls below the horizontal.

(b) Case (ii): $c - \lambda p_1 =$ zero, or expected annual claims equals annual premium

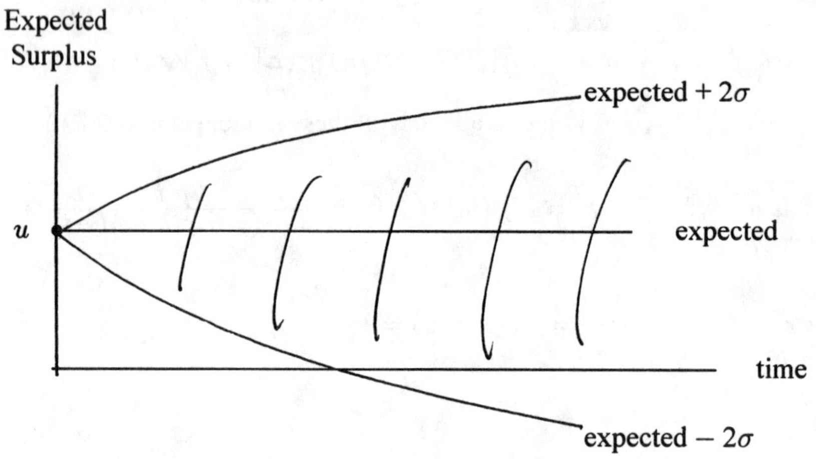

Again $\psi(u) = 1$. Ruin is certain since $\lim_{t\to\infty}(\text{expected} - 2\sigma) = -\infty$.

(c) Case (iii): $c - \lambda p_1 =$ positive, or expected annual claims are less than annual premium

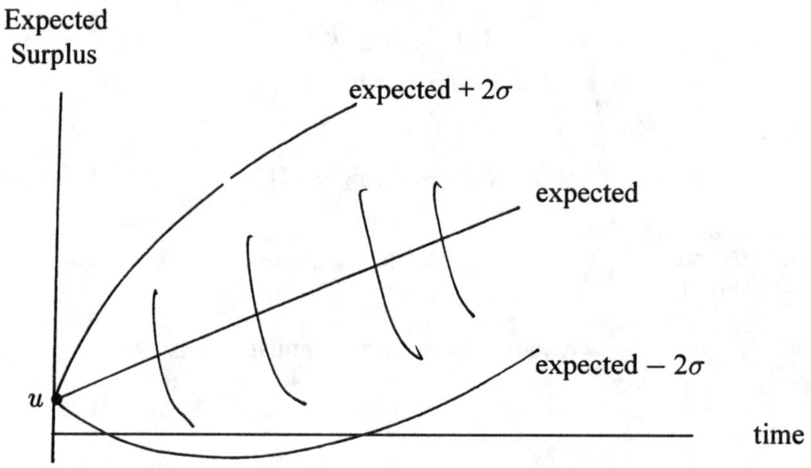

In this case there is a safety margin

$$c - \lambda p_1 > 0 \Rightarrow \frac{c}{\lambda p_1} = \frac{\text{annual premium}}{\text{expected annual claims}} = 1 + \theta,$$

where $\theta > 0$; $\theta =$ relative security loading.

This time $\psi(u) < 1$ (ruin is not certain but can happen as the cross-hatched region in the picture suggests). As u and θ increase the probability of ruin decreases. Exact expressions are given below.

2. The Adjustment Coefficient

R denotes the "adjustment coefficient" which is defined as the unique positive solution[11] of

$$\lambda + cR = \lambda \cdot M_X(R) = \lambda\left(1 + p_1 R + p_2 \frac{R^2}{2!} + \cdots\right)$$

$$\Leftrightarrow \quad \tfrac{c}{\lambda} \cdot R = p_1 R + p_2 R^2/2! + \cdots \quad \left(\text{Note } \tfrac{c}{\lambda} = (1+\theta)p_1\right)$$

With the proper reformulation this defining equation of R is equivalent to the defining equation of $\widetilde{R}$ in the discrete time model in IV. below. If $S(1)$ is the aggregate claims for a 1-year period, then from compound-Poisson results

$$M_{S(1)}(t) = e^{\lambda[M_X(t)-1]}.$$

The equation $M_{S(1)}(R) = e^{cR}$ (equivalent to the defining equation of $\widetilde{R}$) is thus equivalent, after taking logs, to

$$\lambda[M_X(R) - 1] = cR$$

$$\Leftrightarrow \lambda + cR = \lambda M_X(R).$$

Thus, even though the definitions of R and $\widetilde{R}$ look different, they are in fact identical.

(a) Special Case: Claims exponentially distributed

$$p(x) = \beta e^{-\beta x} \text{ for } x \geq 0, \quad p_1 = E[X] = \tfrac{1}{\beta}, \; M_X(t) = \tfrac{\beta}{\beta - t}$$

$$\Rightarrow \quad R = \frac{\theta\beta}{1+\theta}, \; L_1 \text{ is exponential with parameter } \beta.$$

(b) Special Case: Constant claim amount x_0

R is the solution of $\lambda + cR = \lambda e^{x_0 R}$

Solve iteratively using $R = \dfrac{\lambda(e^{x_0 R} - 1)}{c}$.

3. Expressions for $\psi(u)$

(a) Most general

$$\psi(u) = \frac{e^{-Ru}}{E\left[e^{-R \cdot U(T)} \,|\, T < \infty\right]}$$

$T =$ time of ruin

where $U(T) =$ surplus at time of ruin with initial capital u given that ruin occurs.

[11] If it exists. If X is inverse Gaussian it is possible R fails to exist.

(b) Approximations

(i) Since $-R\cdot U(T) > 0$, the denominator is bigger than one so $\psi(u) < e^{-Ru}$.

(ii) If all claim amounts are $\leq m$, the max claim amount, then $e^{-R(u+m)} < \psi(u)$.

(iii) $\psi(u) \approx \frac{1}{1+\theta}\cdot e^{-(2\theta p_1 u/(1+\theta)p_2)}$, which is exact if claims are exponentially distributed. Recall $p_k = E[X^k]$.

(c) Exact Expressions

(i) $\psi(0) = \frac{1}{1+\theta}$, the probability of ruin with no initial capital.

(ii) Exponentially Distributed Claims

$$\psi(u) = \left(\frac{1}{1+\theta}\right)\cdot e^{-(\theta\beta u/1+\theta)} = \left(\frac{1}{1+\theta}\right)e^{-Ru}$$

θ = rel. security load, $E\,[\text{Claim Amount}] = \frac{1}{\beta} = p_1$

u = initial capital, $E\,[\text{Claim Amount}^2] = \frac{2}{\beta^2} = p_2$

(iii) Mixture of Exponentials for claim Amount Distribution

$$p(x) = \sum_{i=1}^{n} \underbrace{\underbrace{A_i}_{\text{weights}} \cdot \underbrace{\beta_i e^{-\beta_i x}}_{\substack{\text{exponential}\\ \text{density}}}}_{\substack{\text{convex combination}\\ \text{or mixture of exponentials}}} \quad \text{where } \Sigma A_i = 1, \quad A_i > 0$$

Step 1

$$M_X(r) = \sum_{i=1}^{n} A_i \cdot \frac{\beta_i}{\beta_i - r} \qquad \text{(rewrite with a common denominator)}$$

Step 2

Partial Fraction Expansion: substitute the above into

$$\left(\frac{\theta}{1+\theta}\right)\frac{M_X(r)-1}{1+(1+\theta)p_1 r - M_X(r)}$$

and expand by partial fractions to obtain $\frac{C_1 r_1}{r_1 - r} + \cdots + \frac{C_n r_n}{r_n - r}$

Step 3

$$\psi(u) = C_1 e^{-r_1 u} + \cdots + C_n e^{-r_n u}$$

Note: With $n = 2$ above, the following steps may be used in place of the partial fraction expansion:

(i) Find r_1, r_2 as roots of the quadratic equation resulting from

$$1 + (1+\theta)E[X]t = M_X(t) = \frac{A_1\beta_1}{\beta_1 - t} + \frac{(1-A_1)\beta_2}{\beta_2 - t},$$

(ii) Find C_1, C_2 as simultaneous solutions of

$$\frac{1}{1+\theta} = \psi(0) = C_1 + C_2$$

$$\frac{1}{\theta} \cdot \frac{E[X^2]}{2E[X]} = E[L] = \psi'(0) = \frac{C_1}{r_1} + \frac{C_2}{r_2}.$$

IV. RECURSIVE APPROXIMATE CALCULATION OF $\psi(u)$ FOR THE COMPOUND POISSON SURPLUS PROCESS MODEL

1. $\psi(u) = 1 - F_L(u)$ and $L = L_1 + \cdots + L_N$ where N is geometric with $p = \frac{\theta}{1+\theta}$, $q = \frac{1}{1+\theta}$. Hence, from the theory of compound sums

$$F_L(u) = \sum_{n=0}^{\infty} \underbrace{q^n \cdot p}_{Pr(N=n)} \cdot F_{L_1}^{*n}(u).$$

Obtaining $F_{L_1}^{*n}(u)$ is quite taxing.

2. Use a discretization of L_1, L_1^{disc} as an approximation. Suppose point masses are assigned at L_1^{disc} values of 0, 1, 2, ... (if the span is h, a slight adjustment is needed in the following). Now N is an $(a, b, 0)$ distribution so recursive calculation of $L^{disc} = L_1^{disc} + \cdots + L_N^{disc}$ probabilities can be computed as follows and used to approximate L-probabilities, hence $\psi(u) = 1 - F_L(u)$ values.

3. $a + \frac{b}{k} = \frac{Pr(N=k)}{Pr(N=k-1)} = \frac{q^k p}{q^{k-1} p} = q = \frac{1}{1+\theta}$

Starting Value: $\underbrace{f_{L^{disc}}(0) = P_N(f_{L_1^{disc}}(0)) = \left(1 - \frac{q}{p}(f_{L_1^{disc}}(0) - 1)\right)^{-1}}_{\text{Probability generating function of a Geometric distribution}}$

where $\frac{q}{p} = \frac{1}{\theta}$

Recursion relation:

$$f_{L^{disc}}(k) = \frac{1}{1 - a f_{L_1^{disc}}(0)} \sum_{j=1}^{k} \left(a + \frac{bj}{k}\right) f_{L_1^{disc}}(j) f_{L^{disc}}(k-j)$$

where $a = \frac{1}{1+\theta}$, $b = 0$. Hence

$$f_{L^{disc}}(k) = \frac{1}{(1+\theta) - f_{L_1^{disc}}(0)} \sum_{j=1}^{k} f_{L_1^{disc}}(j) f_{L^{disc}}(k-j)$$

V. EXISTENCE OF THE ADJUSTMENT COEFFICIENT

R is defined as the unique positive solution of $1+(1+\theta)E[X]t = M_X(t)$. If $M_X(t)$ is defined for $t<\infty$ the picture looks like the figure below.

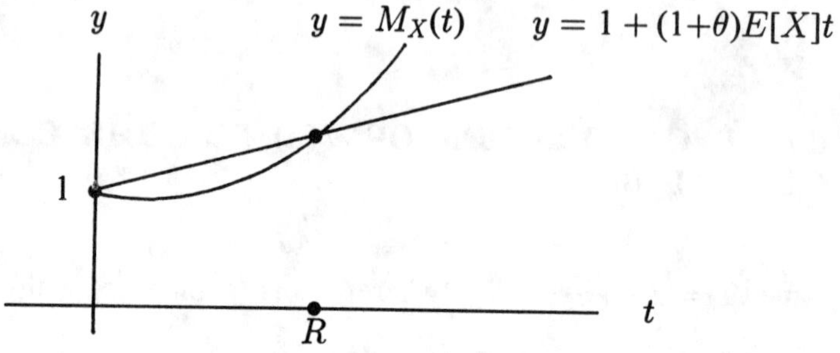

In this case $M_X(t)$ is concave upward and tends to infinity.

However, in some cases the domain of $M_X(t)$ is not $(-\infty,\infty)$. If X is exponential with parameter β, then $M_X(t)=\frac{\beta}{\beta-t}$ diverges unless $t<\beta$ (the right-hand side is still defined if $t>\beta$ but technically it is no longer $M_X(t)$). Here R still exists since $t=\beta$ is an asymptote of $M_X(t)$.

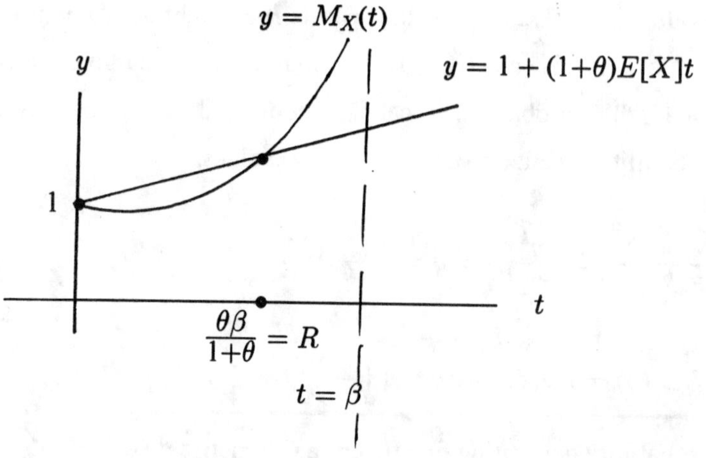

A more extreme case yet occurs when X is inverse Gaussian with parameters α, β. In this case $E[X]=\frac{\alpha}{\beta}$, $M_X(t)=exp\left[\alpha\left(1-\sqrt{1-\frac{2t}{\beta}}\right)\right]$ if $t<\frac{\beta}{2}$. $M_X(t)$ diverges if $t\geq\frac{\beta}{2}$. However, $t=\frac{\beta}{2}$ is not a vertical asymptote. In fact, $\lim_{t\to\beta/2} M_X(t)=exp[\alpha\cdot(1-0)]=e^{\alpha}$. The picture below illustrates how R could fail to exist if the slope of the line $1+(1+\theta)E[X]t$ is too great.

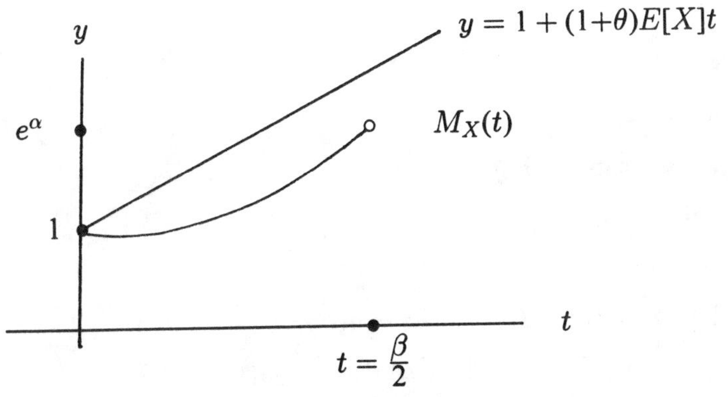

Relation Causing This Picture:

$$1 + (1+\theta)\frac{\alpha}{\beta} \cdot \frac{\beta}{2} \geq e^\alpha \quad \Leftrightarrow \quad \theta \geq 2\left(\frac{e^\alpha - 1}{\alpha}\right) - 1$$

If X is inverse Gaussian and θ satisfies the inequality then R fails to exist.

VI. REINSURANCE AND THE PROBABILITY OF RUIN

Reinsurance is employed by an insurer to reduce risk. Part of claims is assumed by the reinsurer for part of the premium. One measure of risk in a claims process is the probability of ruin. With any reinsurance plan the expected gain of the insurer is diminished and as more of the risk is ceded security tends to increase (i.e., the probability of ruin tends to decrease). However, if the security loading of the reinsurer is greater than that of the original insurer, then there is a point at which greater reinsurance will also tend to diminish security as well. See 1. below.

1. Comparison of expected gain and relative security with and without reinsurance

   (a) Before reinsurance

   θ = insurers relative security loading

   G = premium received by insurer

   relations: $G = (1+\theta) \cdot E[S]$

$$\text{Insurer's expected gain} = G - E[S] = \theta \cdot E[S]$$

$$\theta = \frac{\text{expected gain}}{\text{expected claims}} = \frac{\theta \cdot E[S]}{E[S]}$$

(b) With reinsurance

$h(S)$ = ceded claims

H = reinsurance premium = $(1+\zeta) \cdot E[h(S)]$

ζ = reinsurer's relative security loading

$S - h(S)$ = retained claims

$G - H$ = retained premium

$$\begin{aligned}\text{Insurers expected gain } &= (G-H) - E[S - h(S)] \\ &= G - E[S] - (H - E[h(S)]) \\ &= \theta \cdot E[S] - \underbrace{\zeta \cdot E[h(S)]}_{\substack{\text{amount by which expected}\\ \text{gain is diminished with}\\ \text{reinsurance equal to}\\ \text{reinsurer's expected gain}}}\end{aligned}$$

Measure of security with reinsurance

$$\overline{\theta} = \frac{E[\text{Gain with reinsurance}]}{E[\text{Claims with reinsurance}]} = \frac{\theta \cdot E[S] - \zeta \cdot E[h(S)]}{E[S] - E[h(S)]}$$

$$\begin{cases} < \theta & \text{if } \zeta > \theta \\ = \theta & \text{if } \zeta = \theta \end{cases}$$

A more intuitive from of the equation above is

$$\theta = \frac{E[S_{ret}]}{E[S]} \cdot \overline{\theta} + \frac{E[S_{ceded}]}{E[S]} \cdot \zeta .$$

Here S_{ret}, retained claims (i.e. $S - h(S)$), and S_{ceded}, reinsured claims (i.e. $h(S)$), are viewed as a separation of S into two disjoint pieces. The equation above says that θ (profit margin on the entire portfolio) is a weighted average of the profit margins $\overline{\theta}$, ζ on the two pieces, where the weights correspond to the fraction of expected claims in the pieces.

2. Effect of reinsurance on the adjustment coefficient

The probability of ruin is proportional to e^{-Ru}, so as R goes up the probability of ruin tends to go down. Reinsurance plans tend to increase R (and hence reduce $\psi(u)$, thus increasing security), but, when $\zeta > \theta$, "too much" reinsurance will reduce R (and hence diminish security as well as expected gain).

Meaning of the name "adjustment coefficient": if a certain reinsurance scheme produces an R-value which is not large enough then the arrangement must be adjusted.

(a) The adjustment coefficient without reinsurance

$c =$ continuous annual premium rate

$S =$ compound-Poisson

$\lambda =$ expected annual number of claims

$p_1 =$ expected claim amount $= E[X]$

$\frac{c}{\lambda p_1} = 1 + \theta$

$\lambda + cR = \lambda \cdot M_X(R)$ equation for finding R

(b) The adjustment coefficient with reinsurance based on a piece of each individual claim rather than aggregate claims (simpler mathematics this way)

$X =$ individual claim amount

$h(X) =$ ceded individual claim amount

$c_h = (1{+}\zeta) \cdot E\,[\text{annual ceded claims}] =$ annual reinsurance premium paid continuously

$X - h(X) =$ retained individual claim amount

$c - c_h =$ retained annual premium

$\lambda + (c - c_h)R = \lambda \cdot M_{X-h(X)}(R)$ equation for finding the new adjustment coefficient

$c = \lambda p_1(1{+}\theta)$ and $c_h = \lambda \cdot E\,[h(X)] \cdot (1{+}\zeta)$

(i) Special Case - Proportional Reinsurance

$h(X) = \alpha X$ for $0 < \alpha < 1$ (i.e., $\alpha = .25$ means 25% of ***each*** claim is ceded)

NOTE:

- As α increases the degree of reinsurance increases
- Retained claims $= X - h(X) = (1 - \alpha)X$
- $c_h = \lambda \cdot E\,[h(X)](1{+}\zeta) = \lambda \cdot E\,[\alpha X](1{+}\zeta) = \lambda \alpha p_1(1{+}\zeta)$
- Equation for new adjustment coefficient if $\theta = \zeta$

$$\lambda + (c - c_h)\overline{R} = \lambda \cdot M_{X-h(X)}(\overline{R})$$
$$\Rightarrow \lambda + \lambda p_1(1{+}\theta)(1{-}\alpha)\overline{R} = \lambda \cdot M_{(1-\alpha)X}(\overline{R})$$
$$\Rightarrow 1 + p_1(1{+}\theta)(1{-}\alpha)\overline{R} = M_X\left((1{-}\alpha)\overline{R}\right) \Rightarrow (1{-}\alpha)\overline{R} = R$$
$$\Rightarrow \overline{R} = \frac{R}{1 - \alpha}$$

- If $\zeta > \theta$, then as α increases R goes up for a while and then plummets.
- If $\zeta > \theta$ and X is exponential with parameter β, then $R = \frac{\theta\beta}{1+\theta}$ and $\overline{R} = \frac{\overline{\theta}\,\overline{\beta}}{1+\overline{\theta}}$ where $\overline{\theta}$ is the insurers relative security after proportional reinsurance and $\overline{\beta} = \frac{\beta}{1-\alpha}$.

Note: This relation could be used to find α such that R is maximized: set the derivative with respect to α equal zero and solve for the critical α value.

(ii) Special Case - Excess of Loss

$$h(X) = \begin{cases} 0 & X \le d \\ X - d & X \ge d \end{cases}$$

Note:

- As d decreases the degree of reinsurance increases
- "Stop-loss" refers to S whereas "excess of loss" refers to individual claims X
- Retained claims $= X - h(X) = \begin{cases} X & X \le d \\ d & X \ge d \end{cases}$
- If $\theta = \zeta$ then as the degree of reinsurance increases so does R. However, if $\zeta > \theta$ then R goes up temporarily before dropping.

(c) Optimality of excess of loss reinsurance among reinsurance schemes based on individual claims.

Theorem

Suppose ζ is the relative security loading of a reinsurer providing an excess of loss scheme where $h(X)$ is based on a deductible d. Consider only reinsurance schemes having the same pure premium as $h(X)$ and assume these routines carry the same relative security loading ζ. Then the adjustment coefficient is maximized by the excess of loss scheme based on deductible d.

VII. DISCRETE TIME SURPLUS PROCESS MODEL

1. $U_n = u + nc - S_n \qquad n = 0, 1, 2, \ldots$

   $S_n = W_1 + W_2 + \cdots + W_n,\ W_i =$ claims in i^{th} period $\sim W$

   $\widetilde{T} = min\{n \mid U_n < 0\}$ given that ruin occurs $=$ time of ruin

   $\widetilde{\psi}(u) = Pr(\widetilde{T} < \infty) = Pr($ruin occurs with initial capital $u)$

   $G = Gain = c - W, U_n = u + G_1 + \cdots + G_n$

2. $\widetilde{R}$ – adjustment coefficient; the positive solution of the equation $M_W(\widetilde{R}) = e^{c\widetilde{R}}$ or equivalently, $M_G(-\widetilde{R}) = 1$

   (i) W distributed as $N(\mu,\sigma^2) \Rightarrow \widetilde{R} = \dfrac{2(c-\mu)}{\sigma^2}$

   (ii) W a compound distribution: random sum with N terms

   $1 + \theta = \dfrac{c}{E[W]}$ assumed $> 1, \Rightarrow \theta > 0 \Rightarrow \widetilde{R} \approx \dfrac{2\theta p_1 \cdot E[N]}{(p_2 - p_1^2) \cdot E[N] + p_1^2 \cdot Var(N)}$

   where $p_k = k^{th}$ moment of claim amount variable which is summed to give W.

3. Probability of Ruin

$$\widetilde{\psi}(u) = \frac{e^{-\widetilde{R}u}}{E\left[e^{-\widetilde{R}\cdot U(\widetilde{T})} \mid \widetilde{T} < \infty\right]} < e^{-\widetilde{R}u}$$

VIII. SPECIFYING A PROCESS

1. Claims Number Process
   (a) Global Method - specify the distribution of $N(t+h) - N(t)$ given $N(s)$ for $s \leq t$
   (b) Infinitesimal Method - $Pr(N(t+dt) - N(t) = 1 \mid N(s), s \leq t)$ is specified and is proportional to dt. This is the probability that exactly one claim occurs in the time interval $[t, t+dt]$. Restricted to situations where

$$\lim_{\Delta t \to 0} \frac{Pr(2 \text{ or more claims in } [t, t+\Delta t])}{\Delta t} = 0.$$

   (c) Discrete or Waiting Time Method - specify the joint distribution of the waiting times W_1, $W_2, \ldots$.

2. Compound Poisson Aggregate Claims Process
   (a) If $t \geq 0$ and $h > 0$, then $S(t+h) - S(t)$ is compound-Poisson with λ expected claims per year and $P(x)$ as the distribution function of claim amount.
   (b) In a time interval of length dt there is either one claim, with probability λdt and $P(x)$ as the distribution function, or there is no claim.
   (c) At time h the probability that the next claim occurs in $[h+t, h+t+dt]$ and is $\leq x$ is

$$\underbrace{e^{-\lambda t}(\lambda\, dt)}_{\substack{\text{probability that} \\ \text{waiting time is} \\ \geq t \text{ and } \leq t+dt}} \cdot \underbrace{P(x)}_{\substack{\text{probability that} \\ \text{claim is } \leq x}}$$

IX. RECURSIVE CALCULATION OF $\psi(u,n)$ FOR $n = 1, 2, \ldots$ IN A DISCRETE TIME SURPLUS MODEL

1. $U(n) = u + cn - S(n)$

   $= u + cn - (W_1+\cdots+W_n)$ ($W_i \sim W$, W = annual claims assumed to be discrete)

   $= u + (c-W_1) + \cdots + (c-W_n)$

   $= u + G_1 + \cdots + G_n$ ($G_i \sim G = c - W$, G = annual gain assumed to be discrete)

   $= U(n-1) + G_n$

2. $\psi(u,n) = Pr(\text{ruin by time } n)$

   $= \sum_{k=1}^{n} Pr(\text{ruin}^{*}\text{at time } k)$

   $= \psi(u,n-1) + Pr(\text{ruin at time } n)$

   $*\, U(j) \geq 0$ for $j \leq k-1$ and $U(k) < 0$

3. Starting Value of Recursion

   $$\psi(u,1) = Pr(u + G < 0)$$

   The distribution of $U(1)$ is that of $u+G$.

4. Recursion Step
   Assume you have calculated $U(n-1)$ and $\psi(u,n-1)$. Convolute $U(n-1)$ and G to obtain $U(n)$. In this convolution you **disregard** cases where ruin has already occurred (there is $1 - \psi(u,n-1)$ of the probability remaining in the $U(n-1)$ cases where $U(n-1) \geq 0$). Use this "restricted" convolution to find $Pr(\text{ruin at time } n)$ and then calculate

   $$\psi(u,n) = \psi(u,n-1) + Pr(\text{ruin at time } n)$$

   (See the example at the end of the introductory reading for this Unit.)

CONCEPTUAL REVIEW TEST

1. Suppose the following data are available for a claims process:

(i)

Claim Number	1	2	3	4	5
Arrival Time	.5	1.25	2.75	3.50	4.25
Amount	2	3	13	6	1

(ii) $c =$ annual premium $= 6$, $u =$ initial capital $= 4$

(iii) For any $t \geq 4.25$, $U(t) \geq U(4.25)$

(a) Describe $S(t)$ for $t \leq 5$

(b) Describe $U(t)$ for $t \leq 5$

(c) Graph $S(t)$ and $U(t)$

(d) Does ruin occur? If so what is the time of ruin?

(e) What is the maximal aggregate loss, L?

(f) Obtain the decomposition $L = L_1 + \cdots + L_N$ by working with record lows on the surplus graph.

2. The following questions pertain to a continuous-time compound-Poisson surplus process model.

(i) What is the relation of $\psi(u)$ to the distribution of the maximal aggregate loss, L?

(ii) Give two verbal descriptions of L_1, and describe its relation to the claim amount model, X.

(iii) Describe the distribution of N, the number of record lows on the surplus graph.

(iv) How is L determined from L_1 and N?

(v) How is the adjustment coefficient R defined?

(vi) What is the most general relation of R and $\psi(u)$?

CONCEPTUAL REVIEW TEST ANSWERS

1. (a)

$$S(t) = \begin{cases} 0 & 0 \le t < .5 \\ 2 & .5 \le t < 1.25 \\ 5 & 1.25 \le t < 2.75 \\ 18 & 2.75 \le t < 3.50 \\ 24 & 3.50 \le t < 4.25 \\ 25 & 4.25 \le t < ? \end{cases}$$

(b)

$$U(t) = \begin{cases} 4 + 6t & 0 \le t < .5 \\ 2 + 6t & .5 \le t < 1.25 \\ -1 + 6t & 1.25 \le t < 2.75 \\ -14 + 6t & 2.75 \le t < 3.50 \\ -20 + 6t & 3.50 \le t < 4.25 \\ -21 + 6t & 4.25 \le t < ? \end{cases}$$

(c)

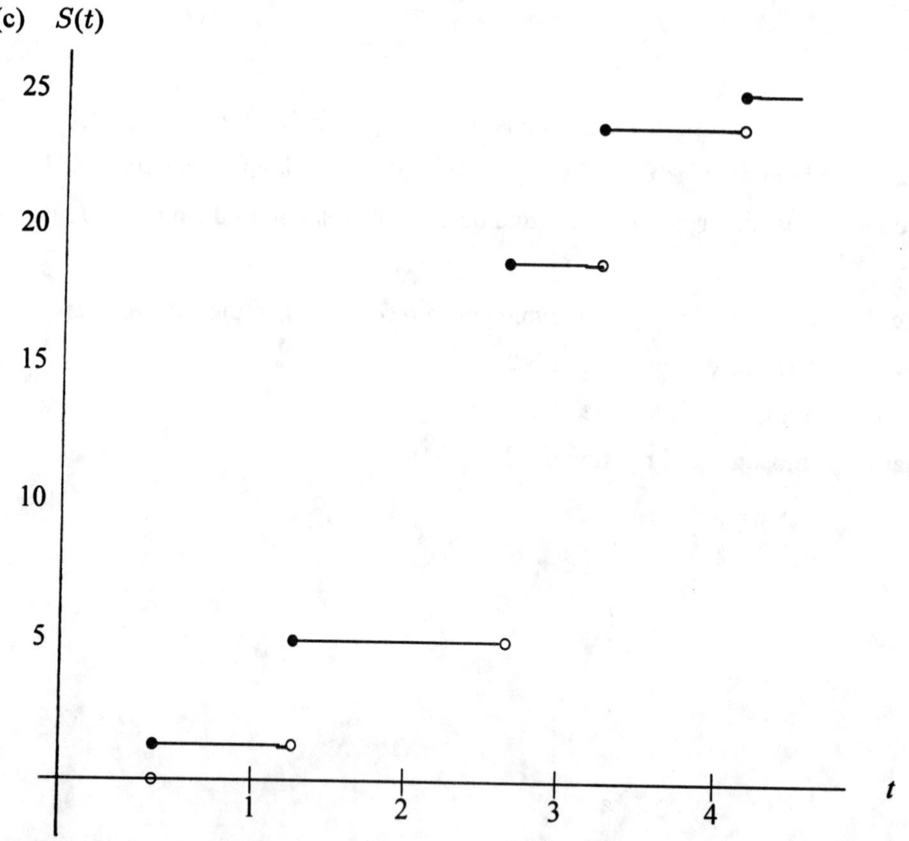

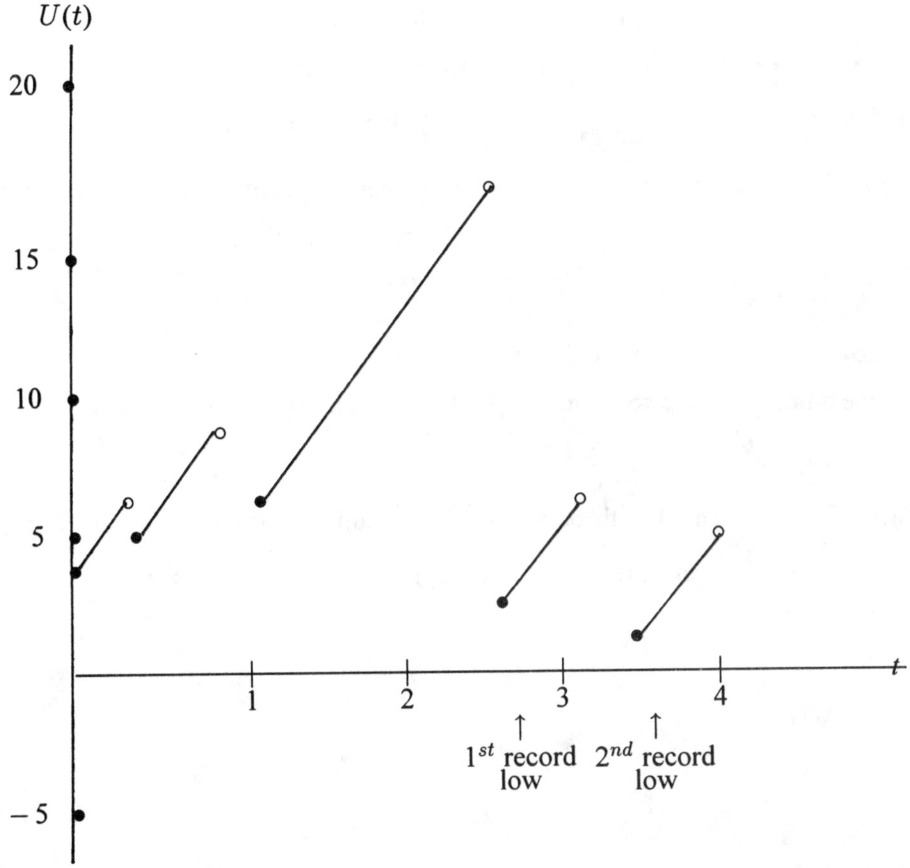

(d) Ruin does not occur since the low point is $U(3.5)$ from the assumption $U(t) \geq U(4.25)$ for $t \geq 4.25$.

(e) $L = U(0) - U(2^{nd}\text{ record low}) = U(0) - U(3.5) = 4 - (-20{+}6(3.5)) = 4 - 1 = 3$

(f) The number of record lows is $N = 2$

Time of low	0	2.75	3.50
U(low)	4	2.5	1
Drop		1.5 ↑ L_1	1.5 ↑ L_2

2. (i) $\psi(u)$ is the probability that the largest aggregate loss over all t exceeds u, i.e., $\psi(u) = Pr(L > u)$, the survival function of the maximal aggregate loss.

(ii) L_1 may be described either as the loss at the first time surplus falls below its initial level, given that this ever happens, or, as the loss at the time of ruin with no initial capital, given that ruin occurs. Note: $\psi(0) = \frac{1}{1+\theta}$ is also the probability that surplus ever drops below its initial level. Also $f_{L_1}(y) = \frac{1}{E[X]}[1 - F_X(x)]$, $E[L_1] = E[X^2]/2E[X]$, and $E[L_1^2] = E[X^3]/3E[X]$ where X is the claim amount model.

(iii) N is geometric. It is the number of failures (i.e. ruins with no initial capital, $q = \psi(0) = \frac{1}{1+\theta}$) until the first success (no further ruins occur, $p = \frac{\theta}{1+\theta}$). $Pr(N = n) = q^n p = \frac{\theta}{(1+\theta)^{n+1}}$, $E[N] = \frac{1}{\theta}$, $Var(N) = \frac{1+\theta}{\theta^2}$.

(iv) $L = L_1 + \cdots + L_N$ where the L_i are independent and identically distributed like L_1, and the L_i together with N are independent. The density function can be calculated from $f_L(x) = \sum_{n=0}^{\infty} Pr(N = n) f_{L_1}^{*n}(x)$, $E[L] = E[N]E[L_1]$,
$Var(L) = E[N]Var(L_1) + (E[L_1])^2 Var(N)$.

(v) R is the unique positive solution of $1 + (1+\theta)E[X]t = M_X(t)$, if it exists.

(vi) $\psi(u) = \dfrac{e^{-Ru}}{E[e^{-RU(T)}|T < \infty]} \leq e^{-Ru}$

When X is exponential with parameter β, the adjustment coefficient is $R = \frac{\theta\beta}{1+\theta}$ and $\psi(u) = \frac{1}{1+\theta}e^{-Ru}$. In general $\psi(0)$ is always $\frac{1}{1+\theta}$.

COMPUTATIONAL REVIEW TEST

For questions 1-11 below, assume a compound-Poisson claims process with $\lambda = 3$ expected claims per period, $u = 10$ in initial capital, $c = 20$ per period in premium, and $p(x) = \frac{1}{5} e^{-x/5}$ for $x > 0$ as the density function for claim amount.

1. Find the expected surplus as a function of t. What happens as $t \to \infty$?

2. What is $Pr(S(2) = 0)$, the probability that aggregate claims is zero for time $t = 2$?

3. What is the distribution of $N(t) - N(2)$ for $t > 2$?

4. What is the distribution of waiting time, W, between claims? What is the expected waiting time between claims?

5. What is the distribution of L_1, the loss at the time surplus first drops below its initial level given that this happens?

6. What is the relative security loading?

7. Find the probability of ruin with no initial capital.

8. What is the expected maximal aggregate loss.

9. What is $\psi(u)$, the probability of ruin with general initial capital u? Find $\psi(u)$ for $u = 10$ as above.

10. Write the equation to determine the adjustment coefficient and solve it.

11. Find the moment generating function of the maximal aggregate loss, and use it to check the result in question 8.

12. Suppose initial surplus is 3 and premium arrives continuously at a rate of 2/yr. Suppose one claim, X, will eventually occur at time T where

T	*Prob.*
1	.30
2	.40
3	.30

X	*Prob.*
2	.40
4	.30
6	.20
8	.10

(a) Calculate $E[U(1)]$, $Var(U(1))$.

(b) Calculate the probability of ruin.

13. For a compound-Poisson surplus process with $Pr(X = 1) = .70$ and $Pr(X = 2) = .30$ calculate:

(a) $Pr(.50 \leq L_1 \leq 1.5)$

(b) $E[L_1]$ using both the density of L_1 used in (a) and the relation to X moments

(c) $Var(L_1)$.

14. In a compound-Poisson surplus model suppose X is a 75%/25% mixture of exponentials with respective parameters $\beta_1 = 2$, $\beta_2 = 4$, and suppose $\theta = \frac{19}{21}$. Calculate $\psi(u)$ in the form $C_1 e^{-r_1 u} + C_2 e^{-r_2 u}$.

15. Consider a compound Poisson surplus model with exponentially distributed claim amounts. Suppose $\theta = .25$ is the relative security loading on the portfolio. Proportional reinsurance $h(x) = \alpha X$, $0 < \alpha < 1$ is to be employed to reduce risk with a reinsurer whose relative security loading is $\zeta = .50$. What value of α will maximize the adjustment coefficient on the retained portfolio?

16. Rework Example 6 if c is changed from 1.5 to 2.

COMPUTATIONAL REVIEW TEST SOLUTIONS

1. $E[U(t)] = E[u + ct - S(t)] = u + ct - (\lambda t) \cdot p_1 = 10 + 20t - (3t) \cdot 5 = 10 + 5t$ since $p_1 = E[X] = \frac{1}{\beta} = \frac{1}{1/5} = 5$ for an exponential $\beta = \frac{1}{5}$ variable.

   $\lim_{t \to \infty} E[U(t)] = \lim_{t \to \infty} (10 + 5t) = \infty$

2. For aggregate claims to be zero, the number of claims, $N(2)$, must be zero. $N(2)$ is Poisson with parameter $\lambda \cdot 2 = 6$. Thus $Pr(S(2) = 0) = e^{-6} \cdot \frac{6^0}{0!} = e^{-6}$.

3. Poisson with parameter $\lambda(t - 2) = 3t - 6$.

4. Since $N(t)$ is Poisson with parameter λt, W is exponential with parameter λ: then $f(w) = \lambda e^{-\lambda w} = 3e^{-3w}$ and $E[W] = \frac{1}{\lambda} = \frac{1}{3}$. Thus there are 3 expected claims per period and an average waiting time of $\frac{1}{3}$ period between claims.

5. The density of L_1 is $f(y) = \underset{\substack{\uparrow \\ 1/p_1}}{\beta}\ [1 - P(y)] = \frac{1}{5}\left[\int_y^\infty \frac{1}{5} e^{-x/5}\,dx\right] = \frac{1}{5} e^{-y/5}, y > 0$. That is, L_1 is also exponential with $\beta = \frac{1}{5}$.

6. $1 + \theta = \frac{\text{annual premium}}{\text{expected annual claims}} = \frac{20}{3 \cdot 5} = \frac{4}{3} \Rightarrow \theta = \frac{1}{3}$.

7. $\psi(0) = \frac{1}{1 + \theta} = \frac{1}{4/3} = \frac{3}{4}$.

8. It follows from $L = L_1 + \ldots + L_N$ where the L_i are independent and identically distributed like L_1, which was seen to be exponential with $\beta = \frac{1}{5}$ in question 5. N has a geometric distribution with $q = \psi(0) = \frac{3}{4}$. By results for random sums,

$$E[L] = E[L_1] \cdot E[N] = \left(\tfrac{1}{\beta}\right) \cdot \left(\tfrac{q}{p}\right) = 5 \cdot \frac{3/4}{1/4} = 15.$$

9. Since X is exponential with $\beta = \frac{1}{5}$ we have

$$\psi(u) = \frac{1}{1+\theta} \cdot e^{-\left(\frac{\theta\beta u}{1+\theta}\right)} = \frac{3}{4}\, e^{-\left(\frac{(1/3)(1/5)u}{4/3}\right)} = \frac{3}{4}\, e^{-u/20}$$

in general, and $\psi(10) = \frac{3}{4}\, e^{-1/2}$

10. $$\lambda + cR = \underbrace{\lambda \cdot M_X\,(R)}_{\text{general}} = \underbrace{\lambda \cdot \frac{\beta}{\beta - R}}_{\text{exponential claims}}$$

$$\Rightarrow\ 3 + 20R = 3 \cdot \frac{1/5}{(1/5) - R} = \frac{3}{1 - 5R}$$

$$\Rightarrow\ (3 + 20R)(1 - 5R) = 3 \ \Rightarrow\ 5R - 100R^2 = 0 \ \Rightarrow\ R = \frac{5}{100} = \frac{1}{20}$$

11. $$M_L(t) = \frac{\theta p_1 t}{1 + (1+\theta)p_1 t - M_X(t)} = \frac{(\frac{1}{3})(5)t}{1 + (\frac{4}{3})(5)t - (\frac{1}{1-5t})}$$

$$\begin{cases} p_1 = E[X] = \frac{1}{\beta} = 5 & \text{(since } X \text{ is exponential with parameter } \beta) \\ \theta = \frac{1}{3} \text{ from above} & \\ M_X(t) = \frac{\beta}{\beta - t} = \frac{1/5}{(1/5) - t} = \frac{1}{1 - 5t} & \text{(since } X \text{ is exponential with parameter } \beta) \end{cases}$$

$$\Rightarrow\ M_L(t) = \frac{5t}{3 + 20t - \frac{3}{1-5t}} = \frac{5t(1-5t)}{5t - 100t^2} = \frac{5t - 1}{20t - 1} \ \Rightarrow\ M_L'(t) = \frac{(20t-1)5 - (5t-1)20}{(20t-1)^2}$$

$$\Rightarrow\ E[L] = M_L'(0) = -5 + 20 = 15.$$

12. (a) $U(t) = 3 + 2t - S(t)$ and the distribution of $S(1)$ is given in the table below:

$S(1)$	Probability
0	$.7 = Pr(T = 2 \text{ or } 3)$
2	$(.3)(.4) = Pr(T = 1 \text{ and } X = 2)$
4	$(.3)(.3) = Pr(T = 1 \text{ and } X = 4)$
6	$(.3)(.2) = Pr(T = 1 \text{ and } X = 6)$
8	$(.3)(.1) = Pr(T = 1 \text{ and } X = 8)$

Thus $E[S(1)] = 1.2$, $E[S(1)^2] = 6$ and $Var(S(1)) = 4.56$. Hence
$E[U(1)] = 3 + 2(1) - E[S(1)] = 5 - 1.2 = 3.8$,
$Var(U(1)) = Var(3 \cdot 2(1) - S(1)) = (-1)^2 Var(S(1)) = 4.56$.

(b) Events making up "ruin"

	T	X	$Probability$
(5 available)	1	6	(.3)(.2)
"	1	8	(.3)(.1)
(7 available)	2	8	(.4)(.1)
	Total: $\psi(3) = .06 + .03 + .04 = .13$		

13. (a) $E[X] = (1)(.7) + 2(.3) = 1.3$ and

$$P(x) = F_X(x) = \begin{cases} 0 & x < 1 \\ .70 & 1 \leq x < 2 \\ 1.0 & 2 \leq x \end{cases}$$

Hence

$$f_{L_1}(x) = \frac{1}{1.3}[1 - F_X(x)] = \begin{cases} \frac{1}{1.3} & 0 \leq x < 1 \\ \frac{.3}{1.3} & 1 \leq x < 2 \\ 0 & \text{otherwise} \end{cases}$$

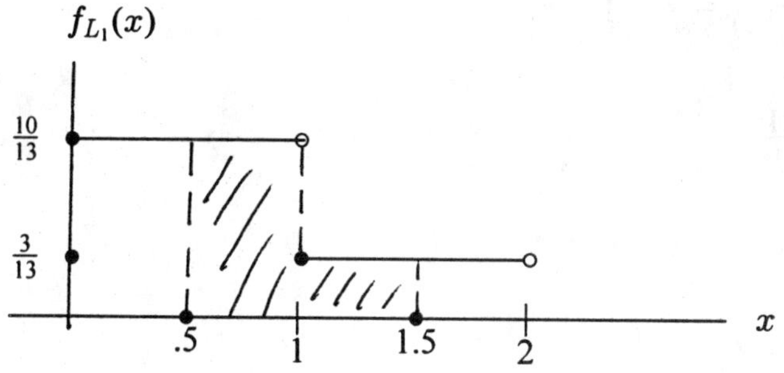

Now $Pr(.5 \leq L_1 \leq 1.5)$, the hashed area in the above figure, is $\frac{10}{13}(1-.5) + \frac{3}{13}(1.5-1) = \frac{13}{26} = .5$.

(b) Using the density for L_1, we have

$$E[L_1] = \int_0^2 x \cdot f_{L_1}(x)\,dx = \int_0^1 x \cdot \frac{10}{13}\,dx + \int_1^2 x \cdot \frac{3}{13}\,dx = \frac{10}{26} + \frac{9}{26} = \frac{19}{26}.$$

In general $E[L_1]$ also equals $E[X^2]/2E[X] = 1.9/2(1.3) = 19/26$.

(c) The easiest variance calculation is as follows:

$$E[L_1^2] = E[X^3]/3E[X] = 3.1/3(1.3) = 31/39$$
$$Var(L_1) = E[L_1^2] - (E[L_1])^2 = \frac{31}{39} - \left(\frac{19}{26}\right)^2.$$

14. Note first that $E[X] = .75\frac{1}{2} + .25\frac{1}{4} = \frac{7}{16}$ and $M_X(t) = .75\left(\frac{2}{2-t}\right) + .25\left(\frac{4}{4-t}\right)$. The values r_1, r_2 are the solutions of $1 + \left(\frac{40}{21}\right)\left(\frac{7}{16}\right)t = 1 + (1+\theta)E[X]t = M_X(t)$: this quadratic equation yields roots of $\frac{24 \pm \sqrt{24^2-20(19)}}{10} = \frac{24 \pm 14}{10} = 1$ or 3.8. Hence $r_1 = 1$, $r_2 = 3.8$. Then C_1 and C_2 are solutions of

$$\frac{1}{1+\theta} = \psi(0) = C_1 + C_2$$

$$E[L] = \psi'(0) = \frac{C_1}{r_1} + \frac{C_2}{r_2}.$$

Now $E[L] = E[N]E[L_1] = \left(\frac{1}{\theta}\right)\frac{E[X^2]}{2E[X]}$ and $E[X^2] = .75\frac{2}{2^2} + .25\frac{2}{4^2} = \frac{13}{32}$. We have already seen $E[X] = \frac{7}{16}$, $\theta = \frac{19}{21}$. Hence the two linear equations to solve are:

$$\frac{21}{40} = \frac{1}{1+\theta} = C_1 + C_2$$

$$\frac{39}{76} = \left(\frac{21}{19}\right)\frac{13/32}{2(7/16)} = E[L] = \frac{C_1}{1} + \frac{C_2}{3.8}$$

$$\Rightarrow \quad C_1(2.8) = 3.8\left(\frac{39}{76}\right) - \frac{21}{40}$$

$$\Rightarrow \quad C_1 = \frac{57}{112}, \quad C_2 = \frac{9}{560}$$

$$\Rightarrow \quad \psi(u) = \frac{57}{112}e^{-u} + \frac{9}{560}e^{-3.8u}.$$

15. $S = X_1 + \cdots + X_N$ where $N \sim$ Poisson(λ), $X \sim$ Exponential β. $S^{ceded} = \alpha X_1 + \cdots + \alpha X_N$ and $S^{ret} = (1-\alpha)X_1 + \cdots + (1-\alpha)X_N$: both are compound-Poissons with the same λ and $\alpha X \sim$ Exponential$\left(\frac{\beta}{\alpha}\right)$, $(1-\alpha)X \sim$ Exponential$\left(\frac{\beta}{(1-\alpha)}\right)$. Let θ' be the security loading on the retained portfolio. Since $\frac{E[S^{ret}]}{E[S]} = (1-\alpha)$, $\frac{E[S^{ceded}]}{E[S]} = \alpha$, we have

$$\theta = (1-\alpha)\theta' + \alpha\zeta$$

or

$$\theta' = \frac{\theta-\alpha\zeta}{1-\alpha} = \frac{.25 - .50\alpha}{1-\alpha} = \frac{1-2\alpha}{4(1-\alpha)}.$$

The adjustment coefficient on the retained portfolio is.

$$R^{ret} = \frac{\theta'(\beta/(1-\alpha))}{1+\theta'} = \beta\frac{(1-2\alpha)}{(5-6\alpha)(1-\alpha)}.$$

To maximize this function of α we solve

$$0 = \frac{dR^{ret}}{d\alpha} = \frac{\beta}{[(5-6\alpha)(1-\alpha)]^2}[1-12\alpha+12\alpha^2]$$

for $\alpha = \frac{12-\sqrt{96}}{24} = .09175.$

16. $U(n) = 1 + 2n - S(n),\ G = 2 - W$

W	Pr	G	$U(1) = 1 + G$
0	.4	2	3
1	.3	1	2
2	.2	0	1
3	.1	−1	0

Thus $\tilde{\psi}(1,1) = 0$. $U(2) = U(1) + G$ (independent):

$U(2)$	Pr
5	.16
4	.24
3	.25
2	.20
1	.10
0	.04
−1	.01

$\Rightarrow Pr(\text{ruin at time 2}) = .01$

$$\Rightarrow \tilde{\psi}(1,2) = \tilde{\psi}(1,1) + .01 = 0 + .01 = .01$$

To calculate the probability of ruin at time 3, disregard $U(2) = -1$ (ruin already at $t = 2$) and see which other combinations give ruin at $t = 3$. The only combination is $U(2) = 0$ and $G = -1$. Hence $\tilde{\psi}(1,3) = .01 + (.04)(.10) = .014$.

UNIT REVIEW QUESTIONS

1. A surplus process has (i) a compound Poisson claims process; (ii) initial surplus of 0; (iii) a claim amount distribution that is uniform over the interval $(0, 30)$; and (iv) a relative security loading of .50. Determine the expected value, given that ruin occurs, of the deficit at ruin.

(A) 5 (B) 10 (C) 15 (D) 20 (E) 25

2. A surplus process has a compound Poisson claims process with $\lambda = 2$, and an exponential claim amount distribution with mean 2. The premium rate is twice the expected claims rate. Reinsurance is purchased which covers 50% of each claim. The loading for the reinsurer is 80%. Determine the adjustment coefficient for the ceding company.

(A) $\frac{4}{11}$ (B) $\frac{5}{11}$ (C) $\frac{6}{11}$ (D) $\frac{7}{11}$ (E) $\frac{8}{11}$

3. An insurance company issues ordinary life policies that pay 1000 at the death of the insured. Insureds have constant annual rates of mortality of .20. All deaths occur at the end of the year of age. No other terminations occur. The premium payable annually in advance is 164 per policy. The company has a portfolio of policies on four individuals whose future lifetimes are independent. The annual expenses per policy are 10 paid at the beginning of the year. The company's effective annual yield rate on its investments is 30 percent. Determine $\psi(500, 2.5)$.

(A) .23 (B) .28 (C) .50 (D) .72 (E) .77

4. For a compound Poisson surplus process, the probability of ruin, as a function of the initial surplus, u, is:

$$\psi(u) = \frac{e^{-6u}}{2}, \; u \geq 0$$

Determine $M_L(2)$.

(A) .75 (B) 1.00 (C) 1.25 (D) 1.50 (E) 1.75

5. A surplus process with $\theta = 1$ has a compound Poisson claims process. Claim amounts have an exponential distribution with mean 2. L is the maximum aggregate loss random variable. Which of the following are true?

I. $\psi(0) = .50$ II. $Pr(L > u) = .50e^{-.50u}$ III. $M_L(r) = \frac{1-2r}{1-4r}$

(A) I and II only (B) I and III only (C) II and III only (D) I, II and III
(E) The correct answer is not given by (A), (B), (C), or (D)

6. For a compound Poisson process, the probability that the surplus will ever fall below its initial level u and will be between $u-y$ and $u-y-dy$ when it happens for the first time is $\left(\frac{4}{3}\right)e^{-2y}\,dy, y>0$. Determine the adjustment coefficient.

(A) 1/2 (B) 2/3 (C) 3/4 (D) 4/5 (E) 5/6

7. An insurance portfolio has the following characteristics:

(i) Claims are certain to occur at times .50, 1.50, 2.50, … .
(ii) Claim amounts have a uniform distribution over $[0, 2]$.
(iii) The relative security loading is .20.
(iv) Premiums are paid only at the beginning of each period.
(v) Initial surplus is 1.

Determine the probability of ruin before time 2.

(A) .015 (B) .030 (C) .045 (D) .060 (E) .075

8. An insurer's portfolio consists of a single possible claim. The probability that the claim will eventually occur is .50. The claim amount will be 10 if it occurs. The time of occurrence, W_1, has a Pareto distribution[12] with $x_0 = 1$ and $\alpha = 3$. The annual premium is 7, payable continuously. Determine the probability that surplus falls below its initial level.

(A) .30 (B) .40 (C) .50 (D) .60 (E) .70

9. An aggregate claims process is compound Poisson. The probability that the waiting time until the next claim will be at least 2 years is .60.

Determine the probability that exactly four claims will occur within 5 years.

(A) .03 (B) .11 (C) .19 (D) .24 (E) .28

10. An insurer has a surplus process with an aggregate claims process that is compound Poisson with:

(i) $\lambda = 1$;
(ii) $p(x) = 1/2, 0 \le x \le 2$; and
(iii) Premium rate 2.

With no reinsurance, the adjustment coefficient is .90.

The insurer purchases proportional reinsurance where the reinsurer pays 25 percent of each individual claim. The reinsurer has a relative security loading of 100 percent.

Determine the adjustment coefficient with reinsurance.

(A) .90 (B) 1.0 (C) 1.1 (D) 1.2 (E) 1.3

[12] $f(x) = \alpha x_0^{\alpha}/x^{\alpha+1}$ for $x \ge x_0$

11. (2 points) A surplus process has a compound Poisson claims process with parameter $\lambda = 2$ and an exponential claim amount distribution with parameter $\beta = 1$. Premiums are received continuously at the rate of 4. L is the maximal aggregate loss. u is the initial surplus such that $Pr\{L > u\} = .05$. Determine u.

(A) $\frac{1}{2}log_e 50$ (B) $log_e 50$ (C) $2\,log_e 50$ (D) $log_e 100$ (E) $2\,log_e 100$

12. (3 points) Two independent compound Poisson claims processes with exponential claim size distribution and mean claim size 10 are insured by separate insurers as follows:

Insurer	Expected Claim Frequency	Relative Security Loading	Surplus
I	8	0.4	10
II	2	0.6	5

The two insurers merge and continue to insure the two processes at the previous premium levels. Determine the probability of ruin for the merged insurer.

(A) 0.36 (B) 0.40 (C) 0.44 (D) 0.48 (E) 0.52

13. (2 points) A surplus process has:
(i) a compound Poisson claims process;
(ii) $p(x) = \frac{1}{2}e^{-x} + \frac{3}{4}e^{-3x} + e^{-4x}$, as the individual claim amount p.d.f.; and
(iii) $1 + 2R = \frac{1}{2}\left(\frac{1}{1-R}\right) + \frac{1}{4}\left(\frac{3}{3-R}\right) + \frac{1}{4}\left(\frac{4}{4-R}\right)$
as the equation for the adjustment coefficient R.

Determine the relative security loading.

(A) 2.0 (B) 2.1 (C) 2.2 (D) 2.3 (E) 2.4

14. (2 points) For a claim number process $\{N(t), t \geq 0\}$ you are given:

(i) the waiting times between successive claims are independent and identically and uniformly distributed over $(0, 2)$
(ii) $N(4.5) = 4$; and
(iii) $T_4 = 4.1$.

Determine the conditional probability that T_5 will be between 4.5 and 4.9.

(A) 0.15 (B) 0.20 (C) 0.25 (D) 0.30 (E) 0.35

15. (2 points) A surplus process has a compound Poisson claims process and probability of ruin $\psi(u) = .2e^{-2u}$. L is the maximal aggregate loss. Determine $E[L]$.

(A) 0.1 (B) 0.2 (C) 0.3 (D) 0.4 (E) 0.5

16. (2 points) For a claim number process $\{N(t), t \geq 0\}$, you are given that the waiting times between successive claims are independent and identically distributed with distribution function $F(t) = 1 - e^{-2t}$. Determine the probability that exactly three claims will occur in an interval of length 1.5.

(A) 0.20 (B) 0.22 (C) 0.24 (D) 0.26 (E) 0.28

17. (3 points) For a discrete time surplus process U_n, $n = 0, 1, 2, \ldots$, let $G_n = U_n - U_{n-1}$. You are given:

(i) $G_1, G_2, \ldots$ are mutually independent and identically distributed random variables; and
(ii) $Pr\{G_n = -1\} = Pr\{G_n = 0\} = \frac{1}{6}$ and $Pr\{G_n = 1\} = \frac{2}{3}$.

Determine the adjustment coefficient $\widetilde{R}$.

(A) 1.36 (B) 1.39 (C) 1.42 (0) 1.45 (E) 1.48

18. For a discrete surplus process $U_n = u + \sum_{i=1}^{n} c_i - \sum_{i=1}^{n} W_i$:

(i) $W_1, W_2, W_3, \ldots$ are mutually independent;
(ii) W_i can take only the values $i+1$ and $i-1$;
(iii) $c_i = i$; and
(iv) $u = 2.3$

Determine $U_{\widetilde{T}}$.

(A) −.7 (B) −.6 (C) −.5 (D) −.4 (E) −.3

19. For a surplus process with a compound Poisson claims process, you are given:

(i) $p(x) = \frac{1}{2}e^{-x} + \frac{3}{2}e^{-3x}$;
(ii) the adjustment coefficient $R = \frac{1}{2}$

Determine θ.

(A) .20 (B) .40 (C) .80 (D) 1.00 (E) 1.80

20. A new business has initial capital 700 and will have annual net earnings of 1000. It faces the risk of a one-time loss with the following characteristics:

(i) $Pr(\text{loss in year } n) = (.35^{n-1})(.65)$
(ii) the size of the loss is uniformly distributed on the ten integers 500, 1000, 1500, ..., 5000; and
(iii) loss occurs at the end of the year

Determine the probability of ruin.

(A) .00 (B) .41 (C) .46 (D) .60 (E) .65

21. For a discrete surplus process, you are given:

(i) initial surplus is 1000;
(ii) level amount of premiums received in each period is 100;
(iii) level amount of expenses incurred by the insurer in each period is 8; and
(iv) $W_1, W_2, \ldots$ are independent and identically distributed $N(10,4)$.

Determine $\widetilde{R}$.

(A) 20.5 (B) 22.5 (C) 41.0 (D) 45.00 (E) 82.0

22. $U(t) = u + ct - S(t)$ is a surplus process such that:

(i) aggregate claims $S(t)$ is a compound Poisson process; and
(ii) individual claim amounts follow the distribution:

x	$p(x)$
1	.25
2	.50
3	.25

Let L_1 be the random variable that denotes the amount by which the surplus falls its initial level for the first time, given that this ever happens.

Determine $Var(L_1)$.

(A) .57 (B) .68 (C) 1.27 (D) 1.78 (E) 1.83

23. For a claim process $\{N(t), t > 0\}$ you are given that the elapsed times between successive claims are mutually independent and identically distributed with distribution function

$$F(t) = 1 - e^{-3t}, \ t \geq 0$$

Determine the probability of exactly 4 claims in an interval of length 2.

(A) .11 (B) .13 (C) .15 (D) .17 (E) .19

24. A compound Poisson surplus process has an exponential claim amount distribution. You are given:

(i) the initial surplus is 16;
(ii) the relative security loading is .4; and
(iii) the probability of ruin is .04.

Determine the adjustment coefficient.

(A) .18 (B) .25 (C) .32 (D) .39 (E) .46

25. In a surplus process:

(i) aggregate claims follows a compound Poisson process; and
(ii) claim amounts have an inverse Gaussian[13] distribution with $\alpha = 1.0$ and $\beta = .20$

Let θ be the greatest value of the relative security loading for which the adjustment coefficient exists.

Determine θ.

(A) 2.3 (B) 2.4 (C) 2.5 (D) 2.6 (E) 2.7

26. For a surplus process with a compound Poisson claim process, you are given:

(i) the adjustment coefficient is .25;
(ii) the claim amount distribution is $p(x) = e^{-2x} + \frac{5}{2}e^{-5x}$, $x > 0$; and
(iii) L is the maximal aggregate loss.

Determine $Pr(L = 0)$.

(A) .10 (B) .20 (C) .30 (D) .40 (E) .50

27. An insurer's portfolio consists of a single possible claim. You are given:

(i) the claim amount is uniformly distributed over (100, 500);
(ii) the probability that the claim occurs after time t is $e^{-.10t}$, $t > 0$
(iii) the claim time and amount are independent;
(iv) the insurer's initial surplus is 20; and
(v) premium income is received continuously at the rate of 40 per annum.

Determine the probability of ruin.

(A) .30 (B) .40 (C) .50 (D) .60 (E) .70

---

13 $M_X(t) = exp\left[\alpha\left(1 - \sqrt{1-\frac{2t}{\beta}}\right)\right]$ if $t < \frac{\beta}{2}$.

28. For an insurer's surplus process, you are given:

(i) aggregate claims follow a compound Poisson process;
(ii) the claim amount distribution has mean 100 and standard deviation 100; and
(iii) the relative security loading is .20.

Proportional reinsurance is available at a premium equal to 130% of the expected reinsured claims. Let α be the proportion of each claim reinsured that minimizes the expected maximal aggregate loss.

Determine α.

(A) 0 (B) $\frac{1}{5}$ (C) $\frac{1}{4}$ (D) $\frac{1}{3}$ (E) $\frac{1}{2}$

29. For a surplus process with a compound Poisson claims process, you are given:

(i) all claims are size 10; and
(ii) the adjustment coefficient is .01.

Determine the relative security loading.

(A) 5.0% (B) 5.1% (C) 5.2% (D) 5.3% (E) 5.4%

30. An asset is purchased for 1000. Its value increases continuously at a uniform rate of 200 and decreases at random times $T_1, T_2, \ldots$ by random amounts $X_1, X_2, \ldots$

You are given:

(i) the intervals $W_1 = T_1$, $W_2 = T_2 - T_1$, $\ldots$ are identically distributed with an exponential distribution with mean .005;
(ii) $X_1, X_2, \ldots$ are identically distributed with $p(.5) = .75$ and $p(1.0) = .25$; and
(iii) $W_1, W_2, \ldots$ and $X_1, X_2, \ldots$ are mutually independent.

Determine the probability that the asset value ever falls below the purchase price.

(A) $\frac{3}{8}$ (B) $\frac{2}{5}$ (C) $\frac{1}{2}$ (D) $\frac{3}{5}$ (E) $\frac{5}{8}$

31. For a surplus process with a compound Poisson claims process, you are given:

(i) $\lambda = 1$;
(ii) all claims are of size 1; and
(iii) the rate of premium collection is 1.

Determine $\psi(1, 1)$.

(A) .00 (B) .25 (C) .50 (D) .75 (E) 1.00

32. For a surplus process with a compound Poisson claims process, you are given:

(i) $\psi(u) = .10e^{-7u} + .2e^{-4u} + .3e^{-2u}$, $u \geq 0$; and
(ii) N denotes the number of new record highs for the aggregate loss process.

Determine $Pr(N = 1)$.

(A) .12 (B) .24 (C) .36 (D) .48 (E) .60

33. An insurer has a surplus process that has a compound Poisson claims process with individual claim amount distribution:

x	$p(x)$
1	.95
10	.05

The insurer charges a premium with relative security loading of 25%. The insurer purchases excess-of-loss reinsurance for claims over 1 for a premium of 150% of expected claims reinsured.

Determine the expected value of the maximal aggregate loss random variable for the insurer with reinsurance.

(A) 3.64 (B) 4.10 (C) 4.22 (D) 5.87 (E) 8.21

34. S_n has a Poisson inverse Gaussian distribution with mean λ and variance $\lambda\left(1 + \frac{1}{\beta_n}\right)$ for $n = 1, 2, \ldots$. As $n \to \infty$ and $\beta_n \to \infty$ the distribution of S_n approaches which of the following?

(A) Inverse Gaussian distribution with mean and variance λ
(B) Poisson distribution with mean λ
(C) Negative binomial distribution with mean and variance λ
(D) Normal distribution with mean and variance λ
(E) The correct answer is not given by (A), (B), (D), or (D)

35. For a surplus process, you are given:

(i) the claim number process is Poisson;
(ii) the claim amount distribution is inverse Gaussian with $\alpha = 1.0$ and $\beta = .02$; and
(iii) the adjustment coefficient does not exist.

How many of $\{0.1, 0.2, 0.3, 0.4\}$ are possible values for $\psi(0)$?

(A) 0 (B) 1 (C) 2 (D) 3 (E) 4

UNIT REVIEW QUESTION SOLUTIONS

1. With $u = 0$, if ruin occurs it occurs at the first time surplus is below its initial level. The deficit (loss) at this time is denoted by L_1 (see Condensed Review Notes of this manual) and the density of L_1 is

$$f(y) = \frac{1}{p_1}[1 - P(y)] \quad y \geq 0,$$

where p_1 is the expected claim amount and $P(y)$ is the distribution function of claim amount. Since claim amount is given to be uniform over [0, 30] we have

$$p_1 = 15, \; P(y) = \begin{cases} y/30 & 0 \leq y \leq 30 \\ 1 & 30 \leq y \end{cases}.$$

Hence

$$E[L_1] = \int_0^\infty y f(y)\,dy = \int_0^{30} y \cdot \tfrac{1}{15}(1 - y/30)\,dy = 30 - 20 = 10,$$ ANSWER B

Note: Notice that the given information $\theta = .5$ is irrelevant! $E[L_1]$ can also be computed as

$$\frac{p_2}{2p_1} = \frac{\left(\frac{30^2}{3}\right)}{2 \cdot 15} = 10.$$

2. We must analyze the portfolio of retained claims which requires analyzing the original and ceded claims:

Original: Compound Poisson $\lambda = 2, p_1 = 2, c = 2(\lambda p_1) = 8$

Ceded: Compound Poisson $\lambda = 2, p_1 = 1, c = 1.8(\lambda p_1) = 3.6$

Retained: Compound Poisson $\lambda = 2, p_1 = 1, c = 8 - 3.6 = 4.4$

Claim amount $= \frac{1}{2}X$ where $M_X(t) = \frac{\beta}{\beta - t} = \frac{1/2}{1/2 - t}$ since X is exponential with mean 2.

Equation for Adjustment Coefficient

$$\underset{\lambda}{\underset{\uparrow}{2}} + 4.4\underset{c}{\underset{\uparrow}{R}} = \underset{\lambda}{\underset{\uparrow}{2}}\, M_{\frac{1}{2}X}(R) = 2\,\frac{\frac{1}{2}}{\frac{1}{2} - \frac{R}{2}} = \frac{2}{1 - R}$$

$$\Rightarrow 2 + 2.4R - 4.4R^2 = 2$$

$$\Rightarrow 2.4R - 4.4R^2 = 0 \quad \Rightarrow \quad R = \underset{\frac{6}{11}}{\underset{\uparrow}{\frac{2.4}{4.4}}} \text{ or } 0$$ Recall R is positive, ANSWER C

Note: This problem can also be attacked by standard formulas. If $I(X) = \alpha X$ (proportional reinsurance) and X is exponential with parameter β then:

retained claim: $X - I(X) = (1-\alpha)X \sim$ Exponential $(\beta/1-\alpha)$
security loading: $\theta = (1-\alpha)\theta' + \alpha\zeta$ where θ is security loading on the original portfolio, ζ is the reinsurers security loading and θ' is the security loading on retained claims

adjustment coefficient: $$R = \frac{\theta\beta}{1+\theta} \quad \text{(original)}$$

$$R' = \frac{\theta'\beta/(1-\alpha)}{1+\theta'} \quad \text{(retained)}$$

Here $\beta = \frac{1}{2}$, $\alpha = \frac{1}{2}$, $\theta = 1$, $\zeta = .8$ so $\theta = \frac{1}{2}\theta' + \frac{1}{2}\zeta$ results in $\theta' = 1.2$. Hence

$$R = \frac{(1.2)(.5/.5)}{2.2} = \frac{1.2}{2.2} = \frac{6}{11}.$$

3. At the end of year one we have $(500 + 4(164-10))(1.3) = 1450.80$ in available cash before any benefits are paid. Consider the following table

Yr 1 Deaths	Yr 1 Ending Fund	Yr 2 Fund Before Benefits
0	1450.80	$(1450 + 4(164-10))(1.3) = 2687^*$
1	450.80	$(450 + 3(164-10))(1.3) = 1186^{**}$
≥ 2	negative (ruin occurs)	

* ruin occurs with 3 or 4 deaths
** ruin occurs with 2 or 3 deaths.

Thus the combinations resulting in ruin are

Yr 1 Deaths	Yr 2 Deaths	Probability
0	3 or 4	$.8^4\left[\binom{4}{3}(.8)^1(.2)^3 + \binom{4}{4}(.2)^4\right] = .01114$
1	2 or 3	$\binom{4}{1}(.8)^3(.2)\left[\binom{3}{2}(.8)^1(.2)^2 + \binom{3}{3}(.2)^3\right] = .04260$
2, 3 or 4	____	$1 - \binom{4}{0}(.8)^4 - \binom{4}{1}(.8)^3(.2)^1 = .18080$
		total $= .2345$

ANSWER A

Note: $\Psi(500, 2.5)$ is the probability of ruin before time 2.5 given initial capital of 500. Ruin can only occur at times $t = 1, 2, \ldots$.

4. Recall that for a compound-Poisson process with exponentially distributed claim amount variable we have

$$\Psi(u) = \left(\frac{1}{1+\theta}\right) e^{-Ru}, \quad R = \frac{\theta\beta}{1+\theta}.$$

By comparison with the given $\Psi(u) = \frac{1}{2}e^{-6u}$ we see that $\theta = 1$ and $\beta = 12$.

Hence $p_1 = E[X] = \frac{1}{\beta} = \frac{1}{12}$ and

$$M_X(t) = (1-t/\beta)^{-1} = (1-t/12)^{-1}$$

$$M_L(t) = \frac{\theta p_1 t}{1+(1+\theta)p_1 t - M_X(t)} = \frac{t/12}{1+(t/6)-(1-t/12)^{-1}}$$

$$M_L(2) = \frac{15}{12}.$$

ANSWER C

Note: This solution can also be obtained as follows:
$F_L(u) = 1-\psi(u) = 1-\frac{1}{2}e^{-6u} = \frac{1}{2}(1)+\frac{1}{2}(1-e^{-6u})$ where 1 is the distribution function of a discrete variable with all probability at 0 and $1-e^{-6u}$ is the distribution function of an exponential with parameter $\beta = 6$. Thus L is a 50/50 mix of 0 and $exp(\beta = 6)$. As a result

$$M_L(t) = \frac{1}{2}\cdot \underset{\substack{\uparrow \\ \text{gen. fnc.} \\ \text{of } 0}}{1} + \frac{1}{2}\cdot \underset{\substack{\uparrow \\ \text{gen. fnc.} \\ \text{of } Exp}}{\frac{6}{6-t}}$$

$$M_L(2) = \frac{1}{2}+\frac{1}{2}\cdot\frac{6}{4} = 1.25.$$

5. I. In general $\Psi(0) = \frac{1}{1+\theta}$. So $\theta = 1$ means $\Psi(0) = \frac{1}{2}$. *True.*

II. The event that the maximal aggregate loss exceeds initial capital, $L > u$, is the same as saying that ruin has occurred. Thus

$$Pr(L>u) = \Psi(u) = \underbrace{\frac{1}{1+\theta}e^{-Ru},\ R = \frac{\theta\beta}{1+\theta}}_{\text{(for } X \text{ exponential, parameter } \beta)}$$

results in $Pr(L>u) = \frac{1}{2}e^{-u/4}$. *False.*

III. With X having an exponential distribution with parameter $\beta = 1/2$ we have $M_X(t) = (1-t/\beta)^{-1} = (1-2t)^{-1}$. Hence

$$M_L(t) = \frac{\theta p_1 t}{1+(1+\theta)p_1 t - M_X(t)} = \frac{(1)(2)t}{1+(2)(2)t-(1-2t)^{-1}} = \frac{1-2t}{1-4t}.\ \textit{True.}$$

ANSWER B

6. In general terms the probability given as $\left(\frac{4}{3}\right)e^{-2y}\,dy$ is expressed as $\frac{\lambda}{c}[1 - P(y)]\,dy$ (see Condensed Review Notes of this manual). Dropping the dy's and differentiating with respect to y yields

$$-\tfrac{\lambda}{c}\,p(y) = \left(\tfrac{4}{3}\right)(-2e^{-2y}),$$

or equivalently,

$$p(y) = \frac{8c}{3\lambda}e^{-2y}, \; y > 0.$$

Since this a constant multiple of an exponential density, $2e^{-2y}$, the uniqueness of that constant implies that

$$2 = \frac{8c}{3\lambda}, \text{ that is } \frac{c}{\lambda} = \frac{3}{4}.$$

Now with an exponential claim amount density $\beta e^{-\beta x}$ it is known that the adjustment coefficient is

$$R = \frac{\theta\beta}{1+\theta},$$

and here β is 2. It remains to calculate θ. In general

$$\frac{c}{\lambda p_1} = \frac{\text{annual premium}}{\text{exp. annual claims}} = 1+\theta\,.$$

Here $p_1 = \frac{1}{\beta} = \frac{1}{2}$, so $1+\theta = \frac{c}{\lambda\left(\frac{1}{2}\right)} = 2\cdot\frac{c}{\lambda} = 2\left(\frac{3}{4}\right)$ from the above calculation of $\frac{c}{\lambda}$. This yields $\theta = \frac{1}{2}$. Finally,

$$R = \frac{\theta\beta}{1+\theta} = \frac{\left(\frac{1}{2}\right)(2)}{1+\left(\frac{1}{2}\right)} = \frac{2}{3},$$

ANSWER B

7. Since there is exactly (non-random) 1 claim per year, expected annual claims are $E[X] = 1$ because the claim amount variable X is uniform on [0,2]. Since the relative security loading is .2, annual premium is $(1 + (.2))E[X] = 1.2$.

Year 1: At $t = 0^+$the available funds are $1 + 1.2 = 2.2$ (surplus + premium). Since the one claim, X_1, is less than 2, ruin cannot occur. As a result the fund available at year end is $2.2 - X_1 > 0$.

Year 2: At $t = 1^+$ the available funds are $(2.2 - X_1) + 1.2$. Ruin can occur at $t = \frac{3}{2}$ with a claim of amount X_2 if $3.4 - X_1 - X_2 < 0$.

Hence

$$Pr(\text{ruin}) = Pr(3.4 < X_1 + X_2).$$

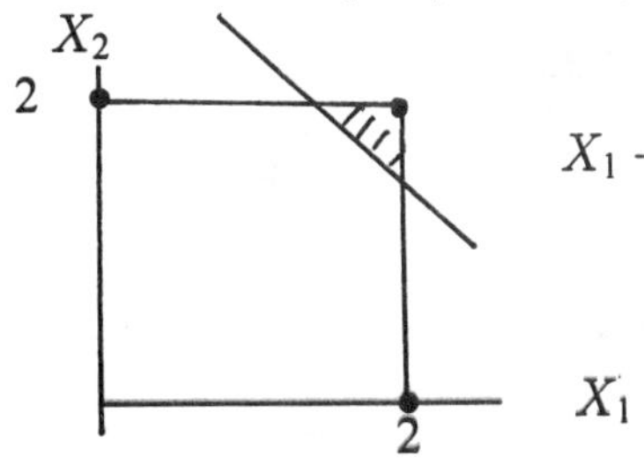

Since X_1, X_2 has a joint uniform density on the square in the figure above, the probability of ruin (hashed region in figure) is proportional to its area:

$$Pr(\text{ruin}) = \frac{\text{Area hashed region}}{\text{Total Area}} = \frac{\frac{1}{2}(.6).6}{2\cdot 2} = .045,$$

ANSWER C

8. If the claim never occurs it is clear that surplus never falls below the initial level. Hence the probability that surplus falls below initial level is

Pr(claim occurs *and* premium up until the time of claim is less than the claim amount, 10)

$$= Pr(\text{claim occurs})\, Pr(7\underbrace{W_1}_{\text{premium}} < 10),$$

where W_1 is assumed to have the Pareto distribution

$$f(w_1) = \frac{3}{w_1^4} = \frac{\alpha}{w_1^{\alpha+1}}, \quad w_1 \geq 1.$$

Hence

$$Pr(7W_1 < 10) = Pr\left(W_1 < \tfrac{10}{7}\right) = \int_1^{10/7} \frac{3}{w_1^4}\, dw_1 = 1 - \left(\tfrac{7}{10}\right)^3.$$

Finally

$$Pr(\text{Surplus falls below initial level}) = \left(\tfrac{1}{2}\right)\left(1 - \left(\tfrac{7}{10}\right)^3\right) = .3285, \qquad \text{ANSWER A}$$

9. Since $N(t)$, the number of claims occurring in t years, is distributed like a Poisson with parameter λt, the waiting time between claims, W, is exponential with parameter λ:

$$f(w) = \lambda e^{-\lambda w},\ Pr(W > w) = \int_w^\infty \lambda e^{-\lambda t}\, dt = e^{-\lambda w}.$$

We are given $.6 = e^{-\lambda 2}$ or $\lambda = -\frac{1}{2} ln(.6)$. The number of claims in 5 years is Poisson with parameter $5\lambda = 1.277075$. Hence the probability of exactly 4 claims in 5 years is the Poisson probability

$$e^{-(5\lambda)} \frac{(5\lambda)^4}{4!} = .0309 \qquad \text{ANSWER A}$$

10. With proportional reinsurance on each claim and $\theta = \zeta$ the insurer's adjustment coefficient after reinsurance is

$$R' = \frac{R}{1 - \alpha}$$

where R is the adjustment coefficient on the original portfolio and αX is reinsured for each claim X. Here we are given $\zeta = 1$ and it follows from given information that $\theta = 1$ since

$$1 + \theta = \frac{c}{\lambda p_1} = \frac{2}{1 \cdot 1}.$$

Thus $R' = \frac{.9}{1 - .25} = 1.2.$ ANSWER D

11. Straightforward: $.05 = Pr(L > u) = \psi(u) = \frac{1}{1+\theta}e^{-Ru}$ due to exponentially distributed claim amounts. Also

$$1+\theta = \frac{c}{\lambda \cdot E[X]} = \frac{4}{2 \cdot \left(\frac{1}{\beta}\right)} = \frac{4}{2 \cdot 1} = 2$$

$$R = \frac{\theta\beta}{1+\theta} = \frac{(1)(1)}{1+1} = \frac{1}{2}$$

$$.05 = \frac{1}{2}e^{-\frac{1}{2}u} \quad \Rightarrow \quad .10 = e^{-\frac{1}{2}u} \quad \Rightarrow \quad ln(.10) = -\frac{1}{2}(u)$$

$$\Rightarrow \quad u = -2ln(.10) = ln(.10)^{-2} = ln(100)$$

ANSWER D

12. The merged claims portfolio is $S = S_I + S_{II}$. It is also compound Poisson with $\lambda = 8 + 2 = 10$ and $p(x) = .8[.10e^{-.10x}] + .2[.10e^{-.10x}] = .10e^{-.10x}$, $\therefore$ $E[X] = 10$. For total premiums we have

$$C = C_I + C_{II} = (1+(.4))(8 \cdot 10) + (1+.6)(2 \cdot 10) = 144.$$

Also $1+\theta = \frac{144}{(10)(10)} = 1.44$, $R = \frac{\theta\beta}{1+\theta} = \frac{(.44)(\frac{1}{10})}{1.44} = .03056$

$$u = u_I + u_{II} = 10 + 5 = 15$$

$$\psi(u) = \frac{1}{1+\theta}e^{-Ru} = \frac{1}{1.44}e^{-.45833} = .43912$$

ANSWER C

13. Compare $1 + (1+\theta)p_1 R = M_X(R)$ to the given equation. Conclusion: $(1+\theta)p_1 = 2$ and $M_X(R) =$ right side. The claim amount distribution is a weighted average of exponentials

$$p(x) = \frac{1}{2}[1e^{-x}] + \frac{1}{4}[3e^{-3x}] + \frac{1}{4}[4e^{-4x}]$$

$$\therefore \quad p_1 = E[X] = \frac{1}{2}\left[\frac{1}{1}\right] + \frac{1}{4}\left[\frac{1}{3}\right] + \frac{1}{4}\left[\frac{1}{4}\right] = .64583$$

$$\therefore \quad 1+\theta = \frac{2}{p_1} = \frac{2}{.64583} \quad \Rightarrow \quad \theta = 2.09677$$

ANSWER B

14. The 4th claim occurs at time 4.1 and there are still 4 claims at time 4.5. So we are given that $W_5 > 4.5 - 4.1 = .4$. Thus

$$Pr(4.5 \le T_5 \le 4.9 | W_5 > .4) = Pr(4.5 - 4.1 \le W_5 \le 4.9 - 4.1 | W_5 > .4)$$

$$= Pr(.4 \le W_5 \le .8 | W_5 > .4)$$

$$= \frac{Pr(.4 < W_5 \le .8)}{Pr(.4 < W_5)} \underset{\substack{\uparrow \\ \text{Uniform} \\ \text{on } [0,2]}}{=} \frac{.4/2}{1.6/2} = .25$$

ANSWER C

15. In general $\psi(u) = 1 - F_L(u)$, so here

$$F_L(u) = 1 - \psi(u) = 1 - .2e^{-2u} = .8(1) + .2(1-e^{-2u}).$$

Now $1 - e^{-2u}$ is the distribution function of an exponential distribution with parameter $\beta = 2$ (mean $= \frac{1}{2}$, $Var = \frac{1}{4}$) and 1 is the distribution function of a zero-variable. Hence L is an 80%/20% mixture of zero and an exponential with parameter $\beta = 2$:

$$E[L] = .80E[0] + .20E[\text{exponential}] = (.2)\left(\tfrac{1}{2}\right) = .10$$

$$E[L^2] = .80E[0^2] + .20E[\text{exponential}^2] = (.2)\left(\tfrac{1}{4} + \left(\tfrac{1}{2}\right)^2\right) = .10$$

$Var(L) = .10 - (.10)^2 = .09$ ANSWER A

16. For a Poisson process with parameter λ, the waiting times are independent exponentials with $\beta = \lambda$. Here $\lambda = 2$ since the waiting time c.d.f. is $F(t) = 1 - e^{-2t}$. The number of claims in an interval of length 1.5, $N(1.5)$, is Poisson with parameter $1.5\lambda = 3$. So

$$Pr(N(3) = 3) = e^{-3}\frac{3^3}{3!} = .224$$ ANSWER B

17. $M_W(\widetilde{R}) = e^{c\widetilde{R}}$, $G_n = U_n - U_{n-1} = c - \underbrace{W_n}_{\text{claims}} \Rightarrow W = c - G$

$$\Rightarrow e^{c\widetilde{R}} = M_W(\widetilde{R}) = M_{c-G}(\widetilde{R}) = M_c(\widetilde{R})M_{-G}(\widetilde{R}) = e^{c\widetilde{R}}M_G(-\widetilde{R})$$

$$\Rightarrow 1 = M_G(-\widetilde{R}) = E[e^{-\widetilde{R}G}] = \sum_g e^{-\widetilde{R}g}pr(g)$$

$$\Rightarrow 1 = e^{\widetilde{R}}\tfrac{1}{6} + e^0\tfrac{1}{6} + e^{-\widetilde{R}} \cdot \tfrac{4}{6} \quad \Rightarrow \quad 6e^{\widetilde{R}} = \left(e^{\widetilde{R}}\right)^2 + e^{\widetilde{R}} + 4$$

Quadratic in $e^{\widetilde{R}}$ $\Rightarrow$ $e^{\widetilde{R}}$ = root of $0 = x^2 - 5x + 4 = (x-4)(x-1)$, i.e., 1 or 4
If $e^{\widetilde{R}} = 1$, then $\widetilde{R} = 0$ (impossible, it is positive) $\therefore$ $e^{\widetilde{R}} = 4$, $\widetilde{R} = ln4 = 1.386$.

18. The gain for year i, $G_i = c_i - W_i$, is $i - \begin{cases} i+1 \\ i-1 \end{cases} = \begin{cases} -1 \\ 1 \end{cases}$. Thus if initial surplus is 2.3 and ruin occurs at time n, $U(n-1) = .3$ and $U(n) = .3 - 1 = -.7$. ANSWER A

19. From the claim amount density $p(x) = \frac{1}{2}e^{-x} + \frac{3}{2}e^{-3x} = \frac{1}{2}(1e^{-1x}) + \frac{1}{2}(3e^{-3x})$ it follows that X is a 50/50 mixture of $Exp(\beta = 1)$ and $Exp(\beta = 3)$. Thus $E[X] = \frac{1}{2}\left(\frac{1}{1}\right) + \frac{1}{2}\left(\frac{1}{3}\right) = \frac{2}{3}$ and $M_X(t) = \frac{1}{2} \cdot \frac{1}{1-t} + \frac{1}{2} \cdot \frac{3}{3-t}$. So the adjustment coefficient R is the unique positive solution of

$$1 + (1+\theta)E[X]R = M_X(R).$$

Since $R = \frac{1}{2}$ and $M_X\left(\frac{1}{2}\right) = 1 + \frac{1}{2} \cdot \frac{3}{2.5} = \frac{8}{5}$ we have

$$1 + (1+\theta)\left(\frac{2}{3}\right)\left(\frac{1}{2}\right) = \frac{8}{5},\ \theta = \frac{4}{5}$$

ANSWER C

20. Available funds by time n are $700 + 1000n$. By time 5 this amount exceeds the largest value of the one-time loss. Hence, ruin may occur at $n = 1, 2, 3, 4$ if the loss amount exceeds 1700, 2700, 3700, 4700, respectively. So

$$Pr(\text{Ruin}) = \sum_{n=1}^{4} Pr(\underset{\substack{\uparrow \\ \text{yr of loss}}}{N} = n)Pr(X > 700 + 1000n)$$

$$= \underbrace{(.65)\left(\frac{7}{10}\right)}_{\substack{\text{uniform with} \\ 7\ X\text{-values} \\ \text{out of } 10}} + (.35)(.65)\left(\frac{5}{10}\right) + (.35)^2(.65)\left(\frac{3}{10}\right) + (.35)^3(.65)\left(\frac{1}{10}\right) = .5954$$

ANSWER D

21. With a discrete-time surplus process model

$$U(n) = 1000 + \underbrace{(100-8)n}_{c=\text{Prem/yr}} - \underbrace{(W_1+\cdots+W_n)}_{\text{agg. claims}}$$

if follows that $\tilde{R} = \frac{2(c-\mu)}{\sigma^2}$ if $W \sim N(\mu, \sigma^2)$. Here $c = 92$, $\mu = 10$, $\sigma^2 = 4$, hence $\tilde{R} = \frac{2(82)}{4} = 41$.

ANSWER C

22. In general moments of L_1 can be calculated in terms of moments of the claim amount variable X via

$$E[L_1] = \frac{E[X^2]}{2E[X]} = \frac{4.5}{2(2)} = 1.125.$$

$$E[L_1^2] = \underbrace{\frac{E[X^3]}{3E[X]}}_{\text{general}} = \underbrace{\frac{11}{3(2)} = \frac{11}{6}}_{\text{here}}.$$

Hence, $Var(L_1) = \frac{11}{6} - 1.125^2 = .567.$ ANSWER A

Note: One could do the problem using the L_1-density to compute $E[L_1^k]$. It takes considerably more effort. Just for practice with $f_{L_1}(y) = \frac{1}{E[X]}[1 - F_X(y)]$ try showing it equals the following:

$$f_{L_1}(y) = \begin{cases} \frac{1}{2.00} & 0 \le y < 1 \\ \frac{.75}{2.00} & 1 \le y < 2 \\ \frac{.25}{2.00} & 2 \le y < 3 \\ 0 & 3 \le y \end{cases}$$

23. $N(t)$ is Poisson with parameter λt $\Leftrightarrow$ W, the waiting time model, is exponential with parameter λ. Here $\lambda = 3$ since $F_W(t) = 1 - e^{-3t}$ means $f_W(t) = 3e^{-3t}$. So $N(2)$ is Poisson with parameter $2\lambda = 6$:

$$Pr(N(2) = 4) = e^{-6}\frac{6^4}{4!} = .1338$$ ANSWER B

24. Standard formulas if claim amounts are exponentially distributed

$$\psi(u) = \frac{1}{1+\theta}e^{-Ru}, \quad R = \frac{\theta\beta}{1+\theta}$$

$$\Rightarrow\ .04 = \frac{1}{1.4}e^{-R(16)} \quad \Rightarrow \quad R = \frac{-ln(.056)}{16} = .180$$ ANSWER A

Note: $\beta = \frac{(1+\theta)R}{\theta} = \left(\frac{1.4}{.4}\right)(.180) = .63.$

25. The Inverse Gaussian has parameters α, β with $E[X] = \frac{\alpha}{\beta}$, $Var(X) = \frac{\alpha}{\beta^2}$, $M_X(t) = exp\left(\alpha\left(1-\sqrt{1-\frac{2t}{\beta}}\right)\right)$ for $t < \frac{\beta}{2}$. The following graph indicates how the adjustment coefficient R, the unique positive solution of $1 + (1+\theta)E[X]t = M_X(t)$, can fail to exist!

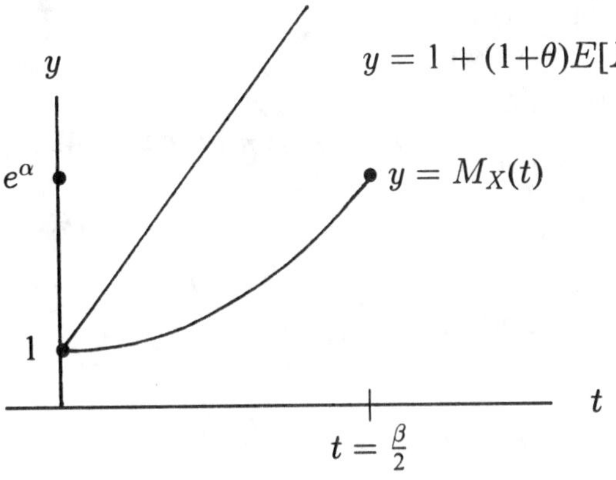

In the picture $1 + (1+\theta)\left(\frac{\alpha}{\beta}\right)\left(\frac{\beta}{2}\right) > e^\alpha$, that is

$$\theta > \frac{2(e^\alpha - 1)}{\alpha} - 1 = \underbrace{\frac{2(e-1)}{1}}_{\text{here}} - 1 = 2.44$$

ANSWER B

26. Since $L = 0$ means surplus never drops below its initial level (same as saying that ruin does not occur if $u = 0$) it follows that $Pr(L = 0) = 1 - \psi(0) = \frac{\theta}{1+\theta}$. Now the equation for R is

$$1 + (1+\theta)E[X]R = M_X(R)$$

and $p(x) = \frac{1}{2}(2e^{-2x}) + \frac{1}{2}(5e^{-5x})$ means that X is a 50/50 mixture of $Exp\ (\beta = 2)$ and $E(\beta = 5)$. Thus $E[X] = \frac{1}{2} \cdot \frac{1}{2} + \frac{1}{2} \cdot \frac{1}{5} = .35$, $M_X(t) = \frac{1}{2} \cdot \frac{2}{2-t} + \frac{1}{2} \cdot \frac{5}{5-t}$, $M_X(R = .25) = \frac{1}{2} \cdot \frac{2}{1.75} + \frac{1}{2} \cdot \frac{5}{4.75} = 1.0977$. Plugging into the equation for R results in $1+\theta = \frac{1.0977 - 1}{(.35)(.25)} = 1.117$. Finally $Pr(L = 0) = \frac{\theta}{1+\theta} = \frac{.117}{1.117} = .105$

ANSWER A

27. Surplus is $20 + 40T - X$ at the time T when the single claim occurs. So

$$Pr(\text{Ruin}) = Pr(20 + 40T - X < 0) = Pr(20 + 40T < X)$$

$$= \iint_D \underbrace{f_T(t) f_X(x)}_{\substack{\text{joint density} \\ \text{(independence)}}} \, dt \, dx$$

$$= \int_{x=100}^{500} \int_{t=0}^{\frac{1}{40}(x-20)} (.1e^{-.1t}) \left(\frac{1}{400}\right) dt \, dx = .4825$$

ANSWER C

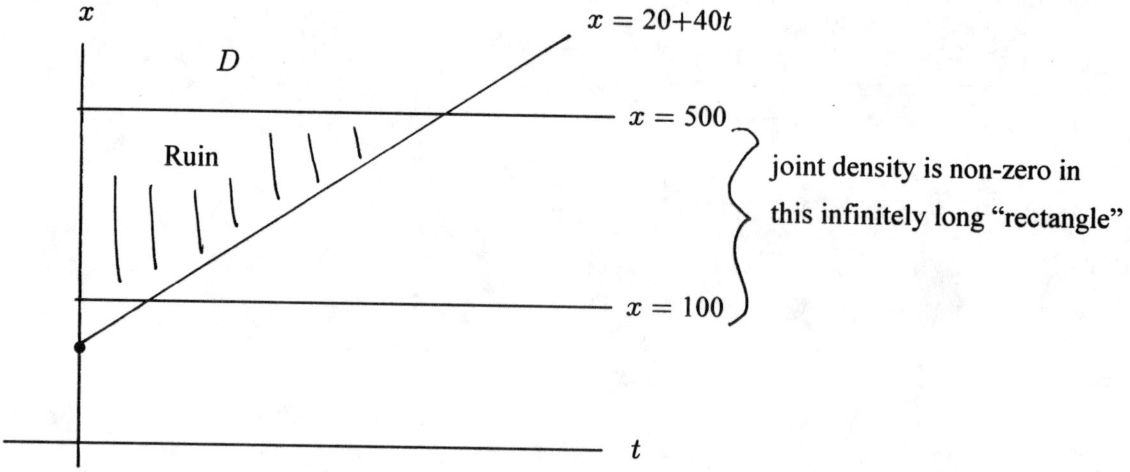

28. In general $E[L] = E[N]E[L_1] = \frac{1}{\theta} \cdot \frac{E[X^2]}{2E[X]}$, so we must compute θ^r, $E[(X^r)^2]$, $E[X^r]$ for the retained portfolio as a function of α. Since $E[S] = \lambda \cdot E[X]$ and $X^r = (1-\alpha)X$ we have $E[S^r] = \lambda \cdot E[X^r] = (1-\alpha)\lambda \cdot E[X] = (1-\alpha)E[S]$,
$E[(X^r)^k] = E[(1-\alpha)^k X^k] = (1-\alpha)^k E[X^k]$.
Also

$$\theta = \underbrace{(1-\alpha)}_{\frac{E[S^r]}{E[S]}} \theta^r + \alpha\zeta, \; \theta = .20 \text{ and } \zeta = .30$$

means $\theta^r = \frac{.2 - .3\alpha}{1-\alpha}$. Finally

$$E[L^r] = \frac{1}{\theta^r} \cdot \frac{E[(X^r)^2]}{2E[(X^r)]} = \left[\frac{1-\alpha}{.2 - .3\alpha}\right] \frac{(1-\alpha)^2 E[X^2]}{(1-\alpha)2E[X]} = c\left(\frac{(1-\alpha)^2}{2-3\alpha}\right)$$

$$\left(c = \frac{10E[X^2]}{2E[X]}\right).$$

To minimize $E[L^r]$ set $\frac{d}{d\alpha}(E[L^r]) = c\frac{(1-\alpha)(-1+3\alpha)}{(2-3\alpha)^2} = 0$ resulting in $\alpha = \frac{1}{3}$. ANSWER D

Note: $\alpha = 1$ reinsures the entire portfolio.

29. $X = 10 \Rightarrow E[X] = 10,\ M_X(t) = E[e^{10t}] = e^{10t}$

$1 + (1{+}\theta)E[X]R = M_X(R),\ R = .01$

$\Rightarrow\ 1 + (1{+}\theta)(10)(.01) = e^{10(.01)}$

$\Rightarrow\ \theta = \dfrac{e^{.10} - 1}{.10} - 1 = .0517$ ANSWER C

30. The probability sought is the same as $\psi(0)$ in a compound-Poisson surplus model where

$$c = \text{annual premium} = 200$$
$$\lambda = \frac{1}{.005} = 200$$
$$u = \text{initial surplus} = 1000$$
$$E[X] = (.5)(.75) + (1.0)(.25) = \tfrac{5}{8}$$

Thus

$$\psi(0) = \frac{1}{1{+}\theta} = \frac{\lambda E[X]}{c} = \frac{200(5/8)}{200} = \frac{5}{8}$$ ANSWER E

31. $\psi(1,1)$ is the probability of ruin by time 1 if $u = 1$. Now $U(t) = u + ct - S(t) = 1 + t - N(t)$ since $u = c = 1$ and $X = 1$. If 1 or 0 claims of 1 happen by $t = 1$ surplus is positive over $[0,1]$. However, if two or more claims occur in $(0,1]$ then ruin happens since $S(1) \geq 2$ and $1 + 1(1) = 2$ is available. (Since $Pr(T_2 = 1) = 0$ we may disregard the situation where the 2nd claim arrives exactly at $t = 1$ leaving a surplus of 0 (no ruin by $t = 1$)). Hence

$$\psi(1,1) = Pr(N(1) \geq 2) = 1 - Pr(N(1) = 0 \text{ or } 1)$$
$$= 1 - \left(e^{-\lambda}\frac{\lambda^0}{0!} + e^{-\lambda}\frac{\lambda^1}{1!}\right) \qquad (\lambda = 1)$$
$$= 1 - (e^{-1} + e^{-1}) = .264$$ ANSWER B

32. N is geometric with $p = \frac{\theta}{1{+}\theta},\ q = \frac{1}{1{+}\theta}$ so $Pr(N = n) = q^n p = \frac{\theta}{(1{+}\theta)^{n+1}}$. Also $\frac{1}{1{+}\theta} = \psi(0) = .10e^0 + .20e^0 + .3e^0 = .60$. Hence $1{+}\theta = \frac{5}{3}, \theta = \frac{2}{3}$ and

$Pr(N = 1) = \dfrac{\theta}{(1{+}\theta)^2} = \frac{2}{3} \cdot \left(\frac{3}{5}\right)^2 = \dfrac{6}{25} = .24$ ANSWER B

33. In general $E[L] = E[N]E[L_1]$. N is geometric with $q = \frac{1}{1+\theta}$, $p = \frac{\theta}{1+\theta}$ so $E[N] = \frac{q}{p} = \frac{1}{\theta}$. Also $E[L_1] = E[X^2]/2E[X]$. We must compute θ, $E[X]$, $E[X^2]$ for the retained portfolio.

(i) Determination of $E[X^{(r)}]$, $E[X^{(r)2}]$

X	$p(x)$	$X^{(c)}$	$X^{(r)}$
1	.95	0	1
10	.05	9	1

mean 1.45 (for X), mean .45 (for $X^{(c)}$), mean 1 (for $X^{(r)}$)

$\Rightarrow$ $E[S] = \lambda \cdot E[X] = 1.45\lambda$
$E[S^{(r)}] = \lambda \cdot E[X^{(r)}] = 1.00\lambda$

$$\Rightarrow \ E[L_1^{(r)}] = \frac{E[X^{(r)2}]}{2E[X^{(r)}]} = \frac{1}{2(1)}$$

(ii) $$\underbrace{\theta}_{.25} = \underbrace{\frac{E[S^{(r)}]}{E[S]}}_{\frac{\lambda}{1.45\lambda}}\theta^{(r)} + \underbrace{\frac{E[S^{(c)}]}{E[S]}}_{\frac{.45\lambda}{1.45\lambda}}\zeta$$

$$\Rightarrow \theta^{(r)} = .1375$$

(iii) $$E[L^{(r)}] = \frac{1}{\theta^{(r)}} \cdot \frac{E[X^{(r)2}]}{2E[X^{(r)}]} = \frac{1}{(.1375)(2)} = 3.64$$

ANSWER A

34. (i) The Poisson-Inverse Gaussian results from a mixing of a Poisson with an Inverse Gaussian. Suppose $N|_\Lambda$ = Poisson Λ, $\Lambda \sim$ Inv. Gaussian (α, β).
Then $E[N] = E[E[N|\Lambda]] = E[\Lambda] = \frac{\alpha}{\beta}$ (Inv. Gaussian fact) and, since $Var(N|\Lambda) = \Lambda$ (Poisson fact), by the double expectation theorem
$Var(N) = E[Var(N|\Lambda)] + Var(E[N|\Lambda]) = E[\Lambda] + Var(\Lambda) = \frac{\alpha}{\beta} + \frac{\alpha}{\beta^2} = \frac{\alpha}{\beta}\left(1 + \frac{1}{\beta}\right)$
Also,

$$M_N(t) = E[e^{tN}] = E[E[e^{tN}|\Lambda]]$$
$$= E[e^{\Lambda(e^t-1)}] \text{ (Poisson fact)}$$
$$= M_\Lambda(e^t-1) = exp\left(\alpha\left(1 - \sqrt{1-\frac{2(e^t-1)}{\beta}}\right)\right) \text{ (Inv. Gaussian fact)}$$

(ii) If S_n has a Poisson Inverse Gaussian distribution with mean λ, variance $\lambda\left(1+\frac{1}{\beta_n}\right)$ and $\beta_n \to \infty$, one way to accomplish this (see above (i)) is to let $\beta_n = n$, $\lambda = \frac{\alpha_n}{\beta_n}$ or $\alpha_n = \lambda n$. With this assumption

$$M_{S_n}(t) = exp\left(\underbrace{n\lambda}_{\substack{\downarrow \\ \infty \\ \text{as } n\to\infty}} \underbrace{\left(1-\sqrt{1-\frac{2(e^t-1)}{n}}\right)}_{\substack{\downarrow \\ 0 \\ \text{as } n\to\infty}}\right).$$

(iii) To find $\lim\limits_{n\to\infty} M_{S_n}(t) = exp\left(\lim\limits_{n\to\infty} n\lambda\left(1-\sqrt{1-\frac{2(e^t-1)}{n}}\right)\right)$ first use Hopital's rule to obtain

$$\lim_{n\to\infty}(\text{inside above}) = \lambda \cdot \lim_{n\to\infty} \frac{1-\sqrt{1-\frac{2(e^t-1)}{n}}}{\frac{1}{n}}$$

$$= \lambda \cdot \lim_{n\to\infty} \frac{-\frac{1}{2}\left(1-\frac{2(e^t-1)}{n}\right)^{-1/2} \cdot \frac{2(e^t-1)}{n^2}}{\left(-\frac{1}{n^2}\right)}$$

$$= \lambda \cdot \lim_{n\to\infty}\left(1-\frac{2(e^t-1)}{n}\right)^{-1/2}(e^t-1)$$

$$= \lambda(e^t-1)\cdot 1^{-1/2} = \lambda(e^t-1)$$

Thus $\lim\limits_{n\to\infty} M_{S_n}(t) = exp(\lambda(e^t-1))$, the generating function of a Poisson-λ distribution.

ANSWER B

35. For the inverse Gaussian with $\alpha = 1, \beta = .02$ the adjustment coefficient does not exist if

$$1 + (1{+}\theta)E[X]t = M_X(t)$$

has no positive solution. Now $M_X(t) = exp\left(\alpha\left(1 - \sqrt{1-\frac{2t}{\beta}}\right)\right)$ if $t < \frac{\beta}{2}$ (diverges otherwise), so the equation has no solution if the following picture illustrates the relation between the left and right sides of the equation above which defines R.

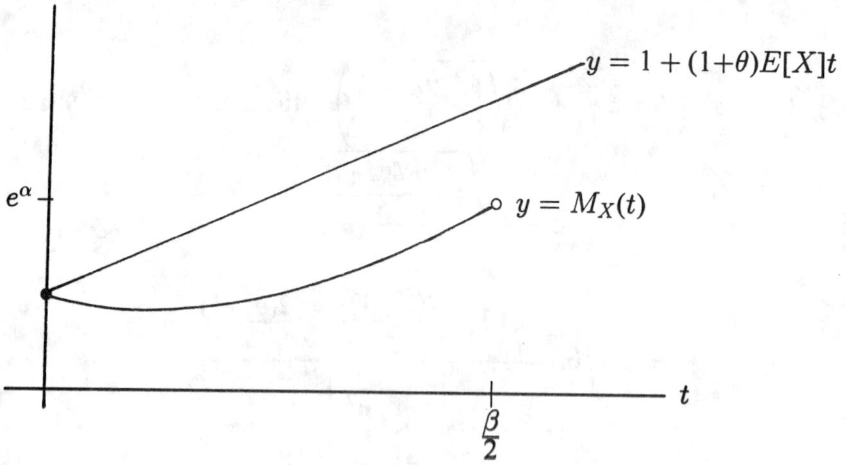

Thus R fails to exist if when we compare these graphs at $t = \frac{\beta}{2}$ the linear graph is higher. R does not exist if

$$1 + (1{+}\theta)E[X]\tfrac{\beta}{2} > exp(\alpha) = \lim_{t\to\frac{\beta}{2}} M_X(t).$$

Equivalently

$$1{+}\theta > \tfrac{2}{\beta}[exp(\alpha) - 1]\frac{1}{E[X]} = \frac{2}{.02}[e - 1]\frac{1}{(1/.02)} = 3.44$$

or

$$\psi(0) = \frac{1}{1{+}\theta} < \frac{1}{3.44} = .291.$$

In the set $\{.10, .20, .30, .40\}$ there are two $\psi(0)$ values satisfying this inequality. ANSWER C

SECTION V

SIMULATION

INTRODUCTORY NOTE

This section of the manual contains one unit, simulation, containing a package of five items:

(1) ***Introductory Notes.*** While not as complete as many textbooks, it is designed to cover all the learning objectives set forth in the SOA - Working Group Report on Course 3.

(2) ***Condensed Review Notes and Advanced Topics.*** These notes constitute a list of the major relations with additional comments on more exotic topics. They should be useful as a reference when solving the Unit Review Questions, and as a final checklist of facts you should be familiar with for the exam.

(3) ***Conceptual Review Test.*** This material should be used in conjunction with reading and rereading the Introductory notes.

(4) ***Computational Review Test.*** These questions are more elementary than the Unit Review Questions and emphasize very basic calculations related to the unit reading.

(5) ***Unit Review Questions.*** No relevant questions from old SOA exams are available. The following questions were constructed by the author, some as imitations of questions from the Course 3 Sample Exam.

UNIT 1: SIMULATION

Introduction

Many stochastic models are sufficiently complex that an exact description of various "state variables" is impossible. By electronically simulating the operation of a stochastic model one can generate data to formulate and test hypotheses or to estimate distributions or model parameters. For example, if $N(t)$ is the number of claims occurring in the time interval $[0, t]$ for a Poisson process with parameter λ, it is difficult to precisely calculate things such as:

(i) the distribution of $S(t)$, aggregate claims over $[0, t]$;

(ii) the distribution of $U(t) = u + ct - S(t)$, surplus at time t ($u =$ initial surplus, premium equal c/year paid continuously);

(iii) $\psi(u, t)$, the probability of ruin by time t; and

(iv) $\psi(u)$, the probability of ruin.

Recent advances in computers have made it possible to do large scale, rapid, and inexpensive simulations resulting in increased understanding of highly complex stochastic processes.

Random Numbers

Suppose $U_1, U_2, \ldots, U_n$ are independent and identically distributed random variables which are uniform on the interval $[0, 1)$. Then $U_1 = u_1, \ldots, U_n = u_n$ are said to be **random numbers**. These numbers are an essential component of simulating a random sample $Y_1 = y_1, \ldots, Y_m = y_m$ from some other random variable Y (i.e., $Y_1, \ldots, Y_m$ are independent and identically distributed like Y). Actually, **pseudo-random numbers** are most often used in place of random numbers since computers can generate them rapidly and inexpensively by procedures such as the multiplicative congruential method or the mixed multiplicative congruential method.

Pseudo-random numbers are deterministically generated from a **seed** (beginning value) **number** but have all the appearances of being independent and uniformly distributed on $[0, 1)$. In the multiplicative congruential method one begins with integers $a < m$ and a seed x_0. One next generates x_1 as the remainder when ax_0 is divided by m (notation: $ax_0 \equiv x_1 \bmod(m)$). One says the ax_0 is **congruent to x_1 modulo m**. Similarly x_2 is the remainder when ax_1 is divided by m and so on. Recursively, x_{n+1} is the remainder when ax_n is divided by m. The sequence $x_1, x_2, \ldots$ is then divided by m to produce the uniform pseudo-random numbers $u_1 = \frac{x_1}{m}, u_2 = \frac{x_2}{m}, \ldots$. With the proper selection of a and m these uniform pseudo-random numbers have the appearance of being a random sample from $U[0, 1)$ (the uniform distribution on $[0, 1)$). For a 32-bit word computer it has been shown that

$m = 2^{32-1}$ (a large prime) and $a = 7^5$ result in the sequence $\frac{x_1}{m}, \frac{x_2}{m}, \ldots$ closely resembling a $U[0,1)$ sample. The uniform pseudo-random numbers used in examples in the unit were generated from a TI-85 calculator using a multiplicative congruential method.

In simulating a sample from a distribution $F_Y(y)$ one begins with uniform pseudo-random numbers $u_1 = \frac{x_1}{m}$, $u_2 = \frac{x_2}{m}$, ... and then **transforms** them into Y-values. This transformation is relatively simple to describe for discrete random variables, though efficiency can be a concern since "searching" is often involved in the transformation. For continuous variables where both $F_Y(y)$ and its inverse function have closed form expressions, the transformation is efficient. If this is not the case one needs a bag of tricks to supplant the inverse transformation method. We begin with the simulation of discrete random variables.

Simulation of Discrete Random Variables: A General Method

Suppose Y is a discrete random variable with possible values $y_1 < y_2 < \ldots$ where $f_Y(y_i) = p_i$ and $1 = p_1 + p_2 + \cdots$. The distribution function is a step function:

$$F_Y(y) = \begin{cases} 0 & y < y_1 \\ p_1 & y_1 \le y < y_2 \\ p_1 + p_2 & y_2 \le y < y_3 \\ \cdots & \cdots \end{cases}$$

Suppose U is uniformly distributed on $[0,1)$. Then $Pr\left(\sum_{i=1}^{j-1} p_i \le U < \sum_{i=1}^{j} p_i\right) = p_j$ since $Pr(a \le U < b) = b - a$ if $0 < a < b < 1$. Consider the transformation which takes $U = u$ and assigns to it $Y = y_j$ if $\sum_{i=1}^{j-1} p_i \le u < \sum_{i=1}^{j} p_i$. Then $Pr(Y = y_j) = Pr\left(\sum_{i=1}^{j-1} p_i \le U < \sum_{i=1}^{j} p_i\right) = p_j$. This method is referred to here as the **standard search transformation.** $U = u$ is transformed into the smallest y_j such that $F_Y(y_j)$ exceeds u.

Example 1 Suppose Y is discrete with $f_Y(1) = .20$, $f_Y(2) = .40$, $f_Y(3) = .30$, and $f_Y(4) = .10$. Simulate a sample of size 10 from the Y distribution.

Solution Using the process outlined above, the transformation can be described by the table below:

U interval	Corresponding Y value
$[0, .20)$	1
$[.20, .60)$	2
$[.60, .90)$	3
$[.90, 1)$	4

The following ten uniform pseudo-random numbers (rounded to three places) were generated on a TI-85 calculator: .451, .989, .698, .544, .638, .930, .674, .798, .552, .338. These $U_1, U_2, \ldots, U_{10}$ values are then transformed to $Y_1, \ldots, Y_{10}$ values 2, 4, 3, 2, 3, 4, 3, 3, 2, 2. Each time we transform a U value we need to search to discover which U interval the observation falls in. □

Because of the searching that takes place it can make sense to order the p_j in decreasing size rather than using the y_j in increasing order. For example, in Example 1 above it might take fewer searches to transform the U values if we used the following rule:

U interval	Corresponding Y value
$[0, .40)$	2
$[.40, .70)$	3
$[.70, .90)$	1
$[.90, 1)$	4

If you search for the proper interval this way 70% of the transformations would be expected to require 2 or fewer searches, whereas with the assignment in Example 1 60% of the transformations would be expected to require 2 or fewer searches. This may seem like a minor improvement but this technique can save big chunks of time if there are many Y values with very small probabilities and you desire a large sample. Algorithms which minimize the expected number of searches are quite valuable tools. It is sometimes possible to improve on the standard search transformation by lowering the expected number of searches. Occasionally a functional transformation is possible.

Simulating a Discrete Uniform Variable

Suppose we desire a sample from a variable Y where $Pr(Y = i) = \frac{1}{n}$ for $i = 1, 2, \ldots, n$ (a **discrete uniform distribution** where the values 1, 2, …, n are "equally likely"). Using the method described prior to Example 1 we see that a U value in $\left[\frac{j-1}{n}, \frac{j}{n}\right)$ gets transformed into $Y = j$. This transformation can be described functionally as $Y = [nU] + 1$, where [ ] is the **greatest integer function**. This works more efficiently than searching and follows from

$$\tfrac{j-1}{n} \le U < \tfrac{j}{n} \quad \Leftrightarrow \quad j-1 \le nU < j \quad \Leftrightarrow \quad [nU] + 1 = j.$$

This method can be used in the process of randomly selecting a subset of size m from a set of size $n > m$ in such a way that each m element subset has the same chance of being selected (i.e., $\frac{1}{\binom{n}{m}}$).

Suppose we wish to randomly select a 3-element subset of a 10-element set. Number the objects in the set 1, 2, …, 10, and form the permutation (1, 2, …, 10).

Step 1:	Set $n = 10$
Step 2:	Generate a uniform pseudo-random number $U = u$ and let $Y = [nU] + 1$.
Step 3:	Interchange the elements in the Yth and n^{th} positions. Stop when 3 interchanges have been performed.
Step 4:	Reset n to $n-1$ and return to Step 2.

Using pseudo-random numbers .219, .622, .871 would result in the following calculations:

interchange

$$n = 10, \quad y = [10(.219)] + 1 = 3, \quad (1, 2, \overset{\downarrow}{3}, 4, 5, 6, 7, 8, 9, \overset{\downarrow}{10}) \quad \rightarrow \quad (1, 2, 10, 4, 5, 6, 7, 8, 9, 3)$$

$$n = 9, \quad y = [9(.622)] + 1 = 6, \quad (1, 2, 10, 4, 5, \overset{\downarrow}{6}, 7, 8, \overset{\downarrow}{9}, 3) \quad \rightarrow \quad (1, 2, 10, 4, 5, 9, 7, 8, 6, 3)$$

$$n = 8, \quad y = [8(.871)] + 1 = 7, \quad (1, 2, 10, 4, 5, 9, \overset{\downarrow}{7}, \overset{\downarrow}{8}, 6, 3) \quad \rightarrow \quad (1, 2, 10, 4, 5, 9, 8, 7, 6, 3)$$

Our random 3-element subset now consists of the last 3 entries of the final permutation {7, 6, 3}. If we had desired a random 7-element subset it would be more efficient to randomly select a 3-element subset to throw away than to do 7 operations as above. This type of selection is always employed in a double-blind clinical trial where a randomly selected subgroup is given a "treatment" while the remainder receives a placebo.

Simulating a Geometric Random Variable

Let Y be the number of the trial in a sequence of Bernoulli trials which results in the first success. Then $Y = 1, 2, \ldots$ and $f_Y(y) = q^{y-1}p$. $F_Y(y) = p + qp + \cdots + q^{y-1}p = p \cdot \dfrac{1-q^y}{1-q} = 1 - q^y$, so $Pr(1 - q^{y-1} \le U < 1 - q^y) = q^{y-1} - q^y = q^{y-1} \cdot p$. If $U = u$ is in the interval $[1 - q^{y-1}, 1 - q^y)$ we transform u to $Y = y$. Now

$$Y = y \quad \Leftrightarrow \quad 1 - q^{y-1} \le u < 1 - q^y$$

$$\Leftrightarrow \quad q^{y-1} \ge 1 - u > q^y$$

$$\Leftrightarrow \quad (y-1)ln(q) \ge ln(1-u) > y\,ln(q) \qquad (ln(q) \text{ is an increasing function of } q),$$

so $$Y = min\{y | y\,ln(q) < ln(1-U)\}$$

$$= min\left\{y | y > \frac{ln(1-U)}{ln(q)}\right\} \qquad (ln(q) < 0))$$

$$= \left[\frac{ln(1-U)}{ln(q)}\right] + 1 \qquad \text{(since } y \text{ is an integer).}$$

We have seen that if U is uniform on $[0, 1)$, then $Y = \left[\frac{ln(1-U)}{ln(q)}\right] + 1$ is geometric with parameter $p = 1 - q$. A slight increase in efficiency is achieved in replacing $1 - U$ by U. This is allowable since $1 - U$ is also uniform on $[0, 1)$. Once again a functional transformation has replaced a searching process.

Example 2 Suppose Y is Geometric with parameter $p = .40$. Simulate a sample of size 5.

Solution The following 5 pseudo-random numbers were generated on a TI-85 calculator: .124, .450, .467, .286, .817. The corresponding Y values are listed in the table below:

U	.124	.450	.467	.286	.817
$Y = \left[\frac{ln(U)}{ln(q)}\right] + 1$	5	2	2	3	1

□

Simulating a Poisson Random Variable

Y has a Poisson λ distribution if $f_Y(y) = e^{-\lambda} \cdot \frac{\lambda^y}{y!}$ for $y = 0, 1, 2, \ldots$. The standard search transformation of U to Y described earlier is very time-consuming here because there are infinitely many possible y values with most having rather minute probability. The number of searches is one more than the value of Y which is produced since you successively test $Y = 0$, $Y = 1$, ... Hence the expected number of searches is $\lambda+1$, which can be time-consuming if λ is large. In the searching process it is efficient to calculate $Pr(Y = y)$ recursively. Since

$$\frac{Pr(Y = y)}{Pr(Y = y - 1)} = \frac{e^{-\lambda}\lambda^y/y!}{e^{-\lambda}\lambda^{y-1}/(y-1)!} = \frac{\lambda}{y},$$

the first step in this recursion is $Pr(Y = 0) = e^{-\lambda}$ and the recursion relation is $Pr(Y = y) = \frac{\lambda}{y} Pr(Y = y - 1)$. The following flow chart describes the standard search transformation from a uniform $[0, 1)$ variable to a Poisson λ variable, Y. In the algorithm we need to keep track of y, $p = f_Y(y)$, and $F = F_Y(y)$. The notation $y + 1 \rightarrow y$ means to increase the y value by one. Similarly $p \cdot \frac{\lambda}{y} \rightarrow p$ means to reset p to the next value of $f_Y(y)$.

Poisson Simulation Flow Chart

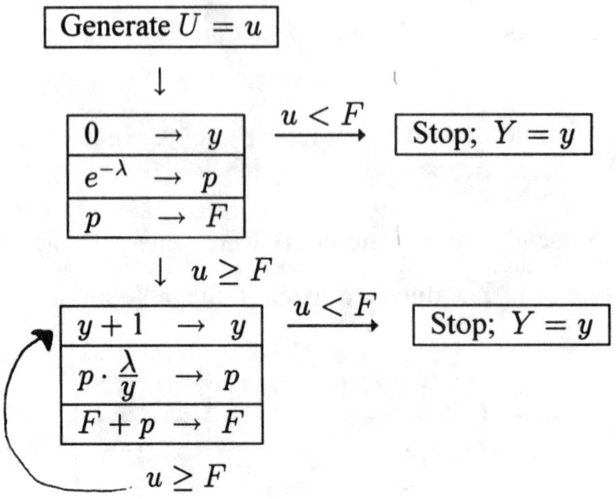

Example 3 With $\lambda = 3$ and $U = .628$ illustrate the above algorithm transforming U into Y having the Poisson $\lambda = 3$ distribution.

Solution

$0 = y$
$.050 = p$
$.050 = F$

$.05 = f_Y(0),\ .05 = F_Y(0)$

$\downarrow\ U = .628 \geq F$

$1 = y$
$.149 = p$
$.199 = F$

$.149 = f_Y(1),\ .199 = F_Y(1) = F_Y(0) + f_Y(1)$

$\downarrow\ U = .628 \geq F$

$2 = y$
$.224 = p$
$.423 = F$

$\downarrow\ U = .628 \geq F$

$3 = y$
$.224 = p$
$.647 = F$

$\xrightarrow{u < F}$ Stop; $Y = 3$

Note: (1) In generating subsequent Y values we would not need to recompute $F_Y(0), \ldots, F_Y(3)$

(2) For large λ this search can take an enormous amount of time. If $\lambda = 24.6$ we might first compute $f_Y(0), \ldots, f_Y(25)$ and then compute $F_Y(23)$, $F_Y(24)$, $F_Y(25)$. The highest probabilities are $f_Y(24)$ and $f_Y(25)$ (i.e., $f_Y([\lambda])$, $f_Y([\lambda]+1)$). If $U < F_Y(24)$ we could test $y = 24$ and begin searching downward. If $U \geq F_Y(24)$ we could test $y = 25$ and begin searching upward. This technique would lower the expected number of searches

from $\lambda+1$ with the standard search transformation method beginning with smallest y values to about $1+.8\sqrt{\lambda}$.

(3) The flow chart in the solution above replicates the algorithm. The following table was produced with a TI-85 by initially setting $0=y$, $e^{-3}=p$, $e^{-3}=F$ and then repeatedly executing the statement

$$y+1 \rightarrow y\text{: } 3p \div y \rightarrow p\text{: } p+F \rightarrow F\text{: } [y, p, F].$$

Table (nearest .001)

y	$f_Y(y)$	$F_Y(y)$
0	.050	.050
1	.149	.199
2	.224	.423
3	.224	.647
4	.168	.815
5	.101	.916
6	.050	.966

Simulating a Binomial Random Variable

The number of successes in a series of n Bernoulli trials where p is the probability of success is a Binomial variable Y where $f_Y(y)=\binom{n}{y}p^y(1-p)^{n-y}$ for $y=0, 1, \ldots, n$. Since

$$\frac{f_Y(y)}{f_Y(y-1)}=\frac{n+1-y}{y}\cdot\frac{p}{1-p} \qquad y=1, 2, \ldots$$

values of $f_Y(y)$ could be recursively generated beginning with $f_Y(0)=(1-p)^n$. The standard search transformation algorithm is then nearly identical to the flow chart above for the Poisson distribution. The expected number of searches is $1+np$ (i.e., one more than the expected value of the variable generated).

An alternative method of generating Y values requires n random numbers $u_1, \ldots, u_n$ and comparisons of each to p. Y is the number of the u_i which are less than p. The description is simpler but more random numbers and comparisons are required than with the standard search transformation algorithm.

Simulation of Continuous Random Variables via the Inverse Function of the Distribution Function

Suppose Y is a continuous random variable whose density function is non-zero on the interval I (the **support**). Then $F_Y(y)$ is continuous and increasing on I and hence has an inverse. If U is uniformly distributed on $[0, 1)$ the following shows that $F_Y^{-1}(U)$ has the same distribution as Y:

$$Pr(F_Y^{-1}(U) \leq y) = Pr(F_Y(F_Y^{-1}(U)) \leq F_Y(y) = Pr(U \leq F_Y(y)) = F_Y(y)$$

since $Pr(a < U \leq b) = b - a$ if $(a, b] \subset [0, 1]$. In cases where both $F_Y(y)$ and its inverse have closed form expressions this observation provides a simple way to transform random numbers $U_1 = u_1, \ldots, U_n = u_n$ into a sample $y_1 = F_Y^{-1}(u_1), \ldots, y_n = F_Y^{-1}(u_n)$ from Y.

If Y is exponentially distributed with parameter λ, $f_Y(y) = \lambda \cdot e^{-\lambda y}$ for y in $I = (0, \infty)$. It easily follows that $F_Y(y) = 1 - e^{-\lambda y}$. If $u = F_Y(y)$ then $y = F_Y^{-1}(u) = -\frac{1}{\lambda} ln(1 - u)$. In other words, if U is $U[0, 1)$ then $-\frac{1}{\lambda} ln(1 - U)$ is exponential with parameter λ. Since $1 - U$ is also $U[0, 1)$, a slightly more efficient transformation is $-\frac{1}{\lambda} ln(U)$.

Although the distribution function of a gamma distribution with parameters $\alpha = n$ (an integer) and λ (i.e., $f(y) = \frac{\lambda^\alpha}{\Gamma(\alpha)} y^{\alpha-1} e^{-\lambda y}$) does not exist in a closed form expression, the preceding idea for generating exponential distributions can be used to generate observations from the gamma distribution with α integral. If $Y_1, \ldots, Y_n$ are independent and identically distributed exponentials with the same parameter λ, then $\sum_{i=1}^{n} Y_i$ is Gamma with parameters n and λ. So suppose $U_1, \ldots, U_n$ are independent and identically distributed $U[0, 1)$ variables. Setting $Y_i = -\frac{1}{\lambda} ln(U_i)$ we have

$$Z = \underbrace{Y_1 + \cdots + Y_n}_{\text{gamma}} = \sum_{i=1}^{n} -\frac{1}{\lambda} ln(U_i) = -\frac{1}{\lambda} ln(U_1 U_2 \cdots U_n)$$

is a Gamma variable.

Example 4 Simulate a sample of size 6 from an exponential distribution with parameter $\lambda = .40$. Use the same data to simulate a sample of size 3 from a Gamma distribution with $\alpha = 2$, $\lambda = .40$.

Solution The following 6 pseudo-random numbers were generated on a TI-85 calculator (rounded to 3 places): .617, .807, .773, .464, .925, .624.

	U_i	.617	.807	.773	.464	.925	.624
(exp.)	$Y_i = -\frac{1}{.40} ln(U)$	1.207	.536	.644	1.920	.195	1.179
(gamma)	$Z = Y_{2i-1} + Y_{2i}$	1.743		2.564		1.374	

□

Recall that in a Poisson process with rate λ the waiting times between successive events, W_i, are independent exponentials with parameter λ. Furthermore, $N(1)$, the number of counted events occurring by time $t = 1$, is Poisson with parameter $\lambda \cdot 1$. Now $\{N(1) = n\}$ is equivalent to the event $\{W_1 + \cdots + W_n \leq 1\} \cap \{W_1 + \cdots + W_{n+1} > 1\}$. Recall that $T_n = W_1 + \cdots + W_n$ is the time of occurrence of the nth event. Thus

$$N(1) = max\{n|T_n \leq 1\} = min\{m|T_m > 1\} - 1.$$

Now if U_1, U_2, ... is a sample from $U[0, 1)$ we know that $W_1 = -\frac{1}{\lambda}ln(U_1)$, $W_2 = -\frac{1}{\lambda}ln(U_2)$, ... is a sample from the Exponential λ distribution. Hence

$$\begin{aligned} N(1) &= min\{m|\sum_{i=1}^{m} -\frac{1}{\lambda}ln(U_i) > 1\} - 1 \\ &= min\{m|ln(U_1 \cdots U_m) < -\lambda\} - 1 \\ &= min\{m|U_1U_2 \cdots U_m < e^{-\lambda}\} - 1. \end{aligned}$$

has a Poisson distribution with parameter λ. This relation offers an alternative way to simulate a Poisson distribution from a sequence of uniform pseudo-random numbers.

Example 5 Generate as many Poisson $\lambda = 2$ observations as possible from a list of 10 pseudo-random numbers.

Solution $e^{-2} = .135$

U_i	.257	.717	.468
$\prod_{j=1}^{i} U_j$	.257	.184	.086

$\Rightarrow \quad N_1 = 3 - 1 = 2$

U_i	.361	.634	.140
$\prod_{j=1}^{i} U_j$	.361	.229	.032

$\Rightarrow \quad N_2 = 3 - 1 = 2$

U_i	.667	.012
$\prod_{j=1}^{i} U_j$	.667	.008

$\Rightarrow \quad N_3 = 2 - 1 = 1$

U_i	.598	.278
$\prod_{j=1}^{i}$	.598	.166

$.166 > e^{-2}$ and 10 pseudo-random numbers have been used.

□

The Rejection Method

Suppose $f(y)$ and $g(y)$ are density functions of continuous random variables having the same support I. Suppose there is a constant k such that $k \cdot g(y) \geq f(y)$ for all y in I. Now $k = \int_I k \cdot g(y)\,dy \geq \int_I f(y)\,dy = 1$ since $\int_I f = \int_I g = 1$. One choice for k would be the least upper bound of $\frac{f(y)}{g(y)}$ on I. If there is a method of generating (i.e., simulating) an observation $Y = y$ from a distribution having density $g(y)$ the **rejection method** uses this value and a random number $U = u$ to either accept y as a value of X or to reject it. A number of repetitions of this process may be required until an X-value is produced. It will be shown that the variable X has density function $f(y)$.

Flow Chart

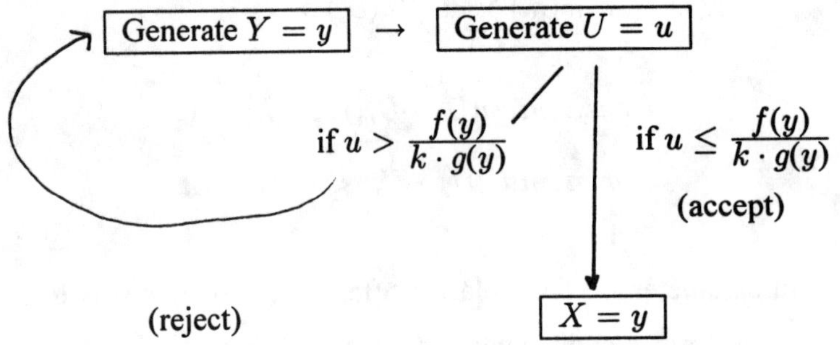

On any iteration of this process the probability that $Y \leq y$ and it is accepted is

$$Pr\left(Y \leq y \text{ and } U \leq \frac{f(Y)}{k \cdot g(Y)}\right) = \int_{s=a}^{y} \int_{t=0}^{f(s)/kg(s)} \underbrace{g(s) \cdot 1}_{\substack{\text{joint density} \\ \text{of } Y,U}} \,dt\,ds$$

$$= \int_{s=a}^{y} g(s)\left[\frac{f(s)}{k \cdot g(s)}\right] ds = \frac{1}{k}\int_{s=a}^{y} f(s)\,ds = \frac{1}{k}F(y),$$

where F is the distribution function corresponding to f and $I = [a, b]$.

On any iteration the probability that the Y value is accepted is $Pr(Y \leq \infty \text{ and } U \leq \frac{f(Y)}{k \cdot g(Y)}) = \frac{1}{k}F(\infty) = \frac{1}{k} \cdot 1$. So the number of iterations required to accept a Y value, N, has a Geometric distribution with parameter $p = \frac{1}{k}$. The expected number of required iterations is thus $E[N] = \frac{1}{p} = k$. Furthermore,

$$Pr(X \le y) = \sum_{n=1}^{\infty} Pr(N = n \text{ and } Y_n \le y)$$

$$= \sum_{n=1}^{\infty} \underbrace{\left(1 - \frac{1}{k}\right)^{n-1}}_{(n-1)\text{ rejections}} Pr\left(Y_n \le y \text{ and } U \le \frac{f(Y_n)}{k \cdot g(Y_n)}\right)$$

$$= \sum_{n=1}^{\infty} \left(1 - \tfrac{1}{k}\right)^{n-1} \left(F(y)\tfrac{1}{k}\right) = F(y) \underbrace{\sum_{n=1}^{\infty} \left(1 - \tfrac{1}{k}\right)^{n-1} \cdot \tfrac{1}{k}}_{=1;\text{ geometric series}} = F(y).$$

Now suppose one wanted to simulate values from a standard normal distribution. If N is standard normal, then $X = |N|$ has density $f(y) = 2 \cdot \frac{1}{\sqrt{2\pi}} e^{-y^2/2}$ for $0 \le y < \infty$. If one simulated values of X they could be multiplied by randomly chosen, equally likely $\pm$ 1's to obtain values from N. The rejection method with $g(y) = e^{-y}$ (exponential with parameter 1) works reasonably well since it is easy to find k with

$$k \ge \frac{f(y)}{g(y)} = \frac{\frac{2}{\sqrt{2\pi}} e^{-y^2/2}}{e^{-y}} = \frac{2}{\sqrt{2\pi}} e^{y - y^2/2}$$

for $y \ge 0$. The maximum $y - \frac{y^2}{2}$ value occurs when $y = 1$ and is $\frac{1}{2}$. Thus $k = \frac{2}{\sqrt{2\pi}} e^{.5} = 1.315$ and the expected number of iterations required, k, is small. Furthermore, we have seen that $-\frac{1}{\lambda} ln(U)$ is exponential with parameter λ if U is $U[0, 1)$.

For each iteration of the rejection method we need random numbers U_1, U_2:

1. $Y = -ln(U_1)$
2. If $U_2 \le \frac{f(Y)}{k \cdot g(Y)} = \frac{2}{1.315\sqrt{2\pi}} e^{Y - Y^2/2} = .607 e^{Y - Y^2/2}$ then $X = -ln(U_1) = Y$ is accepted.

Example 6 Use 8 pairs of pseudo-random numbers to generate as many values as possible from the $|N(0, 1)|$ distribution via the rejection method described above.

Solution

U_1	$Y = -ln(U_1)$	U_2	$.607e^{Y-Y^2/2}$	X
.921	.083	.836	.657	(reject)
.255	1.366	.726	.936	1.365
.247	1.400	.101	.924	1.400
.731	.313	.222	.791	.313
.594	.521	.820	.892	.521
.934	.068	.492	.648	.068
.095	2.357	.402	.399	(reject)
.646	.438	.352	.854	.438

□

Simulation of a Poisson Process

Suppose $\{N(t)|t \geq 0\}$ is a Poisson-process with rate λ. Hence $N(t)$ is Poisson with parameter λt. The waiting times between occurrences of the events being counted, $W_1, W_2, \ldots,$ are independent exponentials with parameter λ. The time of occurrence of the nth event, $T_n = W_1 + \cdots + W_n$, is a Gamma distribution with parameters $\alpha = n, \lambda$. With random numbers $U_1, U_2, \ldots$ we can simulate waiting times $W_1 = -\frac{1}{\lambda} ln(U_1)$, $W_2 = -\frac{1}{\lambda} ln(U_2)$, ... and event occurrence times $T_1 = W_1 = -\frac{1}{\lambda} ln(U_1)$, $T_2 = W_1 + W_2 = -\frac{1}{\lambda} ln(U_1 U_2)$, ... These ideas could be used to simulate the first t_0 units of time in a Poisson process:

$$N(t_0) = min\{n|T_n > t_0\} - 1 = n(t_0)$$

Occurrence times are $T_1 < T_2 < \cdots < T_{n(t_0)}$

Simulation of a Non-Homogeneous Poisson Process

Suppose $\{N(t)|t \geq 0\}$ is a non-homogeneous Poisson-process with intensity function $\lambda(t)$. Then if $m(t) = \int_0^t \lambda(s)\,ds$ we know that the process increment $N(t+s) - N(s)$ is Poisson with parameter $m(t+s) - m(s)$. Suppose one desires to simulate the first t_0 time units of this process. If $\lambda(t) \leq \lambda$ for all $t \leq t_0$ this can be accomplished by simulating a Poisson process with rate λ and accepting events that occur at time t if a random number U is less than or equal to $\frac{\lambda(t)}{\lambda}$. This method is called the **thinning method.**

Example 7 Use the thinning method to generate the first 4 time units of a non-homogenous Poisson process with $\lambda(t) = 1 + .05t$.

Solution For $t \leq 4$, $\lambda(t) = 1 + .05t \leq 1 + .05(4) = 1.2$. So we first must generate a Poisson $\lambda = 1.2$ process on the time interval $[0, 4]$:

U_i	.815	.729	.020	.389
$W_i = -ln(U_i)/1.2$	.171	.263	3.260	.788
$T_i = \sum_{j=1}^{i} W_j$	.171	.434	3.694	4.470
$\frac{\lambda(T_i)}{1.2}$	.840	.851	.987	

Since $T_4 = 4.470 > 4$ we have 3 events occurring in $[0, 4]$ at times $T_1 = .171$, $T_2 = .434$ and $T_3 = 3.694$. We next generate random numbers V_1, V_2, V_3 and accept the event at time T_i if $V_i \leq \frac{\lambda(T_i)}{1.2}$.

T_i	.171	.434	3.682
$\frac{\lambda(T_i)}{1.2}$	.840	.851	.987
V_i	.367	.933	.187
Decision	Accept	Reject	Accept

Thus for the non-homogeneous process we have simulated $N(4) = 2$ with occurrence times of .171 and 3.694. □

Simulation of a Compound Poisson Surplus Process

Suppose the aggregate claim amount over $[0, t]$ is $S(t) = X_1 + \cdots + X_{N(t)}$ where $\{N(t)|t \geq 0\}$ is a Poisson process with rate λ and discrete claim amount model X. If initial surplus is u and c/year in premium arrives continuously, then

$$U(t) = u + ct - S(t)$$

is the surplus at time t. Recall from Unit Four of Section IV of this manual that $\psi(u)$ is the probability of ruin with initial capital u. Also $\psi(u) = \lim_{t \to \infty} \psi(u, t)$ where $\psi(u, t)$ is the probability that ruin occurs by time t. Closed form expressions for $\psi(u)$ and $\psi(u, t)$ are difficult to come by. But for any t_0 we could repeatedly simulate the interval $[0, t_0]$ of the surplus process and estimate $\psi(u, t_0)$ by the relative frequency with which ruin occurs.

The steps are as follows:

1. From random numbers U_1, U_1, ... generate claim occurrence times $T_1 = -\frac{1}{\lambda} ln(U_1)$, $T_2 = -\frac{1}{\lambda} ln(U_1) - \frac{1}{\lambda} ln(U_2) = -\frac{1}{\lambda} ln(U_1 U_2)$, ... until you exceed t_0. Suppose $T_n \leq t_0$ and $T_{n+1} > t_0$.
2. From random numbers V_1, V_2, ..., V_n generate claim amounts X_1, X_2, ..., X_n at times $T_1, \ldots, T_n$ by the standard search transformation and then calculate $S(T_j) = X_1 + \cdots + X_j$.
3. Compare $S(T_j)$ to $u + cT_j$ to see if ruin occurs by time T_j for $j = 1, 2, \ldots, n$.
4. Repeat steps 1-3 and estimate $\psi(u, t_0)$ by the relative frequency with which ruin occurred during the simulations over $[0, t_0]$.

Example 8 With $t_0 = 1$, $\lambda = 4$, $f_X(1) = .70$, $f_X(2) = .30$, $u = 1$, and $c = 6$, simulate the time interval $[0, 1]$ of a compound-Poisson surplus process.

Solution

Step 1: Simulate claim occurrence times until the times exceed 1.

U_i	.235	.784	.451	.331	.718	.730
$T_i = -\frac{1}{4}ln(U_1 \cdots U_i)$	.362	.423	.622	.898	.981	$\underbrace{1.060}_{\text{too big}}$

We have generated 5 claim occurrence times in [0, 1].

Step 2: Simulate 5 claim amounts from X using the standard search transformation. Recall $f_X(1) = .70$, $f_X(2) = .30$.

V-Interval	X-Value
$[0, .70)$	1
$[.70, 1)$	2

V_i	.132	.377	.897	.583	.567
X_i	1	1	2	1	1
$S(T_i)$	1	2	4	5	6

Step 3: Compare $S(T_i)$ to $u + cT_i = 1 + 6T_i$

T_i	.362	.423	.622	.898	.981
$S(T_i)$	1	2	4	5	6
$U(T_i) = 1 + 6T_i$	3.172	3.538	4.732	6.388	6.886

For this simulation over [0, 1] ruin did not occur by $t = 1$ since $U(T_i) > S(T_i)$ for all $T_i \leq 1$.

Step 4: After repeating steps 1-3, twenty times, suppose one observed ruin on 3 occasions. Then $\psi(1, 1)$ would be estimated as the relative frequency $\frac{3}{20}$. □

CONDENSED REVIEW NOTES AND ADVANCED TOPICS

Random and Pseudo-Random Numbers

If $U_1, \ldots, U_n$ are independent and uniformly distributed on $[0, 1)$ then $U_1 = u_1, U_2 = u_2, \ldots, U_n = u_n$ are called **random numbers**. Pseudo-random numbers are generated deterministically but have the appearance of being a $U[0, 1)$ random sample.

1. Multiplicative Congruential Method.
   Beginning with integers $a < m$ and a **seed** x_0 one recursively calculates x_{n+1} as the remainder when ax_n is divided by m (notation: $ax_n \equiv x_{n+1} \text{ mod}(m)$). Then $u_1 = \frac{x_1}{m}$, $u_2 = \frac{x_2}{m}$, ..., $u_n = \frac{x_n}{m}$ are called pseudo-random numbers. For choices such as $m = 2^{32} - 1$ (a large prime) and $a = 7^5$ the pseudo random numbers above appear to be a $U[0, 1)$ sample.
2. Mixed Congruential Method
   Here x_{n+1} is calculated as the remainder when ax_n+b is divided by m ($ax_n+b \equiv x_{n+1}\text{mod}(m)$).

A Standard Search Algorithm for Simulation of a Discrete Random Variable

Suppose Y has values $y_1 < y_2 < \cdots$ where $Pr(Y = y_i) = p_i > 0$ and $\sum_i p_i = 1$. Then $F_Y(y_i) = p_1 + p_2 + \cdots + p_i$. A random (or pseudo-random) number $U = u$ is transformed to y_i if u belongs to $[p_1 + \cdots + p_{i-1},\ p_1 + \cdots + p_i)$, that is, y_i is the smallest y_i value such that $F_Y(y_i) > u$. In effect, one must search for the interval $[F_Y(y_{i-1}),\ F_Y(y_i))$ to which $U = u$ belongs. If possible Y values are 0, 1, 2, ... the expected number of searches is $E[Y] + 1$, one more than the expected value of the Y produced. To improve efficiency (i.e., reduce the expected number of searches) one might order the p_i in decreasing size rather than use the standard search based on the y_i in increasing order. (See the discussion after Example 1.) Occasionally the search can be replaced by a functional transformation. (See Discrete Uniform and Geometric Simulation to follow.)

Simulating a Discrete Uniform (Equally Likely) Model

$Y = 1, 2, \ldots, n$ and $Pr(Y = i) = \frac{1}{n}$ for all $i = 1, \ldots, n$. The standard search transformation can be expressed functionally as

$$Y = [nU] + 1$$

where [ ] means greatest integer.

Simulating a Geometric Model

Let $Y = 1, 2, \ldots$ and $f_Y(y) = q^{y-1}p$ $(q = 1 - p)$. Y is the number of the trial on which the first success occurs in a sequence of Bernoulli trials. The standard search transformation can be expressed functionally as

$$Y = \left[\frac{ln(1-U)}{ln(q)}\right] + 1 \qquad \text{(greatest integer)}$$

Note: (i) If U is $U[0, 1)$ so is $1 - U$. A slight improvement in efficiency is obtained by using $Y = \left[\frac{ln(U)}{ln(q)}\right] + 1$.

(ii) For some authors a variable X is Geometric if it is the **number of failures** before the first success. $X = Y - 1$ here, so one could simulate X by $X = \left[\frac{ln(U)}{ln(q)}\right]$.

Simulating a Poisson Model

The standard search algorithm is more time-consuming since there are infinitely many possible Y values, most having minute probabilities (that a computer may not be able to distinguish from zero). Also, since $f_Y(y) = e^{-\lambda} \cdot \frac{\lambda^y}{y!}$ involves both a yth power and y factorial, calculating $f_Y(0)$, $f_Y(1)$, $f_Y(2) \ldots$ involves redundancy that may be eliminated by working recursively:

$$f_Y(0) = e^{-\lambda}, f_Y(y) = \frac{\lambda}{y} \cdot f_Y(y-1).$$

Since $U = u$ is transformed into the smallest y such that $F_Y(y) > u$, it also makes sense to recursively compute f_Y and F_Y at the same time:

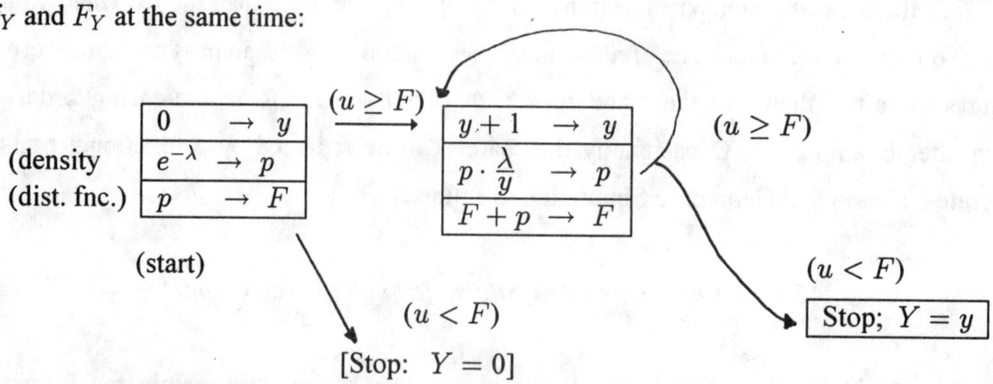

Simulating a Binomial Model

1. Standard Search Transformation. Use the same recursive pattern as with the Poisson above, but recursively generate $f_Y(k) = \binom{n}{k} p^k (q)^{n-k}$ for $k = 0, 1, \ldots, n$ by:

$$f_Y(0) = q^n, \quad f_Y(y) = \frac{n+1-y}{y} \cdot \frac{p}{q} \cdot f_Y(y-1).$$

2. Alternative simulation method requiring more random numbers and comparisons per Y value simulated:

Generate $U_1 = u_1, \ldots, U_m = u_m$ and set Y equal to the number of u_i which are less than p.

Simulating Continuous Random Variables Via the Inverse Function of the Distribution Function

If Y is a continuous random variable with support on the interval I, then $F_Y(y)$ is Uniform $[0, 1)$. Hence if U is Uniform on $[0, 1)$ then $F_Y^{-1}(U)$ has the same distribution as Y.

1. If Y is exponential with parameter λ, then $F_Y(y) = 1 - e^{-\lambda y}$. If $u = 1 - e^{-\lambda y}$ then $y = -\frac{1}{\lambda} ln(1-u) = F_Y^{-1}(u)$. Hence if U is $U[0, 1)$, then $Y = -\frac{1}{\lambda} ln(1-U)$ is exponential with parameter λ. $1 - U$ is also $U[0, 1)$ so it is slightly more efficient to use $Y = -\frac{1}{\lambda} ln(U)$.

2. A gamma distribution with $\alpha = n$ (positive integer) and $\beta = \lambda$ is a sum $Y_1 + \cdots + Y_n$ where the Y_i are independent and identically distributed Exponentials with parameter λ. So if $U_1, \ldots, U_n$ are independent $U[0, 1)$ variables, $\sum_{i=1}^{n} -\frac{1}{\lambda} ln(U_i) = -\frac{1}{\lambda} ln[U_1 \cdots U_n]$ is Gamma with $\alpha = n$, $\beta = \lambda$.

3. Suppose $f_Y(y) = \frac{\alpha y_0^\alpha}{y^{\alpha+1}}$ for $y \geq y_0$ (Pareto distribution). Then $F_Y(y) = 1 - \left(\frac{y_0}{y}\right)^\alpha$ for $y_0 \leq y$. If $u = 1 - \left(\frac{y_0}{y}\right)^\alpha$, then $y = \frac{y_0}{(1-U)^{1/\alpha}}$. Hence if U is $U[0, 1)$, $Y = \frac{y_0}{(1-U)^{1/\alpha}}$ is Pareto. Once again one can use $1 - U$ is $U[0, 1)$ to also conclude that $Y = \frac{y_0}{U^{1/\alpha}} = y_0 U^{-1/\alpha}$ is Pareto.

The Rejection Method

Suppose $f(y)$ and $g(y)$ are density functions with the same support I and there is a constant k with $k \cdot g(y) \geq f(y)$ for all y in I. Suppose $h(U)$ has density $g(y)$ if U is $U[0,1)$. Then if U_1, U_2 are independent and $U[0,1)$, let $Y = h(U_1)$ and accept Y as an X value if $U_2 \leq \frac{f(Y)}{k \cdot g(Y)}$. Then X has density function f.

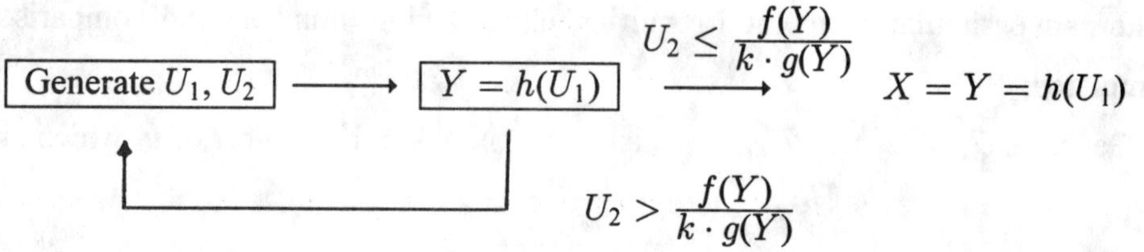

Note: The number of iterations required to accept a Y-value, N, is geometric with expected value equal to k. Thus it is best to choose $g(y)$ with k as small as possible for the sake of efficiency.

Simulating a Poisson Process

Suppose $\{N(t)|t \geq 0\}$ is a Poisson-process with rate λ. If $W_1, W_2, \ldots$, are independent exponentials with parameter λ (i.e., waiting times between counted events), then $T_1 = W_1, T_2 = W_1 + W_2, \cdots$ are the event occurrence times. If U_1, U_2, ... are random numbers, then T_1, T_2, ... can be simulated by $-\frac{1}{\lambda} ln(U_1), -\frac{1}{\lambda} ln(U_1 U_2), \ldots$. Then:

$$\begin{aligned} N(t_0) &= min\{n|T_n > t_0\} - 1 \\ &= min\{n|-\tfrac{1}{\lambda} ln(U_1 \cdots U_n) > t_0\} - 1 \\ &= min\{n|(U_1 \cdots U_n) < e^{-\lambda t_0}\} - 1 \end{aligned}$$

provides a simulation of $N(t_0)$.

Simulating a Non-Homogenous Poisson Process

If $\lambda \geq \lambda(t)$ for all $t \leq t_0$, then the interval $[0, t_0]$ of a non-homogeneous Poisson process with intensity function $\lambda(t)$ can be simulated by the **thinning method**:

1. Generate a Poisson process over $[0, t_0]$ with rate λ
2. Accept the event at time T_i if a random number U_i is $\leq \frac{\lambda(T_i)}{\lambda}$.

CONCEPTUAL REVIEW TEST

1. Explain the standard search transformation for a discrete random variable.

2. Give functional forms of the standard search transformation for the discrete uniform and Geometric distributions.

3. In simulating a Poisson λ variable by the standard search transformation it is best to compute $f_Y(y)$ and $F_Y(y)$ recursively. Why is this? Describe the recursion.

4. How can the distribution function of a continuous random variable be used to simulate the variable?

5. Explain how to simulate an exponential distribution with parameter λ.

6. Describe the rejection method.

CONCEPTUAL REVIEW TEST ANSWERS

1. If $y_1 < y_2 < \ldots$ and $f_Y(y_i) = p_i > 0$, then $Pr(p_1 + \cdots + p_{i-1} \leq Y < p_1 + \cdots + p_i) = p_i$. So if U is $U[0,1)$, transform U into the smallest $Y = y_i$ such that $F_Y(y_i) = p_1 + \cdots + p_i > U$. In other words, if $p_1 + \cdots + p_{i-1} \leq U < p_1 + \cdots + p_i$ transform U into $Y = y_i$.

2. Discrete Uniform: $f_Y(y) = \frac{1}{n}$ for $y = 1,\ 2,\ \ldots,\ n$. A $U = u$ value in $\left[\frac{y-1}{n}, \frac{y}{n}\right)$ gets transformed into $Y = y$. Thus
$\left[\frac{y-1}{n} \leq u < \frac{y}{n}\right) \Leftrightarrow y - 1 \leq nu < y \quad \Leftrightarrow Y = y = [nu] + 1$. In general $Y = [nU] + 1$.
Geometric: $f_Y(y) = q^{y-1}p$ for $y = 1, 2, \ldots$ where $p+q = 1$. Then $F_Y(y) = p + qp + \cdots + q^{y-1}p = 1 - q^y$. Hence a $U = u$ value in $[1 - q^{y-1},\ 1 - q^y)$ gets transformed into $Y = y$. Also $1 - q^{Y-1} \leq U < 1 - q^Y \quad \Leftrightarrow \quad q^{Y-1} \geq 1 - U > q^Y \quad \Leftrightarrow$ $Y - 1 \leq \frac{ln(1-U)}{ln\, q} < Y$. Hence $Y = \left[\frac{ln(1-U)}{ln\, q}\right] + 1$. Since $1 - U$ is $U[0,1)$ it is slightly more efficient to use $Y = \left[\frac{ln(U)}{ln\, q}\right] + 1$.

3. Since $f_Y(y) = e^{-\lambda} \cdot \frac{\lambda^y}{y!}$ it is very inefficient to compute $f_Y(0),\ f_Y(1), \ldots$ which involve powers and factorials, when most of the arithmetic needed for $f_Y(y)$ has already been done in the $f_Y(y-1)$ calculation. The $f_Y(y)$ values can be computed recursively from $\frac{f_Y(y)}{f_Y(y-1)} = \frac{\lambda}{y}$ beginning with $f_Y(0) = e^{-\lambda}$.

Flow Chart

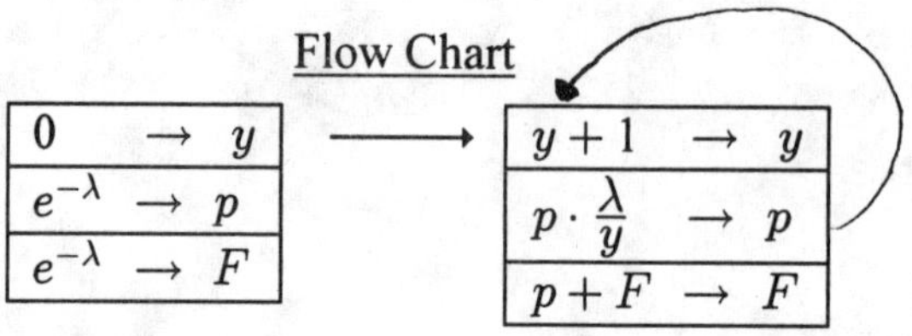

4. $F_Y(Y)$ is $U[0,1)$, so $F_Y^{-1}(U)$ has the same distribution as Y if U is $U[0,1)$.

5. If Y is exponential λ we know $F_Y(y) = 1 - e^{-\lambda y}$. So $F^{-1}(U) = \frac{-ln(1-U)}{\lambda}$ is exponential if U is $U[0,1)$. It is slightly more efficient to use $\frac{-ln(U)}{\lambda}$.

6. If $f(y)$ and $g(y)$ are densities and $\frac{f(y)}{g(y)} \leq k$ for all y, then a variable X with density f is simulated as follows: Suppose U_1, U_2 are random numbers and $Y = h(U_1)$ has density $g(y)$. $Y = h(U_1)$ is accepted as an X value if $U_2 \leq \frac{f(Y)}{k \cdot g(Y)}$.

COMPUTATIONAL REVIEW TEST

1. Simulate the time interval [0, 5] of a Compound Poisson surplus process with initial surplus $u = 3$, annual premium rate $c = 3.25$, $\lambda = 2$ expected claims per year and claim amount distribution

$X = x$	1	2	5
$f_X(x)$	.75	.20	.05

.

List the claim occurrence times, the claim amounts and compute surplus at each occurrence. Does ruin occur?

COMPUTATIONAL REVIEW TEST SOLUTION

1. **Solution Outline - Imitate Example 8**

Step 1: From random numbers U_1, U_2, ... generate $T_1 = -\frac{1}{\lambda}ln(U_1) = -\frac{1}{2}ln(U_1)$, $T_2 = -\frac{1}{2}ln(U_1U_2), \ldots, T_n$ until $T_{n+1} > t_0 = 5$.

Step 2: From random numbers $V_1, V_2, \ldots, V_n$ generate claims $X_1, \ldots, X_n$ by the standard search transformation:

V-value	X-Value
[0, .75)	1
[.75, .95)	2
[.95, 1.00)	5

Step 3: Compute $U(T_i) = u + cT_i - S(T_i)$ for $i = 1, 2, \ldots, n$

UNIT REVIEW QUESTIONS

1. If U is uniformly distributed on $[0, 1)$, which of the following are exponentially distributed with mean 2?

I. $ln(1-U)$ II. $-\frac{1}{2}ln(U)$ III. $-2ln(1-U)$

(A) I and II (B) I and III (C) II and III (D) I, II and III (E) III only

2. Suppose $U_1, \ldots, U_{10}$ are random numbers and Y is the number of U_i values $\leq .75$. The expected value and variance of Y are

	Mean	Variance
(A)	10	7.5
(B)	7.5	.5025
(C)	10	100
(D)	7.5	1.875
(E)	$\frac{4}{3}$	$\frac{16}{9}$

3. Suppose $g(y) = \frac{3}{2}(1-\frac{y}{2})^2$ for $0 \leq y \leq 2$. If U is uniform on $[0, 1)$, which of the following random variables has density function $g(y)$?

(A) $2[1-(1-U)^{-3}]$ (B) $.5[1-(1-U)^{1/3}]$ (C) $2[1-U^{-3}]$
(D) $2[1-U^{1/3}]$ (E) $-2[1-U^{-1/3}]$

Use the following information for Questions 4-7. Let $f(y) = \frac{2}{\sqrt{2\pi}}e^{-y^2/2}$ for $0 \leq y < \infty$ and let $g(y) = \lambda e^{-\lambda y}$ be the exponential density with mean λ. Let $k(\lambda)$ be the maximum value of $\frac{f(y)}{g(y)}$ for $y \geq 0$, and let $F(y) = \int_0^y f(s)\,ds$ be c.d.f..

4. What value of λ makes $k(\lambda)$ as small as possible?

(A) $\frac{1}{2}$ (B) $\frac{3}{4}$ (C) $\frac{4}{5}$ (D) 1 (E) $\frac{3}{2}$

5. Suppose U_1, U_2 are independent and uniformly distributed on $[0, 1)$. Let $Y = \frac{-ln(U_1)}{\lambda}$. Calculate $Pr\left(Y \leq 2 \text{ and } U_2 \leq \frac{f(Y)}{k(\lambda)g(Y)}\right)$.

(A) $\frac{1}{\lambda}\sqrt{\frac{2}{\pi}}e^{\lambda^2/2}F(2)$ (B) $\lambda\sqrt{\frac{\pi}{2}}e^{-\lambda^2/2}F(2)$ (C) $\frac{\lambda^2}{2}(1-e^{-2\lambda})$
(D) $\frac{2}{\lambda^2}(1-e^{-2\lambda})$ (E) $\lambda\sqrt{\frac{\pi}{2}}e^{-\lambda^2/2}(1-e^{-2\lambda})$

The following additional information applies to 6 and 7. Suppose U_1 and U_2 are independent and uniformly distributed on $[0, 1)$. Set $Y = \frac{-ln(U_1)}{\lambda}$ and accept Y as an X-value if

$$U_2 \leq \frac{f(Y)}{k(\lambda)g(Y)}$$

Iterate this process until an X-value is accepted.

6. If N is the number of required iterations, then with $\lambda = 2$ the density of N is $f_N(n) = Pr(N = n) =$

(A) $\left(1 - \frac{\sqrt{2\pi}F(2)}{e^2}\right)^n \left(\frac{\sqrt{2\pi}F(2)}{e^2}\right)$

(B) $\left(1 - \frac{\sqrt{2\pi}F(2)}{e^2}\right)^{n-1} \left(\frac{\sqrt{2\pi}F(2)}{e^2}\right)$

(C) $\left(1 - \frac{\sqrt{2\pi}}{e^2}\right)^n \left(\frac{\sqrt{2\pi}}{e^2}\right)$

(D) $\left(1 - \frac{\sqrt{2\pi}}{e^2}\right)^{n-1} \left(\frac{\sqrt{2\pi}}{e^2}\right)$

(E) None of the above

7. If N is the number of required iterations what is $E[N]$ when $\lambda = 2$?

(A) $\frac{e^2}{\sqrt{2\pi}}$ (B) $\frac{e^2}{\sqrt{2\pi}}\left(1 - \frac{\sqrt{2\pi}}{e^2}\right)$ (C) $e^2\sqrt{2\pi}$

(D) $e^2\sqrt{2\pi}\left(1 - \frac{e^{-2}}{\sqrt{2\pi}}\right)$ (E) None of the above

8. Suppose U_1, U_2, ... are random numbers and $N = min\{m \mid U_1U_2 \cdots U_m \leq e^{-3}\}$. Then $E[N]$ equals

(A) 3 (B) 4 (C) 5 (D) 6 (E) 7

9. Suppose $f(x) = \frac{18}{x^3}$ for $3 < x$. If U is uniformly distributed on $[0, 1)$, which of the following functions of U has density function $f(x)$?

(A) $2(1 - U)^{-1/3}$ (B) $2U^{-1/3}$ (C) $3(1 - U)^{1/2}$ (D) $3U^{1/2}$ (E) $3U^{-1/2}$

UNIT REVIEW QUESTION SOLUTIONS

1. If U is $U[0,1)$ and $F_Y(y) = 1 - e^{-\lambda y}$ (d.f. of an exponential with mean $\frac{1}{\lambda}$), then $F_Y^{-1}(U) = \frac{-ln(1-U)}{\lambda}$ is exponential with mean $\frac{1}{\lambda}$. Since $1 - U$ is also $U[0,1)$, $\frac{-ln(U)}{\lambda}$ has the same exponential distribution. Here $\lambda = \frac{1}{2}$ so that $-2ln(1-U)$ and $-2ln(U)$ are both exponential with mean 2.

ANSWER E

2. Y is Binomial with $n = 10$ trials and $p = .75$ as the probability of success: $E[Y] = np = 7.5$, $V(Y) = np(1-p) = 1.875$

ANSWER D

3. $G(y) = \int_0^y g(x)\,dx = -\left(1 - \frac{x}{2}\right)^3\Big|_0^y = 1 - \left(1 - \frac{y}{2}\right)^3$ is the distribution function. Thus $G^{-1}(U)$ has density function $g(\ )$: $\quad u = 1 - \left(1 - \frac{y}{2}\right)^3 \quad \Rightarrow \quad 1 - \frac{y}{2} = (1-u)^{1/3}$
$\Rightarrow \; G^{-1}(u) = 2[1 - (1-u)^{1/3}] = y$. Since $1 - U$ is also $U[0,1)$, $2[1 - U^{1/3}]$ has density $g(\ )$ as well.

ANSWER D

4. $\frac{f(y)}{g(y)} = \frac{2}{\sqrt{2\pi}} \cdot \frac{1}{\lambda} \cdot e^{\lambda y - y^2/2}$ for $y \geq 0$. $\lambda y - y^2/2$ is a concave down parabola (in y) whose maximum value, $\frac{\lambda^2}{2}$, occurs when $\lambda - y = 0$. Thus $k(\lambda) = \frac{2}{\lambda\sqrt{2\pi}} e^{\lambda^2/2}$. Now
$\frac{dk(\lambda)}{d\lambda} = \frac{2}{\sqrt{2\pi}} \cdot \frac{\lambda e^{\lambda^2/2}(\lambda) - e^{\lambda^2/2}}{\lambda^2} = \frac{2}{\sqrt{2\pi}} \cdot \frac{e^{\lambda^2/2}}{\lambda^2}[\lambda^2 - 1] = 0$ if $\lambda = 1$ (λ must be positive).
Since $k'(\lambda) < 0$ if $\lambda < 1$ and $k'(\lambda) > 0$ if $\lambda > 1$ we see that $\lambda = 1$ is where the minimum occurs.

ANSWER D

5. Y is exponentially distributed with mean $\frac{1}{\lambda}$ so the joint density of Y and U_2 is $g(y) \cdot 1 = \lambda e^{-\lambda y}$ for $y \geq 0$ and $0 \leq u < 1$. Hence

$$Pr\left(Y \leq 2 \text{ and } U_2 \leq \frac{f(Y)}{k(\lambda)g(Y)}\right) = \int_{y=0}^{2} \int_{u=0}^{\frac{f(y)}{k(\lambda)g(y)}} g(y) \cdot 1\,du\,dy$$

$$= \int_{y=0}^{2} g(y) \cdot \frac{f(y)}{k(\lambda)g(y)}\,dy = \int_{y=0}^{2} f(y)\,dy/k(\lambda) = \frac{1}{k(\lambda)} \cdot F(2)$$

where $F(y)$ is the distribution function corresponding to the density function $f(y) = \frac{2}{\sqrt{2\pi}} e^{-y^2/2}$.
Since $k(\lambda) = \frac{2}{\lambda\sqrt{2\pi}} e^{\lambda^2/2} = \frac{1}{\lambda}\sqrt{\frac{2}{\pi}} \cdot e^{\lambda^2/2}$, we have

$$Pr\left(Y \leq 2 \text{ and } U_2 \leq \frac{f(Y)}{k(\lambda)g(Y)}\right) = \frac{1}{k(\lambda)} \cdot F(2) = \lambda \cdot \sqrt{\frac{\pi}{2}} \cdot e^{-\lambda^2/2} \cdot F(2).$$

ANSWER B

6. In general N is geometric (the number of the trial on which the first success takes place) where $p = Pr(\text{Success}) = \frac{1}{k(\lambda)}$. The reason is that (similar to the solution of Question 5) success is accepting and

$$Pr(\text{Accepting on a given iteration}) = Pr\left(Y < \infty \text{ and } U_2 \le \frac{f(Y)}{k(\lambda)g(Y)}\right)$$
$$= \int_{y=0}^{\infty}\int_{u=0}^{\frac{f(y)}{k(\lambda)g(y)}} g(y)\cdot 1\,du\,dy$$
$$= \int_{y=0}^{\infty} g(y)\cdot\left(\frac{f(y)}{k(\lambda)g(y)}\right)dy$$
$$= \frac{1}{k(\lambda)}\int_{y=0}^{\infty} f(y)\,dy = \frac{1}{k(\lambda)}\cdot 1 = \frac{1}{k(\lambda)}.$$

Thus

$$Pr(N = n) = q^{n-1}p = \left(1 - \frac{1}{k(\lambda)}\right)^{n-1}\frac{1}{k(\lambda)}$$
$$= \left(1 - \frac{1}{k(2)}\right)^{n-1}\frac{1}{k(2)}$$
$$= (1 - \sqrt{2\pi}\,e^{-2})^{n-1}(\sqrt{2\pi}\,e^{-2}).$$

ANSWER D

7. $E[N] = \frac{1}{p} = k(\lambda) = k(2) = \frac{e^2}{\sqrt{2\pi}}$ ANSWER A

Note: Questions 4 - 7 deal with the rejection method. If one uses $g(y) = \lambda e^{-\lambda y}$, then $k(\lambda) = \sqrt{\frac{2}{\pi}}\cdot\frac{e^{\lambda^2/2}}{\lambda}$ and the number of iterations required to accept a Y-value as an X-value (having density $f(x)$ above) is Geometric with mean $\frac{1}{p} = \frac{1}{(1/k(\lambda))} = k(\lambda)$. This simulation is most efficient when $E[N]$ is as small as possible. We saw in the solution to Question 4 that $k(\lambda)$ is minimized when $\lambda = 1$. In this case the expected number of iterations is

$$k(1) = \sqrt{\frac{2}{\pi}}\frac{e^{.5}}{1} \approx 1.315.$$

So the best choice for $g(y;\lambda) = \lambda e^{-\lambda y}$ is $\lambda = 1$.

8. $U_1U_2\cdots U_m < e^{-\lambda} \Leftrightarrow \sum_{i=1}^{m} ln(U_i) < -\lambda \Leftrightarrow \sum_{i=1}^{m} -\frac{1}{\lambda}ln(U_i) > 1$. Each term $-\frac{1}{\lambda}ln(U_i)$ is exponential with parameter λ. Let $W_i = -\frac{1}{\lambda}ln(U_i)$. In a Poisson process with rate λ the W_i are waiting times between counted events. So N is the smallest m such that $W_1 + \cdots + W_m$ (time of mth occurrence) exceeds 1. This means $m-1$ events occurred in $(0, 1]$. Hence $N = 1 + N(1)$ where $N(1)$ is Poisson with $\lambda = 3$. $E[N] = 1 + 3 = 4$ ANSWER B

9. $F(x) = \int_3^x \frac{18}{y^3}dy = -\frac{9}{y^2}\Big|_{y=3}^{x} = 1 - \frac{9}{x^2}$ for $x \ge 3$. So if $u = F(x) = 1 - \frac{9}{x^2}$ it follows that $x = 3(1-u)^{-1/2}$. Hence both $3(1-U)^{-1/2}$ and $3U^{-1/2}$ have the density function $f(x)$.

ANSWER E